THEORY
OF THE
INTEGRAL

THEORY

OF THE

INTEGRAL

BY

DR. STANISLAW SAKS

(SECOND REVISED EDITION)

ENGLISH TRANSLATION

BY

L. C. YOUNG, M. A.

WITH TWO ADDITIONAL NOTES

BY

PROF. DR. STEFAN BANACH

DOVER PUBLICATIONS, INC.

NEW YORK

This Dover edition, first published in 1964, is an unabridged and corrected republication of the second revised edition, published by G. E. Stechert & Company in 1937 as Volume VII in the "Monografie Matematyczne" Series.

Library of Congress Catalog Card Number: 64-15517

Manufactured in the United States of America

Dover Publications, Inc.
180 Varick Street
New York 14, N.Y.

PREFACE.

This edition differs from the first[1]) by the new arrangement of the contents of several chapters, some of which have been completed by more recent results, and by the suppression of a number of errors, obligingly pointed out by Mr. V. Jarnìk, which formed the object of the two pages of Errata in the first edition. It is probable that fresh errors have slipped in owing to modifications of the text, but the reader would certainly find many more, if the author had not received the valuable help of Messrs J. Todd, A. J. Ward and A. Zygmund in reading the proofs. Also, Mr. L. C. Young has greatly exceeded his rôle of translator in his collaboration with the author. To all these I express my warmest thanks.

This volume contains two Notes by S. Banach. The first of them, on Haar's measure, is the translation (with a few slight modifications) of the note already contained in the French edition of this book. The second, which concerns the integration in abstract spaces, is published here for the first time and completes the considerations of Chapter I.

The numbers given in the bibliographical references relate to the list of cited works which will be found at the end of the book. The asterisks preceding certain titles indicate the parts of the book which may be omitted on first reading.

S. Saks.

Warszawa-Żoliborz, July, 1937.

---

[1]) S. Saks, *Theorie de l'Intégrale*, Monografie Matematyczne, Volume II, Warszawa 1933.

FROM THE PREFACE TO THE FIRST EDITION.

The modern theory of real functions became distinct from classical analysis in the second half of the 19-th century, as a result of researches, unsystematic at first, which dealt with the foundations of the Differential Calculus or which concerned the discovery of functions whose properties appeared to be very strange and unexpected.

The distrust with which this new field of investigation was regarded is typified by the attitude of H. Poincaré who wrote: "*Autrefois quand on inventait une fonction nouvelle, c'était en vue de quelque but pratique; aujourd'hui on les invente tout exprès pour mettre en défaut les raisonnements de nos pères et on n'en tirera jamais que celà*".

This view was by no means isolated. Ch. Hermite, in a letter to T. J. Stieltjes, expressed himself in even stronger terms: "*Je me détourne avec effroi et horreur de cette plaie lamentable des fonctions qui n'ont pas de dérivées*". Researches dealing with non-analytic functions and with functions violating laws which one hoped were universal, were regarded almost as the propagation of anarchy and chaos where past generations had sought order and harmony. Even the first attempts to establish a positive theory were rather sceptically received: it was feared that an excessively pedantic exactitude in formulating hypotheses would spoil the elegance of classical methods, and that discussions of details would end by obscuring the main ideas of analysis. It is true that the first researches hardly went beyond the traditional, formal apparatus, fixed by Cauchy and Riemann, which was difficult to adapt to the requirements of the new problems. Nevertheless, these researches succeeded in opening the way to applications of the Theory of Sets to Analysis, and — to quote H. Lebesgue's inaugural lecture at the Collège de France — "*the great authority of Camille Jordan gave to the new school a valuable encouragement which amply compensated the few reproofs it had to suffer*".

R. Baire, E. Borel, H. Lebesgue — these are the names which represent the Theory of Real Functions, not merely as an object of researches, but also as a method, names which at the same time recall the leading ideas of the theory. The names of Baire and Borel will be always associated with the method of classification of functions and sets in a transfinite hierarchy by means of certain simple operations to which they are subjected. Excellent accounts of this subject are to be found in the treatises: Ch. J. de la Vallée Poussin, *Fonctions d'ensemble, Intégrale de Lebesgue, Classes de Baire*, 1916, F. Hausdorff, *Mengenlehre*, 1927, H. Hahn, *Theorie der reellen Funktionen*, 1933 (recent edition), C. Kuratowski, third volume of the present collection, and finally in the book of W. Sierpiński, *Topologja ogólna* (in Polish), and its English translation, *General Topology*, to be published in 1934 by the Toronto University Press.

The other line of researches, which arises directly from the study of the foundations of the Integral Calculus, is still more intimately connected with the great trains of thought of Analysis in the last century. On several occasions attempts were made to generalize the old process of integration of Cauchy-Riemann, but it was Lebesgue who first made real progress in this matter. At the same time, Lebesgue's merit is not only to have created a new and more general notion of integral, nor even to have established its intimate connection with the theory of measure: the value of his work consists primarily in his theory of derivation which is parallel to that of integration. This enabled his discovery to find many applications in the most widely different branches of Analysis and, from the point of view of method, made it possible to reunite the two fundamental conceptions of integral, namely that of definite integral and that of primitive, which appeared to be forever separated as soon as integration went outside the domain of continuous functions.

The theory of Lebesgue constitutes the subject of the present volume. While distinguishing it from that of Baire, we have no wish to erect an artificial barrier between two streams of thought which naturally intermingle. On the contrary, we shall have frequent occasion, particularly in the last chapters of this book, to show explicitly how Lebesgue's theory comes to be bound up not only with the results, but also with the very methods, of the theory of Baire. Is not the idea of Denjoy integration at bottom merely a striking adaptation of the idea which guided Baire? Where Baire, by repeated application of passage to the limit, widened the class of functions, Denjoy constructed a transfinite hierarchy of methods of integration starting with that of Lebesgue and whose successive stages are connected by two operations: one corresponding exactly to the generalized integral of Cauchy and the other to the generalized integral of Harnack-Jordan.

Now that the Theory of Real Functions, while losing perhaps a little of the charm of its first youth, has ceased to be a "new" science, it seems superfluous to discuss its importance. It is known that the theory has brought to light regularity and harmony, unhoped for by the older methods, concerning, for instance, the existence of a limit, a derivative, or a tangent. It is enough to mention the theorems, now classical, on the behaviour of a power series on, or near, the boundary of its circle of convergence. Also, many branches of analysis, to cite only Harmonic Analysis, Integral Equations, Functional Operations, have lost none of their elegance where they have been inspired by methods of the Theory of Real Functions. On the contrary, we have learnt to admire in the arguments not only cleverness of calculation, but also the generality which, by an apparent abstraction, often enables us to grasp the real nature of the problem.

The object of the preceding remarks has been to indicate the place occupied by the subject of this volume in the Theory of Real Functions[1]). Let us now say a few words about the structure of the book. It embodies the greater part of a course of lectures delivered by the author at the University of Warsaw (and published in Polish in a separate book[2])), which has been modified and completed by several chapters. The reader need only be acquainted with a few elementary principles of the Theory of Sets, which are to be found in most courses of lectures on elementary analysis. Actually a summary of the elements of the theory of sets of points is given in one of the opening paragraphs.

Several pages of the book are inspired by suggestions and methods which I owe to the excellent university lectures of my teacher, W. Sierpiński, the influence of whose ideas has often guided my personal researches. Finally, I wish to express my warmest thanks to all those who have kindly assisted me in my task, particularly to my friend A. Zygmund, who undertook to read the manuscript. I thank also Messrs C. Kuratowski and H. Steinhaus for their kind remarks and bibliographical indications.

S. Saks.

Warszawa, May, 1933.

---

[1]) In this preface, I made no attempt to write a history of the early days of the theory, and still less to settle questions of priority of discovery. But, since an English Edition of this book is appearing now, I think I ought to mention the name of W. H. Young, whose work on the theory of integration started at the same period as that of Lebesgue.

[2]) *Zarys teorji całki,* Warszawa 1930, Wydawnictwo Kasy im. Mianowskiego, Instytutu Popierania Nauki.

CONTENTS.

pages

CHAPTER III. **Functions of bounded variation and the Lebesgue-Stieltjes integral.**

CHAPTER IV. **Derivation of additive functions of a set and of an interval.**

CHAPTER V. **Area of a surface $z=F(x, y)$.**

CHAPTER VI. **Major and minor functions.**

CHAPTER VII. **Functions of generalized bounded variation.**

CHAPTER VIII. **Denjoy integrals.**

CHAPTER IX. **Derivates of functions of one or two real variables.**

NOTATIONS.

CHAPTER I. ϵ, 4; $\subset$, 4 (254); $\supset$, $=$, 4; Σ, 5 (258); Π, $+$, $-$, lim inf, lim sup, 5; lim, 5 (39); $(\mathfrak{E})$, $\mathfrak{E}_\delta$, $\mathfrak{E}_\sigma$ (where $\mathfrak{E}$ is a class of sets), 5; C, 6; c_E (where E is a set), 6; $\{v_1, E_1; \ldots; v_n, E_n\}$ (where $E_1, \ldots, E_n$ are sets and $v_1, \ldots, v_n$ numbers), 7; $\overline{\mathrm{W}}$, $\underline{\mathrm{W}}$, W, 10 (61, 96); E, 12; $\mathring{f}$, $\underset{\circ}{f}$ (where f is a function), 13; $(\mathfrak{X})\int f\,d\mu$ (where $\mathfrak{X}$ is a class of sets, f a function of a point and μ a measure), 20.

CHAPTER II. ϱ, 39 (40); lim, 39 (5); ϱ, δ, Δ, 40; S, 41 (122, 165); $\overline{\mathrm{S}}$, 41; A', $\bar{A}$, A° (where A is a set), 42; $\mathfrak{G}$, $\mathfrak{F}$, 40; $\mathfrak{B}$, 41; M, m, 42; o, 42 (60); $\mathfrak{L}_\Gamma$ (where Γ is an outer Carathéodory measure), 44; (Γ), $\int f d\Gamma$ (where Γ is an outer Carathéodory measure and f a function of a point), 46; N, 47; Λ, 53.

CHAPTER III. $\boldsymbol{R}$, 56; $(x_1, \ldots, x_m)$ (where $x_1, \ldots, x_m$ are real numbers), 56; $[a_1, b_1; \ldots; a_m, b_m]$, $[a_1, b_1; \ldots; a_m, b_m)$, $(a_1, b_1; \ldots; a_m, b_m]$, $(a_1, b_1, \ldots; a_m, b_m)$ (where $a_1, b_1, \ldots, a_m, b_m$ are real numbers), 57; $\odot$, $\ominus$, 59; O, 60 (254); o, 60 (42); $\overline{\mathrm{W}}$, $\underline{\mathrm{W}}$, W, 61 (10, 96); U^* (where U is a function of an interval), 64; $\int f dU$ (where f is a function of a point and U a function of an interval), 64; L, $|\,|$, 65 (117); $\int f(x)\,dx$ (where f is a function of a point), 66; $\times$, 76 (82); UV (where U and V are functions of an interval), 76; $\times$, 82 (76); $\mathfrak{X}\mathfrak{Y}$ (where $\mathfrak{X}$ and $\mathfrak{Y}$ are classes of sets), 82; $\mu\nu$ (where μ and ν are measures), 86; $\overline{\mathfrak{T}}^\tau$ (where $\mathfrak{T}$ is a class of sets and τ a measure), 87; A, 88; B, 88 (121); $Q^{(a)}$ (where Q is a set and a a point), 91; $\overline{\mathrm{W}}$, $\underline{\mathrm{W}}$, W, 96 (10, 61); $f(a+)$, $f(a-)$ (where f is a function and a a point), 97; $F(I)$ (where F is a function of a real variable and I an interval), 99; $F[E]$ (where F is a function of a real variable and E a set), 100.

CHAPTER IV. r, $\overline{\mathrm{D}}$, $\underline{\mathrm{D}}$, D, 106 (154); $\overline{\Phi}$, $\underline{\Phi}$, Φ', $\overline{\Phi}_{\mathrm{s}}$, $\underline{\Phi}_{\mathrm{s}}$, Φ'_{s}, 106; $\overline{F}^+$, $\underline{F}^+$, $\overline{F}^-$, $\underline{F}^-$, $\overline{F}_E$, $\underline{F}_E$, F'_E, $\overline{F}^+_U$, $\underline{F}^+_U$, $\overline{F}^-_U$, $\underline{F}^-_U$, F'_U (where E is a set, and F, U functions of a real variable), 108, 109; L, 117 (65); p, 121; B, 121 (88); S, 122 (41, 165); f^α, f^{β_1}, f^{β_2}, f^β (where f is a function of a real variable), 144; f^β (where f is a function of two real variables), 147; $\overline{\mathrm{D}}_{\mathrm{sym}}$, $\underline{\mathrm{D}}_{\mathrm{sym}}$, 149; $(\mu, \mathfrak{M})\,\overline{\mathrm{D}}$, $(\mu, \mathfrak{M})\,\underline{\mathrm{D}}$, $(\mu, \mathfrak{M})\,\mathrm{D}$ (where μ is a measure and $\mathfrak{M}$ a sequence of nets), 154 (106); Q_ω, 157; Q_m, ξ'_m, ξ''_m (where m is an integer and ξ a point in the torus space), 157; L_ω, L^*_ω, 157; $\dotplus$, 158.

CHAPTER V. S_0, S 165 (41, 122); $U(\mathfrak{J})$ (where U is a function of an interval and $\mathfrak{J}$ a system of intervals), 165; $\overline{\int} U$, $\underline{\int} U$, $\int U$ (where U is a function of an interval), 166; W_1, W_2, 169; G_1, G_2, G, 171; H_1, H_2, H, 174.

CHAPTER VI. $(\mathfrak{N})\overline{F}$, $(\mathfrak{N})\underline{F}$, $(\mathfrak{N})F'$ (where $\mathfrak{N}$ is a sequence of nets of intervals and F a function of an interval), 188; J_1, J_2, J, 195; $(\mathscr{P})\int$, 201; $(\mathscr{PS})\int$, 208.

CHAPTER VII. $(-\infty, a)$, $(-\infty, a]$, $(a, +\infty)$, $[a, +\infty)$ (where a is a real number), 215; lim sup ap, lim inf ap, lim ap, 219; $\overline{F}^+_{\mathrm{ap}}$, $\underline{F}^+_{\mathrm{ap}}$, $\overline{F}^-_{\mathrm{ap}}$, $\underline{F}^-_{\mathrm{ap}}$, $\overline{F}_{\mathrm{ap}}$, $\underline{F}_{\mathrm{ap}}$, F'_{ap} (where F is a function), 220; V, 221; V_*, 228.

CHAPTER VIII. $(\mathscr{D})\int$, $(\mathscr{D}_*)\int$, 241; $(\mathscr{S})\int$, 244; O, 254 (60); $\subset$, 254 (4); $\mathfrak{T}^{\mathrm{C}}$, $\mathfrak{T}^{\mathrm{H}}$, $\mathfrak{T}^{\mathrm{H}_*}$ (where $\mathfrak{T}$ is an integral), 255 and 256; Σ, 258 (5).

CHAPTER IX. contg, 263; $\overline{F}^+_{\mathrm{ap}_x}$, $\underline{F}^+_{\mathrm{ap}_x}$, $\overline{F}^-_{\mathrm{ap}_x}$, $\underline{F}^-_{\mathrm{ap}_x}$, F'_{ap_x}, $\overline{F}^+_{\mathrm{ap}_y}$, $\underline{F}^+_{\mathrm{ap}_y}$, $\overline{F}^-_{\mathrm{ap}_y}$, $\underline{F}^-_{\mathrm{ap}_y}$, F'_{ap_y} (where F is a function of two variables), 298; lim $\inf_E$, lim $\sup_E$, $\lim_E$ (where E is a set), 304.

CHAPTER I.

The integral in an abstract space.

§ 1. Introduction. Apart from functions having as argument a variable number, or system of n numbers (point in n-dimensional space), we shall discuss in this book functions for which the independent variable is a set of points. Functions of this kind have occurred already in classical Analysis, in several important particular cases. But they only began to be studied in their full generality during the growth of the Theory of Sets, and in close relation to the parts of Analysis directly based on that theory.

If we are, for instance, given a function $f(x)$ integrable on every interval, then by associating with each interval I the value of the integral of $f(x)$ over I, we obtain a function $F(I)$ that is a function of an interval. Similarly, by taking multiple integrals of functions $f(x_1, x_2, ..., x_n)$ of n variables, we are led to consider functions of more general sets lying in spaces of several dimensions, the argument I of our function $F(I)$ being now replaced by any set for which the integral of our given function $f(x_1, x_2, ..., x_n)$ is defined.

We dwell on these examples in order to emphasize the natural connection between the notion of integral (in any sense) and that of function of a set. Needless to say, there are many other examples of functions of a set. Thus in elementary geometry, we have for instance, the length of a segment or the area of a polygon. The class of values of the argument of these two functions (the length and the area) is in the first case, the class of segments and in the second, that of polygons. The problem of extending these classes gave birth to the general theories of measure, in which the notions of length, area, and volume, defined in elementary geometry for a restricted number of figures, are now extended to sets of points of much greater diversity. It is, nevertheless, remarkable that these researches arose far less from problems of Geometry than from their connection with problems of Analysis, above all with the tendency to generalize, and to render more precise, the notion of definite integral. This connection has occasionally found expression even in the terminology. Thus du Bois-Reymond called *integrable* the sets that to-day are said to be of measure zero in the Jordan sense.

The theories of measure have, in the course of their development, been modified in accordance with the changing requirements of the Theory of Functions. In our account, the most important part will be played by the theory of H. Lebesgue.

Lebesgue's theory of measure has made it possible to distinguish in Euclidean spaces a vast class of sets, called *measurable*, in which measure has the property of *complete additivity* — by this we mean that the measure of the sum of a sequence, even infinite, of measurable sets, no two of which have points in common, is equal to the sum of the measures of these sets. The importance of this class of sets is due to the fact that it includes, in particular, (with their classical measures), all the sets of points occurring in problems of classical Analysis, and further, that the fundamental operations applied to measurable sets lead always to measurable sets.

It is nevertheless to be observed that the ground was prepared for Lebesgue's theory of measure by earlier theories associated with the names of Cantor, Stolz, Harnack, du Bois-Reymond, Peano, Jordan, Borel, and others. These earlier theories have, however, to-day little more than historical value. They, too, were suitable instruments for studying and generalizing the notion of integral understood in the classical sense of Riemann, but their results in this direction have been largely artificial and accidental. It is only Lebesgue's theory of measure that makes a decisive step in the development of the notion of integral. This is the more remarkable in that the definition of Lebesgue apparently requires only a very small modification of a formal kind in the definition of integral due to Riemann.

To fix the ideas, let us consider a bounded function $f(x, y)$ of two variables, or what comes to the same thing, a bounded function of a variable point defined on a square K_0. In order to determine its Riemann integral, or more precisely, its lower Riemann-Darboux integral over K_0, we proceed as follows. We divide the square K_0 into an arbitrary finite number of non-overlapping rectangles $R_1, R_2, \ldots, R_n$, and we form the sum

$$\sum_{i=1}^{n} v_i \cdot m(R_i) \tag{1.1}$$

where v_i denotes the lower bound of the function f on R_i, and $m(R_i)$ denotes the area of R_i. The upper bound of all sums of this form is, by definition, the *lower Riemann-Darboux integral* of the function f over K_0. We define similarly the upper integral of f over K_0. If these two extreme integrals are equal, their common value is called the *definite Riemann integral* of the function f over K_0, and the function f is said to be *integrable in the Riemann sense* over K_0.

The extension of measure to all sets measurable in the Lebesgue sense, has rendered necessary a modification of the process of Riemann-Darboux, it being natural to consider sums of the form (1.1) for which $\{R_i\}_{i=1,2,\ldots,n}$ is a subdivision of the square K_0 into a finite number of arbitrary measurable sets, not necessarily either rectangles or elementary geometrical figures. Accordingly, $m(R_i)$ is to be understood to mean the measure of R_i. The v_i retain their former meaning, i. e. represent the lower bounds of f on the corresponding sets R_i. We might call the upper bound of the sums (1.1) interpreted in this way the *lower Lebesgue integral* of the function f over K_0. But actually, this process is of practical importance only for a class of functions, called *measurable*, and for these the number obtained as the upper bound of the sums (1.1) is called simply the *definite Lebesgue integral* of f over K_0. What is important, is that the functions which are measurable in the sense of Lebesgue, and whose definition is closely related to that of the measurable sets, form a very general class. This class includes, in particular, all the functions integrable in the Riemann sense.

Apart from this, the method of Lebesgue is not only more general, but even, from a certain point of view, simpler than that of Riemann-Darboux. For, it dispenses with the simultaneous introduction of two extreme integrals, the lower and the upper. Thanks to this, Lebesgue's method lends itself to an immediate extension to unbounded functions, at any rate to certain classes of the latter, for instance, to all measurable functions of constant sign (cf. below § 10). Finally, the Lebesgue integral renders it permissible to integrate term by term sequences and series of functions in certain general cases where passages to the limit under the integral sign were not allowed by the earlier methods of integration. The reason for this is to be found in the complete additivity of Lebesgue measure. The fundamental theorems of Lebesgue (cf. below § 12) stating the precise circumstances under which term by term integration is permissible, are justly regarded by Ch. J. de la Vallée Poussin [I, p. 44] as one of the finest results of the theory.

Lebesgue's theory of measure has, in its turn, led naturally to further important generalizations. Instead of starting with area, or volume, of figures, we may imagine a mass distributed in the Euclidean space under consideration, and associate with each set as its measure, (its "weight" according to Ch. J. de la Vallée Poussin [I, Chap. VI; 1]), the amount of mass distributed on the set. This, again, leads to a generalization of the integral, parallel to Lebesgue's, known as the Lebesgue-Stieltjes integral. In order to present a unified account of the latter, we shall consider in this chapter an additive class of measurable sets given *a priori* in an arbitrary abstract space. We shall suppose further, that in this class, a completely additive measure is determined for the measurable sets. These hypotheses determine completely a corresponding method of integration in the Lebesgue sense. All the essential properties of the ordinary Lebesgue integral, except at most those implying the process of derivation, remain valid for this abstract integral. From this point of view, in a more or less general form, the Lebesgue integral has been studied by a number of authors, among whom we may mention J. Radon [1], P. J. Daniell [1; 4; 5], O. Nikodym [2] and B. Jessen [1]. For further generalizations (of a somewhat different kind) see also A. Kolmogoroff [1], G. Birkhoff [1], S. Bochner [1], N. Dunford [2; 3], G. Fichtenholz and L. Kantorovitch [1], and M. Gowurin [1].

§ 2. Terminology and notation. Given two sets A and B, we write $A \subset B$ when the set A is a *subset* of the set B, i. e. when every *element* of A is an element of B. When we have both $A \subset B$ and $B \subset A$, i. e. when the sets A and B consist of the same elements, we write $A = B$. Again, $a \in A$ means that a is an element of the set A (*belongs* to A). By the *empty* set, we mean the set without any element; we denote it by 0. A set A is *enumerable* if there exists an infinite sequence of distinct elements $a_1, a_2, \ldots, a_n, \ldots$ consisting of all the elements of the set A.

Given a class $\mathfrak{A}$ of sets, we call *sum* of the sets belonging to this class, the set of all the objects each of which is an element of at least one set belonging to the class $\mathfrak{A}$. We call *product*, or *common part*, of the sets belonging to the class $\mathfrak{A}$, the set of all the objects that belong at the same time to all the sets of this class. We call *difference* of two sets A and B, and we denote by $A - B$, the set of all the objects that belong to A without belonging to B.

Given a sequence of sets $\{A_n\}$ — a finite sequence $A_1, A_2, \ldots, A_n$, or an infinite sequence $A_1, A_2, \ldots, A_n, \ldots$ — we denote the sum by $\sum_i A_i$, by $\sum_{i=1}^{n} A_i$, or by $A_1 + A_2 + \ldots + A_n$, in the finite case, and by $\sum_i A_i$, by $\sum_{i=1}^{\infty} A_i$, or by $A_1 + A_2 + \ldots + A_n + \ldots$ in the infinite case. Similarly, merely replacing the sign Σ by Π, we have the expression for the product of a sequence of sets. If the sequence $\{A_n\}$ is infinite, we call *upper limit* of this sequence, the set of all the elements a such that $a \in A_n$ holds for an infinity of values of the index n. The set of all the elements a belonging to all the sets A_n from some n (in general depending on a) onwards, we call *lower limit* of the sequence $\{A_n\}$. The upper and lower limits of the sequence $\{A_n\}_{n=1,2,\ldots}$, we denote by $\limsup_n A_n$ and $\liminf_n A_n$ respectively. We have

$$(2.1) \qquad \liminf_n A_n = \sum_{k=1}^{\infty} \prod_{n=k}^{\infty} A_n \subset \prod_{k=1}^{\infty} \sum_{n=k}^{\infty} A_n = \limsup_n A_n.$$

If $\limsup_n A_n = \liminf_n A_n$, the sequence $\{A_n\}$ is said to be *convergent*; its upper and lower limits are then called simply *limit* and denoted by $\lim_n A_n$.

If, for a sequence $\{A_n\}$ of sets, we have $A_n \subset A_{n+1}$, for each n, the sequence $\{A_n\}$ is said to be *ascending*, or *non-decreasing*; if, for each n, we have $A_{n+1} \subset A_n$, the sequence $\{A_n\}$ is said to be *descending* or *non-increasing*. Ascending and descending sequences are called *monotone*. We see directly that every monotone sequence is convergent, and that we have $\lim_n A_n = \sum_n A_n$ for every ascending sequence $\{A_n\}$, and $\lim_n A_n = \prod_n A_n$ for every descending sequence $\{A_n\}$.

Finally, given a class $\mathfrak{C}$ of sets, we shall often call the sets belonging to $\mathfrak{C}$, for short, sets ($\mathfrak{C}$). The class of the sets which are the sums of sequences of sets ($\mathfrak{C}$) will be denoted by $\mathfrak{C}_\sigma$. The class of the sets which are the products of such sequences will be denoted by $\mathfrak{C}_\delta$ (see F. Hausdorff [II, p. 83]).

§ 3. Abstract space X. In the rest of this chapter, a set X will be fixed and called *space*. The elements of X will be called *points*. If A is any set contained in X the set $X - A$ will be called *complement of A with respect to X*; the expression "with respect to X" will, however, generally be omitted, since sets outside the space X will not be considered. The complement of a set A will be denoted by $\mathrm{C}A$. We evidently have, for every pair of sets A and B,

$$A - B = A \cdot \mathrm{C}B, \tag{3.1}$$

and for every sequence $\{X_n\}$ of sets

$$\prod_n X_n = \mathrm{C}\sum_n \mathrm{C}X_n, \qquad \sum_n X_n = \mathrm{C}\prod_n \mathrm{C}X_n,$$

(3.2)

$$\limsup_n X_n = \mathrm{C}\liminf_n \mathrm{C}X_n, \qquad \liminf_n X_n = \mathrm{C}\limsup_n \mathrm{C}X_n.$$

In the space X we shall consider functions of a set, and functions of a point. The values of these functions will always be real numbers, finite or infinite. A function will be called *finite*, when it assumes only finite values.

To avoid misunderstanding, let us agree that when infinite functions are subjected to the elementary operations of addition, subtraction etc., we make the following conventions: $a+(\pm\infty)=(\pm\infty)+a=\pm\infty$ for $a \neq \mp\infty$; $(+\infty)+(-\infty)=(-\infty)+(+\infty)=(\pm\infty)-(\pm\infty)=0$; $a\cdot(\pm\infty)=(\pm\infty)\cdot a=\pm\infty$ and $a\cdot(\pm\infty)=(\pm\infty)\cdot a=\mp\infty$, according as $a>0$ or $a<0$; $0\cdot(\pm\infty)=(\pm\infty)\cdot 0=0$; $a/(\pm\infty)=0$; $a/0=\pm\infty$ according as $a\geqslant 0$ or $a<0$.

We call *characteristic function* $\mathrm{c}_E(x)$ of a set E, the function (of a point) equal to 1 at all points of the set, and to 0 everywhere else. The following theorem is obvious:

(3.3) *If $E=\sum_n E_n$, and $E_i \cdot E_k=0$ whenever $i \neq k$, then $\mathrm{c}_E(x)=\sum_n \mathrm{c}_{E_n}(x)$.*

If $\{E_n\}$ is a monotone sequence of sets, the sequence of their characteristic functions is also monotone, non-decreasing or non-increasing according as the sequence $\{E_n\}$ is ascending or descending.

If $\{E_n\}$ is any sequence of sets, A and B denoting its upper and lower limits respectively, we have

$$\mathrm{c}_A(x)=\limsup_n \mathrm{c}_{E_n}(x), \quad \textit{and} \quad \mathrm{c}_B(x)=\liminf_n \mathrm{c}_{E_n}(x);$$

so that, in order that a sequence of sets $\{E_n\}$ converge to a set E, it is necessary and sufficient that the sequence of their characteristic functions $\{\mathrm{c}_{E_n}(x)\}$ converge to the function $\{\mathrm{c}_E(x)\}$.

A function assuming only a finite number of different values on a set E is called a *simple function* on E. If $v_1, v_2, \ldots, v_n$ are all the distinct values of a simple function $f(x)$ on a set E, the function $f(x)$ may on E be written in the form

$$f(x)=\sum_{k=1}^{n} v_k c_{E_k}(x) \quad \textit{where} \quad E=E_1+E_2+\ldots+E_k \quad \textit{and} \quad E_i \cdot E_j=0 \quad \textit{for} \quad i \neq j.$$

The function f given by this formula over the set E will be denoted by $\{v_1, E_1; v_2, E_2; \ldots; v_n, E_n\}$.

The notion of characteristic function is due to Ch. J. de la Vallée Poussin [1] and [I, p. 7].

§ 4. Additive classes of sets. A class $\mathfrak{X}$ of sets in the space X will be called *additive* if (i) the empty set belongs to $\mathfrak{X}$, (ii) when a set X belongs to $\mathfrak{X}$ so does its complement CX, and (iii) the sum of a sequence $\{X_n\}$ of sets selected from the class $\mathfrak{X}$, belongs also to the class $\mathfrak{X}$.

The classes of sets, additive according to this definition, are sometimes termed *completely* additive. We get the definition of a class of sets additive *in the weak sense* if we replace the condition (iii) of the preceding definition by the following: (iii-bis) *the sum of two sets belonging to* $\mathfrak{X}$ *also belongs to* $\mathfrak{X}$.

The sets of an additive class $\mathfrak{X}$ will be called *sets measurable* ($\mathfrak{X}$), or, in accordance with the definition given in § 2 (p. 5), simply *sets* ($\mathfrak{X}$). We see at once that, on account of the conditions (i) and (ii), the space X, as complement of the empty set, belongs to every additive class of sets. Making use of the relations (2.1), (3.1), and (3.2), we obtain immediately the following:

(4.1) ***Theorem.*** *If* $\mathfrak{X}$ *is an additive class of sets, the sum, the product, and the two limits, upper and lower, of every sequence of sets measurable* ($\mathfrak{X}$), *and the difference of two sets measurable* ($\mathfrak{X}$), *are also measurable* ($\mathfrak{X}$).

In later chapters we shall consider certain additive classes of sets that present themselves naturally to us, in connection with the theory of measure, in metrical or in Euclidean spaces. In the abstract space X, about which we have made practically no hypothesis, we can only mention a few trivial examples of additive classes of sets, such as the class of all sets in X, or the class of all finite or enumerable sets and their complements. Let us still mention one further general theorem:

(4.2) ***Theorem.*** *Given any class $\mathfrak{M}$ of sets in X, there exists always a smallest additive class of sets containing $\mathfrak{M}$, i. e. an additive class $\mathfrak{N}_0 \supset \mathfrak{M}$ contained in every other additive class that contains $\mathfrak{M}$.*

For let $\mathfrak{N}_0$ be the product of all the additive classes that contain $\mathfrak{M}$. Such classes evidently exist, one such class being the class of all sets in X. We see at once that the class $\mathfrak{N}_0$ thus defined has the required properties.

§ 5. Additive functions of a set. In the rest of this chapter we suppose that *a definite additive class $\mathfrak{X}$ of sets is fixed in the space X.* In accordance with this hypothesis, we may often omit the symbol $\mathfrak{X}$ in our statements, without causing any ambiguity.

A function of a set, $\Phi(X)$, will be called *additive function of a set* ($\mathfrak{X}$) *on a set E*, if (i) E is a set ($\mathfrak{X}$), (ii) the function $\Phi(X)$ is defined and finite for each set $X \subset E$ measurable ($\mathfrak{X}$), and if (iii) $\Phi(\sum_n X_n) = \sum_n \Phi(X_n)$ for every sequence $\{X_n\}$ of sets ($\mathfrak{X}$) contained in E and such that $X_i \cdot X_k = 0$ whenever $i \neq k$. For simplicity, we shall speak of an "additive function" instead of an "additive function of a set ($\mathfrak{X}$)" whenever there is no mistaking the meaning. An additive function of a set ($\mathfrak{X}$) will be called *monotone* on E if its values for the subsets ($\mathfrak{X}$) of E are of constant sign. A non-negative function $\Phi(\mathfrak{X})$ additive and monotone, will also be termed *non-decreasing*, on account of the fact that, for each pair of sets A and B measurable ($\mathfrak{X}$), the inequality $A \subset B$ implies $\Phi(B) = \Phi(A) + \Phi(B \dot{-} A) \geqslant \Phi(A)$. For the same reason, non-positive monotone functions will be termed *non-increasing*.

(5.1) ***Theorem.*** *If $\Phi(x)$ is an additive function on a set E, then*

(5.2)
$$\Phi(\lim_n X_n) = \lim_n \Phi(X_n)$$

for every monotone sequence $\{X_n\}$ of sets ($\mathfrak{X}$) contained in E. If $\Phi(X)$ is a non-negative monotone function, then

(5.3)
$$\Phi(\liminf_n X_n) \leqslant \liminf_n \Phi(X_n) \quad \textit{and} \quad \Phi(\limsup_n X_n) \geqslant \limsup_n \Phi(X_n)$$

for every sequence $\{X_n\}$ of sets ($\mathfrak{X}$) in E.

Proof. Let $\{X_n\}_{n=1,2,...}$ be a sequence of sets $(\mathfrak{X})$ contained in E.

If $\{X_n\}$ is an ascending monotone sequence, then

$$\lim_n X_n = \sum_{n=1}^{\infty} X_n = X_1 + \sum_{n=1}^{\infty}(X_{n+1} - X_n),$$

and consequently, $\Phi(X)$ being an additive function on E,

$$\Phi(\lim_n X_n) = \Phi(X_1) + \sum_{n=1}^{\infty}\Phi(X_{n+1} - X_n) =$$
$$= \lim_n [\Phi(X_1) + \sum_{k=1}^{n-1}\Phi(X_{k+1} - X_k)] = \lim_n \Phi(X_n).$$

If $\{X_n\}$ is a descending sequence, the sequence $\{E - X_n\}$ is ascending, and, by the result already proved,

$$\Phi(E) - \Phi(\lim_n X_n) = \Phi[\lim_n (E - X_n)] = \lim_n \Phi(E - X_n) = \Phi(E) - \lim_n \Phi(X_n),$$

from which (5.2) follows at once.

Finally, if $\{X_n\}$ is any sequence, but $\Phi(X)$ is a non-negative monotone function, we put

$$Y_n = \prod_{k=n}^{\infty} X_k \quad \textit{for} \quad n = 1, 2, ... \tag{5.4}$$

The sets Y_n are measurable $(\mathfrak{X})$ on account of (4.1), and form an ascending sequence. We therefore have, by the part of our theorem proved already,

$$\Phi(\lim_n Y_n) = \lim_n \Phi(Y_n). \tag{5.5}$$

Now, it follows from (5.4) that $Y_n \subset X_n$, and so, $\Phi(Y_n) \leqslant \Phi(X_n)$, for each n. On the other hand, $\liminf_n X_n = \lim_n Y_n$, and therefore the first of the relations (5.3) is an immediate consequence of (5.5). We establish similarly (or, if preferred, by changing X_n to $E - X_n$) the second of these relations, and this completes the proof of the theorem.

Every function of a set $\Phi(X)$, additive on a set E, can easily be extended to the whole space $\boldsymbol{X}$. In fact, if we write, for instance, $\Phi_1(X) = \Phi(X \cdot E)$ for every set X measurable $(\mathfrak{X})$, we see at once that $\Phi_1(X)$ is a function additive on the whole space $\boldsymbol{X}$, that coincides with $\Phi(X)$ for measurable subsets of E and vanishes for measurable sets containing no points of E. We shall call the function $\Phi_1(X)$, thus defined, the *extension* of $\Phi(X)$ from the set E to the space $\boldsymbol{X}$.

§ 6. The variations of an additive function. The upper and lower bounds of the values that a function of a set $\Phi(X)$, additive on a set E assumes for the measurable subsets of this set E, will be called *upper variation* and *lower variation* of the function Φ over E, and denoted by $\overline{\mathrm{W}}(\Phi; E)$ and $\underline{\mathrm{W}}(\Phi; E)$ respectively. Since every additive function vanishes for the empty set, we evidently have $\underline{\mathrm{W}}(\Phi; E) \leqslant 0 \leqslant \overline{\mathrm{W}}(\Phi; E)$. The number $\overline{\mathrm{W}}(\Phi; E) + |\underline{\mathrm{W}}(\Phi; E)|$ will be called *absolute variation* of the function Φ on E and denoted by $\mathrm{W}(\Phi; E)$.

(6.1) *Theorem. If $\Phi(X)$ is an additive function on a set E, its variations over E are always finite.*

Proof. Suppose that $\mathrm{W}(\Phi; E) = +\infty$. We shall show firstly that there then exists a sequence $\{E_n\}_{n=1,2,...}$ of sets $(\mathfrak{X})$ such that

(6.2) $$E_n \subset E_{n-1} \text{ for } n > 1; \quad \mathrm{W}(\Phi; E_n) = \infty; \quad |\Phi(E_n)| \geqslant n - 1.$$

For let us choose $E_1 = E$ and suppose the sets E_n for $n = 1, 2, ..., k$ defined so as to satisfy the conditions (6.2). By the second of these conditions with $n = k$, there exists a measurable set $A \subset E_k$ such that

(6.3) $$|\Phi(A)| \geqslant |\Phi(E_k)| + k.$$

If $\mathrm{W}(\Phi; A) = \infty$, we have only to choose $E_{k+1} = A$ in order to satisfy the conditions (6.2) for $n = k + 1$. If, on the other hand, $\mathrm{W}(\Phi; A)$ is finite, we must have $\mathrm{W}(\Phi; E_k - A) = +\infty$, and, by (6.3), $|\Phi(E_k - A)| \geqslant |\Phi(A)| - |\Phi(E_k)| \geqslant k$, so that the conditions (6.2) will be satisfied for $n = k + 1$, if we choose $E_{k+1} = E_k - A$. The sequence $\{E_n\}$ is thus obtained by induction.

Now, on account of Theorem 5.1 and of the third of the conditions (6.2), we should have the equality $\Phi(\lim_n E_n) = \lim_n \Phi(E_n) = \infty$, and since every additive function of a set is, by definition, finite, this is evidently impossible. Q. E. D.

It follows from the theorem just proved that every function $\Phi(X)$ additive on a set E is not only finite for the subsets $(\mathfrak{X})$ of E, but also *bounded*; in fact, the values it assumes are bounded in modulus by the finite number $\mathrm{W}(\Phi; E)$.

Theorem 6.1 can be further completed as follows:

(6.4) ***Theorem.*** *For every function* $F(X)$ *additive on a set* E, *the variations* $\overline{\mathrm{W}}(\Phi;X)$, $\underline{\mathrm{W}}(\Phi;X)$ *and* $\mathrm{W}(\Phi;X)$ *are also additive functions of a set* $(\mathfrak{X})$ *on* E, *and we have, for every measurable set* $X \subset E$

$$\Phi(X) = \overline{\mathrm{W}}(\Phi;X) + \underline{\mathrm{W}}(\Phi;X). \tag{6.5}$$

Proof. To fix the ideas, consider the function $\Omega_1(X) = \overline{\mathrm{W}}(\Phi;X)$. Since this function is finite by Theorem 6.1, we have to show that for every sequence $\{X_n\}$ of measurable sets contained in E, and such that $X_i \cdot X_k = 0$ whenever $i \neq k$,

$$\Omega_1(\sum_n X_n) = \sum_n \Omega_1(X_n). \tag{6.6}$$

For this purpose, let us observe that for every measurable set $X \subset \sum_n X_n$ we have $\Phi(X) = \sum_n \Phi(X \cdot X_n) \leqslant \sum_n \Omega_1(X_n)$, and hence

$$\Omega_1(\sum_n X_n) \leqslant \sum_n \Omega_1(X_n). \tag{6.7}$$

On the other hand, denoting generally by Y_n any measurable set variable in X_n, we have $\Omega_1(\sum_n X_n) \geqslant \Phi(\sum_n Y_n) = \sum_n \Phi(Y_n)$, and therefore also $\Omega_1(\sum_n X_n) \geqslant \sum_n \Omega_1(X_n)$. Combining this with (6.7) we get the equality (6.6).

Finally, to establish (6.5), we observe that for every measurable subset Y of X we have $\Phi(Y) = \Phi(X) - \Phi(X - Y) \leqslant \Phi(X) - \underline{\mathrm{W}}(\Phi;X)$, and so $\overline{\mathrm{W}}(\Phi;X) \leqslant \Phi(X) - \underline{\mathrm{W}}(\Phi;X)$. Similarly $\underline{\mathrm{W}}(\Phi;X) \geqslant \Phi(X) - \overline{\mathrm{W}}(\Phi;X)$. These two inequalities give together the equality (6.5), and the proof of Theorem 6.4 is complete.

It follows from this theorem that every function of a set $\Phi(X)$ additive on a set E is, on E, the difference of two non-negative additive functions. The formula (6.5) expresses, in fact, $\Phi(X)$ as the sum of two variations of $\Phi(X)$, of which the one is non-negative and the other non-positive; this particular decomposition of an additive function of a set will be termed the *Jordan decomposition*.

We can now complete Theorem 5.1 as follows:

(6.8) ***Theorem.*** *If* $\Phi(X)$ *is additive on a set* E, *we have* $\Phi(\lim_n X_n) = \lim_n \Phi(X_n)$ *for every convergent sequence* $\{X_n\}$ *of sets* $(\mathfrak{X})$ *contained in* E.

In fact, making use of the Jordan decomposition, we may restrict ourselves to non-negative functions $\Phi(X)$, and for these Theorem 6.8 follows at once from the second part of Theorem 5.1.

§ 7. Measurable functions. Given an arbitrary condition, or property, (V) of a point x, let us denote generally by $\underset{x}{\mathrm{E}}[(V)]$ the set of all the points x of the space considered that fulfill this condition, or have this property. Thus, for instance, if $f(x)$ denotes a function of a point defined on a set E and a is a real number, the symbol

$$(7.1) \qquad \underset{x}{\mathrm{E}}[x \in E; f(x) > a]$$

denotes the set of the points x of E at which $f(x) > a$.

A function of a point, $f(x)$, defined on a set E, will be termed *measurable* $(\mathfrak{X})$, or simply *function* $(\mathfrak{X})$, if the set E, and the set (7.1) for each finite a, are measurable $(\mathfrak{X})$. It is easy to see that

(7.2) *In order that a function* $f(x)$ *be measurable on a measurable set* E, *it suffices that the set* (7.1) *should be so for all values of* a *belonging to an arbitrary everywhere dense set* R *of real numbers (the same holds with the set* (7.1) *replaced by the set* $\underset{x}{\mathrm{E}}[x \in E;\, f(x) \geqslant a]$).

In fact, for every real a, the set R contains a decreasing sequence of numbers $\{r_n\}$ converging to a. We therefore have $\underset{x}{\mathrm{E}}[x \in E; f(x) > a] = \sum_{n=1}^{\infty} \underset{x}{\mathrm{E}}[x \in E; f(x) > r_n]$ and, each term of the sum on the right being measurable by hypothesis, the same holds for the sum itself (cf. Theorem 4.1).

Every function $f(x)$ measurable on a set E, can be continued in various ways, so as to become a measurable function on the whole space X. For definiteness, we shall understand by the *extension* of the function $f(x)$ from the set E to the space X, the function $f_0(x)$ equal to $f(x)$ on E and to 0 everywhere else. For brevity, we shall often deal only with functions measurable on the whole space X, but it is easy to see that all the theorems and the reasonings of this, and of the succeeding, § could be taken relative to an arbitrary set $(\mathfrak{X})$.

The equations

$$\underset{x}{\mathrm{E}}[f(x)\leqslant a]=\mathrm{C}\underset{x}{\mathrm{E}}[f(x)>a], \qquad \underset{x}{\mathrm{E}}[f(x)\geqslant a]=\prod_{n=1}^{\infty}\underset{x}{\mathrm{E}}\left[f(x)>a-\frac{1}{n}\right],$$

$$\underset{x}{\mathrm{E}}[f(x)<a]=\mathrm{C}\underset{x}{\mathrm{E}}[f(x)\geqslant a], \qquad \underset{x}{\mathrm{E}}[f(x)=a]=\underset{x}{\mathrm{E}}[f(x)\geqslant a]\cdot\underset{x}{\mathrm{E}}[f(x)\leqslant a],$$

$$\underset{x}{\mathrm{E}}[f(x)<+\infty]=\sum_{n=1}^{\infty}\mathrm{E}[f(x)<n], \qquad \underset{x}{\mathrm{E}}[f(x)>-\infty]=\sum_{n=1}^{\infty}\underset{x}{\mathrm{E}}[f(x)>-n],$$

$$\underset{x}{\mathrm{E}}[f(x)=+\infty]=\mathrm{C}\underset{x}{\mathrm{E}}[f(x)<+\infty], \qquad \underset{x}{\mathrm{E}}[f(x)=-\infty]=\mathrm{C}\underset{x}{\mathrm{E}}[f(x)>-\infty]$$

show that for every measurable function $f(x)$ and for every number a, the left hand sides are measurable sets. Conversely, in the definition of measurable function, we may replace the set (7.1) by any one of the sets $\underset{x}{\mathrm{E}}[f(x)\geqslant a]$, $\underset{x}{\mathrm{E}}[f(x)\leqslant a]$ or $\underset{x}{\mathrm{E}}[f(x)<a]$; this follows at once from the identity

$$\underset{x}{\mathrm{E}}[f(x)>a]=\sum_{n=1}^{\infty}\underset{x}{\mathrm{E}}\left[f(x)\geqslant a+\frac{1}{n}\right]=\mathrm{C}\underset{x}{\mathrm{E}}[f(x)\leqslant a]=\mathrm{C}\prod_{n=1}^{\infty}\underset{x}{\mathrm{E}}\left[f(x)<a+\frac{1}{n}\right].$$

To any function $f(x)$ on a set E, we attach two functions $f(x)$ and $f(x)$ on E, called, respectively, the *non-negative part* and the *non-positive part* of $f(x)$ and defined as follows:

$$\overset{\circ}{f}(x)=f(x) \quad \text{or} \quad 0 \quad \text{according as} \quad f(x)\geqslant 0 \quad \text{or} \quad f(x)<0,$$

$$\underset{\circ}{f}(x)=f(x) \quad \text{or} \quad 0 \quad \text{according as} \quad f(x)<0 \quad \text{or} \quad f(x)\geqslant 0.$$

We see at once, *that in order that a function be measurable on a set E, it is necessary and sufficient that its two parts, the non-negative and the non-positive, be measurable.*

Returning now to the notions of characteristic function, and simple function introduced in § 3, we have the theorem:

(7.3) ***Theorem.*** *In order that a set E be measurable $(\mathfrak{X})$, it is necessary and sufficient that its characteristic function be measurable. More generally, in order that, on a set E, a simple function $f(x)$ be measurable $(\mathfrak{X})$, it is necessary and sufficient that, for each value of $f(x)$, the points at which this value is assumed on E, should constitute a measurable subset of E.*

Another theorem, of great utility in applications, is the following:

(7.4) ***Theorem.*** *Every function $f(x)$ that is measurable $(\mathfrak{X})$ and non-negative on a set E, is the limit of a non-decreasing sequence of simple functions, finite, measurable and non-negative on E.*

In fact, if we write for each positive integer n and for $x \in E$,

$$f_n(x) = \begin{cases} \dfrac{i-1}{2^n}, & \text{if } \dfrac{i-1}{2^n} \leqslant f(x) < \dfrac{i}{2^n}, \quad 1 \leqslant i \leqslant 2^n \cdot n, \\ n \;, & \text{if } f(x) \geqslant n, \end{cases}$$

the functions $f_n(x)$ thus defined are evidently simple and non-negative, and, on account of Theorem 7.3, measurable on E. Further, as is easily seen, the sequence $\{f_n(x)\}$ is non-decreasing. Finally $\lim\limits_n f_n(x) = f(x)$ for every $x \in E$; for, if $f(x) < +\infty$, we have, as soon as n exceeds the value of $f(x)$, the inequalities $0 \leqslant f(x) - f_n(x) \leqslant 1/2^n$, while, if $f(x) = +\infty$, we have $f_n(x) = n$ for $n = 1, 2, \ldots$, and so $\lim\limits_n f_n(x) = +\infty = f(x)$.

§ 8. Elementary operations on measurable functions. We shall now show that elementary operations effected on measurable functions always lead to measurable functions.

(8.1) ***Theorem.*** *Given two measurable functions $f(x)$ and $g(x)$, the sets*

$$\mathop{\mathrm{E}}_x[f(x) > g(x)], \quad \mathop{\mathrm{E}}_x[f(x) \geqslant g(x)] \quad \text{and} \quad \mathop{\mathrm{E}}_x[f(x) = g(x)],$$

are measurable.

The proof follows at once from the identities

$$\mathop{\mathrm{E}}_x[f(x) > g(x)] = \sum_{n=-\infty}^{+\infty} \sum_{m=1}^{+\infty} \mathop{\mathrm{E}}_x\left[f(x) > \frac{n}{m}\right] \cdot \mathop{\mathrm{E}}_x\left[g(x) < \frac{n}{m}\right],$$

$$\mathop{\mathrm{E}}_x[f \geqslant g] = \mathrm{C}\mathop{\mathrm{E}}_x[g > f] \quad \text{and} \quad \mathop{\mathrm{E}}_x[f = g] = \mathop{\mathrm{E}}_x[f \geqslant g] \cdot \mathop{\mathrm{E}}_x[g \geqslant f].$$

(8.2) ***Theorem.*** *If the function $f(x)$ is measurable, $|f(x)|^\alpha$ is also a measurable function.*

For $\alpha > 0$, the proof is a consequence of the identity

$$\mathop{\mathrm{E}}_x[|f(x)|^\alpha > a] = \mathop{\mathrm{E}}_x[f(x) > a^{1/\alpha}] + \mathop{\mathrm{E}}_x[f(x) < -a^{1/\alpha}],$$

which is valid for every $a \geqslant 0$, while for $a < 0$ its left hand side coincides with the whole space and therefore constitutes a measurable set. For $\alpha < 0$, the proof is similar.

(8.3) ***Theorem.*** *Every linear combination of measurable functions with constant coefficients represents a measurable function.*

The identities

$$\mathop{\mathrm{E}}_x[\alpha\cdot f(x)+\beta>a]=\mathop{\mathrm{E}}_x\left[f(x)>\frac{a-\beta}{\alpha}\right] \qquad \text{for} \quad \alpha>0,$$

$$\mathop{\mathrm{E}}_x[\alpha\cdot f(x)+\beta>a]=\mathop{\mathrm{E}}_x\left[f(x)<\frac{a-\beta}{\alpha}\right] \qquad \text{for} \quad \alpha<0,$$

valid for every function $f(x)$ and for all numbers a, $\alpha\neq 0$, and β, show, in the first place, that $\alpha.\ f(x)+\beta$ is a measurable function, if $f(x)$ is measurable. It follows further, from Theorem 8.1 and from the identities:

$$\mathop{\mathrm{E}}_x[\alpha\cdot f+\beta\cdot g>a]=\mathop{\mathrm{E}}_x\left[f>-\frac{\beta}{\alpha}g+\frac{a}{\alpha}\right] \qquad \text{for} \quad \alpha>0$$

$$\mathop{\mathrm{E}}_x[\alpha\cdot f+\beta\cdot g>a]=\mathop{\mathrm{E}}_x\left[f<-\frac{\beta}{\alpha}g+\frac{a}{\alpha}\right] \qquad \text{for} \quad \alpha<0$$

that if $f(x)$ and $g(x)$ are measurable functions, so is $\alpha\cdot f(x)+\beta\cdot g(x)$.

(8.4) ***Theorem.*** *The product of two measurable functions $f(x)$ and $g(x)$ is a measurable function.*

Measurability of the product $f\cdot g$ is derived by applying Theorems 8.2 and 8.3 to the identity $fg=\frac{1}{4}[(f+g)^2-(f-g)^2]$, the completion of the proof, by taking into account possible infinities of f and g, being trivial.

(8.5) ***Theorem.*** *Given a sequence of measurable functions $\{f_n(x)\}$, the functions*

$$\mathop{\text{upper bound}}_n f_n(x), \quad \mathop{\text{lower bound}}_n f_n(x), \quad \limsup_n f_n(x) \quad \textit{and} \quad \liminf_n f_n(x)$$

are also measurable.

The measurability of $h(x)=\mathop{\text{upper bound}}_n f_n(x)$ follows from the identity $\mathop{\mathrm{E}}_x[h(x)>a]=\sum_n \mathop{\mathrm{E}}_x[f_n(x)>a]$. For the lower bound, the corresponding proof is derived by change of sign.

Hence, the functions $h_n(x)=\text{upper bound}\,[f_{n+1}(x), f_{n+2}(x), \ldots]$ are measurable, and the same is therefore true of the function $\limsup_n f_n(x)=\lim_n h_n(x)=\mathop{\text{lower bound}}_n h_n(x)$. By changing the sign of $f_n(x)$, we prove the same for lim inf.

§ 9. Measure. A function of a set $\mu(X)$ will be called a *measure* ($\mathfrak{X}$), if it is defined and non-negative for every set ($\mathfrak{X}$), and if

$$\mu(\sum_n X_n) = \sum_n \mu(X_n)$$

for every sequence $\{X_n\}$ of sets ($\mathfrak{X}$) no two of which have points in common. The number $\mu(X)$ is then termed, for every set X measurable ($\mathfrak{X}$), the *measure* (μ) of X. If every point of a set E, except at most the points belonging to a subset of E of measure (μ) zero, possesses a certain property V, we shall say that the condition V is satisfied *almost everywhere* (μ) in E, or, that *almost every* (μ) point of E has the property V. We shall suppose, in the sequel of this Chapter, that, just as the class $\mathfrak{X}$ was chosen once for all, a measure μ corresponding to this class is also kept fixed. Accordingly, we shall often omit the symbol (μ) in the expressions "measure (μ)", "almost everywhere (μ)", etc. Clearly $\mu(X) \leqslant \mu(Y)$ for any pair of sets X and Y measurable ($\mathfrak{X}$) such that $X \subset Y$, and $\mu(\sum_n X_n) \leqslant \sum_n \mu(X_n)$ for every sequence of measurable sets $\{X_n\}$.

A measure may also assume infinite values, and is therefore not in general an additive function according to the definition of § 5.

The results established in this chapter concerning perfectly arbitrary measures will be interpreted in the sequel for more special theories of measure, (for instance, those of Lebesgue and Carathéodory). For the present, we shall be content mentioning a few examples.

Let us take for $\mathfrak{X}$, the class of all sets in a space $\mathcal{X}$. We obtain a trivial example of measure ($\mathfrak{X}$) by writing $\mu(X) = 0$ identically, (or else $\mu(X) = +\infty$) for every set $X \subset \mathcal{X}$. Another example consists in choosing an element a in $\mathcal{X}$ and writing $\mu(X) = 1$ or $\mu(X) = 0$, according as $a \in X$ or not. In the case of an enumerable space $\mathcal{X}$, consisting of elements $a_1, a_2, \ldots, a_n, \ldots$, the general form of a measure $\mu(X)$ defined for all subsets X of $\mathcal{X}$ is $\mu(X) = \sum_n k_n f_n(X)$ where $\{k_n\}$ is a sequence of non-negative real numbers and $f_n(X)$ is equal to 1 or 0 according as $a_n \in X$ or not. It follows that every measure defined for all subsets of an enumerable space, and vanishing for the sets that consist of a single point, vanishes identically. The similar problem for spaces of higher potencies is much more difficult (see S. Ulam [1]). For a space of the potency of the continuum see also S. Banach and C. Kuratowski [1], E. Szpilrajn [1], W. Sierpiński [I, p. 60], W. Sierpiński and E. Szpilrajn [1].

We shall now prove the following theorem analogous to Theorem 5.1:

(9.1) ***Theorem.*** *If $\{X_n\}$ is a monotone ascending sequence of measurable sets, then* $\lim_n \mu(X_n) = \mu(\lim_n X_n)$. *The same holds for monotone descending sequences provided, however, that* $\mu(X_1) \neq \infty$.

More generally, for every sequence $\{X_n\}$ *of measurable sets,*

(9.2) $$\mu(\liminf_n X_n) \leqslant \liminf_n \mu(X_n)$$

and, if further $\mu(\sum_n X_n) \neq \infty$,

(9.3) $$\mu(\limsup_n X_n) \geqslant \limsup_n \mu(X_n),$$

so that, in particular, if the sequence $\{X_n\}$ *converges and its sum has finite measure,* $\lim_n \mu(X_n) = \mu(\lim_n X_n)$.

Proof. For an ascending sequence $\{X_n\}_{n=1,2,\dots}$ the equation $\lim_n \mu(X_n) = \mu(\lim_n X_n)$ follows at once from the relation

$$\lim_n X_n = \sum_{n=1}^{\infty} X_n = X_1 + \sum_{n=1}^{\infty}(X_{n+1} - X_n),$$

and if the sequence $\{X_n\}$ is descending and $\mu(X_1) \neq \infty$, then the measure $\mu(X)$ is an additive function on the set X_1 and consequently the required result follows from Theorem 5.1.

In exactly the same way, if for an arbitrary sequence $\{X_n\}$ of measurable sets, $\sum_n X_n$ is of finite measure, the measure $\mu(X)$ is an additive function on this set, and the two inequalities (9.2) and (9.3) follow from Theorem 5.1. To establish the first of these inequalities without assuming that the sum of the sets X_n has finite measure, we write as in the proof of Theorem 5.1

$$Y_n = \prod_{k=n}^{\infty} X_k.$$

Since the sequence is ascending, and $Y_n \subset X_n$ for every n, we have $\mu(\liminf_n X_n) = \mu(\lim_n Y_n) = \lim_n \mu(Y_n) \leqslant \liminf_n \mu(X_n)$.

We conclude this § with an important theorem due to D. Egoroff, concerning sequences of measurable functions (cf. D. Egoroff [1], and also W. Sierpiński [14], F. Riesz [2; 3], H. Hahn [I, pp. 556—8]). We shall first prove the following lemma:

(9.4) **Lemma.** *If E is a measurable set of finite measure* (μ) *and if* $\{f_n(x)\}$ *is a sequence of finite measurable functions on E, converging on this set to a finite measurable function* $f(x)$, *there exists, for each pair of positive numbers* ε, η, *a positive integer N and a measurable subset H of E such that* $\mu(H) < \eta$ *and*

(9.5) $$|f_n(x) - f(x)| < \varepsilon$$

for every $n > N$ *and every* $x \in E - H$.

Proof. Let us denote generally by E_m the subset of E consisting of the points x for which (9.5) holds whenever $n > m$. Thus defined, the sets E_m are measurable and form a monotone ascending sequence, since for each integer m, we have

$$E_m = \prod_{n=m+1}^{\infty} \mathop{\mathrm{E}}_{x}[x \in E; |f(x) - f_n(x)| < \varepsilon].$$

Further, since $\{f_n(x)\}$ converges to $f(x)$ on the whole of E, we have $E = \sum_m E_m$, and so, by Theorem 9.1, $\mu(E) = \lim_m \mu(E_m)$, i. e. $\lim_m \mu(E - E_m) = 0$, and therefore, from a sufficiently large m_0 onwards, $\mu(E - E_m) < \eta$. We have now only to choose $N = m_0$ and $H = E - E_{m_0}$, and the lemma is proved.

(9.6) ***Egoroff's Theorem.*** *If E is a measurable set of finite measure (μ) and if $\{f_n(x)\}$ is a sequence of measurable functions finite almost everywhere on E, that converges almost everywhere on this set to a finite measurable function $f(x)$, then there exists, for each $\varepsilon > 0$, a subset Q of E such that $\mu(E - Q) < \varepsilon$ and such that the convergence of $\{f_n(x)\}$ to $f(x)$ is uniform on Q.*

Proof. By removing from E, if necessary, a set of measure (μ) zero, we may suppose that on E, the functions $f_n(x)$ are everywhere finite, and converge everywhere to $f(x)$. By the preceding lemma, we can associate with each integer $m > 0$ a set $H_m \subset E$ such that $\mu(H_m) < \varepsilon/2^m$ and an index N_m such that

(9.7) $|f_n(x) - f(x)| < 1/2^m$ *for* $n > N_m$ *and for* $x \in E - H_m$.

Let us write $Q = E - \sum_{m=1}^{\infty} H_m$. We find

$$\mu(E - Q) \leqslant \sum_{m=1}^{\infty} \mu(H_m) \leqslant \sum_{m=1}^{\infty} \varepsilon/2^m = \varepsilon,$$

and since the sequence $f_n(x)$ converges uniformly to $f(x)$ on the set Q on account of (9.7), the theorem is proved.

The theorem of Egoroff can be given another form (cf. N. Lusin [I, p. 20]), and, at the same time, the hypothesis concerning finite measure of E can be slightly relaxed.

(9.8) *If E is the sum of a sequence of measurable sets of finite measure (μ) and if $\{f_n(x)\}$ is a sequence of measurable functions finite almost everywhere on this set, converging almost everywhere on E to a finite function, then the set E can be expressed as the sum of a sequence of measurable sets H, E_1, E_2, ... such that $\mu(H)=0$ and that the sequence $\{f_n(x)\}$ converges uniformly on each of the sets E_n.*

For the proof, it suffices to take the case in which the set E is itself of finite measure. With this hypothesis, we can, on account of Theorem 9.6, define by induction a sequence $\{E_k\}_{k=1,2,...}$ of measurable sets such that $\mu(E-\sum_{k=1}^{n}E_k)\leqslant 1/n$, and that the sequence $\{f_n(x)\}$ converges uniformly on the set E_k for each k. Choosing $H=E-\sum_{k=1}^{\infty}E_k$, we have $\mu(H)=0$, and the theorem is proved.

As we may observe, the hypothesis that the set E is the sum of a sequence of sets of finite measure, is essential for the validity of Theorem 9.8. For this purpose, let us take as a space X_0 the interval $[0, 1]$, and as an additive class $\mathfrak{X}_0$ of sets, that of all subsets of X_0. Further, let us define a measure μ_0 by writing $\mu_0(X)=\infty$ whenever the set $X\in\mathfrak{X}_0$ is infinite and $\mu_0(X)=n$, if X is a finite set and n denotes the number of its elements. The sets of measure (μ_0) zero then coincide with the empty set. Finally, let $\{g_n(x)\}$ be an arbitrary sequence of functions, continuous on the interval $[0, 1]$, converging everywhere on this interval, but not uniformly on any subinterval of $[0, 1]$.

To justify our remark concerning Theorem 9.8, it suffices to show that the interval $X_0=[0, 1]$ is not representable as the sum of a sequence $\{E_n\}$ of sets such that the sequence of functions $\{g_n(x)\}$ converges uniformly on each of them. But if such a decomposition were to exist, we might suppose firstly — since the functions $g_n(x)$ are continuous — all the sets E_n closed. Then, however, by the theorem of Baire (cf. Chap. II, § 9) one of them at least would contain a subinterval of $[0, 1]$. This gives a contradiction, since by hypothesis, the sequence $\{g_n(x)\}$ does not converge uniformly on any interval whatsoever.

§ 10. Integral.

If we are given in the space X an additive class of sets $\mathfrak{X}$ and a measure μ defined for the sets of this class, we can attach to them a process of integration for functions of a point. In fact:

(i) If $f(x)$ is a function ($\mathfrak{X}$) non-negative on a set E, we shall understand by the *definite integral* ($\mathfrak{X}$, μ) of $f(x)$ over E the upper bound of the sums

$$\sum_{k=1}^{n} v_k\,\mu(E_k),$$

where $\{E_k\}_{k=1,2,...,n}$ is an arbitrary finite sequence of sets ($\mathfrak{X}$) such that $E=E_1+E_2+...+E_n$ and $E_i\cdot E_k=0$ for $i\neq k$, and where v_k, for $k=1, 2, ..., n$, denotes the lower bound of $f(x)$ on E_k.

(ii) If $f(x)$ is an arbitrary function measurable ($\mathfrak{X}$) on a set E, we shall say that $f(x)$ *possesses a definite integral* ($\mathfrak{X}$, μ) *over* E, if one at least of the non-negative functions $\mathring{f}(x)$ and $-\underset{\circ}{f}(x)$ (cf. § 3) possesses a finite integral over E according to definition (i). And, if this condition is satisfied, we shall understand by the *definite integral* ($\mathfrak{X}$, μ) of the function $f(x)$ over E the difference between the integral of $\mathring{f}(x)$ and that of $-\underset{\circ}{f}(x)$ over E. The definite integral ($\mathfrak{X}$, μ) of $f(x)$ over E will be written $(\mathfrak{X})\int_E f(x)\,d\mu(x)$. If this integral is finite, the function $f(x)$ is said to be *integrable* ($\mathfrak{X}$, μ). For every function $f(x)$ possessing a definite integral over a set E, we evidently have

$$(\mathfrak{X})\int_E f\,d\mu = (\mathfrak{X})\int_E \mathring{f}\,d\mu - (\mathfrak{X})\int_E (-\underset{\circ}{f})\,d\mu = (\mathfrak{X})\int_E \mathring{f}\,d\mu + (\mathfrak{X})\int_E \underset{\circ}{f}\,d\mu.$$

We see at once that the two definitions (i) and (ii) are compatible, i. e. that they give the same value of the integral to any non-negative measurable function. Moreover:

(10.1) *If* $g = \{v_1, X_1; v_2, X_2; \ldots; v_m, X_m\}$ *is a simple non-negative function on the set* $E = X_1 + X_2 + \ldots + X_m$, *the sets* X_i *being measurable* ($\mathfrak{X}$), *then*

$$\int_E g\,d\mu = \sum_{i=1}^{m} v_i\,\mu(X_i).$$

For, if $\{E_j\}_{j=1,2,\ldots,n}$ is an arbitrary subdivision of E into a finite number of sets ($\mathfrak{X}$) without points in common, and if w_j denotes the lower bound of $g(x)$ on E_j, we have $w_j \leqslant v_i$ whenever $E_j \cdot X_i \neq 0$. Hence $\sum_{j=1}^{n} w_j\,\mu(E_j) = \sum_{j=1}^{n}\sum_{i=1}^{m} w_j\,\mu(E_j \cdot X_i) \leqslant \sum_{j=1}^{n}\sum_{i=1}^{m} v_i\,\mu(E_j \cdot X_i) = \sum_{i=1}^{m} v_i\,\mu(X_i)$, and therefore $\int_E g\,d\mu \leqslant \sum_i v_i\,\mu(X_i)$. The opposite inequality is obvious, since the sets $X_1, X_2, \ldots, X_m$ themselves constitute a subdivision of E into a finite sequence of sets ($\mathfrak{X}$) on which the values of $g(x)$ are $v_1, v_2, \ldots, v_m$ respectively.

§ 11. Fundamental properties of the integral. We shall begin with a few lemmas concerning integration of simple functions. As in the preceding §§, the symbols $\mathfrak{X}$, μ etc. will often be omitted.

(11.1) *Lemma.* 1° *For every pair of functions $g(x)$ and $h(x)$, simple, non-negative, and measurable ($\mathfrak{X}$) on a set E, we have*

$$(11.2)\qquad \int_E [g(x)+h(x)]\,d\mu(x) = \int_E g(x)\,d\mu(x) + \int_E h(x)\,d\mu(x).$$

2° *If the function $f(x)$ is simple, non-negative, and measurable ($\mathfrak{X}$) on the set $A+B$ where A and B are sets ($\mathfrak{X}$) without common points, then*

$$(11.3)\qquad \int_{A+B} f(x)\,d\mu(x) = \int_A f(x)\,d\mu(x) + \int_B f(x)\,d\mu(x).$$

Proof. As regards 1°, let

$g=\{g_1, G_1; g_2, G_2; \dots; g_n, G_n\}$ and $h=\{h_1, H_1; h_2, H_2; \dots; h_m, H_m\}$,

where $E=G_1+\dots+G_n=H_1+\dots+H_m$.

We then have, by (10.1),

$$\int_E [g(x)+h(x)]\,d\mu(x) = \sum_{i=1}^{n}\sum_{j=1}^{m}(g_i+h_j)\,\mu(G_i\cdot H_j) =$$

$$= \sum_{i=1}^{n} g_i \sum_{j=1}^{m}\mu(G_i\cdot H_j) + \sum_{j=1}^{m} h_j \sum_{i=1}^{n}\mu(G_i\cdot H_j) =$$

$$= \sum_{i=1}^{n} g_i\mu(G_i) + \sum_{j=1}^{m} h_j\mu(H_j) = \int_E g(x)\,d\mu(x) + \int_E h(x)\,d\mu(x).$$

As regards 2°, if $E=A+B$ and $f=\{f_1, Q_1; f_2, Q_2; \dots; f_n, Q_n\}$, where $E=Q_1+Q_2+\dots+Q_n$, we have

$$\int_E f(x)\,d\mu(x) = \sum_{i=1}^{n} f_i\cdot\mu(Q_i) = \sum_{i=1}^{n} f_i\cdot\mu(A\cdot Q_i) + \sum_{i=1}^{n} f_i\cdot\mu(B\cdot Q_i) =$$

$$= \int_A f(x)\,d\mu(x) + \int_B f(x)\,d\mu(x).$$

(11.4) *Lemma.* *If $\{g_n(x)\}$ is a non-decreasing sequence of functions that are simple, non-negative, and measurable ($\mathfrak{X}$) on a set E, and if, for a function $h(x)$, simple, non-negative, and measurable, on E, we have $\lim\limits_n g_n(x) \geqslant h(x)$ on E, then*

$$(11.5)\qquad \lim_n \int_E g_n(x)\,d\mu(x) \geqslant \int_E h(x)\,d\mu(x).$$

Proof. Let $h = \{v_1, E_1; v_2, E_2; \ldots; v_m, E_m\}$, where

$$0 \leqslant v_1 < v_2 < \ldots < v_m \quad and \quad E = E_1 + E_2 + \ldots + E_m.$$

We may suppose $v_1 > 0$, for, otherwise, we should have $\int\limits_E h\,d\mu = \int\limits_{E-E_1} h\,d\mu$, and, since $\int\limits_E g_n\,d\mu \geqslant \int\limits_{E-E_1} g_n\,d\mu$, we could replace the set E by the set $E - E_1$ on which $h(x)$ does not vanish anywhere. Further we shall assume first that $v_m < +\infty$.

Let us choose an arbitrary positive number $\varepsilon < v_1$, and let us denote, for each positive integer n, by Q_n the set of the points x of E for which $g_n(x) > h(x) - \varepsilon$. The sets Q_n evidently form an ascending sequence converging to E, and, by Theorem 9.1, we have $\mu(Q_n) \to \mu(E)$. This being so we have two cases to distinguish:

(i) $\mu(E) \neq \infty$. We then can find an integer n_0 such that for $n > n_0$ we have $\mu(E - Q_n) < \varepsilon$, and therefore, by Lemma 11.1,

$$\int\limits_E g_n\,d\mu \geqslant \int\limits_{Q_n} g_n\,d\mu \geqslant \int\limits_{Q_n} [h(x) - \varepsilon]\,d\mu(x) =$$

$$= \int\limits_{Q_n} h\,d\mu - \varepsilon\mu(Q_n) \geqslant \int\limits_E h\,d\mu - v_m \cdot \mu(E - Q_n) - \varepsilon\mu(Q_n) \geqslant \int\limits_E h\,d\mu - [v_m + \mu(E)] \cdot \varepsilon;$$

and, passing to the limit, making first $n \to \infty$, and then $\varepsilon \to 0$, we obtain the inequality (11.5).

(ii) $\mu(E) = \infty$. Then, since $\int\limits_E g_n\,d\mu \geqslant (v_1 - \varepsilon)\,\mu(Q_n)$, we obtain $\lim\limits_n \int\limits_E g_n\,d\mu = \infty$, so that the inequality (11.5) is evidently satisfied.

Suppose now $v_m = +\infty$. Then by (10.1) and by what has already been proved, $\lim\limits_n \int\limits_E g_n\,d\mu \geqslant v \cdot \mu(E_m) + \sum\limits_{i=1}^{m-1} v_i \cdot \mu(E_i)$ for any finite number v, and consequently for $v = +\infty = v_m$ also; whence, in virtue of (10.1) the inequality (11.5) follows at once.

(11.6) *Lemma. If the functions of a non-decreasing sequence* $\{g_n(x)\}$ *are simple, non-negative, and measurable* ($\mathfrak{X}$) *on a set* E, *and if* $g(x) = \lim\limits_n g_n(x)$, *then* $\lim\limits_n \int\limits_E g_n(x)\,d\mu(x) = \int\limits_E g(x)\,d\mu(x)$.

Proof. Let $E_1, E_2, \ldots, E_m$ be an arbitrary subdivision of E into a finite number of measurable sets, and let $v_1, v_2, \ldots, v_m$ be the lower bounds of $g(x)$ on these sets respectively. Let us write $v = \{v_1, E_1; v_2, E_2; \ldots; v_m, E_m\}$. We evidently have $\lim\limits_n g_n(x) = g(x) \geqslant v(x)$ on E, and hence, by Lemma 11.4 and by Theorem 10.1

$$\lim_n \int_E g_n \, d\mu \geqslant \int_E v \, d\mu = \sum_{i=1}^{m} v_i \, \mu(E_i).$$

It follows that $\lim_n \int_E g_n \, d\mu \geqslant \int_E g \, d\mu$, and since the opposite inequality is obvious, the proof is complete.

We are now in a position to generalize Lemma 11.1 as follows:

(11.7) ***Theorem.*** *The relation* (11.2) *holds for every pair of functions, $g(x)$ and $h(x)$, non-negative and measurable* ($\mathfrak{X}$) *on the set E, and the relation* (11.3) *holds for every function $f(x)$ non-negative and measurable* ($\mathfrak{X}$) *on the set $A+B$, where A and B are sets* ($\mathfrak{X}$) *without points in common.*

Proof. By Theorem 7.4 there exist two non-decreasing sequences $\{g_n(x)\}$ and $\{h_n(x)\}$ of simple non-negative functions measurable ($\mathfrak{X}$) on E, such that $g(x) = \lim_n g_n(x)$ and $h(x) = \lim_n h_n(x)$. Now, by Lemma 11.1 (1^0), we have $\int_E (g_n + h_n) \, d\mu = \int_E g_n d\mu + \int_E h_n d\mu$ and hence, making $n \to \infty$, we obtain, on account of Lemma 11.6, the relation (11.2). Similarly, if we approximate to $f(x)$ on $A+B$ by a non-decreasing sequence of simple non-negative functions and make use of Lemma 11.1 (2^0), we obtain the relation (11.3).

(11.8) ***Theorem.*** 1^0 *For any function measurable* ($\mathfrak{X}$), *the integral over a set of measure zero is equal to zero.* 2^0 *If the functions $g(x)$ and $h(x)$ measurable on a set E are almost everywhere equal on E, and if one of the two is integrable on E, so is the other, and their integrals over E have the same value.* 3^0 *If a function $f(x)$ measurable* ($\mathfrak{X}$) *on a set E has an integral over E different from $+\infty$, the set of the points x of E at which $f(x) = +\infty$ has measure zero. In particular, if the integral of $f(x)$ over E is finite, the function $f(x)$ is finite almost everywhere on E.*

Proof. We obtain at once part 1^0 of this theorem by making successive use of the definitions (i) and (ii) of § 10.

As regards 2^0, it is evidently sufficient to consider the case of non-negative functions $g(x)$ and $h(x)$. If we denote by E_1 the set of the points x of E at which $g(x) \neq h(x)$, we have by hypothesis $\mu(E_1) = 0$, and, on account of (1^0) and of Theorem 11.7, we obtain $\int_E g \, d\mu = \int_{E-E_1} g \, d\mu = \int_{E-E_1} h \, d\mu = \int_E h \, d\mu$, as required.

Finally, as regards 3°, let us suppose that for a function $f(x)$ measurable ($\mathfrak{X}$) on E we have $f(x) = +\infty$ on a set $E_0 \subset E$ of positive measure. We then have $\int_E \mathring{f}\, d\mu \geqslant \int_{E_0} \mathring{f}\, d\mu \geqslant n\cdot\mu(E_0)$ for every n, and so $\int_E \mathring{f}\, d\mu = +\infty$. Consequently, the integral of $f(x)$ over E, if it exists, is positively infinite, and this completes the proof.

We now generalize Lemma 11.1 (1°) and also complete Theorem 11.7, as follows:

(11.9) ***Theorem of distributivity of the integral.*** *Every linear combination with constant coefficients, $a\cdot g(x) + b\cdot h(x)$ of two functions $g(x)$ and $h(x)$, integrable ($\mathfrak{X}$, μ) over a set E, is also integrable over E, and we have*

$$(11.10) \qquad \int_E (ag + bh)\, d\mu = a \int_E g\, d\mu + b \int_E h\, d\mu.$$

Proof. By Theorem 11.8 (3°), the set of the points at which either of the functions $g(x)$ and $h(x)$ is infinite, has measure zero, and if we replace on this set the values of both functions by 0, we shall not affect the values of the integrals appearing in the relation (11.10). We may therefore suppose that the given functions g and h are finite on E. Further, the relations

$$\int_E ag\, d\mu = a \int_E g\, d\mu, \qquad \int_E bh\, d\mu = b \int_E h\, d\mu$$

being obvious, we need only prove the formula (11.10) for the case $a=b=1$. Finally, the set E can be decomposed into four sets on each of which the two functions $g(x)$ and $h(x)$ are of constant sign. So that, on account of Theorem 11.7, we may assume that the functions $g(x)$ and $h(x)$ are of constant sign on the whole set E. Now, by the same theorem, the relation

$$(11.11) \qquad \int_E (g+h)\, d\mu = \int_E g\, d\mu + \int_E h\, d\mu$$

holds whenever the functions g and h are both non-negative or both non-positive on E, and it only remains, therefore, to show that this relation is valid when g and h have, on E, opposite signs, the one, $g(x)$ say, being non-negative, the other, $h(x)$, non-positive.

This being so, let E_1 and E_2 be the sets consisting of the points x of E for which we have $g(x)+h(x)\geqslant 0$ and $g(x)+h(x)<0$, respectively. The functions g, $g+h$, and $-h$ are non-negative on E_1 and we therefore have, by Theorem 11.7,

$$\int_{E_1} g\,d\mu=\int_{E_1}(g+h)\,d\mu+\int_{E_1}(-h)\,d\mu=\int_{E_1}(g+h)\,d\mu-\int_{E_1}h\,d\mu.$$

Similarly

$$-\int_{E_2} h\,d\mu=\int_{E_2}(-h)\,d\mu=\int_{E_2}(-g-h)\,d\mu+\int_{E_2}g\,d\mu=-\int_{E_2}(g+h)\,d\mu+\int_{E_2}g\,d\mu.$$

Therefore, for $i=1, 2$, we have $\int_{E_i}(g+h)\,d\mu=\int_{E_i}g\,d\mu+\int_{E_i}h\,d\mu$, and by Theorem 11.7 we obtain the relation (11.11).

(11.12) ***Theorem on absolute integrability.*** 1⁰ *In order that a function $f(x)$ measurable ($\mathfrak{X}$) on a set E should be integrable ($\mathfrak{X}$, μ) on E, it is necessary and sufficient that its absolute value should be so.* 2⁰ *If, for a function $g(x)$ measurable ($\mathfrak{X}$) on a set E, there exists a function $h(x)$, integrable ($\mathfrak{X}$, μ) and such that $|g(x)|\leqslant h(x)$ on E, then the function $g(x)$ also is integrable on E; in particular, every function measurable ($\mathfrak{X}$) and bounded on a set E of finite measure (μ) is integrable ($\mathfrak{X}$, μ) on E.*

Proof. As regards 1⁰, we have by Theorem 11.7

$$\int_E |f|\,d\mu=\int_E \mathring{f}\,d\mu+\int_E(-\underset{\circ}{f})\,d\mu,$$

and integrability of $|f|$ is therefore equivalent to that of $\mathring{f}$ and that of $-\underset{\circ}{f}$ holding together, i. e. to integrability of f.

As regards 2⁰, we have the inequalities $g(x)\leqslant|g(x)|\leqslant h(x)$ and $-g(x)\leqslant|g(x)|\leqslant h(x)$ on E, and, since $h(x)$ is, by hypothesis, integrable on E, it follows that the same is true of the non-negative functions $\mathring{g}$ and $-\underset{\circ}{g}$, and therefore of the function $g(x)$.

As an immediate consequence of Theorem 11.12 we have the following theorem, known as the

(11.13) ***First Mean Value Theorem.*** *Given, on a set E, a function $f(x)$ bounded and measurable ($\mathfrak{X}$) on E and a function $g(x)$ integrable ($\mathfrak{X}, \mu$) on E, the function $f(x) \cdot g(x)$ is integrable on E and there exists a number γ lying between the bounds of $f(x)$ on E, such that*

$$\int_E f(x)\,|g(x)|\,d\mu(x) = \gamma \cdot \int_E |g(x)|\,d\mu(x). \tag{11.14}$$

Proof. If we denote by m and M respectively the lower and the upper bound of $f(x)$ on E, and make use of Theorem 11.12, we verify successively, that the functions $(|M|+|m|)\cdot|g(x)|$, $|f(x)\,g(x)|$, $f(x)\,|g(x)|$ and $f(x)\,g(x)$ are integrable on E. Further, we have $m\,|g(x)| \leqslant f(x)\cdot|g(x)| \leqslant M\,|g(x)|$ over E, and, therefore also, $m\int_E |g|\,d\mu \leqslant \int_E f\cdot|g|\,d\mu \leqslant M\int_E |g|\,d\mu$, and so choosing $\gamma = [\int_E f\cdot|g|\,d\mu] : [\int_E |g|\,d\mu]$ (or, if the denominator vanishes, an arbitrary γ between m and M), we obtain the formula (11.14) with $m \leqslant \gamma \leqslant M$.

§ 12. Integration of sequences of functions. In this §, we shall establish some theorems on term by term integration of sequences and series of functions.

(12.1) ***Theorem.*** *If the functions of a sequence $\{g_n(x)\}$ are finite and integrable ($\mathfrak{X}, \mu$) on a set E of finite measure, and the sequence converges uniformly on E to a function $g(x)$, then the function $g(x)$ also is integrable over E, and we have*

$$\lim_n \int_E g_n(x)\,d\mu(x) = \int_E g(x)\,d\mu(x). \tag{12.2}$$

Proof. By Theorem 8.5, the function $g(x)$ is measurable ($\mathfrak{X}$) on E. The functions $g(x) - g_n(x)$ are therefore all measurable also, and, further, since the sequence $\{g_n(x)\}$ converges uniformly to $g(x)$ the functions $g(x) - g_n(x)$ are all bounded, at any rate from some value of the index n onwards. These functions are thus, by Theorem 11.12 (2°), integrable on E, and it follows, by Theorem 11.9, that the function $g(x) = [g(x) - g_n(x)] + g_n(x)$ is integrable too. Finally, denoting by ε_n the upper bound of $|g(x) - g_n(x)|$ on E, we have

$$\left|\int_E g(x)\,d\mu(x) - \int_E g_n(x)\,d\mu(x)\right| \leqslant \int_E |g(x) - g_n(x)|\,d\mu(x) \leqslant \varepsilon_n \mu(E),$$

and this establishes the relation (12.2) since, by hypothesis, $\varepsilon_n \to 0$ and $\mu(E) \neq \infty$.

Neither the theorem thus established, nor its proof, contains, at bottom, anything new, as compared with the similar result for the classical processes of integration of Cauchy, or of Riemann. We now pass on to the proof of theorems more closely related to Lebesgue integration. Among these theorems, a fundamental part is played by the following one, which is due to Lebesgue:

(12.3) ***Theorem.*** *Let* $f(x) = \sum_{n=1}^{\infty} f_n(x)$ *be a series of non-negative functions measurable* $(\mathfrak{X})$ *on a set* E. *Then*

(12.4) $$\int_E f(x)\,d\mu(x) = \sum_{n=1}^{\infty} \int_E f_n(x)\,d\mu(x).$$

Proof. From Theorem 11 7, we derive in the first place, that $\int_E f\,d\mu \geqslant \int_E [\sum_{n=1}^{m} f_n\,d\mu] = \sum_{n=1}^{m} \int_E f_n\,d\mu$ for every m, and so

(12.5) $$\int_E f\,d\mu \geqslant \sum_{n=1}^{\infty} \int_E f_n\,d\mu.$$

To establish the opposite inequality, let us attach, in accordance with Theorem 7.4, to each function $f_n(x)$ a non-decreasing sequence $\{g_n^{(k)}(x)\}_{k=1,2,\ldots}$ of simple functions measurable and non-negative on E, in such a manner that $\lim_k g_n^{(k)}(x) = f_n(x)$ for $n = 1, 2, \ldots$ Let us write $s_k(x) = \sum_{i=1}^{k} g_i^{(k)}(x)$. The functions $s_k(x)$ are clearly simple, measurable, and non-negative, on E, and they form a non-decreasing sequence. Further, for each m, and for $k \geqslant m$, we have $\sum_{i=1}^{m} g_i^{(k)}(x) \leqslant s_k(x) \leqslant f(x)$. Making $k \to \infty$, we derive $\sum_{i=1}^{m} f_i(x) \leqslant \lim_k s_k(x) \leqslant f(x)$ for every m, and so, $f(x) = \lim_k s_k(x)$. Therefore, by Lemmas 11.6 and 11.1 (1°),

$$\int_E f\,d\mu = \lim_k \int_E s_k\,d\mu = \lim_k \sum_{i=1}^{k} \int_E g_i^{(k)}\,d\mu \leqslant \sum_{i=1}^{\infty} \int_E f_i\,d\mu,$$

and this, combined with (12.5), gives the equality (12.4).

Theorem 12.3 may also be stated in the following form:

(12.6) ***Lebesgue's Theorem on integration of monotone sequences of functions.*** *If* $\{f_n(x)\}$ *is a non-decreasing sequence of non-negative functions measurable* ($\mathfrak{X}$) *on a set* E, *and* $f(x) = \lim_n f_n(x)$, *then* $\int_E f(x)\,d\mu(x) = \lim_n \int_E f_n(x)\,d\mu(x)$.

Proof. If we write $g_n(x) = f_{n+1} - f_n(x)$, we obtain

$$f(x) = f_1(x) + \sum_{n=1}^{\infty} g_n(x),$$

and the functions $g_n(x)$ will be non-negative and measurable on E, so that by Theorem 12.3

$$\int_E f\,d\mu = \int_E f_1\,d\mu + \sum_{n=1}^{\infty} \int_E g_n\,d\mu = \lim_k \int_E [f_1 + \sum_{n=1}^{k-1} g_n]\,d\mu = \lim_k \int_E f_k\,d\mu.$$

Q. E. D.

(12.7) ***Theorem of additivity for the integral.*** *If* $\{E_n\}$ *is a sequence of sets measurable* ($\mathfrak{X}$) *no two of which have common points, and* $E = \sum_n E_n$, *then*

(12.8)
$$\int_E f\,d\mu = \sum_n \int_{E_n} f\,d\mu$$

for every function $f(x)$ *possessing a definite integral (finite or infinite) over* E.

Proof. It is clearly sufficient to prove (12.8) in the case of a function $f(x)$ non-negative on E. Supposing this to be the case, let us write $f_n(x) = f(x)$ for $x \in E_n$, and $f_n(x) = 0$ for $x \in E - E_n$. We then have $f(x) = \sum_n f_n(x)$ on E, and, the functions f_n being measurable and non-negative, we may apply Lebesgue's Theorem 12.3. This gives, by Theorem 11.7,

$$\int_E f\,d\mu = \sum_n \int_E f_n\,d\mu = \sum_n \int_{E_n} f_n\,d\mu = \sum_n \int_{E_n} f\,d\mu. \qquad \text{Q. E. D.}$$

If a function $f(x)$ has a definite integral ($\mathfrak{X}, \mu$) over a set E, then $f(x)$ also has a definite integral over any subset of E measurable ($\mathfrak{X}$). We may therefore associate with it the function of a set ($\mathfrak{X}$) defined as follows:

(12.9) $F(X) = \int_X f(x)\,d\mu(x)$ *where* $X \subset E$ *and* $X \in \mathfrak{X}$.

The latter will be called the *indefinite integral* $(\mathfrak{X}, \mu)$ of $f(x)$ on E. It follows from Theorem 12.7 that, whenever the function $f(x)$ is integrable $(\mathfrak{X}, \mu)$ on E, its indefinite integral is an additive function of set $(\mathfrak{X})$ on E.

We end this § with two simple but important theorems. The first is known as *Fatou's lemma*, and appears for the first time (in a slightly less general form) in the classical memoir of P. Fatou [1, p. 375] on trigonometric series. The second is due to Lebesgue [5, in particular p. 375], and is called the *theorem on term by term integration of sequences of functions*; cf. also Ch. J. de la Vallée Poussin [1, p. 445—453], R. L. Jeffery [1] and T. H. Hildebrandt [2].

(12.10) ***Theorem (Fatou's Lemma).*** *If $\{f_n(x)\}$ is any sequence of non-negative functions measurable $(\mathfrak{X})$ on a set E, we have*

$$\int_E \liminf_n f_n(x)\, d\mu(x) \leqslant \liminf_n \int_E f_n(x)\, d\mu(x).$$

Proof. Let us write $g_i(x) = \text{lower bound}\,[f_i(x), f_{i+1}(x), f_{i+2}(x), \ldots]$ where $i = 1, 2, \ldots$. Thus defined $\{g_i(x)\}$ is a non-decreasing sequence of non-negative functions measurable on E, and converges on the set E to $\liminf_i f_i(x)$. We therefore have, by Lebesgue's Theorem 12.6,

$$\int_E \liminf_i f_i(x)\, d\mu(x) = \lim_i \int_E g_i(x)\, d\mu(x) \leqslant \liminf_i \int_E f_i(x)\, d\mu(x).$$

(12.11) ***Lebesgue's Theorem on term by term integration.*** *Let $\{f_n(x)\}$ be a sequence of functions measurable $(\mathfrak{X})$ on a set E, fulfilling, for a function $s(x)$ integrable $(\mathfrak{X})$ on E, the inequality $|f_n(x)| \leqslant s(x)$ for $n = 1, 2, \ldots$ Then*

$$\liminf_n \int_E f_n\, d\mu \geqslant \int_E \liminf_n f_n\, d\mu,$$
(12.12)
$$\limsup_n \int_E f_n\, d\mu \leqslant \int_E \limsup_n f_n\, d\mu.$$

If, further, the sequence $\{f_n\}$ converges on E to a function f, the sequence is integrable term by term, i. e. we have

$$\lim_n \int_E f_n\, d\mu = \int_E f\, d\mu. \tag{12.13}$$

Proof. Let $g(x) = \liminf\limits_n f_n(x)$ and let $h(x) = \limsup\limits_n f_n(x)$. We may clearly suppose $s(x) < +\infty$ throughout E. We then derive from Fatou's Lemma 12.10, $\liminf\limits_n \int\limits_E (s+f_n)\,d\mu \geqslant \int\limits_E (s+g)\,d\mu$ and $\liminf\limits_n \int\limits_E (s-f_n)\,d\mu \geqslant \int\limits_E (s-h)\,d\mu$, which gives at once the relations (12.12).

Further, if $\lim\limits_n f_n(x) = f(x)$, we derive from (12.12) the relation $\liminf\limits_n \int\limits_E f_n d\mu \geqslant \int\limits_E f d\mu \geqslant \limsup\limits_n \int\limits_E f_n d\mu$ which gives the equality (12.13).

§ 13. Absolutely continuous additive functions of a set. The fact that the indefinite integral of a function integrable $(\mathfrak{X}, \mu)$ on a set E is, on E, an additive function of a set $(\mathfrak{X})$, raises the problem of characterizing directly the additive functions expressible as indefinite integrals.

If we restrict ourselves to the Lebesgue integral of functions of a real variable, we may regard indefinite integrals as functions of an interval, or, what comes to the same thing, as functions of a real variable. In that case, a necessary and sufficient condition for a function to be expressible as the indefinite integral of a real function was given, in 1904, still by Lebesgue [I, p. 129, footnote]. A little later (in 1905), G. Vitali [1] explicitly distinguished the class of functions possessing the Lebesgue property by introducing the name of "absolutely continuous functions".

The condition of Lebesgue and Vitali was later extended to functions of a set by J. Radon [1] (cf. also P. J. Daniell [4]). But Radon considered only additive functions of sets measurable in the Borel sense in Euclidean spaces, and only measures determined by additive functions of intervals (cf. below Chapter III). The final form of the condition of Lebesgue-Vitali, as given in Theorem 14.11 below, is due to O. Nikodym [2].

An additive function of a set $(\mathfrak{X})$ on a set E, will be said to be *absolutely continuous* $(\mathfrak{X}, \mu)$ on E, if the function vanishes for every subset $(\mathfrak{X})$ of E whose measure (μ) is zero. An additive function $\Phi(X)$ of a set $(\mathfrak{X})$ on a set E will be termed *singular* $(\mathfrak{X}, \mu)$ on E, if there exists a subset $E_0 \subset E$ measurable $(\mathfrak{X})$, of measure (μ) zero, such that $\Phi(X)$ vanishes identically on $E - E_0$, i. e. $\Phi(X) = \Phi(E_0 \cdot X)$ for every subset X of E measurable $(\mathfrak{X})$. The following statements are at once obvious:

(13.1) ***Theorem.*** 1^0 *In order that an additive function of a set* ($\mathfrak{X}$) *on a set* E *should be absolutely continuous* ($\mathfrak{X}$, μ) [*or should be singular*] *it is necessary and sufficient that its two variations, the upper and the lower, should both be so.* 2^0 *Every linear combination, with constant coefficients, of two additive functions absolutely continuous* [*or singular*] *on a set* E *is itself absolutely continuous* [*or singular*] *on* E. 3^0 *If a sequence* $\{\Phi_n(X)\}$ *of additive functions, absolutely continuous* [*singular*] *on a set* E, *converges to an additive function* $\Phi(X)$ *for each measurable subset* X *of* E, *then the function* $\Phi(X)$ *is also absolutely continuous* [*singular*]. 4^0 *If a function of a set* ($\mathfrak{X}$) *is additive and absolutely continuous* [*singular*] *on a set* E, *the function is so on every measurable subset of* E. 5^0 *If* $E = \sum_n E_n$, *where* $\{E_n\}$ *is a sequence of sets* ($\mathfrak{X}$), *and if an additive function* $\Phi(X)$ *on* E *is absolutely continuous* [*singular*] *on each of the sets* E_n, *the function is absolutely continuous* [*singular*] *on the whole set* E. 6^0 *An additive function of a set cannot be both absolutely continuous and singular on a set* E, *without vanishing identically on* E.

For sets of finite measure, it is sometimes convenient to apply the following test for absolute continuity:

(13.2) ***Theorem.*** *In order that a function* $\Phi(X)$ *additive on a set* E *of finite measure, be absolutely continuous* ($\mathfrak{X}$, μ) *on* E, *it is necessary and sufficient that to each* $\varepsilon>0$ *there correspond an* $\eta>0$, *such that* $\mu(X)<\eta$ *imply* $|\Phi(X)|<\varepsilon$ *for every set* $X\subset E$ *measurable* ($\mathfrak{X}$).

Proof. It is evident that the condition is sufficient. To prove it also necessary, let us suppose the function $\Phi(X)$ absolutely continuous in E. We may assume, replacing if necessary, $\Phi(X)$ by its absolute variation, that $\Phi(X)$ is a non-negative monotone function on E. This being so, let us suppose, if possible, that there exists a sequence $\{E_n\}_{n=1,2,\ldots}$ of measurable subsets of E, such that $\mu(E_n)<1/2^n$ and that $\Phi(E_n)>\eta_0$, where η_0 is a fixed positive number. Let us write $E_0 = \limsup_n E_n$. For every n, we then have $\mu(E_0) \leqslant \sum_{k=n}^{\infty} \mu(E_k) \leqslant 1/2^{n-1}$, and therefore $\mu(E_0)=0$. On the other hand, by Theorem 5.1, we have $\Phi(E_0) \geqslant \limsup_n \Phi(E_n) \geqslant \eta_0$. This is a contradiction, since $\Phi(X)$ is absolutely continuous, and the proof is complete.

(10.0) ***Theorem.*** *In order that a function $\Phi(X)$, additive on a set E, be singular $(\mathfrak{X}, \mu)$ on E, it is necessary and sufficient that for each $\varepsilon > 0$ there exist a set $X \subset E$ measurable $(\mathfrak{X})$ and fulfilling the two conditions* $\mu(X) < \varepsilon$, $\mathrm{W}(\Phi; E - X) < \varepsilon$.

Proof. The condition is clearly necessary. To prove it sufficient, let us suppose that for each n there is a set $X_n \subset E$ measurable $(\mathfrak{X})$ such that $\mu(X_n) < 1/2^n$ and $\mathrm{W}(\Phi; E - X_n) < 1/2^n$, and let us write $E_0 = \limsup_n X_n$. We then have $\mu(E_0) \leqslant \sum_{k=n}^{\infty} \mu(X_k) \leqslant 1/2^{n-1}$ for each n, and so $\mu(E_0) = 0$. On the other hand, by Theorem 5.1 we have $\mathrm{W}(\Phi; E - E_0) \leqslant \liminf_n \mathrm{W}(\Phi; E - X_n) = 0$. The function $\Phi(X)$ is therefore singular on E.

§ 14. The Lebesgue decomposition of an additive function. Before proving the result announced in the preceding §, we shall establish some auxiliary theorems. We begin with the following theorem due to H. Hahn [I, p. 404] (cf. also W. Sierpiński [11]):

(14.1) ***Theorem.*** *If $\Phi(X)$ is an additive function of a set $(\mathfrak{X})$ on a set E, there exists always a set $P \subset E$ measurable $(\mathfrak{X})$, such that $\underline{\mathrm{W}}(\Phi; P) = 0 = \overline{\mathrm{W}}(\Phi; E - P)$, or, what comes to the same thing, such that $\Phi(X) \geqslant 0$ for every measurable set $X \subset P$ and $\Phi(X) \leqslant 0$ for every measurable set $X \subset E - P$.*

Proof. For each positive integer n, we choose a set E_n such that $\Phi(E_n) \geqslant \overline{\mathrm{W}}(\Phi; E) - 1/2^n$. By Theorem 6.4 we then have,

$$(14.2) \qquad \underline{\mathrm{W}}(\Phi; E_n) \geqslant -1/2^n \quad \textit{and} \quad \overline{\mathrm{W}}(\Phi; E - E_n) \leqslant 1/2^n.$$

Writing $P = \liminf_n E_n$, we see that $E - P = \limsup_n (E - E_n) \subset \sum_{n=m}^{\infty} (E - E_n)$ for every m, and therefore, by (14.2),

$$\overline{\mathrm{W}}(\Phi; E - P) \leqslant \sum_{n=m}^{\infty} \overline{\mathrm{W}}(\Phi; E - E_n) \leqslant \frac{1}{2^{m-1}}$$

which gives $\overline{W}(\Phi; E - P) = 0$. On the other hand, the lower variation $\underline{\mathrm{W}}(\Phi; X)$ is a non-positive monotone function of a measurable set $X \subset E$, and, by Theorem 5.1 and the first inequality (14.2), we must have the relation $|\underline{\mathrm{W}}(\Phi; P)| \leqslant \liminf_n |\underline{\mathrm{W}}(\Phi; E_n)| = 0$, which gives $\underline{\mathrm{W}}(\Phi; P) = 0$ and completes the proof.

(14.3) ***Lemma.*** *If $\Phi(X)$ is a non-negative additive function of a set ($\mathfrak{X}$) on a set E, there exists, for each $a>0$, a decomposition of E into a sequence of measurable sets without common points, $H, E_1, E_2, \ldots, E_n, \ldots$ such that $\mu(H)=0$ and that*

$$(14.4)\qquad a\cdot(n-1)\cdot\mu(X)\leqslant\Phi(X)\leqslant an\cdot\mu(X)$$

for every set $X\subset E_n$ measurable ($\mathfrak{X}$).

Proof. By Theorem 14.1, there exists, for each positive integer n, a measurable set A_n such that $\Phi(X)-an\cdot\mu(X)\geqslant 0$ for every measurable set $X\subset A_n$ and $\Phi(X)-an\cdot\mu(X)\leqslant 0$ for every measurable set $X\subset E-A_n$. Write $B_n=\sum_{k=n}^{\infty}A_k$. Any measurable subset X of B_n may be represented in the form $X=\sum_{k=n}^{\infty}X_k$, where X_k are measurable sets, $X_k\subset A_k$ for $k=n, n+1, \ldots$, and $X_i\cdot X_j=0$ for $i\neq j$; and so $\Phi(X)=\sum_{k=n}^{\infty}\Phi(X_k)\geqslant\sum_{k=n}^{\infty}ak\cdot\mu(X_k)\geqslant an\cdot\mu(X)$. We obtain thus a descending sequence of measurable sets $\{B_n\}$ such that

$$(14.5)\qquad \begin{aligned}&\Phi(X)\geqslant an\cdot\mu(X) \quad \text{if} \quad X\subset B_n, && X\in\mathfrak{X},\\ &\Phi(X)\leqslant an\cdot\mu(X) \quad \text{if} \quad X\subset E-B_n, && X\in\mathfrak{X},\end{aligned}$$

the second relation being obvious, since $E-B_n$ is a subset of $E-A_n$.

Let us now write $E_1=E-B_1$, $E_n=B_{n-1}-B_n$ for $n=2, 3, \ldots$, and $H=\lim_n B_n$. Thus defined the sets $H, E_1, E_2, \ldots, E_n, \ldots$ are measurable and without common points, and $E=H+\sum_{n=1}^{\infty}E_n$. Taking into account the relations (14.5), we see at once that the inequality (14.4) holds whenever X is a measurable subset of E_n. Finally, $H\subset B_n$ for each positive integer n, and therefore, by the first of the relations (14.5), we get $\Phi(H)\geqslant an\cdot\mu(H)$, which requires $\mu(H)=0$ and completes the proof.

(14.6) ***Theorem.*** *If E is a set ($\mathfrak{X}$) of finite measure (μ), or, more generally, a set expressible as the sum of a sequence of sets ($\mathfrak{X}$) of finite measure, every additive function of a measurable set $\Phi(X)$ on E is expressible as the sum of an absolutely continuous additive function $\Psi(X)$ and a singular additive function $\Theta(X)$ on E. Such a decomposition of $\Phi(X)$ on E is unique, and the function $\Psi(X)$ is, on E,* *the indefinite integral of a function integrable* $(\mathfrak{X}, \mu)$ *on* E. *If* $\Phi(X)$ *is a non-negative monotone function on* E, *so are the corresponding functions* $\Psi(X)$ *and* $\Theta(X)$.

Proof. Since every additive function of a set is the difference of two non-negative functions of the same kind (cf. § 6), we may restrict ourselves to the case of a non-negative $\Phi(X)$. Further, we shall assume to begin with that the set E has finite measure. By the preceding lemma, there exists, for every positive integer m, a decomposition of E into a sequence of measurable sets $H_1^{(m)}, E_1^{(m)}, E_2^{(m)}, \ldots$, without common points and subject to the conditions:

$$(14.7) \qquad E = H^{(m)} + E_1^{(m)} + \ldots + E_n^{(m)} + \ldots, \qquad \mu(H^{(m)}) = 0,$$

$$(14.8) \quad 2^{-m} \cdot (n-1) \cdot \mu(X) \leqslant \Phi(X) \leqslant 2^{-m} \cdot n \cdot \mu(X), \text{ if } X \subset E_n^{(m)},\ X \in \mathfrak{X}.$$

We therefore have, for all positive integers m, n, and k,

$$2^{-m} \cdot n \cdot \mu(E_n^{(m)} \cdot E_k^{(m+1)}) \geqslant \Phi(E_n^{(m)} \cdot E_k^{(m+1)}) \geqslant 2^{-m-1} \cdot (k-1) \cdot \mu(E_n^{(m)} \cdot E_k^{(m+1)}),$$

and

$$2^{-m-1}\, k \cdot \mu(E_n^{(m)} \cdot E_k^{(m+1)}) \geqslant \Phi(E_n^{(m)} \cdot E_k^{(m+1)}) \geqslant 2^{-m} \cdot (n-1) \cdot \mu(E_n^{(m)} \cdot E_k^{(m+1)}),$$

from which it follows that $(2n-k+1)\, \mu(E_n^{(m)} \cdot E_k^{(m+1)}) \geqslant 0$, and that $(k-2n+2)\, \mu(E_n^{(m)} \cdot E_k^{(m+1)}) \geqslant 0$. Hence $\mu(E_n^{(m)} \cdot E_k^{(m+1)}) = 0$ whenever either $k > 2n+1$, or $k < 2n-2$.

We may therefore write

$$(14.9) \quad E_n^{(m)} \subset E_{2n-2}^{(m+1)} + E_{2n-1}^{(m+1)} + E_{2n}^{(m+1)} + E_{2n+1}^{(m+1)} + Q_n^{(m)} \text{ where } \mu(Q_n^{(m)}) = 0.$$

This being so, let $H = \sum_{m=1}^{\infty} H^{(m)} + \sum_{m,n=1}^{\infty} Q_n^{(m)}$. We write $f^{(m)}(x) = 2^{-m} \cdot (n-1)$ for $x \in E_n^{(m)} - H$, $n = 1, 2, \ldots$, and $f^{(m)}(x) = 0$ for $x \in H$. We thus obtain a sequence $\{f^{(m)}(x)\}$ of non-negative functions measurable $(\mathfrak{X})$ on the set E. By (14.9) we have clearly $|f^{(m+1)}(x) - f^{(m)}(x)| \leqslant 2^{-m}$ on E, so that the sequence $\{f^{(m)}(x)\}$ converges uniformly on E to a non-negative measurable function $f(x)$.

The set H being of measure zero, we have, by (14.7) and (14.8), for every measurable set $X \subset E$ and for every positive integer m,

$$\Phi(X) \geqslant \Phi(X \cdot H) + \sum_n 2^{-m} \cdot (n-1) \cdot \mu(X \cdot E_n^{(m)}) = \Phi(X \cdot H) + \int_X f^{(m)}\, d\mu,$$

and

$$\Phi(X) \leqslant \Phi(X \cdot H) + \sum_n 2^{-m} \cdot n \cdot \mu(X \cdot E_n^{(m)}) = \Phi(X \cdot H) + \int_X f^{(m)}\, d\mu + 2^{-m} \cdot \mu(X).$$

Hence, making $m\to\infty$, we derive $\Phi(X)=\int\limits_X f(X)\,d\mu(x)+\Phi(X\cdot H)$.

This decomposition, so far established subject to the hypothesis that the set E is of finite measure, extends at once to sets expressible as the sum of an enumerable infinity of sets of finite measure. In fact, if $E=\sum\limits_{n=1}^{\infty} A_n$, where the A_n are sets $(\mathfrak{X})$ without common points and of finite measure, then, by what we have already proved, there exists on A_n a non-negative function $f_n(x)$ integrable on A_n, and a measurable set $H_n\subset A_n$ having measure zero, such that $\Phi(X\cdot A_n)=\int\limits_{X\cdot A_n} f_n\,d\mu+\Phi(X\cdot H_n)$, for $n=1, 2, \ldots$ If we now write $H=\sum\limits_n H_n$, and $f(x)=f_n(x)$ for $x\in A_n$, we obtain a measurable set $H\subset E$ of measure zero, and a function $f(X)$, non-negative and integrable on E, such that, by Theorem 12.7, for every measurable set $X\subset E$

$$(14.10)\quad \Phi(X)=\sum_n \int\limits_{X\cdot A_n} f\,d\mu+\sum_n \Phi(X\cdot H_n)=\int\limits_X f\,d\mu+\Phi(X\cdot H).$$

Now, the indefinite integral vanishes for every set of measure zero, and therefore is an absolutely continuous function; on the other hand, we have $\Phi(X\cdot H)=0$ for every measurable set $X\subset E-H$. Thus, since the set H has measure zero, formula (14.10) provides a decomposition of $\Phi(X)$ into an absolutely continuous function and a singular function. Finally, to establish the unicity of such a decomposition, suppose that $\Phi(X)=\Psi_1(X)+\Theta_1(X)=\Psi_2(X)+\Theta_2(X)$ on E, the functions $\Psi_1(X)$ and $\Psi_2(X)$ being absolutely continuous, and the functions $\Theta_1(X)$ and $\Theta_2(X)$ being singular. Then $\Psi_1(X)-\Psi_2(X)=$ $=\Theta_2(X)-\Theta_1(X)$ identically on E, whence by Theorem 13.1 (2^0 and 6^0), we have $\Psi_1(X)=\Psi_2(X)$ and $\Theta_1(X)=\Theta_2(X)$, and this completes the proof of our theorem.

The expression of an additive function as the sum of an absolutely continuous function and of a singular function will be termed the *Lebesgue decomposition*. The singular function that appears in it is often called the *function of the singularities* of the given function. From Theorem 14.6, we derive at once

(14.11) ***Theorem of Radon-Nikodym.*** *If E is a set of finite measure, or, more generally the sum of a sequence of sets of finite measure (μ), then, in order that an additive function of a set ($\mathfrak{X}$) on E be absolutely continuous on E, it is necessary and sufficient that this function of a set be the indefinite integral of some integrable function of a point on E.*

The hypothesis that the set E is the sum of an at most enumerable infinity of sets of finite measure, plays an essential part in the assertion of the theorem of Radon-Nikodym, just as in Theorem 9.8. To see this, let us take again the interval [0, 1] as our space X_1, and let the class $\mathfrak{X}_1$ of all subsets of [0, 1] that are measurable in the Lebesgue sense (cf. below Chap. III) be our fixed additive class of sets in the space X_1. A measure μ_1 will be defined by taking $\mu_1(X)=\infty$ for infinite sets and $\mu_1(X)=n$ for finite sets with n elements. This being so, the sets ($\mathfrak{X}_1$) of measure (μ_1) zero coincide with the empty set, and therefore, every additive function of a set ($\mathfrak{X}_1$) on X_1 is absolutely continuous ($\mathfrak{X}_1$, μ_1). In particular, denoting by $\Lambda(X)$ the Lebesgue measure for every set $X \in \mathfrak{X}_1$, we see that $\Lambda(X)$ is absolutely continuous ($\mathfrak{X}_1, \mu_1$) on X_1. We shall show that $\Lambda(X)$ is not an indefinite integral ($\mathfrak{X}_1, \mu_1$) on X_1. Suppose indeed, if possible, that

$$\Lambda(X) = \int_X g(x)\, d\mu_1(x)$$

for every set $X \in \mathfrak{X}_1$, the function $g(x)$ being integrable ($\mathfrak{X}_1, \mu_1$) on X_1. Since $\Lambda(X)$ is non-negative, we may suppose that $g(x)$ is so too. Let $E=\underset{x}{\mathrm{E}}[g(x)>0]$ and $E_n=\underset{x}{\mathrm{E}}[g(x)>1/n]$ for $n=1, 2, \ldots$ We have $\Lambda(X_1 - E)=\int_{X_1-E} g\, d\mu_1=0$, so that $\Lambda(E)=\Lambda(X_1)=1$ and this requires the set E to be non-enumerable. Since $E=\sum_n E_n$, the same must be true of E_{n_0} for some positive integer n_0. Thus

$$\Lambda(E_{n_0}) = \int_{E_{n_0}} g(x)\, d\mu_1(x) \geqslant \mu_1(E_{n_0})/n_0=\infty,$$

which is evidently a contradiction.

§ 15. Change of measure. Any non-negative additive function $\nu(X)$ of a set ($\mathfrak{X}$) may clearly be regarded as a measure corresponding to the given additive class $\mathfrak{X}$. When such a function $\nu(X)$ is defined only on a set E, we can always continue it (cf. § 5, p. 9) on to the whole space. The terms measure (ν), integral ($\mathfrak{X}, \nu$) etc. are then completely determined for all sets ($\mathfrak{X}$), but, in this case, it is most natural to consider only the subsets of E for which the function $\nu(X)$ was originally given.

(15.1) ***Theorem.*** *Whenever, on a set E measurable* ($\mathfrak{X}$), *we have*

$$(15.2)\qquad \nu(X) = (\mathfrak{X}) \int_X g(x) d\mu(x) + \vartheta(X)$$

where $\vartheta(X)$ *is a non-negative function, additive and singular* ($\mathfrak{X}, \mu$) *on E, and where $g(x)$ is a non-negative function integrable* ($\mathfrak{X}, \mu$) *over E, then also*

$$(15.3)\qquad (\mathfrak{X}) \int_X f(x)\, d\nu(x) = (\mathfrak{X}) \int_X f(x)\, g(x)\, d\mu(x) + (\mathfrak{X}) \int_X f(x)\, d\vartheta(x)$$

for every set $X \subset E$ measurable ($\mathfrak{X}$) *and for every function $f(x)$ that possesses a definite integral* ($\mathfrak{X}, \nu$) *over X. If, further, the function $f(x)$ is integrable* ($\mathfrak{X}, \nu$) *over E, the formula* (15.3) *expresses the Lebesgue decomposition of the indefinite integral $\int_X f\, d\nu$ on E, corresponding to the measure μ, the function $\theta(X) = \int_X f\, d\vartheta$ being the function of singularities* ($\mathfrak{X}, \mu$) *of the indefinite integral $\int_X f\, d\nu$.*

Proof. We may clearly assume that $f(x)$ is defined and non-negative on the whole of the set E. We see at once that, for each set $Y \subset E$ measurable ($\mathfrak{X}$), $\int_Y c_Y(x)\, d\nu(x) = \nu(Y) = \int_Y g(x)\, d\mu(x) + \vartheta(Y) = \int_Y c_Y(x)\, g(x)\, d\mu(x) + \int_Y c_Y(x)\, d\vartheta(x)$, and hence also that for every finite function $h(x)$ simple and measurable ($\mathfrak{X}$) on a set $X \subset E$,

$$(15.4)\qquad \int_X h(x)\, d\nu(x) = \int_X h(x)\, g(x)\, d\mu(x) + \int_X h(x)\, d\vartheta(x).$$

Let now $\{h_n(x)\}$ be a non-decreasing sequence of finite simple functions measurable ($\mathfrak{X}$) and non-negative on X, converging to the given function $f(x)$. Substituting $h_n(x)$ for $h(x)$ in (15.4) and making $n \to \infty$, we obtain (15.3), on account of Lebesgue's Theorem 12.6. If, further, $f(x)$ is integrable ($\mathfrak{X}, \nu$) over E, the identity just established shows at once that the product $f(x)\, g(x)$ is integrable ($\mathfrak{X}, \mu$) over E and hence, that the indefinite integral $\int_X f g\, d\mu$ is absolutely continuous ($\mathfrak{X}, \mu$) 'on E. On the other hand, the function $\theta(X)$ vanishes on every set on which the function $\vartheta(X)$ vanishes, and therefore, is singular ($\mathfrak{X}, \mu$) on E together with $\vartheta(X)$. This completes the proof.

The wide scope of Theorem 15.1 is due to the fact that, if $\mu(X)$ and $\nu(X)$ are any two measures associated with the same class $\mathfrak{X}$ of measurable sets and we have at the same time $\mu(E) < +\infty$, and $\nu(E) < +\infty$, for a set $E \epsilon \mathfrak{X}$, then the measure ν can be represented on E in the form (15.2), where $g(x)$ is a function integrable $(\mathfrak{X}, \mu)$ over the set E and $\vartheta(X)$ is a non-negative function, additive and singular $(\mathfrak{X}, \mu)$ on the same set (cf. Th. 14.6). Hence, with the above hypotheses and notation, in order that $\int\limits_X f\,d\nu = \int\limits_X fg\,d\mu$ should hold identically on E, it is necessary and sufficient that the indefinite integral $\int\limits_X f\,d\nu$ be absolutely continuous $(\mathfrak{X}, \mu)$ on E. This condition is clearly satisfied whenever the measure $\nu(X)$ is itself absolutely continuous $(\mathfrak{X}, \mu)$.

CHAPTER II.

Carathéodory measure.

§ 1. Preliminary remarks. In the preceding chapter, we supposed given a priori a certain class of sets, together with a measure defined for the sets of this class. A different procedure is usually adopted in theories dealing with special measures. We then begin by determining, as an outer measure, a non-negative function of a set, defined for all sets of the space considered, and it is only a posteriori that we determine a class of measurable sets for which the given outer measure is additive.

An abstract form of these theories, possessing both beauty and generality, is due to C. Carathéodory [I]. The account that we give of it in this chapter, is based on that of H. Hahn [I, Chap. VI], in which the results of Carathéodory are formulated for arbitrary metrical spaces. This account will be preceded by two §§ describing the notions that are fundamental in general metrical spaces.

§ 2. Metrical space. A space $\boldsymbol{M}$ is metrical if to each pair a and b of its points there corresponds a non-negative number $\varrho(a, b)$, called *distance* of the points a and b, that satisfies the following conditions: (i) $\varrho(a, b)=0$ is equivalent to $a=b$, (ii) $\varrho(a, b)=\varrho(b, a)$, (iii) $\varrho(a, b)+\varrho(b, c)\geqslant\varrho(a, c)$. In this chapter, we shall suppose that a metrical space $\boldsymbol{M}$ is fixed, and that all sets of points that arise, are located in $\boldsymbol{M}$.

The notation that we shall use, is as follows. A point a is *limit* of a sequence $\{a_n\}$ of points in $\boldsymbol{M}$, and we write $a=\lim_n a_n$, if $\lim_n \varrho(a, a_n)=0$. Every sequence possessing a limit point is said to be *convergent*. Given a set M, the upper bound of the numbers $\varrho(a, b)$ subject to $a \in M$ and $b \in M$ is called *diameter* of M and is denoted by $\delta(M)$. The set M is *bounded* if $\delta(M)$ is finite. For a class $\mathfrak{M}$ of sets, the upper bound of the numbers $\delta(M)$ subject to $M \in \mathfrak{M}$ is denoted by $\Delta(\mathfrak{M})$ and called *characteristic number* of $\mathfrak{M}$. By the *distance* $\varrho(a, A)$ *of a point* a *and a set* A, we mean the lower bound of the numbers $\varrho(a, x)$ subject to $x \in A$, and by *the distance* $\varrho(A, B)$ *of two sets* A and B, the lower bound of the numbers $\varrho(x, y)$ for $x \in A$ and $y \in B$.

We call *neighbourhood of a point a with radius* $r > 0$, or *open sphere* $S(a; r)$ *of centre a and radius r*, the set of all points x such that $\varrho(a, x) < r$. The set of all points x such that $\varrho(a, x) \leqslant r$ is called *closed sphere of centre a and radius r*, and is denoted by $\overline{S}(a; r)$.

A point a is termed *point of accumulation of a set* A, if every neighbourhood of a contains infinitely many points of A. The set A' of all points of accumulation of A is termed *derived set* of A. The set $A + A'$, that we denote by $\overline{A}$, is termed *closure* of A. If $A = \overline{A}$, the set A is said to be *closed*. The points of a set, other than its points of accumulation, are termed *isolated*. A set is *isolated*, if all its points are isolated. We call *perfect*, any closed set not containing isolated points.

A point a of a set A is said to be an *internal point* of A, if there exists a neighbourhood of a contained in A. The set of all the internal points of a set A is called *interior* of A and denoted by A°. The set $\overline{A} - A^\circ$ is termed *boundary of A*. If $A = A^\circ$, the set A is said to be *open*. Two sets A and B are called *non-overlapping*, if $A \cdot B^\circ = B \cdot A^\circ = 0$.

The class of all open sets will be denoted by $\mathfrak{G}$ and that of all closed sets by $\mathfrak{F}$. In accordance with the convention adopted in § 2 of Chap. I, p. 5, open and closed sets will also be termed sets ($\mathfrak{G}$) and sets ($\mathfrak{F}$) respectively. We see at once that the complement of any set ($\mathfrak{G}$) is a set ($\mathfrak{F}$) and vice-versa.

The sum of a finite number or of an infinity of open sets, as well as the common part of a finite number of such sets, is always an open set. Any common part of a finite number, or of an infinity, of closed sets, and also any sum of a finite number of such sets, are closed sets. Nevertheless, the sets $(\mathfrak{F}_\sigma)$ and $(\mathfrak{G}_\delta)$ (cf. Chap. I, § 2, p. 5) do not in general coincide with the sets $(\mathfrak{F})$ and $(\mathfrak{G})$, although every set $(\mathfrak{F})$ is clearly a set $(\mathfrak{F}_\sigma)$ and, at the same time, a set $(\mathfrak{G}_\delta)$; for, if F is a closed set and G_n denotes the set of the points x such that $\varrho(x, F) < 1/n$, we have $F = \prod_n G_n$, where G_n are open. The corresponding result for the sets $(\mathfrak{G})$ is obtained by passing to the complementary sets. Moreover, it follows that any set expressible as the common part of a set $(\mathfrak{F})$ and a set $(\mathfrak{G})$ is both a set $(\mathfrak{F}_\sigma)$ and a set $(\mathfrak{G}_\delta)$.

We shall denote by $\mathfrak{B}$, the smallest additive class that includes all closed sets (cf. Chap. I, Th. 4.2). This class, clearly, includes also all sets $(\mathfrak{G}_\delta)$ and $(\mathfrak{F}_\sigma)$. The sets $(\mathfrak{B})$ are also termed *measurable* $(\mathfrak{B})$ (in accordance with Chap. I, § 4, p. 7). They are known as *Borel sets*.

We shall also give a few "relative" definitions having reference to a set M. The common part of M with any closed set is *closed in* M; we see at once that, for a set $P \subset M$ to be closed in M, it is necessary and sufficient that $P = M \cdot \bar{P}$, i. e. that the set P contains all its points of accumulation belonging to M. Similarly, any set expressible as the common part of M and an open set is termed *open in* M.

Any set of the form $M \cdot S(a; r)$, where $a \in M$ and $r > 0$, is called *portion* of M. If every portion of M contains points of a set A, i. e. if $\bar{A} \supset M$, the set A is said to be *everywhere dense in* M. If a set B is not everywhere dense in any portion of M, i. e. if no portion of M is contained in $\bar{B}$, the set B is said to be *non-dense in* M. In other words, a set B is non-dense in M, if, and only if, each portion of M contains a portion in which there are no points of B. It follows at once that the sum of a finite number of sets non-dense in the set M is itself non-dense in M. The sets expressible as sums of a finite or enumerably infinite number of sets non-dense in M are termed (according to R. Baire [1]) *sets of the first category in* M, and the sets not so expressible are termed *sets of the second category in* M. In all these terms, the expression "in M" is omitted when M coincides with the whole space; thus, by "non-dense sets", we mean sets whose closures contain no sphere and by "sets of the first category", enumerable sums of such sets.

A set M is called *separable*, if it contains an enumerable subset everywhere dense in M.

§ 3. Continuous and semi-continuous functions. If $f(x)$ is a function of a point, defined on a set A containing the point a, we shall denote by $\mathrm{M}_A(f; a; r)$ and $\mathrm{m}_A(f; a; r)$, respectively, the upper and lower bounds of the values assumed by $f(x)$ on the portion $A \cdot \mathrm{S}(a; r)$ of the set A. When r tends to 0, these two bounds converge monotonely towards two limits (finite or infinite) which we shall call respectively *maximum* and *minimum of the function $f(x)$ on the set A at the point a*, and denote by $\mathrm{M}_A(f; a)$ and $\mathrm{m}_A(f; a)$. Their difference $\mathrm{o}_A(f; a) = \mathrm{M}_A(f; a) - \mathrm{m}_A(f; a)$ will be called *oscillation of $f(x)$ on A at a*. We clearly have

(3.1) $$\mathrm{m}_A(f; a) \leqslant f(a) \leqslant \mathrm{M}_A(f; a) \quad \textit{for every point } a \in A.$$

If $f(a) = \mathrm{m}_A(f; a)$, the function $f(x)$ is said to be *lower semi-continuous on the set A at the point a*; similarly, if $f(a) = \mathrm{M}_A(f; a)$, the function $f(x)$ is *upper semi-continuous on A at a*. If both conditions hold together, and if $f(x)$ is finite at the point a, i. e. if $\mathrm{m}_A(f; a) = \mathrm{M}_A(f; a) \neq \infty$, the function $f(x)$ is termed *continuous on A at the point a*. Functions having the appropriate property at all points of the set A, will be termed simply *lower semi-continuous*, or *upper semi-continuous*, or *continuous*, *on A*. In all these terms and symbols, we usually omit all reference to A, when the latter is an open set (in particular, the whole space), or when A is kept fixed, in which case the omission causes no ambiguity.

From these definitions we conclude at once that, if $f(x)$ is upper semi-continuous, the function $-f(x)$ is lower semi-continuous, and vice-versa; and further, that, if two functions are upper (or lower) semi-continuous, so is their sum (supposing, of course, that the functions to be added do not assume at any point infinite values of opposite signs).

(3.2) ***Theorem.*** *For every function $f(x)$ defined on a set A, the set of the points of A at which $f(x)$ is not continuous on A, is the common part of the set A with a set $(\mathfrak{F}_\sigma)$.*

Proof. Let us denote by F_n the set of the points x of A at which either $f(x) = \pm\infty$, or $\mathrm{o}_A(f; x) \geqslant 1/n$. The set $F = \sum_n F_n$ consists of all the points of A at which the function $f(x)$ is not continuous. Now it is easy to see that each of the sets F_n is closed in A, i. e. that $F_n = A \cdot \overline{F}_n$. Therefore F is the common part of A and the set $\sum_n \overline{F}_n$, which is a set $(\mathfrak{F}_\sigma)$.

(3.3) ***Theorem.*** *For a function of a point $f(x)$ to be upper [lower] semi-continuous on a set A, it is necessary and sufficient that, for each number a, the set*

$$(3.4) \qquad \mathop{\mathrm{E}}_{x}[x \in A;\ f(x) \geqslant a] \qquad [\mathop{\mathrm{E}}_{x}[x \in A;\ f(x) \leqslant a]]$$

be closed in A, i. e. expressible as the common part of A with a set $(\mathfrak{F})$.

Proof. We need only consider the case of upper semi-continuous functions, as the other case follows by change of sign.

Let $f(x)$ be a function upper semi-continuous on A, a an arbitrary number, and $x_0 \in A$ a point of accumulation of the set (3.4). For each $r>0$, the sphere $S(x_0; r)$ then contains points of that set, and this requires $M_A(f; x_0; r) \geqslant a$ and so $M_A(f; x_0) \geqslant a$. Since by hypothesis $M_A(f; x_0) = f(x_0)$, we derive $f(x_0) \geqslant a$, so that x_0 belongs to the set (3.4). This set is thus closed in A.

Suppose, conversely, that the set (3.4) is closed in A for each a. Since the relation $M_A(f; x) = f(x)$ is evident for any x at which $f(x) = +\infty$, let x_0 be a point at which $f(x_0) < +\infty$, and a any number greater than $f(x_0)$. The set (3.4) is closed in A and does not contain x_0, and so, for a sufficiently small value r_a of r, contains no point of the sphere $S(x_0; r)$. Thus $M_A(f; x_0) \leqslant M_A(f; x_0; r_a) \leqslant a$ for every number $a > f(x_0)$, and hence $M_A(f; x_0) \leqslant f(x_0)$, which, by (3.1), requires $M_A(f; x_0) = f(x_0)$.

An immediate consequence of Theorem 3.3 (cf. Chap. I, § 7, particularly p. 13) is the following

(3.5) ***Theorem.*** *Every function semi-continuous on a set $(\mathfrak{B})$ is measurable $(\mathfrak{B})$ on this set. More generally, if $\mathfrak{X}$ is any additive class of sets including all closed sets (and so all sets measurable $(\mathfrak{B})$), every function semi-continuous on a set $(\mathfrak{X})$ is measurable $(\mathfrak{X})$ on this set.*

§ 4. Carathéodory measure. A function of a set $\Gamma(X)$, defined and non-negative for all sets of the space $\boldsymbol{M}$, will be called *outer measure in the sense of Carathéodory*, if it fulfills the following conditions:

(C_1) $\quad \Gamma(X) \leqslant \Gamma(Y)$ *whenever* $X \subset Y$,

(C_2) $\quad \Gamma(\sum_i X_i) \leqslant \sum_i \Gamma(X_i)$ *for each sequence* $\{X_i\}$ *of sets,*

(C_3) $\quad \Gamma(X+Y) = \Gamma(X) + \Gamma(Y)$ *whenever* $\rho(X, Y) > 0$.

It should be noted that of these three conditions, the last one, only, has a metrical character. Now in this §, as well as in the §§ 5 and 6, we shall use only properties (C_1) and (C_2) of the Carathéodory measure. Hence all the results of these §§ remain valid in a perfectly arbitrary abstract space.

In order to simplify the wording, we shall suppose, in the rest of this chapter, except in § 8 which is concerned with certain special measures, that an outer Carathéodory measure $\Gamma(X)$ is uniquely determined in the space considered.

A set E will be termed *measurable with respect to the given outer measure* $\Gamma(X)$, if the relation $\Gamma(P+Q)=\Gamma(P)+\Gamma(Q)$ holds for every pair of sets P and Q contained, respectively, in the set E and in its complement CE; or, what amounts to the same, if $\Gamma(X)=\Gamma(X\cdot E)+\Gamma(X\cdot CE)$ holds for every set X. By condition (C_2) this last relation may be replaced by the inequality $\Gamma(X)\geqslant \Gamma(X\cdot E)+\Gamma(X\cdot CE)$.

The class of all the sets that are measurable with respect to Γ, will be denoted by $\mathfrak{L}_\Gamma$. We see at once that this class includes the empty set and all the sets X for which $\Gamma(X)=0$. Moreover it is clear that complements of sets ($\mathfrak{L}_\Gamma$) are also sets ($\mathfrak{L}_\Gamma$).

The main object of this § is to establish the additivity of the class $\mathfrak{L}_\Gamma$ (in the sense of Chap. I, § 4) and to prove that the function $\Gamma(X)$ is a measure ($\mathfrak{L}_\Gamma$) in the sense of Chap. I, § 9. This result will constitute Theorems 4.1 and 4.5.

(4.1) ***Theorem.*** *If S is the sum of a sequence $\{X_n\}_{n=1,2,\ldots}$ of sets ($\mathfrak{L}_\Gamma$) no two of which have common points, the set S is again a set ($\mathfrak{L}_\Gamma$) and $\Gamma(S)=\sum_n \Gamma(X_n)$; more generally, for each set Q*

$$\Gamma(Q)=\sum_n \Gamma(Q\cdot X_n)+\Gamma(Q\cdot CS). \tag{4.2}$$

Proof. Let $S_k=\sum_{n=1}^{k} X_n$. We begin by proving inductively that all the sets S_k are measurable with respect to Γ, and that, for each k and for every set Q,

$$\Gamma(Q)\geqslant \sum_{n=1}^{k} \Gamma(Q\cdot X_n)+\Gamma(Q\cdot CS_k). \tag{4.3}$$

Suppose indeed, that S_p is a set ($\mathfrak{L}_\Gamma$) and that the inequality (4.3) holds for every set Q, when $k=p$. Since X_{p+1} is, by hypothesis, a set ($\mathfrak{L}_\Gamma$) and $S_p\cdot X_{p+1}=0$, we then have

$$\Gamma(Q) = \Gamma(Q \cdot X_{p+1}) + \Gamma(Q \cdot CX_{p+1}) =$$
$$= \Gamma(Q \cdot X_{p+1}) + \Gamma(Q \cdot CX_{p+1} \cdot S_p) + \Gamma(Q \cdot CX_{p+1} \cdot CS_p) =$$
$$= \Gamma(Q \cdot X_{p+1}) + \Gamma(Q \cdot S_p) + \Gamma(Q \cdot CS_{p+1}) \geqslant \sum_{n=1}^{p+1} \Gamma(Q \cdot X_n) + \Gamma(Q \cdot CS_{p+1})$$

and this is (4.3) for $k = p + 1$. In view of condition (C_2), p. 43, it follows further that $\Gamma(Q) \geqslant \Gamma(Q \cdot S_{p+1}) + \Gamma(Q \cdot CS_{p+1})$,. which proves that S_{p+1} is a set ($\mathfrak{L}_\Gamma$).

Combining the inequality (4.3), thus established, with the inequality $\Gamma(Q \cdot CS_k) \geqslant \Gamma(Q \cdot CS)$, we obtain, by making $k \to \infty$, the inequality $\Gamma(Q) \geqslant \sum_{n=1}^{\infty} \Gamma(Q \cdot X_n) + \Gamma(Q \cdot CS)$, and from this (4.2) follows on account of condition (C_2).

Finally, the same condition enables us to derive from (4.2) that $\Gamma(Q) \geqslant \Gamma(Q \cdot S) + \Gamma(Q \cdot CS)$, and this shows that S is a set ($\mathfrak{L}_\Gamma$) and completes the proof.

(4.4) ***Lemma.*** *The difference of two sets ($\mathfrak{L}_\Gamma$) is itself a set ($\mathfrak{L}_\Gamma$).*

Proof. Let $X \in \mathfrak{L}_\Gamma$ and $Y \in \mathfrak{L}_\Gamma$, and let P and Q be any two sets such that $P \subset X - Y$ and $Q \subset C(X - Y)$. Write $Q_1 = Q \cdot Y$ and $Q_2 = Q \cdot CY$. Making successive use of the three pairs of inclusions $Q_1 \subset Y$, $Q_2 \subset CY$; $P \subset X$, $Q_2 \subset C(X - Y) \cdot CY \subset CX$; and $Q_1 \subset Y$, $P + Q_2 \subset CY$, we find $\Gamma(P) + \Gamma(Q) = \Gamma(P) + \Gamma(Q_1) + \Gamma(Q_2) = \Gamma(P + Q_2) + \Gamma(Q_1) = \Gamma(P + Q)$, which shows that $X - Y$ is a set ($\mathfrak{L}_\Gamma$).

(4.5) ***Theorem.*** *$\mathfrak{L}_\Gamma$ is an additive class of sets in the space **M**.*

Proof. We have already remarked (p. 44) that the empty set and that complements of sets ($\mathfrak{L}_\Gamma$) are sets ($\mathfrak{L}_\Gamma$). To verify the third condition (iii) for additivity (cf. Chap. I, § 4, p. 7), let us observe firstly that, on account of Lemma 4.4 and of the identity $X \cdot Y = X - CY$, the common part of any two sets ($\mathfrak{L}_\Gamma$) is itself a set ($\mathfrak{L}_\Gamma$). This result extends by induction to common parts of any finite number of sets ($\mathfrak{L}_\Gamma$) and, with the help of the identity $\sum_i X_i = C \prod_i CX_i$, we pass to the similar result for finite sums of sets. Finally, if X is the sum of an infinite sequence $\{X_n\}_{n=1, 2, \ldots}$ of sets ($\mathfrak{L}_\Gamma$), we have $X = S_1 + \sum_{n=1}^{\infty} (S_{n+1} - S_n)$ where $S_n = \sum_{k=1}^{n} X_k$. Now, clearly, of the sets S_1 and $S_{n+1} - S_n$, no two have common points, and, moreover, by the results already proved, they all belong to the class $\mathfrak{L}_\Gamma$. Consequently, to ascertain that X is a set ($\mathfrak{L}_\Gamma$), we have only to apply Theorem 4.1. The class $\mathfrak{L}_\Gamma$ is thus additive.

Theorem 4.5 connects the considerations of this chapter with those of the preceding one. Thus, in accordance with the conventions adopted in Chap. I, pp. 7 and 16, the sets $(\mathfrak{L}_\Gamma)$ may be termed sets measurable $(\mathfrak{L}_\Gamma)$, and $\Gamma(X)$ may, for $X \in \mathfrak{L}_\Gamma$, be regarded as a measure associated with the class $\mathfrak{L}_\Gamma$. This class, together with the measure Γ, determines further the notions of functions measurable $(\mathfrak{L}_\Gamma)$, of integral $(\mathfrak{L}_\Gamma, \Gamma)$, of additive function of a set $(\mathfrak{L}_\Gamma)$ absolutely continuous $(\mathfrak{L}_\Gamma, \Gamma)$, and the other notions defined generally in Chap. I. Since the outer measure Γ determines already the class $\mathfrak{L}_\Gamma$, we shall omit in the sequel the symbol representing this class, whenever the notation makes explicit reference to the outer measure; thus we shall say "function integrable (Γ)" instead of "function integrable $(\mathfrak{L}_\Gamma, \Gamma)$" and the integral (Γ) of a function $f(x)$ over a set E will be denoted simply by $\int_E f(x)\, d\Gamma(x)$, instead of by $(\mathfrak{L}_\Gamma)\int_E f(x)\, d\Gamma(x)$.

In accordance with Chap. I, § 9, the value taken by $\Gamma(X)$ for a set X measurable $(\mathfrak{L}_\Gamma)$ will be termed *measure* (Γ) of X; when X is quite arbitrary, this value will be called its *outer measure* (Γ).

If E_0 is a subset of a set E such that $\Gamma(E - E_0) = 0$, then for any function $f(x)$ on E the measurability $(\mathfrak{L}_\Gamma)$ of f on E is equivalent to its measurability $(\mathfrak{L}_\Gamma)$ on E_0. This remark and Theorem 11.8, Chap. I, justify the following convention:

If a function $f(x)$ is defined only almost everywhere (Γ) on a set E, then, E_0 denoting the set of the points of E at which $f(x)$ is defined, by *measurability* $(\mathfrak{L}_\Gamma)$, *integrability* (Γ) and *integral* (Γ) *of f on the set E* we shall mean those on the set E_0.

Let us note two further theorems.

(4.6) ***Theorem.*** *Given an arbitrary set E,* (i) $\Gamma(E \cdot \sum_n X_n) = \sum_n \Gamma(E \cdot X_n)$ *for every sequence $\{X_n\}$ of sets measurable $(\mathfrak{L}_\Gamma)$ no two of which have common points,* (ii) $\Gamma(E \cdot \lim_n X_n) = \lim_n \Gamma(E \cdot X_n)$ *for every ascending sequence $\{X_n\}$ of sets measurable $(\mathfrak{L}_\Gamma)$, and this relation remains valid for descending sequences provided, however, that $\Gamma(E \cdot X_1) \neq \infty$,* (iii) *more generally, for every sequence $\{X_n\}$ of sets measurable $(\mathfrak{L}_\Gamma)$ $\Gamma(E \cdot \liminf_n X_n) \leqslant \liminf_n \Gamma(E \cdot X_n)$, and, if further $\Gamma(E \cdot \sum_n X_n) \neq \infty$, then also $\Gamma(E \cdot \limsup_n X_n) \geqslant \limsup_n \Gamma(E \cdot X_n)$.*

Part (i) of this theorem is contained in Theorem 4.1, and parts (ii) and (iii) follow easily from (i) (cf. Chap. I, the proofs of Theorems 5.1 and 9.1).

A part of Theorem 4.6 will be slightly further generalized. Given a set E, let us denote, for any set X, by $\Gamma_E^0(X)$ the lower bound of the values taken by $\Gamma(E\cdot Y)$ for the sets Y measurable ($\mathfrak{L}_\Gamma$) that contain X.

(4.7) ***Theorem.*** *Given a set E,* (i) *to every set X corresponds a set $X^0 \supset X$ measurable* ($\mathfrak{L}_\Gamma$) *such that* $\Gamma_E^0(X) = \Gamma(E\cdot X^0)$, (ii) $\Gamma(E\cdot \liminf_n X_n) \leqslant \Gamma_E^0(\liminf_n X_n) \leqslant \liminf_n \Gamma_E^0(X_n)$ *for every sequence* $\{X_n\}$ *of sets, and, in particular,* $\Gamma(E\cdot \lim_n X_n) \leqslant \Gamma_E^0(\lim_n X_n) = \lim_n \Gamma_E^0(X_n)$ *for every ascending sequence* $\{X_n\}$.

Proof. *re* (i). For every positive integer n there is a set $Y_n \supset X$, measurable ($\mathfrak{L}_\Gamma$), such that $\Gamma(E\cdot Y_n) \leqslant \Gamma_E^0(X) + 1/n$. Writing $X^0 = \prod_n Y_n$, we verify at once that the set X^0 has the required properties.

re (ii). Taking (i) into account, let us associate with each set X_n a set $X_n^0 \supset X_n$, measurable ($\mathfrak{L}_\Gamma$) and such that $\Gamma(E\cdot X_n^0) = \Gamma_E^0(X_n)$. The set $\liminf_n X_n^0 \supset \liminf_n X_n$ is measurable ($\mathfrak{L}_\Gamma$) and, we therefore have, by Theorem 4.6 (iii)

$$\Gamma_E^0(\liminf_n X_n) \leqslant \Gamma(E\cdot \liminf_n X_n^0) \leqslant \liminf_n \Gamma(E\cdot X_n^0) = \liminf_n \Gamma_E^0(X_n).$$

The second part of (ii) follows at once from the first part.

* **§ 5. The operation (A).** We shall establish here that measurability ($\mathfrak{L}_\Gamma$) is an invariant of a more general operation than those of addition and multiplication of sets.

We call *determining system*, any class of sets $\mathfrak{A} = \{A_{n_1, n_2, \ldots, n_k}\}$ in which with each finite sequence of positive integers $n_1, n_2, \ldots, n_k$ there is associated a set $A_{n_1, n_2, \ldots, n_k}$. The set

(5.1) $$\sum_{n_1, n_2, \ldots, n_k, \ldots} A_{n_1}\cdot A_{n_1, n_2}\cdot \ldots \cdot A_{n_1, n_2, \ldots, n_k}\cdot \ldots$$

where the summation extends over all infinite sequences of indices $n_1, n_2, \ldots, n_k, \ldots$, is called *nucleus* of the determining system $\mathfrak{A}$ and denoted by $\mathrm{N}(\mathfrak{A})$. The operation leading from a determining system to its nucleus is often called the *operation* (A).

The operation (A) was first defined by M. Souslin [1] in 1917. When applied to Borel sets, it leads to a wide class of sets (following N. Lusin, we call them *analytic*) and these play an important part in the theory of sets, in the theory of real functions, and even in some problems of classical type. A systematic account of the theory of these sets will be found in the treatises of H. Hahn [II], F. Hausdorff [II], C. Kuratowski [I], N. Lusin [II] and W. Sierpiński [II].

We mentioned at the beginning of this § that the operation (A) includes those of addition and of multiplication of sets. This remark must be understood as follows: *If $\mathfrak{M}$ is a class of sets such that the nucleus of every determining system formed of sets* ($\mathfrak{M}$) *itself belongs to $\mathfrak{M}$, then the sum and the common part of every sequence $\{N_i\}$ of sets* ($\mathfrak{M}$) *are also sets* ($\mathfrak{M}$). In fact, writing $P_{n_1, n_2, \ldots, n_k} = N_{n_1}$ and $Q_{n_1, n_2, \ldots, n_k} = N_k$ we see at once that the nuclei of the determining systems $\{P_{n_1, n_2, \ldots, n_k}\}$ and $\{Q_{n_1, n_2, \ldots, n_k}\}$ coincide respectively with the sum and with the common part of the sequence $\{N_i\}$. Thus, Theorem 5.5, now to be proved, will complete the result contained in Theorem 4.5, and in conjunction with Theorem 7.4, establish measurability ($\mathfrak{L}_\Gamma$) for analytic sets in any metrical space (cf. N. Lusin and W. Sierpiński [1], N. Lusin [3, pp. 25—26], and W. Sierpiński [12; 15]). The proof of this can be simplified if we assume regularity of the outer measure Γ (cf. § 6) (see C. Kuratowski [I, p. 58]).

With every determining system $\mathfrak{A} = \{A_{n_1, n_2, \ldots, n_k}\}$, we shall also associate the following sets. $\mathrm{N}^{h_1, h_2, \ldots, h_s}(\mathfrak{A})$ will denote, for each finite sequence $h_1, h_2, \ldots, h_s$ of positive integers, the sum (5.1) extended over all sequences, $n_1, n_2, \ldots, n_k, \ldots$ such that $n_i \leqslant h_i$ for $i = 1, 2, \ldots, s$. We see at once that the sequence $\{\mathrm{N}^h(\mathfrak{A})\}_{h=1,2,\ldots}$, together with every sequence $\{\mathrm{N}^{h_1, h_2, \ldots, h_k, h}(\mathfrak{A})\}_{h=1,2,\ldots}$, is monotone ascending and that

$$(5.2) \qquad \mathrm{N}(\mathfrak{A}) = \lim_h \mathrm{N}^h(\mathfrak{A}), \qquad \mathrm{N}^{h_1, h_2, \ldots, h_k}(\mathfrak{A}) = \lim_h \mathrm{N}^{h_1, h_2, \ldots, h_k, h}(\mathfrak{A}).$$

Further, for every sequence of positive integers $h_1, h_2, \ldots, h_k, \ldots$, we shall write

$$\mathrm{N}_{h_1}(\mathfrak{A}) = \sum_{n_1 \leqq h_1} A_{n_1}, \quad \mathrm{N}_{h_1, h_2}(\mathfrak{A}) = \sum_{n_1 \leqq h_1,\, n_2 \leqq h_2} A_{n_1} \cdot A_{n_1, n_2}, \quad \ldots,$$

$$\mathrm{N}_{h_1, h_2, \ldots, h_k}(\mathfrak{A}) = \sum_{n_1 \leqq h_1,\, n_2 \leqq h_2, \ldots,\, n_k \leqq h_k} A_{n_1} \cdot A_{n_1, n_2} \cdot \ldots \cdot A_{n_1, n_2, \ldots n_k}. \quad \ldots$$

We see directly that if the sets of the determining system $\mathfrak{A}$ belong to a class of sets $\mathfrak{M}$, the sets $\mathrm{N}_{h_1, h_2, \ldots, h_k}(\mathfrak{A})$ belong to the class $\mathfrak{M}_{\delta\sigma}$.

(5.3) ***Lemma.*** *For every determining system* $\mathfrak{A}=\{A_{n_1,n_2,...,n_k}\}$ *and for every sequence of positive integers* $h_1, h_2, ..., h_k, ...$

$$N_{h_1}(\mathfrak{A})\cdot N_{h_1,h_2}(\mathfrak{A})\cdot...\cdot N_{h_1,h_2,...,h_k}(\mathfrak{A})\cdot...\subset N(\mathfrak{A}). \tag{5.4}$$

Proof. Let x be any point belonging to the left-hand side of (5.4). We shall show firstly that a positive integer $n_1^0\leqslant h_1$ can be chosen so that, for each $k\geqslant 2$, the point x belongs to a set $A_{n_1}\cdot A_{n_1,n_2}\cdot...\cdot A_{n_1,n_2,...,n_k}$ for which $n_1=n_1^0$ and $n_i\leqslant h_i$ for $i=2, 3, ..., k$. Indeed, if there were no such integer n_1^0, we could associate with each index $n\leqslant h_1$, a positive integer k_n, such that x belongs to no product $A_n\cdot A_{n,n_2}\cdot...\cdot A_{n,n_2,...,n_{k_n}}$ for which $n_i\leqslant h_i$ when $i=2, 3, ..., k_n$. Denote by p_1 the greatest of the numbers $k_1, k_2, ..., k_{h_1}$. The point x thus belongs to none of the sets $A_{n_1}\cdot A_{n_1,n_2}\cdot...\cdot A_{n_1,n_2,...,n_{p_1}}$ for which $n_i\leqslant h_i$ when $i=1, 2, ..., p_1$, and therefore is not contained in their sum $N_{h_1,h_2,...,h_{p_1}}(\mathfrak{A})$. This is a contradiction since, by hypothesis, x is an element of the left-hand side of (5.4).

After the index n_1^0, we can determine afresh an index $n_2^0\leqslant h_2$, so that, for each $k\geqslant 3$, the point x belongs to a set $A_{n_1}\cdot A_{n_1,n_2}\cdot...\cdot A_{n_1,n_2,...,n_k}$ for which $n_1=n_1^0$, $n_2=n_2^0$ and $n_i\leqslant h_i$ when $i=3, 4, ..., k$. For, if there were no such index, we could find, as previously, a positive integer $p_2\geqslant 3$ such that x belongs to no product $A_{n_1}\cdot A_{n_1,n_2}\cdot...\cdot A_{n_1,n_2,...,n_{p_2}}$ for which $n_1=n_1^0$ and $n_i\leqslant h_i$ when $i=2, 3, ..., p_2$. And this would contradict the definition of the index n_1^0.

Proceeding in this way, we determine an infinite sequence of indices $\{n_i^0\}$ such that $n_i^0\leqslant h_i$ when $i=1, 2, ...$ and such that $x\in A_{n_1^0}\cdot A_{n_1^0,n_2^0}\cdot...\cdot A_{n_1^0,n_2^0,...,n_k^0}\cdot...$. Thus $x\in N(\mathfrak{A})$, and this completes the proof.

Lemma 5.3 is due to W. Sierpiński [13]. The proof contains a slightly more precise result than is expressed by the relation (5.4) and shows that the left-hand side of that relation coincides with the sum (5.1), when the latter is extended only to systems of indices $n_1, n_2, ..., n_k, ...$ restricted to satisfy $n_1\leqslant h_1, n_2\leqslant h_2, ..., n_k\leqslant h_k, ...$.

Let us call *degenerate*, a determining system $\{A_{n_1,n_2,...,n_k}\}$ such that, for some sequence $\{h_k\}$ of positive integers, we have $A_{n_1,n_2,...,n_k}=0$ whenever $n_k>h_k$. Then, for this sequence $\{h_k\}$, the relation of inclusion (5.4) becomes an identity and we are led to the following theorem:

If a degenerate determining system consists of sets belonging to a class $\mathfrak{M}$, *its nucleus is a set* $(\mathfrak{M}_{\delta\sigma\delta})$. A similar theorem cannot hold for non-degenerate systems: in fact, as shown by M. Souslin, the operation (A) applied to Borel sets (and even to linear segments) may lead to sets that are not Borel sets (cf. F. Hausdorff [II, p. 182—184]).

(5.5) **Theorem.** *The nucleus of any determining system* $\mathfrak{A}=\{A_{n_1,n_2,\ldots,n_k}\}$ *consisting of sets measurable* $(\mathfrak{L}_\Gamma)$ *is itself measurable* $(\mathfrak{L}_\Gamma)$.

Proof. Let us write, for short,

$$N=\mathrm{N}(\mathfrak{A}),\qquad N^{n_1,n_2,\ldots,n_k}=\mathrm{N}^{n_1,n_2,\ldots,n_k}(\mathfrak{A}),\qquad N_{n_1,n_2,\ldots,n_k}=\mathrm{N}_{n_1,n_2,\ldots,n_k}(\mathfrak{A}).$$

We have to show that, for any set E

$$\Gamma(E)\geqslant\Gamma(E\cdot N)+\Gamma(E\cdot \mathrm{C}N). \tag{5.6}$$

We may assume that $\Gamma(E)<\infty$, since (5.6) is evidently fulfilled in the opposite case.

Let us denote (as in § 4, p. 47) by $\Gamma_E^0(X)$ the lower bound of the values of $\Gamma(E\cdot Y)$ for sets $Y\supset X$ measurable $(\mathfrak{L}_\Gamma)$ and let ε be an arbitrary positive number. Taking into account (5.2) and Theorem 4.7, we readily define by induction a sequence of positive integers $\{h_k\}$ such that $\Gamma_E^0(N^{h_1})\geqslant\Gamma(E\cdot N)-\varepsilon/2$ and

$$\Gamma_E^0(N^{h_1,h_2,\ldots,h_k})\geqslant\Gamma_E^0(N^{h_1,h_2,\ldots,h_{k-1}})-\varepsilon/2^k\quad \textit{for}\quad k=2,3,\ldots.$$

Thus the sets $N_{n_1,n_2,\ldots,n_k}\supset N^{n_1,n_2,\ldots,n_k}$ being measurable $(\mathfrak{L}_\Gamma)$ together with the $A_{n_1,n_2,\ldots,n_k}$,

$$\Gamma(E\cdot N_{h_1,h_2,\ldots,h_k})\geqslant\Gamma_E^0(N^{h_1,h_2,\ldots,h_k})\geqslant\Gamma(E\cdot N)-\varepsilon$$

for each k, and therefore

$$\begin{aligned}\Gamma(E)&=\Gamma(E\cdot N_{h_1,h_2,\ldots,h_k})+\Gamma(E\cdot\mathrm{C}N_{h_1,h_2,\ldots,h_k})\geqslant\\&\geqslant\Gamma(E\cdot N)+\Gamma(E\cdot\mathrm{C}N_{h_1,h_2,\ldots,h_k})-\varepsilon.\end{aligned} \tag{5.7}$$

Now the sequence of sets $\{N_{h_1,h_2,\ldots,h_k}\}_{k=1,2,\ldots}$ is descending, and by Lemma 5.3 its limit is a subset of N. The sequence $\{\mathrm{C}N_{h_1,h_2,\ldots,h_k}\}_{k=1,2,\ldots}$ is thus ascending and its limit contains the set $\mathrm{C}N$. Hence, making $k\to\infty$ in (5.7), we find, by Theorem 4.6(ii), the inequality $\Gamma(E)\geqslant\Gamma(E\cdot N)+\Gamma(E\cdot\mathrm{C}N)-\varepsilon$, and this implies (5.6) since ε is an arbitrary positive number.

§ 6. Regular sets. A set X will be called *regular* (with respect to the outer measure Γ), if there exists a set A measurable $(\mathfrak{L}_\Gamma)$, containing X and such that $\Gamma(A)=\Gamma(X)$. Every measurable set is evidently regular, and so is also every set X whose outer measure (Γ) is infinite, since we then have $\Gamma(X)=\Gamma(\boldsymbol{M})=\infty$. If every set of the space considered is regular with respect to the outer measure Γ, this measure is itself called *regular*; cf. H. Hahn [I, p. 432], C. Carathéodory [1; I, p. 258].

Denoting by $\Gamma^0(X)$ the lower bound of the values of $\Gamma(Y)$ for sets $Y \supset X$ measurable ($\mathfrak{L}_\Gamma$), we see readily that the relation $\Gamma^0(X) = \Gamma(X)$ expresses a necessary and sufficient condition for the set X to be regular. From Theorem 4.7(ii), taking for the set E the whole space, we derive the following:

(6.1) ***Theorem.*** *For any sequence* $\{X_n\}$ *of regular sets* $\Gamma(\liminf_n X_n) \leqslant \liminf_n \Gamma(X_n)$, *and, if further the sequence* $\{X_n\}$ *is ascending* $\Gamma(\lim_n X_n) = \lim_n \Gamma(X_n)$.

The generality and the importance of this theorem consist in that all outer measures Γ that occur in applications satisfy the condition of regularity, and, for these measures, the last relation of Theorem 6.1 therefore holds for every ascending sequence of sets. Nevertheless, for measures that are not themselves regular, the restriction concerning regularity of the sets X_n is essential for the validity of Theorem 6.1 as is shown by an example of irregular measure due to C. Carathéodory [II, pp. 693—696].

We may observe further that, for any fixed set E, the function of a set $\Gamma_E^0(X)$, defined in § 4, p. 47, is always a regular outer measure, even if the given measure $\Gamma(X)$ is not. Conditions (C_1) and (C_2) together with that of regularity, are at once seen to hold, and (C_3) may be derived from Theorem 7.4, according to which closed sets are measurable ($\mathfrak{L}_\Gamma$).

§ 7. Borel sets. We shall show in this § that, independently of the choice of the outer measure Γ, the class $\mathfrak{L}_\Gamma$ contains all Borel sets.

(7.1) ***Lemma.*** *If* Q *is any set contained in an open set* G, *and* Q_n *denotes the set of the points* a *of* Q *for which* $\varrho(a, CG) \geqslant 1/n$, *then* $\lim_n \Gamma(Q_n) = \Gamma(Q)$.

Proof. Since the sequence $\{Q_n\}$ is ascending and $Q = \lim_n Q_n$, it suffices to show that $\lim_n \Gamma(Q_n) \geqslant \Gamma(Q)$. For this purpose let us write $D_n = Q_{n+1} - Q_n$. We then have $\varrho(D_{n+1}, Q_n) \geqslant 1/n(n+1) > 0$, provided that $D_{n+1} \neq 0$ and $Q_n \neq 0$. Hence, taking into account condition (C_3), p. 43, it is readily verified by induction that

$$(7.2)\quad \Gamma(Q_{2n+1}) \geqslant \Gamma\Big(\sum_{k=1}^{n} D_{2k}\Big) = \sum_{k=1}^{n} \Gamma(D_{2k}),\ \Gamma(Q_{2n}) \geqslant \Gamma\Big(\sum_{k=1}^{n} D_{2k-1}\Big) = \sum_{k=1}^{n} \Gamma(D_{2k-1})$$

for every positive integer n. Writing, for short, $a_n = \sum_{k=n}^{\infty} \Gamma(D_{2k})$ and

$b_n = \sum_{k=n+1}^{\infty} \Gamma(D_{2k-1})$, we obtain at once, by condition (C_2), p. 43,

$$(7.3) \qquad \Gamma(Q) \leqslant \Gamma(Q_{2n}) + a_n + b_n.$$

Now two possibilities arise: either both series, $\sum_{k=1}^{\infty} \Gamma(D_{2k})$ and $\sum_{k=1}^{\infty} \Gamma(D_{2k-1})$ have finite sums, or, one at least has its sum infinite. In the former case $a_n \to 0$ and $b_n \to 0$, so that, the required inequality $\Gamma(Q) \leqslant \lim_n \Gamma(Q_n)$ follows by making $n \to \infty$ in (7.3); while, in the latter case, the inequality is obvious, since by (7.2) we have then $\lim_n \Gamma(Q_n) = \infty$.

(7.4) ***Theorem.*** *Every set measurable* ($\mathfrak{B}$) *is measurable* ($\mathfrak{L}_\Gamma$).

Proof. Since the class $\mathfrak{L}_\Gamma$ is additive and since $\mathfrak{B}$ is the smallest additive class including the closed sets (cf. § 2, p. 41), it is enough to prove that every closed set is measurable ($\mathfrak{L}_\Gamma$), i. e., denoting any such a set by F, that

$$(7.5) \qquad \Gamma(P+Q) \geqslant \Gamma(P) + \Gamma(Q)$$

holds for every pair of sets $P \subset F$ and $Q \subset CF$. Since the set CF is open, there is, by Lemma 7.1, a sequence $\{Q_n\}$ of sets such that $Q_n \subset Q$, $\varrho(Q_n, F) \geqslant 1/n$ for $n=1, 2, \ldots$, and $\lim_n \Gamma(Q_n) = \Gamma(Q)$. Thus $\varrho(Q_n, P) \geqslant \varrho(Q_n, F) > 0$, and so, on account of condition (C_3), p. 43, we derive $\Gamma(P+Q) \geqslant \Gamma(P+Q_n) = \Gamma(P) + \Gamma(Q_n)$ for each n, and, making $n \to \infty$, we obtain (7.5).

The arguments of this § depend essentially on property (C_3) of outer measure, and on the metrical character of the space M, which did not enter into §§ 4—6. It is possible however to give to these arguments a form, independent of condition (C_3), valid for certain topological spaces that are not necessarily metrical (cf. N. Bourbaki [1]).

From the preceding theorem coupled with Theorem 3.5, we derive at once the following

(7.6) ***Theorem.*** (i) *Every function measurable* ($\mathfrak{B}$) *on a set* E *is measurable* ($\mathfrak{L}_\Gamma$) *on* E. (ii) *Every function that is semi-continuous on a set* ($\mathfrak{L}_\Gamma$) *is measurable* ($\mathfrak{L}_\Gamma$) *on this set.*

§ 8. Length of a set. We shall define in this § a class of functions of a set that are outer Carathéodory measures and that play an important part in a number of applications.

Let α be an arbitrary positive number. Given a set X, we shall denote, for each $\varepsilon > 0$, by $\Lambda_\alpha^{(\varepsilon)}(X)$ the lower bound of the sums $\sum_{i=1}^{\infty}[\delta(X_i)]^\alpha$, for which $\{X_i\}_{i=1,2,...}$ is an arbitrary partition of X into a sequence of sets that have diameters less than ε. When $\varepsilon \to 0$, the number $\Lambda_\alpha^{(\varepsilon)}(X)$ tends, in a monotone non-decreasing manner, to a unique limit (finite or infinite) which we shall denote by $\Lambda_\alpha(X)$. The function of a set $\Lambda_\alpha(X)$ thus defined is an outer measure in the sense of Carathéodory. For, when $\varepsilon > 0$, we clearly have (i) $\Lambda_\alpha^{(\varepsilon)}(X) \leqslant \Lambda_\alpha^{(\varepsilon)}(Y)$ if $X \subset Y$, (ii) $\Lambda_\alpha^{(\varepsilon)}(\sum_n X_n) \leqslant \sum_n \Lambda_\alpha^{(\varepsilon)}(X_n)$, if $\{X_n\}$ is any sequence of sets, and (iii) $\Lambda_\alpha^{(\varepsilon)}(X+Y) = \Lambda_\alpha^{(\varepsilon)}(X) + \Lambda_\alpha^{(\varepsilon)}(Y)$, if $\varrho(X, Y) > \varepsilon$. Making $\varepsilon \to 0$, (i), (ii), (iii) become respectively the three conditions (C_1), (C_2), (C_3), p. 43, of Carathéodory for $\Lambda_\alpha(X)$.

We shall prove further that the outer measure Λ_α (for any $\alpha > 0$) is regular in the sense of § 6, i. e. that every set is regular with respect to this measure. We shall even establish a more precise result, namely

(8.1) ***Theorem.*** *For each set X there is a set $H \in \mathfrak{G}_\delta$ such that $X \subset H$ and $\Lambda_\alpha(H) = \Lambda_\alpha(X)$.*

Proof. For each positive integer n, there is a partition of X into a sequence of sets $\{X_i^{(n)}\}_{i=1,2,...}$ such that

(8.2) $\delta(X_i^{(n)}) < 1/2n$ *for* $i=1,2,...,$ *and* $\sum_{i=1}^{\infty}[\delta(X_i^{(n)})]^\alpha \leqslant \Lambda_\alpha(X) + 1/n.$

We can evidently enclose each set $X_i^{(n)}$ in an open set $G_i^{(n)}$ such that

(8.3) $$\delta(G_i^{(n)}) \leqslant (1 + 1/n)\, \delta(X_i^{(n)}).$$

Writing $H = \prod_{n=1}^{\infty} \sum_{i=1}^{\infty} G_i^{(n)}$, we see at once that H is a set ($\mathfrak{G}_\delta$) and that $X \subset H$. Moreover, for each n, $H = \sum_{i=1}^{\infty} H \cdot G_i^{(n)}$ and the relations (8.2) and (8.3) imply that $\delta(H \cdot G_i^{(n)}) < 1/n$ for $i = 1, 2, ...$ and that $\Lambda_\alpha^{(1/n)}(H) \leqslant \sum_{i=1}^{\infty}[\delta(H \cdot G_i^{(n)})]^\alpha \leqslant (1+1/n)^\alpha [\Lambda_\alpha(X) + 1/n]$. Making $n \to \infty$, we find in the limit $\Lambda_\alpha(H) \leqslant \Lambda_\alpha(X)$, and, since the converse inequality is obvious, this completes the proof.

In Euclidean n-dimensional space $\boldsymbol{R}_n$ (see Chap. III), the sets whose measure (Λ_n) is zero may be identified with those of measure zero in the Lebesgue sense. By analogy, in any metrical space, sets whose measure (Λ_α) is zero are termed sets having *α-dimensional volume zero*, and in particular, when $\alpha=1, 2, 3$, sets *of zero length*, *of zero area*, *of zero volume*, respectively. For the same reason, sets of finite measure (Λ_α) are termed sets *of finite α-dimensional volume* (or *of finite length*, *finite area*, *finite volume*, in the cases $\alpha=1, 2, 3$). In particular, in $\boldsymbol{R}_1$, i.e. on the straight line, the outer measure Λ_1 coincides with the Lebesgue measure, and, on this account, we call the number $\Lambda_1(X)$, in general, *outer length* of X, and when X is a set measurable ($\mathfrak{L}_{\Lambda_1}$), simply, *length* of X. For short, we often write Λ instead of Λ_1.

We have mentioned only the more elementary properties of the measures Λ_α, those, namely, that we shall have some further occasion to use. For a deeper study, the reader should consult F. Hausdorff [1]. Among the researches devoted to the notion of length of sets in Euclidean spaces, special mention must be made of the important memoir of A. S. Besicovitch [1]; cf. also W. Sierpiński [1] and J. Gillis [1].

§ 9. Complete space. A metrical space is termed *complete*, if a sequence $\{a_n\}$ of its points converges whenever $\lim\limits_{m,n\to\infty} \varrho(a_m, a_n)=0$. In any metrical space, this is evidently a necessary condition for convergence of the sequence $\{a_n\}$, but, as a rule, not a sufficient one. The following theorem concerns a characteristic property of complete spaces:

(9.1) ***Theorem.*** *In a complete space, when $\{F_n\}$ is a descending sequence of closed and non-empty sets whose diameters tend to zero, the common part $\prod\limits_n F_n$ is not empty.*

Proof. Let a_n be an arbitrarily chosen point of F_n. For $n \geqslant m$, we have $\varrho(a_m, a_n) \leqslant \delta(F_m)$, and hence $\lim\limits_{m,n\to\infty} \varrho(a_m, a_n)=0$. The sequence $\{a_n\}$ is thus convergent. Now the limit point of this sequence clearly belongs to all the sets F_m, since $a_n \in F_n \subset F_m$ whenever $n \geqslant m$, and since the sets F_m are closed by hypothesis.

(9.2) ***Baire's theorem.*** *In a complete space $\boldsymbol{M}$, every non-empty set ($\mathfrak{G}_\delta$) is of the second category on itself, i.e. if H is a set ($\mathfrak{G}_\delta$) in $\boldsymbol{M}$ and $H=\sum\limits_n H_n$, one at least of the sets H_n is everywhere dense in a portion of H.*

Proof. Suppose, accordingly, that $H=\prod_{n=1}^{\infty} G_n$ where G_n are open sets, and further that

$$H=\sum_{n=1}^{\infty} H_n \tag{9.3}$$

where H_n are non-dense in H. The partial sums of the series (9.3) are then also non-dense in H (cf. § 2, p. 41), and it is easy to define inductively a descending sequence of portions S_n of H such that (i) $\overline{S}_n \subset G_n$, (ii) $\overline{S}_n \cdot \sum_{j=1}^{n} H_j = 0$, (iii) $\delta(S_n) \leqslant 1/n$. On account of Theorem 9.1 and of (iii), the sets $\overline{S}_n$ have a common point, which by (i), belongs to all the sets G_n, and so to H, while at the same time, by (ii) it belongs to none of the H_n. This contradicts (9.3) and proves the theorem.

The case of Theorem 9.2 that occurs most frequently, is that in which H is a closed set. For closed sets in Euclidean spaces the theorem was established in 1899 by R. Baire [1]. To Baire, we owe also the fundamental applications of the theorem, which have brought out the fruitfulness and the importance of the result for modern real function theory. As regards the theorem by itself however, it was found, almost at the same time and independently by W. F. Osgood [1] in connection with some problems concerning functions of a complex variable (cf. in this connection, the interesting article by W. H. Young [7]). The general form of Theorem 9.2 is due to F. Hausdorff [I, pp. 326—328; II, pp. 138—145].

If a is a non-isolated point (cf. § 2, p. 40) of a set M, the set (a) consisting of the single point a is clearly non-dense in M. It therefore follows from Theorem 9.2 that

(9.4) ***Theorem.*** *In a complete metrical space, every non-empty set ($\mathfrak{G}_\delta$) without isolated points, and in particular every perfect set, is non-enumerable.*

More precisely, by a theorem of W. H. Young [1], every set that fulfills the condition of Theorem 9.4 has the power of the continuum; cf. also F. Hausdorff [II, p. 136].

CHAPTER III.

Functions of bounded variation and the Lebesgue-Stieltjes integral.

§ 1. Euclidean spaces. In this chapter, the notions of measure that we consider undergo a further specialization. Accordingly we introduce for Euclidean spaces, a particular class of outer measures of Carathéodory, determined in a natural way by non-negative additive functions of an interval. These outer measures in their turn determine the corresponding classes of measurable sets and measurable functions, and lead to processes of integration usually known as those of Lebesgue-Stieltjes.

By *Euclidean space of m dimensions* $\boldsymbol{R}_m$, we mean the set of all systems of m real numbers $(x_1, x_2, ..., x_m)$. The number x_k is termed k-th *coordinate* of the point $(x_1, x_2, ..., x_m)$. The point $(0, 0, ..., 0)$ will be denoted by 0.

By *distance* $\varrho(x, y)$ of two points $x=(x_1, x_2, ..., x_m)$ and $y=(y_1, y_2, ..., y_m)$ in the space $\boldsymbol{R}_m$, we mean the non-negative number $[(y_1-x_1)^2+(y_2-x_2)^2+...+(y_m-x_m)^2]^{1/2}$. Distance, thus defined, evidently fulfills the three conditions of Chap. II, p. 40, and hence Euclidean spaces may be regarded as metrical spaces. All the definitions adopted in Chap. II therefore apply in particular to spaces $\boldsymbol{R}_m$. In § 2 we supplement them by some definitions more exclusively restricted to Euclidean spaces.

The space $\boldsymbol{R}_1$ is also termed *straight line* and the space $\boldsymbol{R}_2$, *plane*. Accordingly, the sets in $\boldsymbol{R}_1$ will often be called *linear*, and those in $\boldsymbol{R}_2$ *plane sets.*

§ 2. Intervals and figures. Suppose given a Euclidean space $\boldsymbol{R}_m$.

The set of the points $(x_1, x_2, ..., x_m)$ of $\boldsymbol{R}_m$ that fulfill a linear equation $a_1x_1+a_2x_2+...+a_mx_m=b$, where $b, a_1, a_2, ..., a_m$ are real numbers and, of these, the coefficients $a_1, a_2, ..., a_m$ do not all vanish together, is called *hyperplane* $a_1x_1+a_2x_2+...+a_mx_m=b$. For each fixed $k=1, 2, ..., m$, the hyperplanes $x_k=b$ are said to be *orthogonal to the axis of* x_k. The term *hyperplane* by itself, will be applied exclusively to a hyperplane orthogonal to one of the axes. In $\boldsymbol{R}_1$, hyperplanes coincide with points. In $\boldsymbol{R}_2$ and $\boldsymbol{R}_3$ they are respectively *straight lines* and *planes*.

Given two points $a=(a_1, a_2, ..., a_m)$ and $b=(b_1, b_2, ..., b_m)$ such that $a_k \leqslant b_k$ for $k=1, 2, ..., m$, we term *closed interval* $[a_1, b_1; a_2, b_2; ...; a_m, b_m]$ the set of all the points $(x_1, x_2, ..., x_m)$ such that $a_k \leqslant x_k \leqslant b_k$ for $k=1, 2, ..., m$. The points a and b are called *principal vertices* of this interval. If, in the definition of closed interval, we replace successively the inequality $a_k \leqslant x_k \leqslant b_k$ by the inequalities (1⁰) $a_k < x_k < b_k$, (2⁰) $a_k \leqslant x_k < b_k$ and (3⁰) $a_k < x_k \leqslant b_k$, we obtain the definitions (1⁰) of *open interval* $(a_1, b_1; a_2, b_2; ...; a_m, b_m)$, (2⁰) of *interval half open to the right* $[a_1, b_1; a_2, b_2; ...; a_m, b_m)$ and (3⁰) of *interval half open to the left* $(a_1, b_1; a_2, b_2; ...; a_m, b_m]$. If $a_k=b_k$ for at least one index k, all these intervals are said to be *degenerate*. In what follows, an *interval*, by itself, always means either a closed non-degenerate interval or an empty set, unless another meaning is obvious from the context.

We call *face* of the closed interval $I=[a_1, b_1; a_2, b_2; ...; a_m, b_m]$ the common part of I and any one of the $2m$ hyperplanes $x_k=a_k$ and $x_k=b_k$, where $k=1, 2, ..., m$. If J is an open or half open interval we call *faces* of J those of its closure $\bar{J}$. We see at once that the faces of any non-empty interval I are degenerate intervals and that their sum is the boundary of the interval I.

If $b_1-a_1=b_2-a_2=...=b_m-a_m>0$, the interval $[a_1, b_1; a_2, b_2; ...; a_m, b_m]$ is termed *cube* (*square* in $\boldsymbol{R}_2$). We define similarly *open cubes* and *half open cubes* (half open to the right or to the left).

We call *net of closed intervals* in $\boldsymbol{R}_m$ any system of closed non-overlapping intervals that together cover the space $\boldsymbol{R}_m$. Similarly, by *net of half open intervals*, we mean a system of intervals half open on the same side, no two of which have common points, and whose sum covers $\boldsymbol{R}_m$. A sequence of nets $\{\mathfrak{N}_k\}$ (of closed or of half open intervals) is *regular*, if each interval of $\mathfrak{N}_{k+1}$ is contained in an interval of $\mathfrak{N}_k$ and if the characteristic numbers $\Delta(\mathfrak{N}_k)$ (cf. Chap. II, p. 40) tend to 0 as $k\to\infty$. Given a net of half open intervals, we clearly change it into a net of closed intervals by replacing the half open intervals by their closures. The same operation changes any regular sequence of nets of half open intervals into a regular sequence of nets of closed intervals.

(2.1) ***Theorem.*** *Given an enumerable system of hyperplanes* $x_k=a_j$, *where* $k=1, 2, \ldots, m$, *and* $j=1, 2, \ldots$, *we can always construct a regular sequence* $\{\mathfrak{N}_k\}$ *of nets of cubes (closed or half open) none of which has a face on the given hyperplanes.*

To see this, let b denote a positive number not of the form qa_j/p where p and q are integers and $j=1, 2, \ldots$. Such a number b certainly exists, since the set of the numbers of the form qa_j/p is at most enumerable. This being so, for each positive integer k let us denote by $\mathfrak{N}_k$ the net consisting of all the cubes half open to the left $(p_1b/2^k, (p_1+1)b/2^k; p_2b/2^k, (p_2+1)b/2^k; \ldots; p_mb/2^k, (p_m+1)b/2^k]$, where $p_1, p_2, \ldots, p_m$ are arbitrary integers. The sequence of nets $\{\mathfrak{N}_k\}$ evidently fulfills the required conditions.

Let us observe that, *given a regular sequence* $\{\mathfrak{N}_k\}$ *of nets of half open* [*closed*] *intervals, every open set* G *is expressible as the sum of an enumerable system of intervals* $(\mathfrak{N}_k)$ *without common points* [*non-overlapping*]. To see this, let $\mathfrak{M}_1$ be the set of intervals of $\mathfrak{N}_1$ that lie in G, and let $\mathfrak{M}_{k+1}$, for each $k\geqslant 1$, be the set of intervals $(\mathfrak{N}_{k+1})$ that lie in G but not in any of the intervals $(\mathfrak{M}_k)$. Since $\Delta(\mathfrak{N}_k)\to 0$ as $k\to\infty$, the enumerable system of intervals $\sum_k \mathfrak{M}_k$ covers the set G, and the other conditions required are evidently satisfied also.

On account of Theorem 2.1, we derive at once the following proposition which will often be useful to us in the course of this Chapter:

(2.2) ***Theorem.*** *Given a sequence of hyperplanes* $\{H_i\}$, *every open set* G *is expressible as the sum of a sequence of half open cubes without common points* [*or of closed non-overlapping cubes*] *whose faces do not lie on any of the hyperplanes* H_i.

A set expressible as the sum of a finite number of intervals will be termed *elementary figure*, or simply, *figure*. Every sum of a finite number of figures is itself a figure, but this is not in general the case for the common part, or for the difference, of two figures.

We shall therefore define two operations similar to those of multiplication and subtraction of sets, but which differ from the latter in that, when we perform them on figures, the result is again a figure. These operations will be denoted by $\odot$ and $\ominus$ and are defined by the relations

$$A \odot B = \overline{(A \cdot B)}^{\circ} \qquad \text{and} \qquad A \ominus B = \overline{(A - B)}^{\circ}.$$

The relation $A \odot B = 0$ means that the figures A and B do not overlap (cf. Chap. II, p. 40).

Given an interval $I = [a_1, b_1; a_2, b_2; \ldots; a_m, b_m]$, the number $(b_1 - a_1) \cdot (b_2 - a_2) \cdot \ldots \cdot (b_m - a_m)$ will be called *volume* of I (*length* for $m=1$, *area* for $m=2$), and denoted by $\mathrm{L}(I)$ or by $|I|$. If $I=0$, by $\mathrm{L}(I)=|I|$ we mean 0 also. When several spaces $\boldsymbol{R}_m$ are considered simultaneously, we shall, to prevent any ambiguity, denote the volume of an interval I in $\boldsymbol{R}_m$ by $\mathrm{L}_m(I)$. We see at once that every figure R can be subdivided into a finite number of non-overlapping intervals. The sum of the volumes of these intervals is independent of the way in which we make this subdivision; it is termed *volume* (*length*, *area*) of R and denoted, just as in the case of intervals, by $\mathrm{L}(R)$ or by $|R|$.

§ 3. Functions of an interval. We shall say that $F(I)$ is a *function of an interval* on a figure R [or in an open set G], if $F(I)$ is a finite real number uniquely defined for each interval I contained in R [or in G]. To simplify the wording, we shall usually suppose that functions of an interval are defined in the whole space.

A function of an interval $F(I)$ will be said to be *continuous on a figure* R, if to each $\varepsilon>0$ there corresponds an $\eta>0$ such that $|I|<\eta$ implies $|F(I)|<\varepsilon$ for every interval $I \subset R$. A function of an interval will be said to be *continuous in an open set* G, if it is continuous on every figure $R \subset G$. Finally, functions continuous in the whole space will simply be said to be *continuous*.

The reader will have noticed that we use the terms "on" (or "over") and "in" in slightly different senses. We may express the distinction as follows. Suppose that a certain property (P) of functions of a point, of an interval, or of a set has been defined on figures. We then say that a function has this property *in* an open set G, if it has the property on every figure $R \subset G$. Further, if a function has the property (P) in the whole space, we say simply that *it has the property* (P). Thus, for instance, a function of a set $\Phi(X)$ is additive ($\mathfrak{B}$) (cf. Chap. I, § 5 and Chap. II, § 8) in an open set G, if it is additive ($\mathfrak{B}$) on every figure $R \subset G$; if μ is a measure ($\mathfrak{B}$) (cf. Chap. I, § 9), a function of a point, defined in the whole space, is said to be integrable ($\mathfrak{B}$, μ), if it is integrable ($\mathfrak{B}$, μ) on every figure, and so on.

We shall call *oscillation* $O(F; E)$ of a function of an interval F on a set E, the upper bound of the values $|F(I)|$ for intervals $I \subset E$. If D is an arbitrary set and R a figure, we shall denote by $o_R(F; D)$ the lower bound of the numbers $O(F; R \cdot G)$, where G is any open set containing D; the number $o_R(F; D)$ will be termed *oscillation of F on R at the set D*. Finally we shall say simply *oscillation of F at D*, and use the notation $o(F; D)$, for the upper bound of the numbers $o_R(F; D)$ where R denotes any figure (or, what amounts to the same, interval or cube).

In the sequel, D will usually be a hyperplane (a point in $\boldsymbol{R}_1$, a straight line in $\boldsymbol{R}_2$) or else the boundary of a figure. In these cases we shall say that the function F is *continuous*, or *discontinuous*, *at D on R*, according as $o_R(F; D) = 0$ or $o_R(F; D) > 0$. Similarly, we shall say that F is *continuous*, or *discontinuous*, *at D*, according as $o(F; D) = 0$ or $o(F; D) > 0$.

(3.1) ***Theorem.*** *In order that a function F of an interval be continuous on a figure R [or in the whole space], it is necessary and sufficient that $o_R(F; D) = 0$ [or that $o(F; D) = 0$] for every hyperplane D.*

Proof. Since the condition is clearly necessary, let us suppose that the function F is not continuous on R. There is then a number $\varepsilon_0 > 0$ and a sequence of intervals $\{I^{(n)} = [a_1^{(n)}, b_1^{(n)}; \ldots; a_m^{(n)}, b_m^{(n)}]\}$ contained in R and such that for $n = 1, 2, \ldots$, $|F(I^{(n)})| > \varepsilon_0$, and that $|I^{(n)}| \to 0$. By the second of these conditions, we can extract from the sequence $\{I^{(n)}\}$, a subsequence $\{I^{(n_k)}\}$, in such a manner that $\lim_k (b_i^{(n_k)} - a_i^{(n_k)}) = 0$ for a positive integer $i = i_0 \leqslant m$. The sequences $\{a_{i_0}^{(n_k)}\}_{k=1,2,\ldots}$ and $\{b_{i_0}^{(n_k)}\}_{k=1,2,\ldots}$ then have a common limit point a, and, denoting by D the hyperplane $x_{i_0} = a$, we see that every open set $G \supset D$ contains an infinity of intervals $I^{(n)}$, so that $o_R(F; D) \geqslant \varepsilon_0 > 0$.

§ 4. Functions of an interval that are additive and of bounded variation. A function of an interval $F(I)$ is said to be *additive* on a figure R_0 [or in an open set G], if $F(I_1+I_2)=$ $=F(I_1)+F(I_2)$ whenever I_1, I_2 and I_1+I_2 are intervals contained in R_0 [or in G] and I_1, I_2 are non-overlapping. A function additive in the whole space, is for instance the volume $\mathrm{L}(I)=|I|$. Just as in the case of the function $\mathrm{L}(I)$ (cf. § 2, p. 59), every additive function of an interval $F(I)$ on a figure R_0 [or in an open set G] can be continued on all figures in R_0 [or in G] in such a manner that $F(R_1+R_2)=F(R_1)+F(R_2)$ for every pair of figures $R_1\subset R_0$ and $R_2\subset R_0$ that do not overlap. In the sequel, we shall always suppose every additive function of an interval continued in this way on the figures.

If F is an additive function of an interval on a figure R_0, we shall term respectively *upper* and *lower (relative) variations* of F on R_0 the upper and lower bounds of $F(R)$ for figures $R\subset R_0$. We denote these variations by $\overline{\mathrm{W}}(F; R_0)$ and $\underline{\mathrm{W}}(F; R_0)$ respectively. Since every additive function vanishes on the empty set, we have $\overline{\mathrm{W}}(F; R_0)\geqslant 0\geqslant\underline{\mathrm{W}}(F;R_0)$. The number $\overline{\mathrm{W}}(F;R_0)+|\underline{\mathrm{W}}(F;R_0)|$, clearly non-negative, will be called *absolute variation* of F on R_0 and denoted by $\mathrm{W}(F; R_0)$. If $\mathrm{W}(F; R_0)<+\infty$, the function F is said to be *of bounded variation on* R_0. In accordance with the convention of § 3, p. 59, an additive function of an interval in the whole space is of bounded variation, if it is of bounded variation on every figure.

It is obvious that a function of bounded variation on a figure R_0 is equally so on every figure contained in R_0, and also that the sum, the difference, and, more generally, any linear combination of two additive functions of an interval that are of bounded variation on a figure, is itself of bounded variation on the same figure.

An additive function whose values are of constant sign is termed *monotone*. A non-negative monotone additive function is also termed *non-decreasing* (for the same reason as in the case of non-negative additive functions of a set, cf. Chap. I, p. 8). Similarly, non-positive additive functions are also termed *non-increasing*. Every monotone additive function F of an interval on a figure R_0 is clearly of bounded variation on R_0.

If a function is of bounded variation on a figure R_0, its relative variations on R_0 are evidently finite. Conversely, if for an additive function F of an interval on a figure R_0, one or other of the two relative variations is finite, then both are finite, and therefore the absolute variation is finite. For, if $\overline{\mathrm{W}}(F; R_0) < +\infty$ say, then as $\underline{\mathrm{W}}(F; R_0)$ is the lower bound of the numbers $F(R) = F(R_0) - F(R_0 \ominus R)$, where R is any figure contained in R_0, we find $\underline{\mathrm{W}}(F; R_0) \geqslant F(R_0) - \overline{\mathrm{W}}(F; R_0) > -\infty$. Moreover, this last inequality may also be written in the form $F(R_0) \leqslant \overline{\mathrm{W}}(F; R_0) + \underline{\mathrm{W}}(F; R_0)$. Here we replace F by $-F$ to derive the opposite inequality and then finally the equality $F(R_0) = \overline{\mathrm{W}}(F; R_0) + \underline{\mathrm{W}}(F; R_0)$. Hence *any additive function of bounded variation is the sum of its two relative variations on any figure for which it is defined.* This decomposition is termed the *Jordan decomposition* of an additive function of bounded variation, and is similar to the Jordan decomposition of an additive function of a set (Chap. I, § 6).

If F is an additive function of bounded variation of an interval on a figure R_0, the three monotone functions defined for every figure $R \subset R_0$ by the relations

$$W(R) = \mathrm{W}(F; R), \qquad W_1(R) = \overline{\mathrm{W}}(F; R) \qquad \textit{and} \qquad W_2(R) = \underline{\mathrm{W}}(F; R),$$

are likewise additive on R_0 and are termed, respectively, *absolute*, *upper*, and *lower variations* of F. The first two are non-negative and the third non-positive. It therefore follows from the Jordan decomposition that every additive function of bounded variation on a figure is, on this figure, the difference of two non-decreasing functions. The converse is obvious.

We shall now prove some elementary theorems concerning continuity properties of functions of bounded variation.

(4.1) ***Theorem.*** *If F is an additive function of an interval, of bounded variation on a figure R_0,* (i) *the series $\sum_n \mathrm{o}_{R_0}(F; D_n)$ converges for every sequence $\{D_n\}$ of hyperplanes distinct from one another, and* (ii) *there is at most an enumerable infinity of hyperplanes D such that $\mathrm{o}_{R_0}(F; D) > 0$.*

Proof. In the proof of (i) we may clearly suppose that the hyperplanes D_n are orthogonal to the same axis. Consider now the first k of these D_n. We can associate with them, k non-overlapping intervals $I_1, I_2, \dots, I_k$, contained in R_0 and such that $\mathrm{o}_{R_0}(F; D_n) \leqslant |F(I_n)| + 1/k^2$ for $n = 1, 2, \dots, k$. Hence $\sum_{n=1}^{k} \mathrm{o}_{R_0}(F; D_n) \leqslant \sum_{n=1}^{k} |F(I_n)| + 1/k \leqslant \mathrm{W}(F; R_0) + 1/k$, and, since k is an arbitrary positive integer, $\sum_{n=1}^{\infty} \mathrm{o}_{R_0}(F; D_n) \leqslant \mathrm{W}(F; R_0) < +\infty$.

To establish (ii), suppose that there is a non-enumerable infinity of hyperplanes D such that $o_{R_0}(F; D) > 0$. There would then be a positive number ε, such that $o_{R_0}(F; D) > \varepsilon$ for an infinity, (which would even be non-enumerable) of hyperplanes. But this clearly contradicts part (i) which has just been proved.

We obtain at once from Theorem 4.1 the following

(4.2) ***Theorem.*** *For each additive function of an interval of bounded variation, there is at most an enumerable infinity of hyperplanes of discontinuity.*

(4.3) ***Theorem.*** *If F is an additive function of an interval of bounded variation on a figure R_0 and we write $W(I) = W(F; I)$, the relations $o_{R_0}(F; D) = 0$ and $o_{R_0}(W; D) = 0$ are equivalent for every hyperplane D.*

Proof. Suppose, if possible, that

(4.4) $o_{R_0}(F; D) = 0$ and (4.5) $o_{R_0}(W; D) > \varepsilon$

for a hyperplane D and a number $\varepsilon > 0$. We shall show that it is then possible to define a sequence of figures $\{R_n\}_{n=1,2,\dots}$, non-overlapping, contained in R_0, and such that

(4.6) $R_n \cdot D = 0$ and (4.7) $|F(R_n)| > \varepsilon/2$.

To see this, suppose defined k non-overlapping figures $R_1, R_2, \dots, R_k$ contained in R_0, and let (4.6) and (4.7) hold for $n = 1, 2, \dots, k$. On account of (4.5) there is then an interval $I \subset R_0$ such that $I \cdot R_n = 0$ for $n = 1, 2, \dots, k$, and such that $W(F; I) = W(I) > \varepsilon$. Hence, there exists a figure $R \subset I$ such that $|F(R)| > W(F; I)/2 > \varepsilon/2$. Moreover since (4.4) asserts that F is continuous on R_0 at D, we may suppose that $R \cdot D = 0$. But if we now choose $R_{k+1} = R$, we see that the figure R_{k+1} does not overlap any of the figures R_n for $1 \leqslant n \leqslant k$, and that (4.6) and (4.7) continue to hold for $n = k+1$.

Having obtained our sequence $\{R_n\}$, we conclude from (4.7) that $W(F; R_0) \geqslant \sum_n |F(R_n)| = \infty$, and this contradicts our hypotheses. The conditions (4.4) and (4.5) are thus incompatible, i. e. (4.4) implies $o_{R_0}(W; D) = 0$. And since the converse is obvious, this completes the proof.

From Theorems 4.3 and 3.1, we obtain at once the following

(4.8) ***Theorem.*** *In order that an additive function of bounded variation on a figure R_0 be continuous on R_0, it is necessary and sufficient that its three variations be so.*

§ 5. Lebesgue-Stieltjes integral. Lebesgue integral and measure. We need hardly point out the analogy between additive functions of bounded variation of an interval and additive functions of sets. This analogy will be made clearer and deeper in the present §, by associating a function U^* of a set with each additive function U of bounded variation of an interval. In order to simplify the wording, we shall suppose that the functions of an interval are defined in the whole space.

Suppose given in the first place, a non-negative additive function U of an interval; we then denote for any set E, by $U^*(E)$ the lower bound of the sums $\sum_k U(I_k)$, where $\{I_k\}$ is an arbitrary sequence of intervals such that $E \subset \sum I_k^\circ$. For an arbitrary additive function U of bounded variation, with the upper and lower variations W_1 and W_2, we denote by W_1^* and $(-W_2)^*$ the functions of a set that correspond to the non-negative functions W_1 and $-W_2$, and we write, by definition, $U^* = W_1^* - (-W_2)^*$. The function U^* is thus defined for all sets and is finite for bounded sets.

When U is non-negative, U^* is an outer measure in the sense of Carathéodory, i. e. fulfills the three conditions (C_1), (C_2) and (C_3) of Chap. II, § 4. Condition (C_3) is the only one requiring proof, the other two are obvious. Let therefore A and B be any two sets whose distance does not vanish, and let ε be a positive number. There is then a sequence $\{I_n\}$ of intervals such that $A+B \subset \sum_n I_n^\circ$ and $\sum_n U(I_n) \leqslant U^*(A+B)+\varepsilon$. We may clearly suppose that the intervals of the sequence have diameters less than $\varrho(A, B)$, i. e. that none of them contains both points of A and points of B. We then have $U^*(A)+U^*(B) \leqslant \sum_n U(I_n) \leqslant U^*(A+B)+\varepsilon$. This gives the inequality $U^*(A)+U^*(B) \leqslant U^*(A+B)$ and establishes condition (C_3).

The function U^*, determined by a non-negative function of an interval, itself determines, since it is an outer Carathéodory measure (cf. Chap. II, § 4, p. 46), the class $\mathfrak{L}_{U^*}$ of the sets measurable with respect to U^* and the process of integration (U^*). To simplify the notation, we shall omit the asterisk and write simply $\mathfrak{L}_U$ for $\mathfrak{L}_{U^*}$, integral (U) for integral (U^*), measure (U) of a set instead of measure (U^*), $\int_E f dU$ instead of $\int_E f dU^*$, and so on.

This slight change of notation cannot cause any confusion, since the measure U^* is uniquely determined by the function of an interval U.

When U is a general additive function of an interval, of bounded variation, we shall understand by $\mathfrak{L}_U$ the common part of the classes $\mathfrak{L}_{W_1}$ and $\mathfrak{L}_{-W_2}$, where W_1 and W_2 denote respectively the upper and lower variations of U. A function of a point $f(x)$ will be termed *integrable* (U) on a set E, if $f(x)$ is integrable (W_1) and ($-W_2$) simultaneously; by its *integral* (U) over E we shall mean the number $\int_E f dW_1 - \int_E f d(-W_2)$, and we write it $\int_E f dU$ as in the case of a non-negative function U. This integration with respect to an additive function of bounded variation of an interval is called *Lebesgue-Stieltjes integration*. In the case of the integration over an interval $I=[a, b]$ in $\boldsymbol{R}_1$, we frequently write $\int_a^b f dU$ for $\int_I f dU$.

When the function U is continuous, every indefinite integral (U) vanishes, together with the function U^*, on the boundary of any figure. Consequently, an indefinite integral with respect to a continuous function U of bounded variation of an interval is additive not only as function of a set ($\mathfrak{L}_U$) but also as function of an interval.

The most important case is that in which the given function of an interval U is the special function L (cf. § 2, p. 59) that denotes the volume of an interval. The outer measure (L) is also termed *outer Lebesgue measure*, and the integral (L), *Lebesgue integral*, while functions integrable (L) are often called, as originally, by Lebesgue, *summable*. The class of sets $\mathfrak{L}_{\mathrm{L}}$ will be denoted simply by $\mathfrak{L}$. The outer measure (L) of an arbitrary set E is written $\text{meas}_e E$, and meas E without the suffix when E is measurable ($\mathfrak{L}$). We shall also denote this outer measure by $|E|$ or by $\mathrm{L}(E)$ (or sometimes by $\mathrm{L}_m(E)$ in $\boldsymbol{R}_m$), thus extending to arbitrary sets the notation adopted for all figures R, since for the latter, as we shall see (cf. Th. 6.2), the measure (L) coincides with the values $\mathrm{L}(R)=|R|$. Finally, owing to the special part played by Lebesgue measure in the theory of integration and derivation, the terms "measure of a set", "measurable set", "measurable function", and so on, will, in the sequel, be understood in the Lebesgue sense, whenever another sense has not been explicitly assigned to them.

We also modify slightly the integral notation for a Lebesgue integral; and instead of $\int_E f(x)\,d\mathrm{L}(x)$ we write $\int_E f(x)\,dx$, or else $\int\int_E\ldots\int f(x_1, x_2, \ldots, x_m)\,dx_1\,dx_2\ldots dx_m$, when we wish to indicate the number of dimensions of the space $\boldsymbol{R}_m$ under consideration. This brings us back to the classical notation.

A special part, similar to that of Lebesgue measure in the theory of the integral, is played by Borel sets in the theory of additive classes of sets. In the first place, it follows from Theorem 7.4, Chap. II, that every class $\mathfrak{L}_U$, where U is an additive function of bounded variation of an interval, contains all the sets ($\mathfrak{B}$). In the sequel, we shall agree that additive functions of a set will always mean functions additive ($\mathfrak{B}$), unless there is explicit reference to another additive class of sets. Similarly, additive functions of a set that are absolutely continuous ($\mathfrak{B}$, L) or singular ($\mathfrak{B}$, L), will simply be called *absolutely continuous* or *singular*. In point of fact, Theorem 6.6 below, which asserts that every set measurable ($\mathfrak{L}$) is the sum of a set ($\mathfrak{B}$) and a set of zero measure (L), will show that every additive function of a set, absolutely continuous ($\mathfrak{B}$, L), can be extended in a unique manner to all sets ($\mathfrak{L}$) so as to remain absolutely continuous ($\mathfrak{L}$, L).

The special rôle of the measure (L) and of the sets ($\mathfrak{B}$) showed itself already during the growth of the theory. Lebesgue measure was the starting point for further extensions of the notions of measure and integral, whereas the Borel sets were the origin of general theories of additive classes and functions. The sets ($\mathfrak{B}$) were introduced, with measure (L) defined for them, by E. Borel [I, p. 46—50] in 1898. But it was not until some years later that H. Lebesgue [1; I], by simplifying and extending the definition of measure (L) to all sets ($\mathfrak{L}$), made clear the importance of this measure for the theory of integration and especially for that of derivation of functions. *Vide* E. Borel [1] and H. Lebesgue [6].

We have already seen in § 1 of this book, how, by an apparently very slight modification of the classical definition of Riemann, we obtain the Lebesgue integral. A similar remark may be made with regard to the relationship of Lebesgue measure to the earlier measure of Peano-Jordan. The outer measure of Peano-Jordan for a bounded set E is the lower bound of the numbers $\sum_n |I_n|$ where $\{I_n\}$ is any finite system of intervals covering E. Lebesgue's happy idea was to replace in this definition, the finite systems of intervals by enumerable ones.

We have given in the text a more general form to Lebesgue's definition, relative to an arbitrary non-negative function of an interval. This relativizing of Lebesgue measure is due to J. Radon [1] and to Ch. J. de la Vallée-Poussin [1; I]. The parallel extension of the Lebesgue integral is also due to J. Radon. In the text we have termed it Lebesgue-Stieltjes integral; it is sometimes also termed Lebesgue-Radon integral or Radon integral. For a systematic exposition of the properties of this integral, *vide* H. Lebesgue [II, Chap. XI]. A particularly interesting generalization of the Lebesgue integral, of the Stieltjes type, has been given by N. Bary and D. Menchoff [1]; it differs considerably from the other generalizations of this type. Finally, for an account of the Riemann-Stieltjes integral (which we shall not discuss in this volume) *vide* W. H. Young [2], S. Pollard [1], R. C. Young [1], M. Fréchet [5] and G. Fichtenholz [2].

It was again J. Radon [I, p. 1] who pointed out the importance of the Lebesgue-Stieltjes integral for certain classical parts of Analysis, particularly for potential theory. The modern progress of this theory, which is bound up with the theory of subharmonic functions, has shown up still further the fruitfulness of the Lebesgue-Stieltjes integral in this branch of Analysis (cf. the memoirs of F. Riesz [4] and G. C. Evans [1]).

§ 6. Measure defined by a non-negative additive function of an interval. In this §, U will denote a fixed non-negative additive function of an interval. In the preceding § we made correspond to any such a function U, an outer Carathéodory measure U^*. Besides the properties established in Chap. II for all Carathéodory measures, the function of a set U^* possesses a number of elementary properties of a more special kind which we shall investigate in this §.

(6.1) ***Lemma.*** *If D denotes a hyperplane or a degenerate interval, the relation* $\mathrm{o}(U; D)=0$ *implies* $U^*(D)=0$.

Proof. Since every hyperplane is the sum of a sequence of degenerate intervals (cf. § 2, p. 57), it is enough to prove the lemma in the case in which D is a degenerate interval $[a_1, b_1; a_2, b_2; \ldots; a_m, b_m]$.

Let R be a cube containing D in its interior, G an arbitrary open set such that $D \subset G$, and let

$$D_\varepsilon = [a_1-\varepsilon, b_1+\varepsilon;\ a_2-\varepsilon, b_2+\varepsilon;\ \ldots;\ a_m-\varepsilon, b_m+\varepsilon],$$

where ε is any positive number, sufficiently small to ensure that $D_\varepsilon \subset R \cdot G$. Since D_ε is then an ordinary closed interval containing D in its interior, we find $U^*(D) \leqslant U(D_\varepsilon) \leqslant \mathrm{O}(U; R \cdot G)$, whence $U^*(D) \leqslant \mathrm{o}_R(U; D)=0$.

(6.2) ***Theorem.*** *For every figure R we have*

(6.3) $$U^*(R^\circ) \leqslant U(R) \leqslant U^*(R),$$

and, if the oscillation of U at the boundary of R vanishes,

(6.4) $$U^*(R^\circ) = U(R) = U^*(R).$$

In particular therefore, if U is a continuous function, the equality (6.4) *holds for every figure R.*

Proof. In virtue of Theorems 2.2 and 4.2 the set R° is expressible as the sum of a sequence of non-overlapping cubes $\{I_k\}$ such that the oscillation of U vanishes at all faces of all the I_k. Hence, by the preceding lemma $U^*(R^\circ) = \sum_k U^*(I_k^\circ)$, and since $U(R) \geqslant \sum_{k=1}^n U(I_k) \geqslant \sum_{k=1}^n U^*(I_k^\circ)$ for each positive integer n, we get $U^*(R^\circ) \leqslant U(R)$.

To establish that $U(R) \leqslant U^*(R)$, it is enough to show that $U(R) \leqslant \sum_k U(I_k)$ for every sequence of intervals $\{I_k\}$ such that $R \subset \sum_k I_k^\circ$. Now, if $\{I_k\}$ is such a sequence, we have, by the well-known covering theorem of Borel-Lebesgue, $R \subset \sum_{k=1}^N I_k^\circ$ for some sufficiently large value of N. Hence $U(R) \leqslant \sum_{k=1}^N U(R \odot I_k) \leqslant \sum_{k=1}^N U(I_k)$.

Finally, denoting by B the boundary of R, let us suppose that $o(U; B) = 0$. It then follows from Lemma 6.1 that $U^*(B) = 0$, so that $U^*(R) = U^*(R^\circ)$, and the equality (6.4) follows at once from (6.3).

(6.5) ***Theorem.*** *Given an arbitrary set E and any positive ε, there is* (i) *an open set G such that $E \subset G$ and $U^*(G) \leqslant U^*(E) + \varepsilon$,* (ii) *a set $H \in \mathfrak{G}_\delta$ such that $E \subset H$ and $U^*(H) = U^*(E)$.*

Proof. *re* (i). There exists for each $\varepsilon > 0$, a sequence of intervals $\{I_n\}$ such that $E \subset \sum_n I_n^\circ$ and that $\sum_n U(I_n) \leqslant U^*(E) + \varepsilon$. Hence, writing $G = \sum_n I_n^\circ$, we find, on account of condition (C_2) of Carathéodory (Chap. II, p. 43) and Theorem 6.2, that $U^*(G) \leqslant \sum_n U^*(I_n^\circ) \leqslant \sum_n U(I_n) \leqslant$ $\leqslant U^*(E) + \varepsilon$.

re (ii). Let us make correspond to E, for each positive integer n, an open set G_n containing E and such that $U^*(G_n) \leqslant U^*(E) + 1/n$; this is always possible by (i). The set $H = \prod_n G_n$ clearly fulfills our requirements and this completes the proof.

Every set $(\mathfrak{G}_\delta)$ is of course measurable $(\mathfrak{L}_U)$. Hence it follows at once from Theorem 6.5 that every set is regular (cf. Chap. II, § 6) with respect to the outer measure U^*, and therefore that this measure is itself regular.

(6.6) ***Theorem.*** *Each of the following conditions is necessary and sufficient for a set E to be measurable $(\mathfrak{L}_U)$:*

(i) *for every $\varepsilon > 0$ there is an open set $G \supset E$ such that $U^*(G - E) \leqslant \varepsilon$;*

(ii) *there is a set $(\mathfrak{G}_\delta)$ containing E and differing from E at most by a set of measure (U) zero;*

(iii) *for every $\varepsilon > 0$ there is a closed set $F \subset E$ such that $U^*(E - F) \leqslant \varepsilon$;*

(iv) *there is a set $(\mathfrak{F}_\sigma)$ contained in E and differing from E at most by a set of measure (U) zero.*

Proof. We shall first prove all these conditions necessary. Let E be a set measurable $(\mathfrak{L}_U)$ and ε a positive number. We begin by representing E as the sum of a sequence $\{E_n\}_{n=1,2,\ldots}$ of sets measurable $(\mathfrak{L}_U)$ of finite measure; we may write for instance, $E_n = E \cdot S(0; n)$. This being so, we associate with each set E_n, in accordance with Theorem 6.5, an open set $G_n \supset E_n$ such that $U^*(G_n) \leqslant U^*(E_n) + \varepsilon/2^n$. Hence, the sets E_n being measurable $(\mathfrak{L}_U)$, we have $U^*(G_n - E_n) \leqslant \varepsilon/2^n$ for every n, and if we write $G = \sum_n G_n$, we find $E \subset G$ and $U^*(G - U) \leqslant \sum_n U^*(G_n - E_n) \leqslant \varepsilon$, and this proves condition (i) necessary.

To prove the necessity of condition (ii), we attach to the given set E measurable $(\mathfrak{L}_U)$ a sequence $\{Q_n\}$ of open sets such that $E \subset Q_n$ and $U^*(Q_n - E) \leqslant 1/n$ for each n. Writing $H = \prod_n Q_n$, we see that $H \in \mathfrak{G}_\delta$, $E \subset H$ and $U^*(H - E) = 0$.

Finally, we observe that for any set A, the relation $A \supset CE$ implies $CA \subset E$ and $E - CA = A - CE$; further, if A is a set $(\mathfrak{G})$ or $(\mathfrak{G}_\delta)$, the set CA is a set $(\mathfrak{F})$ or $(\mathfrak{F}_\sigma)$ respectively. Hence every set E measurable $(\mathfrak{L}_U)$ fulfills conditions (iii) and (iv), since, by the results just proved, its complement CE fulfills conditions (i) and (ii).

The sufficiency of conditions (ii) and (iv) is evident, since sets of measure (U) zero, and sets $(\mathfrak{G}_\delta)$ or $(\mathfrak{F}_\sigma)$, are always measurable $(\mathfrak{L}_U)$.

To establish the sufficiency of conditions (i) and (iii), we need only observe that they imply respectively conditions (ii) and (iv). Thus, for instance, if (iii) holds, there is for each positive integer n a closed set $F_n \subset E$ such that $U^*(E-F_n) \leqslant 1/n$. The set $P = \sum_n F_n$ is therefore a set $(\mathfrak{F}_\sigma)$ contained in E and such that $U^*(E-P)=0$.

From Theorem 6.6 it follows in particular that the general form of a set measurable $(\mathfrak{L}_U)$ is $B+N$, where B is a set measurable $(\mathfrak{B})$ and N a set of measure (U) zero. In other words, $\mathfrak{L}_U$ is the smallest additive class containing the Borel sets and the sets of measure (U) zero. It follows that $\mathfrak{L}_U \supset \mathfrak{L}$ whenever the function of an interval U is absolutely continuous (*vide* § 12).

(6.7) ***Theorem.*** *For any set E there is a set $H \in \mathfrak{G}_\delta$ containing E and such that*

(6.8) $U^*(H \cdot X) = U^*(E \cdot X)$ *for every set X measurable* $(\mathfrak{L}_U)$.

Proof. It is enough to show that there is a set $H \supset E$ measurable $(\mathfrak{L}_U)$ for which (6.8) holds. For, by Theorem 6.6 we can always enclose such a set H in a set $(\mathfrak{G}_\delta)$ differing from it by a set of measure (U) zero.

Let us represent E as limit of an ascending sequence $\{E_n\}$ of bounded sets, which are therefore of finite outer measure (U); and let us associate, as we may by Theorem 6.5, with each E_n a set $H_n \in \mathfrak{G}_\delta$ such that $E_n \subset H_n$ and $U^*(H_n) = U^*(E_n)$. Then, for every set X measurable $(\mathfrak{L}_U)$,

$$U^*(H_n \cdot X) = U^*(H_n) - U^*(H_n \cdot CX) \leqslant U^*(E_n) - U^*(E_n \cdot CX) \leqslant U^*(E_n \cdot X);$$

from which, writing $H = \liminf_n H_n$, we deduce by means of Theorem 9.1 of Chap. I, that

$$U^*(H \cdot X) \leqslant \liminf_n U^*(H_n \cdot X) \leqslant \lim_n U^*(E_n \cdot X) \leqslant U^*(E \cdot X),$$

and this implies (6.8), since $H = \liminf_n H_n \supset \lim_n E_n = E$.

In the theorems of this § we have supposed the function U of an interval to be non-negative. But, by slight changes in the wording, the theorems can easily be extended to arbitrary functions of bounded variation. As an example we mention the following theorem which corresponds to Theorem 6.5:

(6.9) ***Theorem.*** *If F is an additive function of bounded variation of an interval, then for any bounded set E and any $\varepsilon>0$ there is an open set $G\supset E$ such that $|F^*(X)—F^*(E)\leqslant\varepsilon$ for every bounded set X satisfying the condition $E\subset X\subset G$.*

Proof. Denoting by W_1 and W_2 two functions of an interval that are respectively the upper and the lower variation of F, we can, by Theorem 6.5, enclose E in each of two open sets G_1 and G_2 such that $W_1^*(G_1)\leqslant W_1^*(E)+\varepsilon$ and $W_2^*(G_2)\geqslant W_2^*(E)-\varepsilon$. Therefore, writing $G=G_1\cdot G_2$ we have $E\subset G$; and for any bounded set X such that $E\subset X\subset G$, we find $0\leqslant W_1^*(X)-W_1^*(E)\leqslant\varepsilon$ and $0\leqslant W_2^*(E)—W_2^*(X)\leqslant\varepsilon$, whence by subtraction $|F^*(X)—F^*(E)|\leqslant\varepsilon$.

Let us still prove a theorem which allows us to regard all non-negative additive functions of a set in $\boldsymbol{R}_m$ as determined by non-negative additive functions of an interval. We recall that, according to the conventions of § 3, p. 59 and § 5, p. 66, we always mean by additive functions of a set, functions of a set that are additive ($\mathfrak{B}$) on every figure.

(6.10) ***Theorem.*** *Given any non-negative additive function Φ of a set, there is always a non-negative additive function F of an interval such that $\Phi(X)=F^*(X)$ for every bounded set X measurable ($\mathfrak{B}$).*

Proof. Let us denote for each interval $I=[a_1, b_1; ...; a_m, b_m]$, by $\tilde{I}$ the interval $(a_1, b_1; ...; a_m, b_m]$ half open to the left, and let us define the non-negative additive function of an interval by writing $F(I)=\Phi(\tilde{I})$ for every interval I.

This being so, we observe that any bounded open set G can be expressed (cf. Theorems 2.2 and 4.2) as the sum of a sequence $\{I_n\}$ of non-overlapping intervals at whose faces the oscillation of F vanishes; and therefore by Theorem 6.2, $\Phi(G)=\sum_n\Phi(\tilde{I}_n)=\sum_n F(I_n)=$ $=\sum_n F^*(\tilde{I}_n)=F^*(G)$. Thus the equation $\Phi(X)=F^*(X)$ holds whenever X is a bounded open set, and therefore also whenever X is a bounded set ($\mathfrak{G}_\delta$), since the latter is expressible as the limit of a descending sequence of bounded open sets. It follows further that $\Phi(X)=$ $=F^*(X)=0$ for every bounded set X of measure (F) zero, since, by Theorem 6.6, such a set X can be enclosed in a bounded set $(\mathfrak{G}_\delta)$ of measure (F) zero. This completes the proof, since every bounded set $(\mathfrak{B})$ is, by Theorem 6.6, the difference of a bounded set $(\mathfrak{G}_\delta)$ and of a set of measure (F) zero.

The proof of Theorem 6.10 could also be attached to the following general theorem concerning functions additive $(\mathfrak{B})$ defined on any metrical space $\boldsymbol{M}$: *if two such functions coincide for every open set, they are identical for all sets* $(\mathfrak{B})$. This theorem is easily proved.

§ 7. Theorems of Lusin and Vitali-Carathéodory. We shall establish in this § two theorems concerning the approximation to measurable functions by continuous functions and by semi-continuous functions. As in the preceding §, U will stand for a non-negative additive function of an interval, fixed in any manner for the space $\boldsymbol{R}_m$.

(7.1) ***Lusin's Theorem.*** *In order that a function $f(x)$, finite on a set E, be measurable $(\mathfrak{L}_U)$ on E, it is necessary and sufficient that for every $\varepsilon>0$, there exists a closed set $F\subset E$ such that $U^*(E-F)<\varepsilon$, and on which $f(x)$ is continuous.*

Proof. To show the condition necessary, we suppose $f(x)$ finite and measurable $(\mathfrak{L}_U)$ on E, and we deal first with two particular cases:

(i) $f(x)$ is a simple function on E. The set E is, in this case, the sum of a finite sequence $E_1, E_2, \ldots, E_n$ of sets measurable $(\mathfrak{L}_U)$ no two of which have common points, such that $f(x)$ is constant on each of these sets. By Theorem 6.6 there exists, for each set E_i, a closed set $F_i\subset E_i$ such that $U^*(E_i-F_i)<\varepsilon/n$. Writing $F=\sum_{i=1}^{n} F_i$, we then have $F\subset E$ and $U^*(E-F)<\varepsilon$, and moreover the function $f(x)$ is clearly continuous on F.

(ii) E is a set of finite measure (U). In this case, by Theorem 7.4, Chap. I, (applied separately to the non-negative and to the non-positive parts of $f(x)$), there is a sequence $\{f_n(x)\}_{n=1,2,\ldots}$ of simple functions, finite and measurable $(\mathfrak{L}_U)$, that converges on E to $f(x)$. By Egoroff's Theorem (Chap. I, Th. 9.6), this sequence converges uniformly on a set $P\subset E$, measurable $(\mathfrak{L}_U)$ and such that $U^*(E-P)<\varepsilon/2$. This set P may further be supposed to be closed, on account of Theorem 6.6. Finally, by (i) we can attach to each function $f_n(x)$, a closed set $P_n\subset E$ such that $U^*(E-P_n)<\varepsilon/2^{n+1}$, and on which $f_n(x)$ is continuous. Hence, writing $F=P\cdot\prod_n P_n$, we get $U^*(E-F)\leqslant U^*(E-P)+\sum_n U^*(E-P_n)\leqslant\varepsilon$; and moreover, all the $f_n(x)$, and therefore also the function $f(x)=\lim_n f_n(x)$, are continuous on F, a set which is evidently closed.

We now come to the general case where E is any set measurable $(\mathfrak{L}_U)$. Let $E_n=E\cdot(S_n-S_{n-1})$, where $S_0=0$ and $S_n=\mathrm{S}(0;n)$ for $n\geqslant 1$. By (ii), there exists, for each $n\geqslant 1$, a closed set $Q_n\subset E_n$ such that $U^*(E_n-Q_n)<\varepsilon/2^n$, and on which $f(x)$ is continuous. Writing $F=\sum_{n=1}^{\infty}Q_n$, the set F is closed, we have $U^*(E-F)\leqslant$ $\leqslant\sum_n U^*(E_n-Q_n)<\varepsilon$, and $f(x)$ is continuous on F.

The proof of the necessity of the condition is thus complete. Let us now suppose, conversely, that the condition is satisfied. The set E is then expressible as the sum of a set N of measure (U) zero and of a sequence $\{F_n\}$ of closed sets on each of which $f(x)$ is continuous. The function f is thus measurable $(\mathfrak{L}_U)$ on N and on each of the sets F_n (cf. Chap. II, Th. 7.6), and therefore on the whole set E.

For the various proofs of Lusin's theorem, *vide* N. Lusin [1], W. Sierpiński [6] and L. W. Cohen [1].

(7.2) ***Lemma.*** *Given a function $f(x)$, measurable $(\mathfrak{L}_U)$ and non-negative in the space $\boldsymbol{R}_m$, there exists, for each $\varepsilon>0$, a lower semi-continuous function $h(x)$ such that*

$$h(x)\geqslant f(x) \text{ at each point } x, \tag{7.3}$$

and

$$\int_{\boldsymbol{R}_m}[h(x)-f(x)]\,dU(x)\leqslant\varepsilon \tag{7.4}$$

(where, in accordance with the convention of Chap. I, p. 6, the difference $h(x)-f(x)$ is to be understood to vanish at any point x for which $h(x)=f(x)=+\infty$).

Proof. (i) First suppose that $f(x)$ is bounded and vanishes outside a bounded set E measurable $(\mathfrak{L}_U)$. Let $\eta=\varepsilon/[1+U^*(E)]$. We write $E_k=\mathrm{E}_x[x\in E;\ (k-1)\eta\leqslant f(x)<k\eta]$ for $k=1,2,\ldots$ and we associate with each set E_k an open set $G_k\supset E_k$ such that

(7.5) $$U^*(G_k - E_k) \leqslant 1/k \cdot 2^k.$$

Further, denoting by $c_k(x)$ the characteristic function of G_k, we write $h(x) = \sum_{k=1}^{\infty} k\eta \cdot c_k(x)$. Since each function $c_k(x)$ is evidently lower semi-continuous, the function $h(x)$ is so too. We also observe that $h(x)$ fulfills condition (7.3). On the other hand

$$\int_{R_m} h(x)\,dU(x) = \sum_{k=1}^{\infty} k\eta \int_{R_m} c_k(x)\,dU(x) = \sum_{k=1}^{\infty} k\eta \cdot U^*(G_k) =$$

$$= \sum_{k=1}^{\infty} (k-1)\eta \cdot U^*(E_k) + \sum_{k=1}^{\infty} \eta \cdot U^*(E_k) + \sum_{k=1}^{\infty} k\eta \cdot U^*(G_k - E_k),$$

whence, by (7.5), we obtain

$$\int_{R_m} h(x)\,dU(x) \leqslant \int_{R_m} f(x)\,dU(x) + \eta \cdot U^*(E) + \eta \leqslant \int_{R_m} f(x)\,dU(x) + \varepsilon.$$

From this, remembering that $f(x)$ is integrable on R_m, (7.4) follows at once.

(ii) We now pass to the general case and represent firstly $f(x)$ in the form $f(x) = \sum_{n=1}^{\infty} f_n(x)$, where the $f_n(x)$ are bounded non-negative functions measurable ($\mathfrak{L}_U$), each of which vanishes outside a bounded set. We may do this, for instance, by writing $f_n(x) = s_n(x) - s_{n-1}(x)$ where

$$s_n(x) = \left\{ \begin{array}{lll} f(x) & \textit{for} \;\; \varrho(0, x) < n & \textit{and} \;\; f(x) \leqslant n, \\ n & \textit{for} \;\; \varrho(0, x) < n & \textit{and} \;\; f(x) > n, \\ 0 & \textit{for} \;\; \varrho(0, x) \geqslant n & \end{array} \right\} \qquad n = 0, 1, 2, \ldots$$

By what has been proved in (i), there exists for each function $f_n(x)$ a lower semi-continuous function $h_n(x)$ such that $h_n(x) \geqslant f_n(x)$ at every point x, and that $\int_{R_m} [h_n(x) - f_n(x)]\,dU(x) < \varepsilon/2^n$. The function $h(x) = \sum_{n=1}^{\infty} h_n(x)$ is then evidently lower semi-continuous and fulfills condition (7.3). Finally $\int_{R_m} [h(x) - f(x)]\,dU(x) \leqslant \sum_{n=1}^{\infty} \int_{R_m} [h_n(x) - f_n(x)]\,dU(x) \leqslant \varepsilon$, and this completes the proof.

(7.6) ***Theorem of Vitali-Carathéodory.*** *Given a function $f(x)$ measurable $(\mathfrak{L}_U)$ in the space $\boldsymbol{R}_m$, there exist two monotone sequences of functions $\{l_n(x)\}$ and $\{u_n(x)\}$ for which the following conditions are satisfied:*

(i) *the functions l_n are lower semi-continuous and the functions u_n are upper semi-continuous,*

(ii) *each of the functions l_n is bounded below and each of the functions u_n is bounded above,*

(iii) *the sequence $\{l_n\}$ is non-increasing and the sequence $\{u_n\}$ is non-decreasing,*

(iv) $l_n(x)\geqslant f(x)\geqslant u_n(x)$ *for every x,*

(v) $\lim\limits_n l_n(x)=f(x)=\lim\limits_n u_n(x)$ *almost everywhere (U),*

(vi) *on every set E on which $f(x)$ is integrable (U), so are the functions $l_n(x)$ and $u_n(x)$ and we have*

$$\lim_n \int_E l_n(x)\,dU(x)=\lim_n \int_E u_n(x)\,dU(x)=\int_E f(x)\,dU(x).$$

Proof. By expressing the function $f(x)$ as the sum of its non-negative and non-positive parts $\overset{\circ}{f}(x)$ and $\underset{\circ}{f}(x)$ (Chap. I, § 7), we may suppose that $f(x)$ is of constant sign, say non-negative. By the preceding lemma, we can associate with $f(x)$ a sequence of lower semi-continuous functions $\{h_n(x)\}_{n=1,2,\dots}$ such that $h_n(x)\geqslant f(x)$ for every x and

$$\lim_n \int_{\boldsymbol{R}} [h_n(x)-f(x)]\,dU(x)=0. \tag{7.7}$$

Writing $l_n(x)=\min\,[h_1(x), h_2(x), \dots, h_n(x)]$ we therefore obtain a non-increasing sequence of lower semi-continuous functions $\{l_n(x)\}$ that evidently fulfills conditions (i), (ii), (iii) and (iv); moreover, it follows from (7.7) that $\lim\limits_n \int_{\boldsymbol{R}_m} [l_n(x)-f(x)]\,dU(x)=0$, and hence that the functions $l_n(x)$ fulfill also conditions (v) and (vi).

In order now to define the sequence $\{u_n(x)\}$, we attach to the function $1/f(x)$ a non-increasing sequence of lower semi-continuous functions $\{g_n(x)\}$ such that $\lim\limits_n g_n(x)=1/f(x)$ almost everywhere (U). Such a sequence certainly exists by what has just been proved. The functions $1/g_n(x)$ then form a non-decreasing sequence of upper semi-continuous functions, that converges almost everywhere (U) to $f(x)$. If we now write $u_n(x)=1/g_n(x)$ when $1/g_n(x)\leqslant n$, and

$u_n(x)=n$ when $1/g_n(x)>n$, we obtain a sequence $\{u_n(x)\}$ of bounded functions with the same properties, which therefore satisfies conditions (i—v). Finally, since the functions $u_n(x)$ are non-negative, we can apply Lebesgue's Theorem (Chap. I, Th. 12.6) to derive from (iii) and (v) that $\lim_n \int_E u_n(x)\,dU(x)=\int_E f(x)\,dU(x)$ on every set E measurable ($\mathfrak{L}_U$), and this implies (vi).

Conditions (i) and (v) of Theorem 7.6 imply that every function measurable ($\mathfrak{L}_U$) is almost everywhere (U) the limit of a convergent sequence (with finite or infinite limit) of semi-continuous functions, and thus coincides almost everywhere (U) with a function of the second class of Baire. This result, due to G. Vitali [2] (cf. also W. Sierpiński [6]) was completed by C. Carathéodory [I, p. 406], who established for every measurable function $f(x)$ the existence of two sequences of functions fulfilling conditions (i)—(v). Condition (vi), which includes, as we shall see later, the theorem of de la Vallée Poussin and Perron on the existence, for summable functions, of majorant and minorant functions, has been added here because its proof is naturally related to those of conditions (i—v).

There is an obvious analogy between the property of measurable functions expressed by the theorem of Vitali-Carathéodory, and the properties of measurable sets stated in conditions (i) and (iii) of Theorem 6.6. By taking into account the geometrical definition of the integral (cf. below § 10), we might even base the proof of Theorem 7.6 directly on Theorem 6.6 (*vide* the first ed. of this book, pp. 88—91).

§ 8. Theorem of Fubini. Given two Euclidean spaces R_p and R_q, if $x=(a_1, a_2, ..., a_p)$ and $y=(a_{p+1}, a_{p+2}, ..., a_{p+q})$ are two points situated respectively in these two spaces, we shall denote by (x, y) the point $(a_1, a_2, ..., a_{p+q})$ in the space R_{p+q}. If X and Y are two sets situated respectively in the spaces R_p and R_q, we shall denote by $X\times Y$ the set of all points (x, y) in R_{p+q} such that $x \epsilon X$ and $y \epsilon Y$. In particular, if X and Y are two intervals — closed, open, or half open on the same side — $X\times Y$ also is an interval in R_{p+q}, which is closed, open, or half open on the same side as X and Y. Every interval $I=[a_1, b_1; ...; a_{p+q}, b_{p+q}]$ can evidently be expressed — and in a unique manner — in the form $I_1\times I_2$ where I_1 and I_2 are intervals in R_p and R_q respectively; we merely have to write $I_1=[a_1, b_1; ...; a_p, b_p]$ and $I_2=[a_{p+1}, b_{p+1}; ...; a_{p+q}, b_{p+q}]$.

Given two additive functions of an interval, U and V, in the spaces R_p and R_q respectively, we determine a function of an interval T in R_{p+q} by writing $T(I_1\times I_2)=U(I_1)\cdot V(I_2)$ for each pair of intervals $I_1\subset R_p$ and $I_2\subset R_q$. The function T thus defined, clearly additive when U and V are, will be denoted by UV. In particular, we see easily that $L_{p+q}=L_pL_q$, where L_p, L_q and L_{p+q} denote the volume in the spaces $\boldsymbol{R}_p$, $\boldsymbol{R}_q$ and $\boldsymbol{R}_{p+q}$ respectively (cf. § 2, p. 59).

It is known since Cauchy that, if I_1 and I_2 are respectively two intervals in the spaces $\boldsymbol{R}_p$ and $\boldsymbol{R}_q$, integration of any continuous function over the interval $I_1 \times I_2 \subset \boldsymbol{R}_{p+q}$ may be reduced to two successive integrations over the intervals I_1 and I_2. By repeating the process, any integral of a continuous function on an m-dimensional interval may be reduced to m successive integrations on linear intervals in $\boldsymbol{R}_1$. This classical theorem was extended by H. Lebesgue [1] to functions measurable ($\mathfrak{L}$) that are bounded, and then by G. Fubini [1] (cf. also L. Tonelli [2]) to all functions integrable (L), whether bounded or not. We shall state this result in the following form:

(8.1) ***Fubini's Theorem.*** *Suppose given two non-negative additive functions U and V of an interval in the spaces $\boldsymbol{R}_p$ and $\boldsymbol{R}_q$ respectively, and let $f(x,y)$ be a non-negative function measurable ($\mathfrak{L}_{UV}$) in $\boldsymbol{R}_{p+q}$. Then*

(i_1) *$f(x, y)$ is a function of x, measurable ($\mathfrak{L}_U$) in $\boldsymbol{R}_p$ for every $y \in \boldsymbol{R}_q$, except at most a set of measure (V) zero,*

(i_2) *$f(x, y)$ is a function of y, measurable ($\mathfrak{L}_V$) in $\boldsymbol{R}_q$ for every $x \in \boldsymbol{R}_p$, except at most a set of measure (U) zero,*

(ii) $$\int_{\boldsymbol{R}_{p+q}} f(x,y)\,dUV(x,y) = \int_{\boldsymbol{R}_q}\Big[\int_{\boldsymbol{R}_p} f(x,y)\,dU(x)\Big]\,dV(y) = \int_{\boldsymbol{R}_p}\Big[\int_{\boldsymbol{R}_q} f(x,y)\,dV(y)\Big]\,dU(x).$$

Proof. Let us write for short, $T=UV$. By symmetry, it is enough to show that every non-negative function $f(x, y)$ measurable ($\mathfrak{L}_T$) in $\boldsymbol{R}_{p+q}$ fulfills condition (i_1) and also the relation

$$\int_{\boldsymbol{R}_{p+q}} f(x,y)\,dT(x,y) = \int_{\boldsymbol{R}_q}\Big[\int_{\boldsymbol{R}_p} f(x,y)\,dU(x)\Big]\,dV(y). \tag{8.2}$$

For brevity, we shall say that a function $f(x, y)$ in $\boldsymbol{R}_{p+q}$ has the property (F), if it is non-negative and measurable ($\mathfrak{L}_T$) in $\boldsymbol{R}_{p+q}$, and if it fulfills condition (i_1) and the relation (8.2). For the sake of clearness, the reasoning that follows is divided into a several auxiliary propositions.

(8.3) *The sum of two functions with the property* (F), *and the limit of any non-decreasing sequence of such functions, have the property* (F). *Also, the difference of two functions with the property* (F), *has the property* (F), *provided that it is non-negative and that one at least of the given functions is finite and integrable* (T) *on the space* $\boldsymbol{R}_{p+q}$.

For the sum, and for the difference, of two functions, the statement is obvious. Let therefore $\{h_n(x, y)\}$ be a non-decreasing sequence of functions in $\boldsymbol{R}_{p+q}$ having the property (F), and let $h(x, y) = \lim_n h_n(x, y)$. The definite integrals $\int_{\boldsymbol{R}_p} h_n(x, y)\, dU(x)$ exist, and constitute a non-decreasing sequence, for every $y \in \boldsymbol{R}_q$ except at most those of a set of measure (V) zero. Consequently, by Lebesgue's theorem on integration of monotone sequences of functions:

$$\int_{\boldsymbol{R}_{p+q}} h(x,y)\, dT(x,y) = \lim_n \int_{\boldsymbol{R}_{p+q}} h_n(x, y)\, dT(x, y) = \lim_n \int_{\boldsymbol{R}_q} \Big[\int_{\boldsymbol{R}_p} h_n(x,y)\, dU(x)\Big] dV(y) =$$

$$= \int_{\boldsymbol{R}_q} \Big[\lim_n \int_{\boldsymbol{R}_p} h_n(x, y)\, dU(x)\Big] dV(y) = \int_{\boldsymbol{R}_q} \Big[\int_{\boldsymbol{R}_p} h(x, y)\, dU(x)\Big] dV(y),$$

and this establishes the property (F) for the function $h(x, y)$.

(8.4) *The characteristic function of any set* $E \subset \boldsymbol{R}_{p+q}$ *measurable* $(\mathfrak{L}_T)$ *has the property* (F).

We shall establish this, first for very special sets E and then, by successive stages, for general measurable sets. Suppose in the first place that

1° $E = A \times B$, where A and B are intervals half open to the left, situated respectively in $\boldsymbol{R}_p$ and $\boldsymbol{R}_q$, and such that the oscillations of U and of V vanish at the boundaries of A and B respectively (cf. § 3, p. 60). The oscillation of the function $T = UV$ therefore vanishes at the boundary of the interval $E = A \times B$, and we find by Theorem 6.2

$$T^*(E) = T(\bar{E}) = U(\bar{A}) \cdot V(\bar{B}) = U^*(A) \cdot V^*(B). \tag{8.5}$$

On the other hand, for every $y \in \boldsymbol{R}_q$ the function $c_E(x, y)$ is in x the characteristic function either of the half open interval A, or of the empty set, according as $y \in B$ or $y \in \boldsymbol{R}_q - B$. This function is therefore measurable $(\mathfrak{L}_U)$, and indeed measurable $(\mathfrak{B})$, for every $y \in \boldsymbol{R}_q$, and, by (8.5)

$$\int\limits_{R_{p+q}} c_E(x,y)\, dT(x,y) = T^*(E) = U^*(A)\cdot V^*(B) = \int\limits_{R_q}\Big[\int\limits_{R_p} c_E(x,y)\, dU(x)\Big]\, dV(y).$$

2° E is an open set. We shall begin by showing that, in this case, E is the sum of a sequence of half open intervals $\{I_n\}$ no two of which have common points, these intervals I_n being of the form $A_n \times B_n$ where (a) A_n and B_n are intervals, half open to the left, situated in R_p and R_q respectively, and (b) the oscillations of U and V vanish at the boundaries of A_n and B_n respectively.

To see this, let $\{\mathfrak{U}^{(k)}\}$ be a regular sequence of nets in R_p formed of intervals half open to the left and such that the oscillation of U vanishes at the boundary of each of these intervals; by Theorems 4.2 and 2.1, such a sequence certainly exists. And let $\{\mathfrak{B}^{(k)}\}$ be a sequence of nets similarly constructed for the space R_q and for the function V. We denote, for each k, by $\mathfrak{T}^{(k)}$ the system of all half open intervals in R_{p+q} which are of the form $A\times B$ where $A\epsilon\mathfrak{U}^{(k)}$ and $B\epsilon\mathfrak{B}^{(k)}$. The systems of intervals $\mathfrak{T}^{(k)}$, thus defined, form a regular sequence of nets of half open intervals in the space R_{p+q}. The set E being open, we can therefore express it (cf. § 2, p. 58) as the sum of a sequence of half open intervals $\{I_n\}$ taken from the nets $\mathfrak{T}^{(k)}$ and without points in common to any two. We see at once that each interval I_n of this sequence is of the form $A_n\times B_n$ where A_n and B_n satisfy conditions (a) and (b).

This being so, we have $c_E(x,y) = \sum\limits_n c_{I_n}(x,y)$, where on account of the result established for the case 1°, each of the characteristic functions $c_{I_n}(x,y)$ has the property (F). Therefore, to verify that the function $c_E(x,y)$ also has this property, we need only apply (8.3).

3° E is a set $(\mathfrak{G}_\delta)$. First suppose that, besides, the set E is bounded. E is then the limit of a descending sequence of bounded open sets $\{G_n\}$. The functions $c_{G_1}(x,y) - c_{G_n}(x,y)$ constitute a non-decreasing sequence of non-negative functions which have, by 2° and (8.3), the property (F). Consequently, again on account of (8.3), the limit function of this sequence $h(x,y) = c_{G_1}(x,y) - c_E(x,y)$ itself has the property (F) and the same is therefore true of the function $c_E(x,y) = c_{G_1}(x,y) - h(x,y)$.

Now if E is an arbitrary set $(\mathfrak{G}_\delta)$, we can express it as the limit of an ascending sequence $\{H_n\}$ of bounded sets $(\mathfrak{G}_\delta)$. By what has just been proved, the characteristic functions of the sets H_n have the property (F) and, consequently, the function $c_E(x,y)=\lim_n c_{H_n}(x,y)$ itself has the property (F).

4° *E is a set of measure* (T) *zero*. There is then, by Theorem 6.5, a set $H \epsilon \mathfrak{G}_\delta$ containing E and of measure (T) zero. By the result established for sets $(\mathfrak{G}_\delta)$, the function $c_H(x,y)$ has the property (F), and therefore $\int_{R_q}\left[\int_{R_p} c_H(x,y)\,dU(x)\right]dV(y) = =\int_{R_{p+q}} c_H(x,y)\,dT(x,y)=T^*(H)=0$. Hence, for every $y \epsilon R_q$, except at most a set Y of measure (V) zero, $\int_{R_p} c_H(x,y)\,dU(x)=0$, i. e. $c_H(x,y)$, as function of x, vanishes almost everywhere (U) in R_p. Hence, *a fortiori*, $c_E(x,y) \leqslant c_H(x,y)$ as function of x, vanishes almost everywhere (U), and is consequently measurable $(\mathfrak{L}_U)$, for all $y \epsilon R_q$, except at most for those of the set Y of measure (V) zero. Finally, we clearly have $\int_{R_q}\left[\int_{R_p} c_E(x,y)\,dU(x)\right]dV(y)=0=T^*(E)=\int_{R_{p+q}} c_E(x,y)\,dT(x,y)$. The function $c_E(x,y)$ thus has the property (F).

On account of Theorem 6.6 every set E measurable $(\mathfrak{L}_T)$ is expressible in the form $E=H-Q$, where H is a set $(\mathfrak{G}_\delta)$ and Q is a set of measure (T) zero contained in H. We thus have $c_E(x,y)= =c_H(x,y)-c_Q(x,y)$, and by (8.3) the proposition (8.4) reduces to the special cases 3° and 4° already treated.

The proposition (8.4) being thus established, let $f(x,y)$ bo any non-negative function measurable $(\mathfrak{L}_T)$ in the space R_{p+q}. By Theorem 7.4, Chap. I, the function f is the limit of a non-decreasing sequence of simple functions, finite, non-negative, and measurable $(\mathfrak{L}_T)$. Now each of these simple functions is a linear combination, with positive coefficients, of a finite number of characteristic functions of sets measurable $(\mathfrak{L}_T)$, and therefore has the property (F) on account of (8.4). Thus the function f is the limit of a non-decreasing sequence of functions with the property (F), and so, by (8.3), f itself has the property (F). This completes the proof of Theorem 8.1.

Let us make special mention of the particular case of the theorem in which $f(x,y)$ is the characteristic function of a measurable set:

(8.6) ***Theorem.*** *If U and V are two non-negative additive functions of an interval in the spaces $\boldsymbol{R}_p$ and $\boldsymbol{R}_q$ respectively, and if Q is a set measurable ($\mathfrak{L}_{UV}$) in the space $\boldsymbol{R}_{p+q}$, then*

(i$_1$) *the set* $\underset{x}{\mathrm{E}}[(x, y) \epsilon Q]$ *is measurable* ($\mathfrak{L}_U$) *for every* $y \epsilon \boldsymbol{R}_q$, *except at most a set of measure* (V) *zero,*

(i$_2$) *the set* $\underset{y}{\mathrm{E}}[(x, y) \epsilon Q]$ *is measurable* ($\mathfrak{L}_V$) *for every* $x \epsilon \boldsymbol{R}_p$, *except at most a set of measure* (U) *zero, and*

(ii) *the measure* (UV) *of* Q *is equal to*

$$\int_{\boldsymbol{R}_q} U^*\{\underset{x}{\mathrm{E}}[(x, y) \epsilon Q]\}\, dV(y) = \int_{\boldsymbol{R}_p} V^*\{\underset{y}{\mathrm{E}}[(x, y) \epsilon Q]\}\, dU(x).$$

Fubini's theorem is frequently stated in the following form:

(8.7) ***Theorem.*** *Let U and V be two additive functions of bounded variation of an interval in the spaces $\boldsymbol{R}_p$ and $\boldsymbol{R}_q$ respectively. Then for every function $f(x, y)$ integrable (UV) on $\boldsymbol{R}_{p+q}$, the relation* (ii) *of theorem* 8.1 *holds good and the function $f(x, y)$ is integrable (U) in x on $\boldsymbol{R}_p$ for every $y \epsilon \boldsymbol{R}_q$, except at most a set of measure (V) zero, and integrable (V) in y on $\boldsymbol{R}_q$ for every $x \epsilon \boldsymbol{R}_p$, except at most a set of measure (U) zero.*

We reduce this statement at once to that of Theorem 8.1 by expressing the function f as the sum of its non-negative and non-positive parts, and by applying to the functions of an interval U and V the Jordan decomposition (§ 4, p. 62).

Further generalizations of Fubini's theorem for the Lebesgue-Stieltjes integration (in particular including the theorems analogous to Theorem 15.1 of Chap. I) were studied by L. C. Young in his Fellowship Dissertation (Cambridge 1931, unpublished). An account of these researches will be given in the bool *The theory of Stieltjes integrals and distribution-functions* by L. C. Young (Oxford, Clarendon Press).

It follows in particular from Theorem 8.6 that for any set Q measurable in the sense of Lebesgue in the space $\boldsymbol{R}_{p+q}$, its measure (L_{p+q}) is given by the definite integrals $\int_{\boldsymbol{R}_q} \mathrm{L}_p\{\underset{x}{\mathrm{E}}[(x, y) \epsilon Q]\}\, d\mathrm{L}_q(y) = \int_{\boldsymbol{R}_p} \mathrm{L}_q\{\underset{y}{\mathrm{E}}[(x, y) \epsilon Q]\}\, d\mathrm{L}_p(x)$. It is nevertheless to be remarked that the existence of these two integrals does not in general enable us to draw any conclusion as to measurability ($\mathfrak{L}$) of the set Q. W. Sierpiński [5] has in fact constructed in the plane a set non-measurable ($\mathfrak{L}$) having exactly one point in common with every parallel to the axes. This construction depends, needless to say, on the axiom of selection of Zermelo.

For an interesting discussion of Fubini's theorem for Lebesgue integration of functions of variable sign, *vide* G. Fichtenholz [1].

We complete the theorems of this § by the following

(8.8) ***Theorem.*** *If* Q *is a set measurable* ($\mathfrak{B}$) *in the space* $\boldsymbol{R}_{p+q}$, *the set* $\underset{x}{\mathrm{E}}[(x, y)\in Q]$ *is measurable* ($\mathfrak{B}$) *in the space* $\boldsymbol{R}_p$ *for every* $y\in \boldsymbol{R}_q$, *and the set* $\underset{y}{\mathrm{E}}[(x, y)\in Q]$ *is measurable* ($\mathfrak{B}$) *in* $\boldsymbol{R}_q$ *for every* $x\in \boldsymbol{R}_p$.

Similarly, if a function $f(x,y)$ *is measurable* ($\mathfrak{B}$) *in the space* $\boldsymbol{R}_{p+q}$, *then in* $\boldsymbol{R}_p$ *the function* $f(x,y)$ *is measurable* ($\mathfrak{B}$) *in* x *for every* $y\in\boldsymbol{R}_q$, *and in* $\boldsymbol{R}_q$ *the function* $f(x,y)$ *is measurable* ($\mathfrak{B}$) *in* y *for every* $x\in\boldsymbol{R}_p$.

Proof. It will be enough to prove the first half of the theorem, since the second half obviously follows from the first. Let us denote by $\mathfrak{B}_0$ the class of all sets Q in $\boldsymbol{R}_{p+q}$ such that the sets $\underset{x}{\mathrm{E}}[(x, y)\in Q]$, for every $y\in\boldsymbol{R}_q$, and the sets $\underset{y}{\mathrm{E}}[(x, y)\in Q]$, for every $x\in\boldsymbol{R}_p$, are measurable ($\mathfrak{B}$) in the spaces $\boldsymbol{R}_p$ and $\boldsymbol{R}_q$ respectively. If a set $Q\subset\boldsymbol{R}_{p+q}$ is closed, so are the sets $\underset{x}{\mathrm{E}}[(x, y)\in Q]$ and $\underset{y}{\mathrm{E}}[(x, y)\in Q]$. The class $\mathfrak{B}_0$ thus contains all closed sets of the space $\boldsymbol{R}_{p+q}$, and on the other hand we see at once that $\mathfrak{B}_0$ is additive. It follows that $\mathfrak{B}_0$ includes all Borel sets in the space $\boldsymbol{R}_{p+q}$ (cf. the definition, Chap. II, p. 41), and this completes the proof.

* **§ 9. Fubini's theorem in abstract spaces.** We shall return in this § to the abstract considerations of Chap. I and show that for abstract spaces, theorems similar to those of the preceding § hold good.

Given any two sets X and Y, we shall denote by $X\times Y$ the set of all pairs of elements (x, y) for which $x\in X$ and $y\in Y$. The set $X\times Y$ is often called *combinatory product* or *Cartesian product* (cf. C. Kuratowski [I, p. 7]) of the sets X and Y. The following identities are obvious

(9.1) $$(X_1\times Y_1)\cdot(X_2\times Y_2)=(X_1\cdot X_2)\times(Y_1\cdot Y_2),$$

(9.2) $$(X_2\times Y_2)-(X_1\times Y_1)=[(X_2-X_1)\times Y_2]+[(X_2\cdot X_1)\times(Y_2-Y_1)],$$

the sets X_1, X_2, Y_1, Y_2 being quite arbitrary.

If $\mathfrak{X}$ and $\mathfrak{Y}$ are additive classes of sets in the spaces X and Y respectively, $\mathfrak{X}\mathfrak{Y}$ will denote the smallest additive class of sets in the space $\boldsymbol{X}\times\boldsymbol{Y}$, containing all product-sets of the form $X\times Y$, where $X\in\mathfrak{X}$ and $Y\in\mathfrak{Y}$.

For auxiliary purposes, we shall make use in this § of the following definition: a class $\mathfrak{N}$ of sets will be termed *normal*, if (i) the sum of every sequence of sets ($\mathfrak{N}$) no two of which have common points is itself a set ($\mathfrak{N}$) and (ii) the limit of every descending sequence of sets ($\mathfrak{N}$) is a set ($\mathfrak{N}$).

We shall begin by proving the following analogue of Theorem 8.8:

(9.3) ***Theorem.*** *Let $\mathfrak{X}$ and $\mathfrak{Y}$ be two additive classes of sets in the spaces X and Y respectively. Then, if Q is a set measurable ($\mathfrak{X}\mathfrak{Y}$) in the space $X \times Y$, the set* $\underset{x}{\mathrm{E}}[(x, y) \in Q]$ *is measurable ($\mathfrak{X}$) for every $y \in Y$, and the set* $\underset{y}{\mathrm{E}}[(x, y) \in Q]$ *is measurable ($\mathfrak{Y}$) for every $x \in X$.*

In the same way a function $f(x, y)$ which is measurable ($\mathfrak{X}\mathfrak{Y}$) in the space $X \times Y$, is measurable ($\mathfrak{X}$) in x for every $y \in Y$ and measurable ($\mathfrak{Y}$) in y for every $x \in X$.

Proof. It is enough to prove only the first part concerning sets. To do this, we denote by $\mathfrak{M}$ the class of all sets Q in $X \times Y$ such that the set $\underset{x}{\mathrm{E}}[(x, y) \in Q]$ is measurable ($\mathfrak{X}$) for every $y \in Y$, and that the set $\underset{y}{\mathrm{E}}[(x, y) \in Q]$ is measurable ($\mathfrak{Y}$) for every $x \in X$ We see at once that the class $\mathfrak{M}$ is additive in the space $X \times Y$ and that, besides, it includes all sets $X \times Y$ for which $X \in \mathfrak{X}$ and $Y \in \mathfrak{Y}$. Hence $\mathfrak{X}\mathfrak{Y} \subset \mathfrak{M}$, and this completes the proof.

Before proceeding further we shall establish the following lemma:

(9.4) ***Lemma.*** *If $\mathfrak{X}$ and $\mathfrak{Y}$ are two additive classes of sets in the spaces X and Y respectively, the class $\mathfrak{X}\mathfrak{Y}$ coincides with the smallest normal class that includes the sets $X \times Y$ for which $X \in \mathfrak{X}$ and $Y \in \mathfrak{Y}$.*

Proof. For brevity let us term elementary any set $X \times Y$ for which $X \in \mathfrak{X}$ and $Y \in \mathfrak{Y}$, and let $\mathfrak{N}_0$ denote the smallest normal class which includes all elementary sets (i. e. the common part of all the normal classes that include these sets). Clearly $\mathfrak{N}_0 \subset \mathfrak{X}\mathfrak{Y}$ since $\mathfrak{X}\mathfrak{Y}$ is also a normal class. In order to establish the opposite inclusion, it is enough to prove that the class $\mathfrak{N}_0$ is additive, and this will be an immediate consequence of the following two properties of the class $\mathfrak{N}_0$:

(9.5) *The common part of any sequence of sets* $(\mathfrak{N}_0)$ *is itself a set* $(\mathfrak{N}_0)$.

(9.6) *The complement (with respect to the space* $X \times Y$*) of any set* $(\mathfrak{N}_0)$ *is again a set* $(\mathfrak{N}_0)$.

To prove (9.5), it is enough, since the class $\mathfrak{N}_0$ is normal, to show that the common part of two sets $(\mathfrak{N}_0)$ is a set $(\mathfrak{N}_0)$.

For this purpose, let $\mathfrak{N}_1$ be the class of all the sets $(\mathfrak{N}_0)$ whose common parts with every elementary set belong to $\mathfrak{N}_0$. From the identity (9.1), it follows that the common part of two elementary sets is an elementary set, and hence that $\mathfrak{N}_1$ includes all the elementary sets. On the other hand, we verify at once that $\mathfrak{N}_1$ is a normal class. This gives $\mathfrak{N}_0 \subset \mathfrak{N}_1$, and since by definition $\mathfrak{N}_1 \subset \mathfrak{N}_0$, we obtain $\mathfrak{N}_1 = \mathfrak{N}_0$.

Let now $\mathfrak{N}_2$ be the class of all the sets $(\mathfrak{N}_0)$ whose common parts with every set $(\mathfrak{N}_0)$ belong to $\mathfrak{N}_0$. Since $\mathfrak{N}_1 = \mathfrak{N}_0$, the class $\mathfrak{N}_2$ includes all elementary sets. Furthermore, $\mathfrak{N}_2$ is clearly a normal class. We therefore have $\mathfrak{N}_2 = \mathfrak{N}_0$, and this proves (9.5).

To establish (9.6), let $\mathfrak{N}_3$ be the class of all the sets $(\mathfrak{N}_0)$ whose complements are also sets $(\mathfrak{N}_0)$. On account of the identity (9.2) the complement of any elementary set is the sum of two elementary sets without common points, and so, a set $(\mathfrak{N}_0)$. Therefore the class $\mathfrak{N}_3$ includes all elementary sets and, to conclude that $\mathfrak{N}_3 = \mathfrak{N}_0$, it suffices to show that the class $\mathfrak{N}_3$ is normal.

Let therefore $\{X_n\}$ be any sequence of sets $(\mathfrak{N}_3)$ without common points to any two of them, and let X be the sum of the sequence. The set X clearly belongs to the class $\mathfrak{N}_0$. On the other hand, the sets CX_n are, by hypothesis, sets $(\mathfrak{N}_0)$; so that, by (9.5), the same is true of their product $CX = \prod_n CX_n$. Thus we have at the same time, $X \in \mathfrak{N}_0$ and $CX \in \mathfrak{N}_0$, and therefore $X \in \mathfrak{N}_3$.

Again, let $\{Y_n\}_{n=1,2,\ldots}$ be a descending sequence of sets $(\mathfrak{N}_3)$, and Y its limit. The set Y clearly belongs to the class $\mathfrak{N}_0$. On the other hand, consider the identity

$$CY = \sum_{n=1}^{\infty} CY_n = CY_1 + \sum_{n=1}^{\infty} Y_n \cdot CY_{n+1},$$

and observe that no two of the sets CY_1 and $Y_n \cdot CY_{n+1}$ for $n=1,2,\ldots$ have common points. Since these sets belong, by (9.5), to the class $\mathfrak{N}_0$, so does the set CY. Thus we have both $Y \in \mathfrak{N}_0$ and $CY \in \mathfrak{N}_0$, whence $Y \in \mathfrak{N}_3$. The class $\mathfrak{N}_3$ is therefore normal, and this establishes (9.6) and completes the proof of Lemma 9.4.

We can restate Lemma 9.4 in the following more general form:

(9.7) *Given in an abstract space $\boldsymbol{T}$ a class $\mathfrak{Q}$ of sets additive in the weak sense, then the smallest class that is additive (in the complete sense) and contains $\mathfrak{Q}$. coincides with the smallest normal class containing $\mathfrak{Q}$.*

The proof is the same as for Lemma 9.4.

If $\mathfrak{X}$ and $\mathfrak{Y}$ are additive classes in the spaces $\boldsymbol{X}$ and $\boldsymbol{Y}$ respectively, the finite sums of the sets $X \times Y$ for which $X \epsilon \mathfrak{X}$ and $Y \epsilon \mathfrak{Y}$, constitute, according to formulae (9.1) and (9.2), a class that is additive in the weak sense (*vide* Chap. I, p. 7) in the space $\boldsymbol{X} \times \boldsymbol{Y}$ Another example of a class of sets additive in the weak sense consists of the class of all the sets of an arbitrary metrical space $\boldsymbol{M}$, that are both sets $(\mathfrak{G}_\delta)$ and $(\mathfrak{F}_\sigma)$. The smallest class that is additive (in the complete sense) and contains these sets is clearly the class of Borel sets in $\boldsymbol{M}$.

The assertion of (9.7) enables us to prove easily the following theorem due to H. Hahn [2, p. 437] and in some respect analogous to Theorem 6.6:

Let $\mathfrak{Q}$ be a class of sets, additive in the weak sense in a space $\boldsymbol{T}$, and let $\mathfrak{T}$ be the smallest class of sets that is additive in the complete sense and contains $\mathfrak{Q}$. Suppose further that τ is a measure $(\mathfrak{T})$ such that the space $\boldsymbol{T}$ either has finite measure (τ), or, more generally, is expressible as the sum of a sequence of sets of finite measure (τ). Then (i) *for every set E measurable $(\mathfrak{T})$ and for every $\varepsilon > 0$, there exists a set $F \epsilon \mathfrak{Q}_\delta$, and a set $G \epsilon \mathfrak{Q}_\sigma$, such that $F \subset E \subset G$ and that $\tau(E - F) < \varepsilon$ and $\tau(G - E) < \varepsilon$;* (ii) *for every set E measurable $(\mathfrak{T})$ there exist a set $(\mathfrak{Q}_{\delta\sigma})$ contained in E, and a set $(\mathfrak{Q}_{\sigma\delta})$ containing E, which differ from E at most by sets of measure (τ) zero.*

(9.8) ***Theorem.*** *Let $\mathfrak{X}$ and $\mathfrak{Y}$ be additive classes of sets in the spaces $\boldsymbol{X}$ and $\boldsymbol{Y}$ respectively, and let μ and ν be measures defined respectively for these classes. Suppose that $\mu(\boldsymbol{X}) < \infty$ and $\nu(\boldsymbol{Y}) < \infty$, or, more generally, that*

(9.9)
$$\boldsymbol{X} = \sum_n X_n, \qquad \boldsymbol{Y} = \sum_n Y_n$$
where $X_n \epsilon \mathfrak{X}$, $Y_n \epsilon \mathfrak{Y}$, $\mu(X_n) < \infty$ and $\nu(Y_n) < \infty$ for $n = 1, 2, \ldots$

Then, for every set $Q \subset \boldsymbol{X} \times \boldsymbol{Y}$ measurable $(\mathfrak{X}\mathfrak{Y})$, (i) $\mu\{\underset{x}{\mathrm{E}}[(x, y) \epsilon Q]\}$, *as function of y, is measurable $(\mathfrak{Y})$ in the space $\boldsymbol{Y}$ and $\nu\{\underset{y}{\mathrm{E}}[(x, y) \epsilon Q]\}$, as function of x, is measurable $(\mathfrak{X})$ in the space $\boldsymbol{X}$; furthermore*

(ii)
$$(\mathfrak{Y}) \int_{\boldsymbol{Y}} \mu\{\underset{x}{\mathrm{E}}[(x, y) \epsilon Q]\} \, d\nu(y) = (\mathfrak{X}) \int_{\boldsymbol{X}} \nu\{\underset{y}{\mathrm{E}}[(x, y) \epsilon Q]\} \, d\mu(x).$$

Proof. We may clearly suppose that no two sets X_n, and also no two sets Y_n, have common points. The same will then be true of the sets $X_n \times Y_m$ in the space $\boldsymbol{X} \times \boldsymbol{Y}$.

Let us denote by $\mathfrak{N}$ the class of all the sets P measurable $(\mathfrak{X}\mathfrak{Y})$ in the space $\boldsymbol{X} \times \boldsymbol{Y}$, such that conditions (i) and (ii) of the theorem hold good for every set $Q = P\cdot(X_n \times Y_m)$ where n and m are arbitrary positive integers. Since $Q = \sum_{n,m} Q\cdot(X_n \times Y_m)$ for every set $Q \subset X \times Y$, and since no two of the sets $X_n \times Y_m$ have common points, it follows easily from Lebesgue's Theorem 12.3, Chap. I, that every set Q belonging to the class $\mathfrak{N}$ fulfills conditions (i) and (ii). We have to prove that this class includes all sets measurable ($\mathfrak{X}\mathfrak{Y}$).

To do this, we observe that it follows at once from the identity (9.1) that every set $X \times Y$ for which $X \epsilon \mathfrak{X}$ and $Y \epsilon \mathfrak{Y}$, belongs to $\mathfrak{N}$. On the other hand, since by hypothesis $\mu(X_n) < \infty$ and $\nu(Y_n) < \infty$ for every n, we easily deduce from Lebesgue's Theorems 12.3 and 12.11 Chap. I, that the sum of any sequence of sets ($\mathfrak{N}$) no two of which have common points, and the limit of any descending sequence of sets ($\mathfrak{N}$), are themselves sets ($\mathfrak{N}$). The class $\mathfrak{N}$ is therefore normal, and by Lemma 9.4, contains all sets ($\mathfrak{X}\mathfrak{Y}$). This proves the theorem.

If we suppose the hypotheses of Theorem 9.8 satisfied, a measure can be defined for the class $\mathfrak{X}\mathfrak{Y}$ so as to correspond naturally to the measures μ and ν that are given for the classes $\mathfrak{X}$ and $\mathfrak{Y}$. We do this by calling *measure* ($\mu\nu$) of a set Q measurable ($\mathfrak{X}\mathfrak{Y}$) the common value of the integrals (ii) of Theorem 9.8. It is immediate that we then have $\mu\nu(X \times Y) = \mu(X)\cdot\nu(Y)$ for every pair of sets $X \epsilon \mathfrak{X}$ and $Y \epsilon \mathfrak{Y}$.

This definition enables us to state Theorem 9.8 in a manner analogous to Theorem 8.6. But the analogy would be incomplete if we neglected to extend at the same time the class $\mathfrak{X}\mathfrak{Y}$. Thus, for instance if $\mathfrak{X}$ and $\mathfrak{Y}$ denote respectively the classes of sets measurable in the Lebesgue sense in Euclidean spaces $\boldsymbol{R}_p$ and $\boldsymbol{R}_q$, the class $\mathfrak{X}\mathfrak{Y}$ does not coincide with that of the sets measurable ($\mathfrak{L}$) in $\boldsymbol{R}_{p+q}$, although it is evidently included in the latter. The extension of the class $\mathfrak{X}\mathfrak{Y}$, that we require in the general case, will be defined as follows.

Given an additive class of sets $\mathfrak{T}$ and a measure τ associated with this class, we shall call the class $\mathfrak{T}$ *complete with respect to the measure* τ if it includes all subsets of sets ($\mathfrak{T}$) of measure (τ) zero. Thus for instance, if Γ denotes any measure of Carathéodory, the class $\mathfrak{L}_\Gamma$ is complete with respect to Γ (cf. Chap. II, p. 44), and in particular, the class $\mathfrak{L}$ in a Euclidean space is complete with respect to Lebesgue measure; whereas the class of sets measurable ($\mathfrak{B}$) is not complete with respect to that measure.

Every additive class of sets $\mathfrak{T}$ may be completed with respect to any measure τ defined for the class, i. e. there is always an additive class $\mathfrak{S} \supset \mathfrak{T}$ such that the function of a set τ can be continued as a measure on all sets ($\mathfrak{S}$) and such that $\mathfrak{S}$ is complete with respect to the measure τ thus continued. Among the classes $\mathfrak{S}$ of this kind, there is a smallest one that we shall denote by $\overline{\mathfrak{T}}^{\tau}$. As is seen directly, this class consists of all sets of the form $T - N_1 + N_2$, where $T \epsilon \mathfrak{T}$ and N_1, N_2 are arbitrary subsets of sets ($\mathfrak{T}$) of measure (τ) zero. The extension of the measure τ to all sets of this form is evident.

We can now state the following theorem which corresponds to Fubini's Theorem 8.1:

(9.10) ***Theorem.*** *Under the hypotheses of Theorem* 9.8, *if* $f(x, y)$ *is a non-negative function measurable* ($\overline{\mathfrak{X}\mathfrak{Y}}^{\mu\nu}$) *in the space* $X \times Y$,

(i_1) $f(x, y)$ *as function of* x *is measurable* ($\overline{\mathfrak{X}}^{\mu}$) *in* X *for every* $y \epsilon Y$, *except at most a set of measure* (ν) *zero*;

(i_2) $f(x, y)$ *as function of* y *is measurable* ($\overline{\mathfrak{Y}}^{\nu}$) *in* Y *for every* $x \epsilon X$, *except at most a set of measure* (μ) *zero*;

(ii) $$\int_{X\times Y} f(x,y)\, d\mu\nu(x,y) = \int_Y \Big[\int_X f(x,y)\, d\mu(x)\Big]\, d\nu(y) = \int_X \Big[\int_Y f(x,y)\, d\nu(y)\Big] d\mu(x).$$

Proof. In the special case in which f is the characteristic function of a set measurable ($\mathfrak{X}\mathfrak{Y}$), the theorem is an immediate consequence of Theorem 9.8. The same is true when f is the characteristic function of a set measurable ($\overline{\mathfrak{X}\mathfrak{Y}}^{\mu\nu}$) of measure ($\mu\nu$) zero, and in consequence Theorem 9.8 remains true when f is the characteristic function of any set ($\overline{\mathfrak{X}\mathfrak{Y}}^{\mu\nu}$).

This being so, we pass as usual to the case in which f is a finite function, simple and measurable ($\overline{\mathfrak{X}\mathfrak{Y}}^{\mu\nu}$) and finally, with the help of Theorems 7.4 and 12.6, Chap. I, to the general case in which f is any non-negative function measurable ($\overline{\mathfrak{X}\mathfrak{Y}}^{\mu\nu}$).

Condition (9.9) is essential to the validity of Theorems 9.8 and 9.10. To see this, let us consider some examples for which the condition is not fulfilled. Put $X = Y = R_1$, and let $\mathfrak{X} = \mathfrak{Y}$ be the class of all sets in R_1 that are measurable in the sense of Lebesgue. We choose for μ the ordinary Lebesgue measure, and we define the measure ν by making $\nu(Y)$ equal to the number of elements of Y (so that $\nu(Y) = \infty$ if Y is an infinite set). Finally, let Q be the set of all the points (x, x) in $R_2 = X \times Y$ such that $0 \leqslant x \leqslant 1$. The integrals occuring in condition (ii) of Theorem 9.8 are then respectively 0 and 1 so that condition (ii) does not hold. (We could also, by a suitable modification of the set Q, choose $Y = R_2$ and take as measure ν the length Λ_1; cf. Chap. II, § 8.)

Another example showing the importance of condition (9.9) is due to A. Lindenbaum. Put $X=Y=R_1$, let $\mathfrak{X}=\mathfrak{Y}$ be the class of all Borel sets in R_1, and let $\mu(X)=\nu(X)$ denote for every set X the number of its elements. By a theorem of the theory of analytic sets (cf., for instance, C. Kuratowski [I, p. 261]) there exists in the plane $R_2=X\times Y$ a Borel set Q such that the set of $x \in R_1$ for which $\underset{y}{\mathrm{E}}[(x, y)\in Q]$ reduces to a single point, is not measurable in the sense of Borel. In other words, the set of $x\in X$ for which $\nu\{\underset{y}{\mathrm{E}}[(x, y)\in Q]\}=1$ is not measurable ($\mathfrak{X}$). Thus condition (i) of Theorem 9.8 does not hold.

For the results of this §, *vide* H. Hahn [2]; cf. also S. Ulam [2], Z. Łomnicki and S. Ulam [1], and W. Feller [1]. For a discussion of Fubini's theorem applied to functions whose values belong to an abstract vector space, *vide* also S. Bochner [2]. Finally we observe that certain theorems, analogous to those established in this § for measurable sets and sets of measure zero, can be stated for the property of Baire and the Baire categories. Cf. on this point C. Kuratowski and S. Ulam [1].

§ 10. Geometrical definition of the Lebesgue-Stieltjes integral. The geometrical definition of an integral is inspired by the older and more natural idea of regarding the integral as the measure of an "area", or of a "volume", attached to the function in a certain way that is well known.

Let us begin by fixing our notation. Given a function $f(x)$ defined on a set $Q\subset R_m$, we call *graph* of $f(x)$ on Q, and we denote by $\mathrm{B}(f; Q)$, the set of all points (x, y) of R_{m+1} for which $x\in Q$ and $y=f(x)\neq\infty$. If $f(x)$ is non-negative on Q, the set of all the points (x, y) of R_{m+1} such that $x\in Q$ and $0\leqslant y\leqslant f(x)$ is termed, according to C. Carathéodory, *ordinate-set* of f on Q and will be denoted by $\mathrm{A}(f; Q)$.

As in §§ 3—7 we shall suppose the space R_m fixed and a non-negative additive function U of an interval given in R_m. And in accordance with § 2, p. 59 and § 5, p. 65, L_1 denotes the Lebesgue measure in R_1.

(10.1) ***Lemma.*** *If $Q\subset R_m$ is a set measurable ($\mathfrak{L}_U$), the set $\underset{(x,y)}{\mathrm{E}}[x\in Q;\ a\leqslant y\leqslant b]$ in R_{m+1} is, for every pair of real numbers a and $b\geqslant a$, measurable ($\mathfrak{L}_{U\mathrm{L}_1}$), and its measure ($U\mathrm{L}_1$) is $(b-a)\cdot U^*(Q)$.*

Proof. Let us write for short, $Q_{a,b}=\underset{(x,y)}{\mathrm{E}}[x\in Q;\ a\leqslant y\leqslant b]$ and $T=U\mathrm{L}_1$. We shall begin by showing that if Q has measure (U) zero, the set $Q_{a,b}$ is of measure (T) zero, and so is certainly measurable ($\mathfrak{L}_T$).

To see this, observe that there is then, for any $\varepsilon>0$, a sequence of intervals $\{I_n\}$ in $\boldsymbol{R}_m$ such that $Q\subset\sum_n I_n^\circ$ and $\sum_n U(I_n)\leqslant\varepsilon$. Writing $J_n=I_n\times[a-\varepsilon, b+\varepsilon]$, we obtain a sequence of intervals $\{J_n\}$ in $\boldsymbol{R}_{m+1}$, such that $Q_{a,b}\subset\sum_n J_n^\circ$ and $\sum_n T(J_n)=\sum_n U(I_n)\cdot(b-a+2\varepsilon)\leqslant(b-a+2\varepsilon)\cdot\varepsilon$. Thus $T^*(Q_{a,b})=0$.

Let now Q be any set measurable ($\mathfrak{L}_U$). By Theorem 6.6, Q is the sum of a sequence of closed sets and a set of measure (U) zero. Therefore, by the above, the set $Q_{a,b}$ is also the sum of a sequence of closed sets and of a set of measure (T) zero, and is thus measurable ($\mathfrak{L}_T$). Finally, for every real number y, we have $\underset{x}{\mathrm{E}}[(x, y)\,\epsilon\, Q_{a,b}]=Q$ if $a\leqslant y\leqslant b$, and $\underset{x}{\mathrm{E}}[(x,y)\,\epsilon\, Q_{a,b}]=0$ if y is outside the interval $[a,b]$. Hence, by Theorem 8.6, we have $T^*(Q_{a,b})=\int_a^b U^*(Q)\,dy=$ $=(b-a)\cdot U^*(Q)$, which completes the proof.

(10.2) ***Theorem.*** *If $f(x)$ is a function measurable ($\mathfrak{L}_U$) on a set $Q\subset\boldsymbol{R}_m$, its graph on Q is of measure ($U\mathrm{L}_1$) zero.*

Proof. Since any set measurable ($\mathfrak{L}_U$) can be expressed as the sum of a sequence of bounded measurable sets, we can restrict ourselves to the case in which Q is bounded.

Let us fix an $\varepsilon>0$ and write $Q_n=\underset{x}{\mathrm{E}}[x\,\epsilon\, Q;\ n\,\varepsilon\leqslant f(x)<(n+1)\varepsilon]$ for every integer n. By Lemma 10.1 the measure ($U\mathrm{L}_1$) of the graph of $f(x)$ on Q_n does not exceed $\varepsilon\cdot U^*(Q_n)$; therefore, on the whole set Q, it does not exceed $\varepsilon\cdot U^*(Q)$, and so vanishes.

We can now prove the following theorem which includes the geometrical definition of the Lebesgue integral:

(10.3) ***Theorem.*** *In order that a function $f(x)$ defined and non-negative on a set $Q\subset\boldsymbol{R}_m$ measurable ($\mathfrak{L}_U$) be measurable ($\mathfrak{L}_U$) on Q, it is necessary and sufficient that its ordinate-set $\mathrm{A}(f;Q)$ on Q be measurable ($\mathfrak{L}_{U\mathrm{L}_1}$). When this condition is fulfilled, the definite integrat (U) of f on Q is equal to the measure ($U\mathrm{L}_1$) of the set $\mathrm{A}(f;Q)$.*

Proof. Write, for short, $T=U\mathrm{L}_1$ and suppose first that $f(x)$ is a simple function, finite, non-negative, and measurable ($\mathfrak{L}_U$) on Q, i.e. that $f=\{v_1,Q_1;\ v_2,Q_2;\ \ldots;\ v_n,Q_n\}$ where Q_i are sets measurable ($\mathfrak{L}_U$)

no two of which have common points. By Lemma 10.1, all the sets $\mathrm{A}(f; Q_i)$ are measurable $(\mathfrak{L}_T)$ and $T^*[\mathrm{A}(f; Q_i)] = v_i \cdot U^*(Q_i)$ for $i = 1, 2, \ldots, n$. Hence, the set $\mathrm{A}(f; Q) = \sum_i \mathrm{A}(f; Q_i)$ is itself measurable $(\mathfrak{L}_T)$, and its measure (T) is equal to $\sum T^*[\mathrm{A}(f; Q_i)] = = \sum_i v_i \cdot U^*(Q_i) = \int_Q f(x)\, dU(x)$.

Let now f be any non-negative function measurable $(\mathfrak{L}_T)$ on Q. There is a non-decreasing sequence $\{h_n(x)\}$ of simple functions, finite, non-negative, and measurable $(\mathfrak{L}_U)$ on Q such that $f(x) = \lim_n h_n(x)$.

We then have

$$\mathrm{A}(f; Q) = \lim_n \mathrm{A}(h_n; Q) + \mathrm{B}(f; Q). \tag{10.4}$$

Now, by the above, all the sets $\mathrm{A}(h_n; Q)$ are measurable $(\mathfrak{L}_T)$ and $T^*[\mathrm{A}(h_n; Q)] = \int_Q h_n\, dU$ for $n = 1, 2, \ldots$. On the other hand, by Theorem 10.2, the set $\mathrm{B}(f; Q)$ has measure (T) zero. It therefore follows at once from (10.4) that the set $\mathrm{A}(f; Q)$ is itself measurable $(\mathfrak{L}_T)$ and that

$$T^*[\mathrm{A}(f; Q)] = \lim_n \int_Q h_n\, dU = \int_Q f\, dU.$$

It remains to prove that, if the set $\mathrm{A}(f; Q)$ is measurable $(\mathfrak{L}_T)$, the function f is measurable $(\mathfrak{L}_U)$. To do this, write for short $A = \mathrm{A}(f; Q)$, and observe that, for every non-negative number y, the set $\mathrm{E}_x[x \in Q;\, f(x) \geqslant y]$ coincides with the set $\mathrm{E}_x[(x, y) \in A]$. Thus, by Theorem 8.6, if A is measurable $(\mathfrak{L}_T)$, the set $\mathrm{E}_x[x \in Q;\, f(x) \geqslant y]$ is measurable $(\mathfrak{L}_U)$ for all numbers y except at most those of a set of measure (L_1) zero. But this suffices for the measurability of f on Q (cf. Chap. I, (7.2)) and so completes the proof.

* **§ 11. Translations of sets.** As an application of Theorem 8.6, we shall prove in this § a theorem on parallel translations of sets. As a matter of course, in what follows, translations could be replaced by rotations, or by certain other transformations constituting continuous groups and preserving Lebesgue measure.

Given two points $x=(x_1, x_2, ..., x_m)$ and $y=(y_1, y_2, ..., y_m)$ in the space $\boldsymbol{R}_m$, we shall denote by $x+y$ the point $(x_1+y_1, x_2+y_2, ..., x_m+y_m)$ and by $|x|$ the number $(x_1^2+x_2^2+...+x_m^2)^{1/2}$. We shall write $x\to 0$ when $|x|\to 0$. If Q is a set in the space $\boldsymbol{R}_m$ and a any point of this space, $Q^{(a)}$ will denote the set of all points $x+a$ where $x \in Q$. The set $Q^{(a)}$ is termed *translation of Q by the vector a*. If Φ is an additive function of a set in $\boldsymbol{R}_m$ and $a\in \boldsymbol{R}_m$, we shall write $\Phi^{(a)}(X)=\Phi(X^{(a)})$ for every set X bounded and measurable $(\mathfrak{B})$.

(11.1) ***Theorem.*** *If Q is a bounded set $(\mathfrak{B})$ of measure* (L) *zero in the space $\boldsymbol{R}_m$ and Φ is an additive function of a set $(\mathfrak{B})$ in $\boldsymbol{R}_m$, the function Φ vanishes for almost all translations of Q, i. e. $\Phi(Q^{(a)})=\Phi^{(a)}(Q)=0$ for almost all points a of $\boldsymbol{R}_m$.*

Proof. We may clearly assume Φ to be a non-negative function, and Q to be a bounded set $(\mathfrak{G}_\delta)$. Hence, by Theorem 6.10, there is a non-negative additive function U of an interval, such that $\Phi(X)=U^*(X)$ for every set X bounded and measurable $(\mathfrak{B})$.

Denote by $\widetilde{M}$, for any set $M\subset \boldsymbol{R}_m$, the set of all points (x, y) of the space $\boldsymbol{R}_{2m}$ which are such that $x\in \boldsymbol{R}_m$, $y\in \boldsymbol{R}_m$ and $x+y\in M$. The set $\widetilde{M}$ is clearly open whenever the set M is open. It follows at once that if M is a set $(\mathfrak{G}_\delta)$, so is the set $\widetilde{M}$. Finally, observe that for every point $z\in \boldsymbol{R}_m$ we have $\underset{x}{\mathrm{E}}[(x, z)\in\widetilde{M}]=\underset{y}{\mathrm{E}}[(z, y)\in\widetilde{M}]=M^{(-z)}$.

Since the given set Q is, by hypothesis, a set $(\mathfrak{G}_\delta)$, so is the set $\widetilde{Q}$, and by Theorem 8.6, $\int_{\boldsymbol{R}_m} U^*(Q^{(-z)})d\mathrm{L}_m(z)=\int_{\boldsymbol{R}_m}\mathrm{L}_m(Q^{(-z)})dU(z)=0$, because all translations $Q^{(-z)}$ of the set Q are of measure (L_m) zero. Hence $\Phi(Q^{(-z)})=U^*(Q^{(-z)})=0$ for every $z\in\boldsymbol{R}_m$, except at most a set of measure (L_m) zero. Replacing $-z$ by a, we obtain the required statement.

(11.2) ***Theorem.*** *Given an additive function of a set Φ, each of the following three conditions is both necessary and sufficient for the function Φ to be absolutely continuous:*

1° $\lim_{a\to 0}\Phi(Q^{(a)})=\lim_{a\to 0}\Phi^{(a)}(Q)=\Phi(Q)$ *for every bounded set Q measurable $(\mathfrak{B})$ and of measure* (L) *zero;*

2° $\lim_{a\to 0}\Phi(Q^{(a)})=\lim_{a\to 0}\Phi^{(a)}(Q)=\Phi(Q)$ *for every bounded set Q measurable $(\mathfrak{B})$;*

3° $\lim_{a\to 0}\mathrm{W}[\Phi^{(a)}-\Phi; I]=0$ *for every interval I.*

Proof. It is evidently sufficient to establish the necessity of condition 3° and the sufficiency of condition 1°.

Suppose first that Φ is an absolutely continuous additive function of a set. In virtue of Theorem 14.11, Chap. I, Φ is thus the indefinite integral of a function f measurable ($\mathfrak{B}$). Let $I=[a_1, b_1; \ldots; a_m, b_m]$ be an interval in the space considered and let J be an interval containing I in its interior, for instance the interval $[a_1-1, b_1+1; \ldots; a_n-1, b_m+1]$.

Let ε be any positive number. Since the function $f(x)$ is integrable over J, there exists a number $\eta>0$ such that $\int_X |f(x)|\, dx<\varepsilon/3$ for every set $X\subset J$ measurable ($\mathfrak{B}$) and of measure (L) less than η. Therefore

$$(11.3)\qquad \int_X |f(x)|\, dx<\varepsilon/3 \quad \textit{and} \quad \int_X |f(x+u)|\, dx=\int_{X^{(u)}} |f(x)|\, dx<\varepsilon/3$$
$$\textit{if} \quad X\epsilon\mathfrak{B},\quad X\subset I,\quad |X|<\eta \quad \textit{and} \quad |u|<1.$$

On the other hand, by Lusin's Theorem 7.1, there exists a closed set $F\subset I^\circ$ such that the function f is continuous on F and such that $|I-F|<\eta/2$. Let $\sigma<1$ be a positive number such that $F^{(u)}\subset I$ whenever $|u|<\sigma$, and such that

$$(11.4)\qquad |f(x+u)-f(x)|<\frac{\varepsilon}{3\cdot|I|} \quad \textit{whenever} \quad x\,\epsilon\, F,\ x+u\,\epsilon\, F, \ \textit{and}\ |u|<\sigma.$$

Let now a be any point of $\boldsymbol{R}_m$ such that $|a|<\sigma$. By (11.4)

$$(11.5)\qquad \int_{F\cdot F^{(-a)}} |f(x+a)-f(x)|\, dx\leqslant|I|\cdot(\varepsilon/3\,|I|)=\varepsilon/3.$$

On the other hand, $|I-F\cdot F^{(-a)}|\leqslant|I-F|+|I-F^{(-a)}|\leqslant2\cdot|I-F|<\eta$, and therefore, by (11.3),

$$\int_{I-F\cdot F^{(-a)}} |f(x+a)-f(x)|\, dx<2\varepsilon/3.$$

If we add this inequality to (11.5) we obtain $\int_I |f(x+a)-f(x)|\, dx<\varepsilon$, i. e. the variation $W[\Phi^{(a)}-\Phi; I]=\int_I |f(x+a)-f(x)|\, dx$ tends to 0 with $|a|$. The function Φ therefore fulfills condition 3°.

It remains to prove the sufficiency of condition 1°. Now, if the function Φ fulfills this condition, Φ vanishes by Theorem 11.1 for every bounded set measurable ($\mathfrak{B}$) of measure (L) zero, and so is absolutely continuous.

It was long known that every absolutely continuous function Φ fulfills conditions 1°, 2° and 3° of Theorem 11.2. The converse, however, (i. e. the sufficiency of these conditions, in order that the function Φ of a set be absolutely continuous) was established more recently. The sufficiency of condition 3° was first proved by A. Plessner [1] (with the help of trigonometric series and for functions of a real variable). As regards the other conditions (1° and 2°), and as regards Theorem 11.1, *vide* H. Milicer-Grużewska [1], and N. Wiener and R. C. Young [1]. In the text we have followed the method used by the latter authors. Cf. also N. Dunford [1].

§ 12. Absolutely continuous functions of an interval.

An additive function F of an interval will be termed *absolutely continuous on a figure* R_0, if to each $\varepsilon>0$ there corresponds a number $\eta>0$ such that for every figure $R\subset R_0$ the inequality $|R|<\eta$ implies $|F(R)|<\varepsilon$. In conformity with § 3, p. 59, we shall understand by absolute continuity in an open set G, absolute continuity on every figure $R\subset G$, and by absolute continuity, absolute continuity in the whole space.

Every additive function of an interval, absolutely continuous on a figure R_0, is of bounded variation on R_0. For, if F is a function that is absolutely continuous on R_0, there exists a number $\eta>0$ such that, for every figure $R\subset R_0$, the inequality $|R|<\eta$ implies $|F(R)|<1$. Therefore, if we subdivide R_0 into a finite number of intervals $I_1, I_2, \ldots, I_n$ of measure less than η, we obtain $\mathrm{W}(F; R_0)\leqslant \sum_{k=1}^{n}\mathrm{W}(F; I_k)\leqslant 2n$.

An additive function of an interval F, of bounded variation on a figure R_0, will be termed *singular on* R_0, if for each $\varepsilon>0$ there exists a figure $R\subset R_0$ such that $|R|<\varepsilon$ and $\mathrm{W}(F; R_0\ominus R)<\varepsilon$.

The reader will observe the analogy between the above definitions and the criteria given in Theorems 13.2 and 13.3, Chap. I, in order that an additive function of a set should be absolutely continuous or singular. This analogy could be pushed further by introducing the notions of absolutely continuous function, and of singular function, with respect to a non-negative additive function of an interval. But this "relativization", although useful in certain cases, would not play an essential part in the remainder of this book.

The following theorem is, almost word for word, a duplicate of Theorem 13.1 of Chapter I.

(12.1) ***Theorem.*** *1⁰ In order that an additive function of an interval be absolutely continuous [singular] on a figure R_0, it is necessary and sufficient that its two variations, the upper and the lower, should both be so. 2⁰ Every linear combination, with constant coefficients, of two additive functions of an interval which are absolutely continuous [singular] on a figure R_0 is itself absolutely continuous [singular] on R_0. 3⁰ The limit of a bounded monotone sequence of additive functions of an interval that are absolutely continuous [singular] on a figure R_0 is also absolutely continuous [singular] on R_0. 4⁰ If an additive function of an interval is absolutely continuous [singular] on a figure R_0, the function is so on every figure $R \subset R_0$. 5⁰ If an additive function of an interval is absolutely continuous [singular] on each of the figures R_1 and R_2, the function is so on the figure R_1+R_2. 6⁰ An additive function of an interval cannot be both absolutely continuous and singular on a figure R_0, without vanishing identically on R_0.*

Part 3⁰, at most, perhaps requires a proof. (It differs slightly from the corresponding part of Theorem 13.1, Chap. I.) Let therefore F be the limit of a bounded monotone sequence $\{F_n\}$ of additive functions of an interval on a figure R_0. Let ε be any positive number. Since the functions $F-F_n$ are monotone on R_0, there exists a positive integer n_0 such that

$$(12.2) \quad |F(R)-F_{n_0}(R)| \leqslant |F(R_0)-F_{n_0}(R_0)| < \varepsilon/2 \quad \textit{for every figure } R \subset R_0.$$

This being so, let us suppose that the functions F_n are absolutely continuous on R_0. There is then an $\eta>0$ such that, for every figure $R \subset R_0$, $|R|<\eta$ implies the inequality $|F_{n_0}(R)|<\varepsilon/2$ and therefore, by (12.2), the inequality $|F(R)|<\varepsilon$. The function F is thus absolutely continuous on R_0.

Suppose next that the functions F_n are singular on R_0. There is then a figure $R_1 \subset R_0$ such that $|R_1|<\varepsilon$ and $W[F_{n_0}; R_0 \ominus R_1]<\varepsilon/2$. Hence, by (12.2), $W[F; R_0 \ominus R_1]<\varepsilon$, which shows that the function F is singular. This completes the proof.

We shall now establish two simple theorems that show explicitly the connection between the absolutely continuous or singular functions of an interval and those of a set. To avoid misunderstanding, we draw the reader's attention to the abbreviations adopted in § 5, p. 66, in the terminology of functions of a set.

(12.3) ***Theorem.*** *In order that a non-negative additive function F of an interval be absolutely continuous, it is necessary and sufficient that the corresponding function of a set F^* should be so.*

Proof. Suppose that the function F is absolutely continuous. In order to prove that the function F^* is so too, it is enough to show that F^* vanishes on every bounded set of measure (L) zero. Let therefore E be such a set, and let J be an interval that contains E in its interior. For any $\varepsilon > 0$, let η be a positive number such that

(12.4) $|R| < \eta$ *implies* $|F(R)| < \varepsilon$ *for every figure* $R \subset J$.

Since $|E|=0$, there exists a sequence of intervals $\{I_n\}$ in J such that

(12.5) $$E \subset \sum_n I_n^\circ \quad \textit{and} \quad \sum_n |I_n| < \eta.$$

Denote by R_k the sum of the k first intervals of this sequence. By Theorem 4.6 (or 6.1) of Chap. II, and Theorem 6.2, the relations (12.4) and (12.5) give $F^*(E) \leqslant \lim_k F^*(R_k^\circ) \leqslant \lim_k F(R_k) \leqslant \varepsilon$, from which it follows that $F^*(E)=0$.

Conversely, if F^* is an absolutely continuous function of a set, the absolute continuity of F follows at once from the inequality $F(R) \leqslant F^*(R)$ which holds by Theorem 6.2 for every figure R.

(12.6) ***Theorem.*** *In order that a non-negative additive function of an interval F be singular, it is necessary and sufficient that the corresponding function of a set F^* should be so.*

Proof. Suppose that the function of an interval F is singular, and let J be any interval. Given any number $\varepsilon > 0$, there is then a figure $R \subset J$ such that $|R| < \varepsilon$ and $F(J \ominus R) < \varepsilon$. Consequently, by Theorem 6.2, we have $F^*(J^\circ - R) \leqslant F(J \ominus R) < \varepsilon$, which shows on account of Theorem 13.3, Chap. I, that the non-negative function of a set F^* is singular in the interior of every interval J, and therefore in the whole space.

Suppose, conversely, that the function of a set F^* is singular, and let ε be any positive number. Given any interval I there is then a set $E \subset I^\circ$ such that $|E|=0$ and $F^*(I^\circ - E)=0$. Consequently, there is a sequence of intervals $\{I_n\}$ in I such that

(12.7) $I^\circ - E \subset \sum_n I_n$ and (12.8) $\sum_n F(I_n) < \varepsilon$.

Denote by R_k the sum of the k first intervals of this sequence. Since $|E|=0$, we obtain from (12.7) that $|R_{k_0}| > |I| - \varepsilon$ for a sufficiently large k_0, and writing $P = I \ominus R_{k_0}$, this gives $|P| < \varepsilon$. Again, by (12.8), $F(I \ominus P) < \varepsilon$, which proves that the function F is singular.

§ 13. Functions of a real variable. The most important of the notions and theorems of this chapter were originally given a rather different form: they were made to refer, not to additive functions of an interval, but to functions of a real variable. It is, however, easy to establish between functions of a real variable and additive functions of a linear interval, a correspondence rendering it immaterial which of these two kinds of functions is considered.

To do this, let $f(x)$ be an arbitrary finite function of a real variable on an interval I_0. Let us term *increment* of $f(x)$ over any interval $I=[a, b]$ contained in I_0, the difference $f(b)-f(a)$. Thus defined the increment is an additive function of a linear interval $I \subset I_0$, and corresponds in a unique manner to the function $f(x)$. Conversely, if we are given any additive function $F(I)$ of a linear interval I, this in itself defines, except for an additive constant, a finite function of a real variable $f(x)$ whose increments on the intervals I coincide with the corresponding values of the function $F(I)$.

We shall understand by *upper*, *lower* and *absolute*, *variations* of a function of a real variable $f(x)$ on an interval I, the upper, lower, and absolute, variations of the increment of $f(x)$ over I. To denote these numbers, we shall use symbols similar, to those adopted for additive functions of an interval, i. e.: $\overline{\mathrm{W}}(f; I)$, $\underline{\mathrm{W}}(f; I)$, and $\mathrm{W}(f; I)$.

A finite function will be termed *of bounded variation* on an interval I_0, if its increment is a function of an interval of bounded variation on I_0. Similarly the function is *absolutely continuous*, or *singular*, if its increment is absolutely continuous, or singular. As we see immediately, in order that a function $f(x)$ be of bounded variation on an interval I_0, it is necessary and sufficient that there exists a finite number M such that $\sum_i |f(b_i)-f(a_i)| < M$ for every sequence of non-overlapping intervals $\{[a_i, b_i]\}$ contained in I_0. Similarly, in order that $f(x)$ be absolutely continuous, it is necessary and sufficient that to each $\varepsilon>0$ there corresponds an $\eta>0$ such that $\sum_i |f(b_i)-f(a_i)| < \varepsilon$ for every sequence of non-overlapping intervals $\{[a_i, b_i]\}$ contained in I_0 and for which $\sum_i |b_i-a_i| < \eta$.

If $f(x)$ and $g(x)$ are two bounded functions on an interval I_0, and M denotes the upper bound of the absolute values of $f(x)$ and $g(x)$ on I_0, we have

$$|f(b)g(b)-f(a)g(a)|\leqslant M[|f(b)-f(a)|+|g(b)-g(a)|]$$

for every interval $[a, b]\subset I_0$. It follows at once that

(13.1) *The product of two functions of bounded variation [absolutely continuous] on an interval is itself of bounded variation [absolutely continuous] on this interval.*

Finally we see that if a function of an interval F corresponds to a finite function of a point f (i. e. is the increment of f), we have $o_I(f; a)=o_I(F; a)$ for any interval I and any point $a \in I$ (cf. Chap. II, § 3, p. 42, and the present Chapter, § 3, p. 60). Thus, in particular, in order that the function f be continuous at a point a according to the definition of § 3, Chap. II, it is necessary and sufficient that the function of an interval F that corresponds to f should be so according to the definition of § 3 of the present Chapter.

If at a point a a function of a real variable f has a unique, limit on the right, this limit will be denoted by $f(a+)$; similarly, $f(a-)$ will stand for a unique limit on the left. If the function f is defined in a neighbourhood of a point a and both limits $f(a+)$, $f(a-)$ exist, then the oscillation $o(f; a)$ (*vide* Chap. II, p. 42) is equal to the largest of the three numbers $|f(a+)-f(a-)|$, $|f(a+)-f(a)|$, and $|f(a-)-f(a)|$.

If both limits $f(a+)$ and $f(a-)$ exist and are finite, and $f(a)=\frac{1}{2}[f(a+)+f(a-)]$ the function $f(x)$ is termed *regular at the point a*. It is *regular* if it is regular at every point.

Let f be any function of a real variable, of bounded variation, and $\{a_n\}$ a sequence of points. Let us put $s(a)=0$ and

$$s(x)=\begin{cases} f(a+)-f(a)+\sum_n^{(a,x)}[f(a_n+)-f(a_n-)]+f(x)-f(x-) & \textit{for } x>a \\ f(a-)-f(a)+\sum_n^{(a,x)}[f(a_n-)-f(a_n+)]+f(x)-f(x+) & \textit{for } x<a, \end{cases}$$

where the summation $\sum_n^{(a,x)}$ is extended to all indices n such that $a<a_n<x$, when $x>a$, and $a>a_n>x$, when $x<a$. The function s thus defined is termed the *saltus-function of f corresponding to the sequence $\{a_n\}$ of points*. It is continuous everywhere except, perhaps,

at the points a_n, and by subtracting it from f we obtain a function of bounded variation, continuous at all points of continuity of f and, besides, at all the points a_n. If $\{a_n\}$ is the sequence of all points of discontinuity of f, the corresponding function s is called simply the *saltus-function of f*. By varying the fixed point a we get the various saltus-functions of f which can obviously differ only by constants. A function of bounded variation which is its own saltus-function, is called a *saltus-function.*

The functions of a real variable whose increments over each interval I coincide respectively with the variations $\overline{W}(f; I)$, $\underline{W}(f; I)$ and $W(f; I)$ of a function f, are also termed (*upper*, *lower*, and *absolute*) *variations of f*. By applying the Jordan decomposition (§ 4, p. 62), we can express any function of a real variable f of bounded variation as the sum of two functions that are respectively its upper and lower variations. Thus any function of bounded variation is the difference of two monotone non-decreasing functions, and consequently is measurable ($\mathfrak{B}$) and has at every point the two unilateral limits, on the right and left. Moreover, the set of its points of discontinuity is at most enumerable, since the sum of its oscillations at the points of discontinuity lying in any finite interval is always finite (this is actually the special case of Theorem 4.1).

In various cases it is more convenient to operate on functions of a real variable than on additive functions of an interval in R_1. The difference is, of course, only formal, and all the definitions adopted for functions of an interval can be stated, with obvious modifications, in terms of functions of a real variable. We need not state them here explicitly. If F is a function of a real variable, of bounded variation, the meaning of expressions such as Lebesgue-Stieltjes integral with respect to F, integral (F), sets ($\mathfrak{L}_F$), and so on, may be regarded as absolutely clear, in view of the definitions of § 5. If F is a continuous function and g a function integrable (F), the integral $\int_I g dF$, where I is a variable interval, is an additive continuous function of an interval I (*vide* § 5, p. 65). There is, consequently, a continuous function of a real variable whose increment on any interval I coincides with the definite integral (F) of g over I. This function, which is determined uniquely except for an additive constant, is also termed *indefinite integral* (F) *of g*.

When there is no ambiguity, the additive function of an interval that is determined by a finite function of a real variable F, will be denoted by the same letter F, i. e. $F(I)$ will stand for the increment of $F(x)$ on an interval I. By means of the corresponding function of an interval, any function of a real variable F of bounded variation determines an additive function of a set which we denote by F^* (cf. § 5). We see at once that $F^*(X)=F(b+)-F(a-)$ when $X=[a, b]$, and that $F^*(X)=F(a+)-F(a-)$ when $X=(a)$, i. e. when X is the set consisting of a single point a.

If $W(x)$ is the absolute variation of a function $F(x)$ of bounded variation, we clearly have $\mathrm{W}(F^*; X)\leqslant W^*(X)$ for every set X bounded and measurable ($\mathfrak{B}$). The opposite inequality does not hold in general. If, for instance, X is a set consisting of one point only, and F is the characteristic function of X, then $\mathrm{W}(F^*; X)= =F^*(X)=0$, while $W^*(X)=2$. We can, however, state the following theorem:

(13.2) ***Theorem.*** *If $F(x)$ is a function of a real variable of bounded variation, and $W(x)$ is the absolute variation of $F(x)$, then $\mathrm{W}(F^*; X)= =W^*(X)$ for every set X bounded and measurable ($\mathfrak{B}$) at all points of which $F(x)$ is continuous.*

Proof. Suppose first that the set X is contained in an open interval J_0 in which the function $F(x)$, and consequently the function $W(x)$ also, is continuous. Let $G\subset J_0$ be an arbitrary open set such that $X\subset G$. Then, expressing G as the sum of a sequence of closed non-overlapping intervals $\{I_n\}$, we get $W^*(X)\leqslant W^*(G)=\sum_n W^*(I_n)= =\sum_n W(I_n)\leqslant\sum_n \mathrm{W}(F^*; I_n)=\mathrm{W}(F^*; G)$; whence $W^*(X)\leqslant \mathrm{W}(F^*; X)$, and since the opposite inequality is obvious, $W^*(X)=\mathrm{W}(F^*; X)$.

Let us pass now to the general case. Let I_0 be an interval containing X in its interior, and let $\varepsilon>0$. Denote by $\{a_n\}$ the sequence of points of discontinuity of $F(x)$ interior to I_0, and by $S_N(x)$ the saltus-function of $F(x)$ corresponding to the points a_n for $n>N$. Let us put $G(x)=F(x)-S_N(x)$, where N is a positive integer sufficiently large in order that $\mathrm{W}(S_N; I_0)\leqslant\varepsilon$. The points $a_1, a_2, ..., a_N$, none of which belongs to X, divide I_0 into a finite number of subintervals $J_0, J_1, ..., J_N$ in the interior of which the function $G(x)$ is continuous. Hence, denoting by $V(x)$ the absolute variation of

$G(x)$, there follows, by what has already been proved, $V^*(X \cdot J_k) = \mathrm{W}(G^*; X \cdot J_k)$ for $k = 0, 1, \ldots, N$, whence $V^*(X) = \mathrm{W}(G^*; X)$. On the other hand, $|W^*(X) - V^*(X)|$ and $|\mathrm{W}(F^*; X) - \mathrm{W}(G^*; X)$ are both at most equal to $\mathrm{W}(S_N; I_0) \leqslant \varepsilon$. Thus $|W^*(X) - \mathrm{W}(F^*; X)| \leqslant 2\varepsilon$, and finally $W^*(X) = \mathrm{W}(F^*; X)$.

If $F(x)$ is a finite function of a real variable and E an arbitrary set in $\boldsymbol{R}_1$, the set of the values of $F(x)$ for $x \in E$ will be denoted by $F[E]$.

(13.3) ***Theorem.*** *If $F(x)$ is a function of a real variable of bounded variation and $\mathrm{W}(x)$ is the absolute variation of $F(x)$, then $|F[E]| \leqslant W^*(E)$ for every set E in $\boldsymbol{R}_1$; and if further the function $F(x)$ is non-decreasing, and continuous at all points of E, then $|F[E]| = F^*(E)$.*

Proof. Let ε be a positive number and $\{I_n\}$ a sequence of intervals such that $E \subset \sum_n I_n$ and $W^*(E) + \varepsilon \geqslant \sum_n W(I_n)$. Then, if m_n and M_n denote the lower and upper bounds, respectively, of $F(x)$ on I_n, the sequence of intervals $\{[m_n, M_n]\}$ covers the set $F[E]$, and consequently $|F[E]| \leqslant \sum_n (M_n - m_n) \leqslant \sum_n W(I_n) \leqslant W^*(E) + \varepsilon$. Hence, $|F[E]| \leqslant W^*(E)$.

Suppose now $F(x)$ continuous at the points of E and non-decreasing. By what has already been proved, $|F[E]| \leqslant F^*(E)$. To establish the opposite inequality, let η be an arbitrary positive number, and $\{J_n\}$ a sequence of intervals subject to the conditions $F[E] \subset \sum_n J_n$ and $|F[E]| + \eta \geqslant \sum_n |J_n|$. Let E_n denote the set of the points $x \in E$ such that $F(x) \in J_n$. Then $F^*(E_n) \leqslant |J_n|$ for each n; and consequently $F^*(E) \leqslant \sum_n |J_n| \leqslant |F[E]| + \eta$, whence $F^*(E) \leqslant |F[E]|$.

The characteristic function of a set consisting of a single point provides the simplest example of a singular function of a real variable, that does not vanish identically. This function is however discontinuous. It is easy to give examples of functions of an interval that are additive, singular, continuous, and not identically zero, in the spaces $\boldsymbol{R}_m$ for $m \geqslant 2$. For simplicity, consider the plane, and denote, for any interval I, by $F(I)$ the length of the segment of the line $y = x$ contained in I; the function of an interval $F(I)$ will evidently have the desired properties. A similar example for $\boldsymbol{R}_1$ is less trivial. We shall therefore conclude this § with a short description of an elementary method for the construction of continuous singular functions of a real variable.

We shall begin with the following remark which frequently proves useful.

(13.4) *Let E be a linear, bounded, perfect and non-dense set, and α and $\beta>\alpha$ two arbitrary numbers. Then, if a and b denote the lower and upper bounds of E, a function $F(x)$ may be defined on the interval $J_0=[a, b]$ so as to satisfy the following conditions:* (i) $F(a)=\alpha$, $F(b)=\beta$, (ii) *$F(x)$ is constant on each interval contiguous to the set E, and* (iii) *$F(x)$ is continuous and non-decreasing on the interval J_0 and strictly increasing on the set E.*

To see this, let $\{I_n\}$ be the sequence of intervals contiguous to E, and let us agree to write $I_n \lessdot I_m$ whenever the interval I_n is situated on the left of I_m. By induction (cf. e. g. F. Hausdorff [II, p. 50]) we can easily establish a one-to-one correspondence between the intervals I_n and the rational numbers of the open interval (α, β) so that, denoting by $u(I_n)$ the number which corresponds to the interval I_n, the relation $I_n \lessdot I_m$ implies $u(I_n)<u(I_m)$. Let us now put $F(x)=u(I_n)$ for $x \in I_n$ where $n=1, 2, \ldots$, and then extend $F(x)$ by continuity to the whole of the interval J_0. We see at once that the function $F(x)$ thus obtained satisfies all the required conditions (i), (ii) and (iii) of (13.4).

Now let us choose for the set E in (13.4) a set of measure zero. Then if $\{I_n\}$ is the sequence of the intervals contiguous to E, we have

$$W(F; \sum_{k=1}^{n} I_k)=\sum_{k=1}^{n} W(F; I_k)=0$$

for each positive integer n; and since $|J_0-\sum_{k=1}^{n} I_k| \to 0$ as $n \to \infty$, the function $F(x)$ is evidently singular on the interval J_0.

The singular function obtained by the foregoing construction is continuous and monotone non-decreasing; the function is not constant on the whole interval J_0, but is so on certain partial intervals. Now, by the method of condensation of singularities, it is easy to derive from it a singular continuous function that increases everywhere.

To do this, suppose in (13.4), $|E|=0$, $a=\alpha=0$, $b=\beta=1$, and extend the function $F(x)$ on to the whole axis $\boldsymbol{R}_1$ by stipulating $F(x+1)=1+F(x)$. Write

$$H(x)=\sum_{n=1}^{\infty} \frac{F(nx)}{2^n}. \tag{13.5}$$

This series is a uniformly convergent series of singular functions, since $F(nx)$ is clearly singular with $F(x)$. Now the functions $F(nx)$ are monotone non-decreasing. By Theorem 12.1 (3°), the function $H(x)$ is thus singular. This function is also continuous, as the limit of a uniformly convergent series. To prove that $H(x)$ is strictly increasing, let x_1 and $x_2>x_1$ denote an arbitrary pair of points in $[0, 1]$. For $n>1/(x_2-x_1)$, we have $nx_2-nx_1>1$, and consequently $F(nx_2)>F(nx_1)$; while for every n, $F(nx_2) \geqslant F(nx_1)$, whence by (13.5), $H(x_2)>H(x_1)$ as asserted.

Various examples of this kind have been constructed by A. Denjoy [1], W. Sierpiński [3], H. Hahn [I, p. 538], L. C. Young [1] and G. Vitali [4]; cf. also O. D. Kellog [1], and E. Hille and J. D. Tamarkin [1].

§ 14. Integration by parts. As in the preceding §, we shall deal only in this § with functions of a real variable. For the latter, we shall establish two classical theorems, of importance on account of their many applications to various branches of Analysis. We shall first prove them for the Lebesgue-Stieltjes integral and then specialize them for the ordinary Lebesgue integral.

(14.1) ***Theorem on integration by parts.*** *If $U(x)$ and $V(x)$ are two functions of bounded variation, we have for every interval $I_0=[a,b]$*

$$\int_a^b U\,dV+\int_a^b V\,dU=U(b+)V(b+)-U(a-)V(a-),$$

provided that at each point of I_0 either one at least of the functions U and V is continuous, or both are regular.

Proof. In order to simplify the notation assume $a=0$ and $b=1$, and consider the triangle $Q=\underset{(x,y)}{\mathrm{E}}[0\leqslant x\leqslant 1; y\leqslant x]$ on the plane $\boldsymbol{R}_2$. The set $\underset{x}{\mathrm{E}}[(x,y)\,\epsilon\,Q]$ is then the interval $[y,1]$ or the empty set, according as y belongs, or does not belong, to the interval $[0,1]$. Similarly, $\underset{y}{\mathrm{E}}[(x,y)\,\epsilon\,Q]$ is the interval $[0,x]$ or the empty set, according as we have, or do not have, $0\leqslant x\leqslant 1$. Hence, by Fubini's theorem in the form (8.6),

$$\int_0^1[U(1+)-U(y-)]\,dV(y)=\int_0^1[V(x+)-V(0-)]\,dU(x),$$

i. e.

$$\text{(14.2)}\quad \int_0^1 U(x-)\,dV(x)+\int_0^1 V(x+)\,dU(x)=U(1+)V(1+)-U(0-)V(0-).$$

Interchanging U and V and adding the corresponding equation to (14.2), we get, on dividing by 2,

$$\text{(14.3)}\quad \int_0^1 \tfrac{1}{2}[U(x+)+U(x-)]\,dV(x)+\int_0^1 \tfrac{1}{2}[V(x+)+V(x-)]\,dU(x)=$$
$$=U(1+)V(1+)-U(0-)V(0-).$$

Let M be the set of the points in $I_0=[0,1]$ at which the function $U(x)$ is regular. Then

$$\text{(14.4)}\quad \int_M \tfrac{1}{2}[U(x+)+U(x-)]\,dV(x)=\int_M U(x)\,dV(x).$$

On the other hand, the set $I_0 - M$ is at most enumerable and, by hypothesis, the function $V(x)$, and consequently both its relative variations, are continuous at each point of $I_0 - M$. Thus, the definite integral (V) of any function over the set $I_0 - M$ is zero, and it follows from (14.4) that $\int_0^1 \frac{1}{2}[U(x+)+U(x-)]\,dV(x) = \int_0^1 U(x)\,dV(x)$. Similarly, the second member on the left-hand side of the relation (14.3) is equal to $\int_0^1 V(x)\,dU(x)$, and this relation may be written

$$\int_0^1 U\,dV + \int_0^1 V\,dU = U(1+)\,V(1+) - U(0-)\,V(0-),$$

which proves the theorem.

The theorem may be also proved independently of Fubini's theorem, but then the proof is slightly longer. The proof given above was communicated to the author by L. C. Young.

(14.5) ***Second Mean Value Theorem.*** *If $U(x)$ and $V(x)$ are two non-decreasing functions and the function $V(x)$ is continuous, then in any interval $[a, b]$ there exists a point ξ such that*

$$(14.6) \qquad \int_a^b U\,dV = U(a)\cdot[V(\xi) - V(a)] + U(b)\cdot[V(b) - V(\xi)].$$

Proof. Since the values of $U(x)$ outside the interval $[a, b]$ do not affect (14.6), we may suppose that $U(a-) = U(a)$ and, $U(b+) = U(b)$. Therefore, making use of Theorem 14.1 and of the first mean value theorem (Chap. I, Th. 11.13), we obtain

$$(14.7) \qquad \int_a^b U\,dV = U(b)\,V(b) - U(a)\,V(a) - \int_a^b V\,dU =$$
$$= U(b)\,V(b) - U(a)\,V(a) - \mu\cdot[U(b) - U(a)],$$

where μ is a number lying between the bounds of the function $V(x)$ on $[a, b]$. But, since this function is by hypothesis continuous, there exists in $[a, b]$ a point ξ such that $\mu = V(\xi)$. Substituting this value for μ in (14.7) we obtain the relation (14.6).

As a special case of Theorem 14.1 we have the following theorem on integration by parts for the Lebesgue integral:

(14.8) ***Theorem.*** *If $u(x)$ and $v(x)$ are two summable functions on an interval $[a, b]$ and $U(x)$ and $V(x)$ are their indefinite integrals* (L), *then*

$$(14.9) \qquad \int_b^b U(x)\,v(x)\,dx + \int_a^b V(x)\,u(x)\,dx = U(b)\cdot V(b) - U(a)\cdot V(a).$$

Proof. Observe first that by writing for instance $u(x)=0$ and $v(x)=0$ outside the interval $[a, b]$, we may suppose that the functions $u(x)$ and $v(x)$, and their indefinite integrals $U(x)$ and $V(x)$, are defined on the whole straight line $\boldsymbol{R}_1$. Also, by altering, if necessary, the values of the functions $u(x)$ and $v(x)$ on a set of measure (L) zero, which does not affect the values of the integrals in (14.9), we may suppose that these functions, together with the functions $U(x)\,v(x)$ and $V(x)\,u(x)$, are measurable ($\mathfrak{B}$) (cf. Theorem 7.6 of Vitali-Carathéodory or else Lusin's Theorem 7.1). We may, therefore write, according to Theorem 15.1, Chap. I,

$$\int_a^b U(x)v(x)\,dx = \int_a^b U(x)\,dV(x) \qquad \text{and} \qquad \int_a^b V(x)u(x)\,dx = \int_a^b V(x)\,dU(x),$$

and (14.9) follows at once from Theorem 14.1.

Similarly, we derive at once from Theorem 14.5 the *second mean value theorem for the Lebesgue integral*:

(14.10) ***Theorem.*** *If $U(x)$ is a non-decreasing function on an interval $[a, b]$ and $v(x)$ is a summable function on this interval, then*

$$\int_a^b U(x)\,v(x)\,dx = U(a)\int_a^{\xi} v(x)\,dx + U(b)\int_{\xi}^b v(x)\,dx,$$

where ξ is a point of $[a, b]$.

CHAPTER IV.

Derivation of additive functions of a set and of an interval.

§ 1. Introduction. In this chapter we shall study Lebesgue's theory of derivation of additive functions in a Euclidean space of any number of dimensions. When other spaces are considered, or when we specialize our space (to be, say, the straight line $\boldsymbol{R}_1$ or the plane $\boldsymbol{R}_2$), we shall say so explicitly.

In what follows, an essential part is played by Vitali's Covering Theorem (*vide*, below, § 3) which is restricted to the case of Lebesgue measure. For this reason, the theorems of the present chapter have not in general any complete or direct extension to other measures, not even when the latter are determined by additive functions of an interval. In accordance with the conventions of § 5, Chap. III, the terms measure, integral, almost everywhere, etc. will be understood in the Lebesgue sense whenever we do not explicitly assign another meaning to them. Similarly, by additive functions of a set we shall always mean functions of a set ($\mathfrak{B}$) (some of which may of course be continued on to wider classes of sets, cf. Chap. III, § 5).

We have already remarked in § 1, Chap. I, that any additive function of a set Φ in a space $\boldsymbol{R}_m$, may be regarded as a distribution of mass. It is then natural to consider the limit of the ratio $\Phi(S)/|S|$ where S denotes a cube, or a sphere, with a fixed centre a and with diameter tending to 0, as the density of the mass at the point a. By the fundamental theorem of Lebesgue (*vide*, below, Theorem 5.4) this limit exists almost everywhere. Moreover Lebesgue has shown that in the above ratio, S may be taken to denote much more general sets than cubes or spheres. Of these, further details will be given in the next §.

§ 2. Derivates of functions of a set and of an interval.

Suppose given a Euclidean space R_m. By *parameter of regularity* $\mathrm{r}(E)$ of a set E lying in this space, we shall mean the lower bound of the numbers $|E|/|J|$ where J denotes any cube containing E. Thus when E is an interval, $l^m/L^m \leqslant \mathrm{r}(E) \leqslant l/L$, where l denotes the smallest and L the largest of the edges of E; in particular, the parameter of regularity of a cube is equal to 1.

A sequence of sets $\{E_n\}$ will be termed *regular*, if there exists a positive number α such that $\mathrm{r}(E_n) > \alpha$ for $n=1, 2, \ldots$.

We shall say that a sequence of sets $\{E_n\}$ *tends* to a point a, if $\delta(E_n) \to 0$ as $n \to \infty$, and the point a belongs to all the sets of the sequence.

Given a function of a set Φ (not necessarily additive) we call *general upper derivate* of Φ at a point a the upper bound of the numbers l such that there exists a regular sequence of closed sets $\{E_n\}$ tending to a, for which $\lim\limits_n \Phi(E_n)/|E_n| = l$. We shall denote this derivate by $\overline{\mathrm{D}}\Phi(a)$. Similarly, merely replacing the closed sets by intervals, we define the *ordinary upper derivate* of Φ at a point a, and we denote it by $\overline{\Phi}(a)$. If we remove the condition of regularity of the sequences of intervals considered, we obtain the definition of strong upper derivate. In other words the *strong upper derivate* of Φ at a point a is the upper limit of the ratio $\Phi(I)/|I|$, where I is any interval containing a, whose diameter tends to zero. This derivate will be denoted by $\overline{\Phi}_s(a)$.

The three *lower* derivates at a point a, general $\underline{\mathrm{D}}\Phi(a)$, ordinary $\underline{\Phi}(a)$, and strong $\underline{\Phi}_s(a)$, have corresponding definitions, and if at a point a the numbers $\underline{\mathrm{D}}\Phi(a)$ and $\overline{\mathrm{D}}\Phi(a)$ are equal, their common value is termed *general derivative* of Φ at the point a and will be denoted by $\mathrm{D}\Phi(a)$. If further $\mathrm{D}\Phi(a) \neq \infty$, the function Φ is said to be *derivable in the general sense* at the point a. Similarly we define the *ordinary derivative* $\Phi'(a)$ and the *strong derivative* $\Phi'_s(a)$, as well as *derivability in the ordinary sense*, and *in the strong sense*, of the function Φ at the point a. Sometimes the derivatives $\mathrm{D}\Phi(a)$, $\Phi'(a)$ and $\Phi_s(a)$ are termed *unique* derivates, while the upper and lower derivates (general, ordinary and strong) are termed *extreme* derivates. At any point a, we clearly have $\underline{\mathrm{D}}\Phi(a) \leqslant \underline{\Phi}(a) \leqslant \overline{\Phi}(a) \leqslant \overline{\mathrm{D}}\Phi(a)$ and similarly $\underline{\Phi}_s(a) \leqslant \underline{\Phi}(a) \leqslant \overline{\Phi}(a) \leqslant \overline{\Phi}_s(a)$; so that the existence either of a general derivative, or of a strong derivative, always implies that of an ordinary derivative. On the other hand, no such relation holds between the general and the strong extreme derivates.

It may be noted that in order that it be possible to determine the general derivates of a function of a set Φ, the latter must be defined at any rate for all closed sets; whereas in order to determine the extreme ordinary derivates, or the extreme strong derivates, we need only have the function Φ defined for the intervals. This is why the process of general derivation is most frequently applied to additive functions of a set, and that of ordinary, or of strong, derivation to functions of an interval. We shall often omit the terms "ordinary", "in the ordinary sense", in expressions such as "ordinary derivate", "derivability in the ordinary sense".

We have seen (Chap. III, § 5) that an additive function of an interval F of bounded variation determines an additive function of a set F^*. Let us mention, in the case in which the function F is non-negative, an almost evident relation between ordinary derivates of F and general derivates of F^*:

(2.1) ***Theorem.*** *If F is an additive non-negative function of an interval, then, at any point x, which belongs to no hyperplane of discontinuity of F, we have* $\underline{\mathrm{D}}F^*(x)\leqslant\underline{F}(x)\leqslant\overline{F}(x)\leqslant\overline{\mathrm{D}}F^*(x)$.

In particular therefore, the ordinary derivative $F'(x)=\mathrm{D}F^*(x)$ exists at almost every point x at which F^* has a general derivative.

Proof. Since $F(I)\leqslant F^*(I)$ for any interval I, the inequality $\overline{F}(x)\leqslant\overline{\mathrm{D}}F^*(x)$ is obvious. On the other hand, let l denote any number exceeding $\underline{F}(x)$. Then there exists a regular sequence of intervals $\{I_n\}$ tending to the point x and such that $\lim\limits_n F(I_n)/|I_n|<l$. Since x does not belong to any plane of discontinuity of F, we may asssume that it is an internal point of all the intervals I_n. Hence we can make correspond to each interval I_n an interval $J_n\subset I_n^\circ$ such that $x\in J_n$, $|J_n|\geqslant(1-1/n)\cdot|I_n|$ and $\mathrm{r}(J_n)=\mathrm{r}(I_n)$. We then have $\limsup\limits_n F^*(J_n)/|J_n|\leqslant\lim\limits_n F(I_n)/|I_n|<l$. Now since $\{J_n\}$ is a regular sequence of intervals tending to x, it follows that $\underline{\mathrm{D}}F^*(x)\leqslant l$, and therefore that $\underline{\mathrm{D}}F^*(x)\leqslant\underline{F}(x)$.

Let us note also the following result:

(2.2) ***Theorem.*** *If f is a summable function and Φ is the indefinite integral of f, then $\overline{\mathrm{D}}\Phi(x)\leqslant f(x)$ and $\overline{\Phi}_s(x)\leqslant f(x)$ at any point x at which the function f is upper semi-continuous, and similarly $\underline{\mathrm{D}}\Phi(x)\geqslant f(x)$ and $\underline{\Phi}_s(x)\geqslant f(x)$ at any point x at which the function f is lower semi-continuous.*

In particular therefore, $\Phi'(x)=\Phi_s'(x)=\mathrm{D}\Phi(x)=f(x)$ at any point x at which the function f is continuous.

In R_1 there is no difference between ordinary and strong derivation. If $F(x)$ is a finite function of a real variable, we understand by its *extreme derivates* $\overline{F}(x)$ and $\underline{F}(x)$, and by its *derivative*, or *unique derivate*, $F'(x)$, the corresponding derivates of the function of an interval that $F(x)$ determines (cf. Chap. III, § 13). Besides these derivates, which we shall often term *bilateral*, we also define, for functions of a real variable, unilateral derivatives and derivates. Thus, if $F(x)$ is a finite function of a real variable defined in the neighbourhood of a point x_0, the upper limit of $[F(x)-F(x_0)]/(x-x_0)$ as x tends to x_0 by values of $x>x_0$ is called *right-hand upper derivate* of the function F at the point x_0 and is denoted by $\overline{F}^+(x_0)$. Similarly we define at the point x_0 the *right-hand lower derivate* $\underline{F}^+(x_0)$ and the two *left-hand, upper* and *lower, derivates*, $\overline{F}^-(x_0)$ and $\underline{F}^-(x_0)$. These four derivates are called *unilateral extreme*, or *Dini, derivates*. If the two derivates on one side (right or left) are equal, their common value is called *unilateral* (*right-hand* or *left-hand*) *derivative* of the function F at the point in question. Finally, we shall call *intermediate derivate* of $F(x)$ at the point x_0, any number l such that there exists a sequence $\{x_n\}$ of points distinct from x_0 for which $\lim_n x_n = x_0$ and $\lim_n [F(x_n)-F(x_0)]/(x_n-x_0)=l$.

Let E be a linear set, x_0 a point of accumulation of E, and $F(x)$ a finite function defined on E and at the point x_0. The upper and lower limit of the ratio $[F(x)-F(x_0)]/(x-x_0)$ as x tends to x_0 by values belonging to the set E, are called respectively the *upper* and *lower derivate* of F at x_0, *relative to the set E*. We shall denote them respectively by $\overline{F}_E(x_0)$ and $\underline{F}_E(x_0)$. When they are equal, their common value is termed *derivative* of F at x_0 *relative to the set E*, and is denoted by $F'_E(x_0)$.

Besides this derivation relative to a set, we define also derivation relative to a function. Suppose given two finite functions $F(x)$ and $U(x)$, and let x_0 be a point such that the function U is not identically constant in any interval containing x_0. We then call *upper derivate* $\overline{F}_U(x_0)$ and *lower derivate* $\underline{F}_U(x_0)$ of the function F *with respect to the function U* at the point x_0, the upper limit and the lower limit of the ratio $[F(x)-F(x_0)]/[U(x)-U(x_0)]$ as x tends to x_0 by values other than those for which $F(x)-F(x_0)=$ $=U(x)-U(x_0)=0$. Similarly, considering unilateral limits of the same ratio, we define four *Dini derivates* of F *with respect to U:* $\overline{F}^+_U(x)$, $\underline{F}^+_U(x)$, $\overline{F}^-_U(x)$ and $\underline{F}_U(x)$.

When all these extreme derivates are equal, their common value is denoted by $F'_U(x_0)$ and called *derivative* of F *with respect to the function* U at the point x_0. The most usual case in which this method of derivation is applied, is when U is a monotone increasing function; and it is then easy, by change of variable, to reduce derivation with respect to U to ordinary derivation.

§ 3. Vitali's Covering Theorem. We shall say that a family $\mathfrak{E}$ of sets covers a set A *in the sense of Vitali*, if for every point x of A there exists a regular sequence of sets ($\mathfrak{E}$) tending to x (cf. p. 106).

(3.1) ***Vitali's Covering Theorem.*** *If in the space* $\boldsymbol{R}_m$ *a family of closed sets* $\mathfrak{E}$ *covers in the sense of Vitali a set* A, *then there exists in* $\mathfrak{E}$ *a finite or enumerable sequence* $\{E_n\}$ *of sets no two of which have common points, such that*

(3.2) $$|A-\sum_n E_n|=0.$$

Proof. a) We first prove the theorem in the special case in which (i) the parameters of regularity of all the sets ($\mathfrak{E}$) exceed a fixed number $\alpha>0$ and (ii) the set A is bounded i. e. contained in an open sphere S. We may clearly assume that, in addition, all the sets ($\mathfrak{E}$) are also contained in S.

This being so, we shall define the required sequence $\{E_n\}$ by induction in the following manner.

For E_1 we choose an arbitrary set ($\mathfrak{E}$), and when the first p sets $E_1, E_2, \ldots, E_p$ no two of which have common points, have been defined, we denote by δ_p the upper bound of the diameters of all the sets ($\mathfrak{E}$) which have no points in common with $\sum_{i=1}^{p} E_i$, and by E_{p+1} any one of these sets with diameter exceeding $\delta_p/2$. Such a set must exist, unless the sets $E_1, E_2, \ldots, E_p$ already cover the whole of the set A, in which case they constitute the sequence whose existence was to be established. We may therefore suppose that this induction can be continued indefinitely.

To show that the infinite sequence $\{E_n\}$ thus defined covers A almost entirely, let us write

(3.3) $$B=A-\sum_n E_n$$

and suppose, if possible, that $|B|>0$. On account of condition (i), we can associate with each set E_n a cube J_n such that $E_n\subset J_n$ and

$|E_n| > \alpha \cdot |J_n|$. Let $\tilde{J}_n$ denote the cube with the same centre as J_n and with diameter $(4m+1)\,\delta(J_n)$. The series

(3.4) $$\sum_n |\tilde{J}_n| = (4m+1)^m \cdot \alpha^{-1} \cdot \sum_n |J_n| \leqslant (4m+1)^m \cdot \alpha^{-1} \cdot \sum_n |E_n| \leqslant (4m+1)^m \cdot \alpha^{-1} \cdot |S|$$

converges; therefore we can find an integer N such that $\sum_{n=N+1}^{\infty} |\tilde{J}_n| < |B|$. It follows that there exists a point $x_0 \in B$ not belonging to any $\tilde{J}_n$ for $n > N$; and since by (3.3) the point x_0 does not belong to $\sum_n E_n$ and the sets E_n are supposed closed, there must exist in $\mathfrak{E}$ a set E containing x_0 and such that

(3.5) $$E \cdot E_n = 0 \qquad \textit{for} \quad n = 1, 2, \ldots, N.$$

Hence the set E has common points with at least one of the sets E_n for $n > N$; for otherwise we should have $0 < \delta(E) \leqslant \delta_n \leqslant 2\delta(E_{n+1}) \leqslant \leqslant 2\delta(J_{n+1})$ for every positive integer n, and this is clearly impossible since by (3.4) we have $\lim_n \delta(J_n) = 0$. Let n_0 be the smallest of the values of n for which $E \cdot E_n \neq 0$. Then on the one hand, $E \cdot E_n = 0$ for $n = 1, 2, \ldots, n_0 - 1$, so that

(3.6) $$\delta(E) \leqslant \delta_{n_0 - 1};$$

and on the other hand, by (3.5), $n_0 > N$, which implies, by definition of x_0, that x_0 does not belong to $\tilde{J}_{n_0}$. Thus we find that there are both some points outside $\tilde{J}_{n_0}$ and some points belonging to the set $E_{n_0} \subset J_{n_0}$, which are contained in the set E; this set must therefore have diameter exceeding $2\delta(J_{n_0}) \geqslant 2\delta(E_{n_0}) > \delta_{n_0 - 1}$, in contradiction to (3.6). The assumption that $|B| > 0$ thus leads to a contradiction and this proves the theorem, subject to the additional hypotheses (i) and (ii).

b) Now let $\mathfrak{E}$ be any family of closed sets covering the set A in the sense of Vitali; and let us denote, for any positive integer n, by S_n the sphere $S(0; n)$ and by A_n the set of the points $x \in A \cdot S_n$ for which there exists a sequence of sets tending to x and consisting of sets $(\mathfrak{E})$ whose parameters of regularity exceed $1/n$. The sets A_n constitute an ascending sequence and $A = \lim_n A_n$.

We can now define by induction a sequence of families of sets $\{\mathfrak{T}_n\}$ subject to the following conditions: 1° each family $\mathfrak{T}_n$ consists of a finite number of sets $(\mathfrak{E})$ no two of which have common points and none of which, for $n > 1$, have points in common with the sets of preceding families $\mathfrak{T}_1, \mathfrak{T}_2, \ldots, \mathfrak{T}_{n-1}$; 2° denoting by T_n the sum of the sets which belong to $\mathfrak{T}_n$,

$$(3.7) \qquad |A_n - \sum_{i=1}^{n} T_i| < 1/n.$$

To see this, suppose that for $n \leqslant p$ we have determined families $\mathfrak{T}_n$ subject to 1° and 2°. Write $\widetilde{A}_{p+1} = A_{p+1} - \sum_{i=1}^{p} T_i$, and consider the family of all the sets ($\mathfrak{E}$) which are contained in the open set $\mathrm{C}\sum_{i=1}^{p} T_i$ and whose parameters of regularity exceed $1/(p+1)$. This family evidently covers the set $\widetilde{A}_{p+1} \subset A_{p+1} \subset S_{p+1}$ in the sense of Vitali, and by what we have already proved we can extract from it a sequence $\{\widetilde{E}_i\}$ of sets, no two of which have common points, so as to cover $\widetilde{A}_{p+1}$ almost entirely. Therefore, for a sufficiently large index i_0,

$$|A_{p+1} - \sum_{i=1}^{p} T_i - \sum_{i=1}^{i_0} \widetilde{E}_i| = |\widetilde{A}_{p+1} - \sum_{i=1}^{i_0} \widetilde{E}_i| < 1/(p+1),$$

and, denoting by $\mathfrak{T}_{p+1}$ the family consisting of the sets $\widetilde{E}_1, \widetilde{E}_2, \ldots, \widetilde{E}_{i_0}$, we find that conditions 1° and 2° hold when $n = p+1$.

Let us now write $\mathfrak{T} = \sum_n \mathfrak{T}_n$. The family $\mathfrak{T}$ consists of a finite number, or of an enumerable infinity, of sets ($\mathfrak{E}$) no two of which have common points. Denoting the sum of these sets by T, we find, by (3.7), $|A - T| = 0$ and this completes the proof.

The proof given above is due to S. Banach [3] (for other proofs cf. C. Carathéodory [II, pp. 299—307] and T. Radó [3]).

Theorem 3.1 was proved by G. Vitali [3] in a slightly less general form; he assumed the family $\mathfrak{E}$ to consist of cubes. H. Lebesgue [5] while retaining the line of argument of Vitali, showed that the conclusion drawn by Vitali could be generalized as follows:

(3.8) ***Theorem.*** *Given a set A and a family $\mathfrak{E}$ of closed sets, suppose that with each point $x \in A$ we can associate a number $\alpha > 0$, a sequence $\{X_n\}$ of sets ($\mathfrak{E}$) and a sequence $\{J_n\}$ of cubes such that*

$$x \in J_n, \quad X_n \subset J_n, \quad |X_n| > \alpha \cdot |J_n| \quad \textit{for} \quad n = 1, 2, \ldots, \quad \textit{and} \quad \lim_n \delta(J_n) = 0.$$

Then $\mathfrak{E}$ contains a sequence of sets no two of which have common points, that covers the set A almost entirely.

This statement, although apparently more general than that of Theorem 3.1, easily reduces to the latter. For let us denote by $\mathfrak{E}^0$ the family of all the sets of the form $E+(x)$, where E is any set of $\mathfrak{E}$ and x any point of the set A. The family $\mathfrak{E}^0$ clearly covers the set A in the Vitali sense, and by Theorem 3.1 we can therefore extract from it a sequence $\{E_n^0\}$ of sets no two of which have common points and which covers the set A almost entirely. Now each set E_n^0 either already belongs to $\mathfrak{E}$, or becomes a set $(\mathfrak{E})$ as soon as we remove from it a suitably chosen point. Therefore, removing where necessary a point from each E_n^0, we obtain a sequence of sets $(\mathfrak{E})$ no two of which have common points and whose sum, since it differs from $\sum_n E_n^0$ by an at most enumerable set, covers A almost entirely.

For further generalizations of Vitali's theorem (which, again, can be proved without introducing fresh methods), see B. Jessen, J. Marcinkiewicz and A. Zygmund [1, p. 224].

It is easy to see that the hypothesis that the family $\mathfrak{E}$ covers the set A in the Vitali sense (and not merely in the ordinary sense) is essential for the validity of Theorem 3.1. But, as has been shown by S. Banach [1] and H. Bohr (*vide* C. Carathéodory [II, p. 689]), this hypothesis cannot be dispensed with in the theorem even in the case where $\mathfrak{E}$ is a family of intervals such that to each point x of the set A there corresponds a sequence $\{I_n\}$ of intervals belonging to $\mathfrak{E}$, of centre x and diameter $\delta(I_n)$ tending to zero as $n \to \infty$.

For covering theorems similar to that of Vitali and which correspond to linear measure (length, cf. Chap. II, § 9) of sets, *vide* W. Sierpiński [7], A. S. Besicovitch [1] and J. Gillis [1].

§ 4. Theorems on measurability of derivates. Of the two theorems which we shall establish in this §, the first is due to S. Banach [4, p. 174] (cf. also A. J. Ward [2, p. 177]) and concerns the extreme derivates of any function of an interval (not necessarily additive). We begin by proving the following lemma:

(4.1) ***Lemma.*** *Any set expressible as the sum of a family of intervals is measurable.*

Proof. Let $\mathfrak{J}$ be any family of intervals and let S be the sum of the intervals of $\mathfrak{J}$. Let $\mathfrak{C}$ denote the family of cubes each of which is contained in one at least of the intervals $(\mathfrak{J})$. The set S is clearly covered by $\mathfrak{C}$ in the Vitali sense and by Theorem 3.1, S is therefore expressible as the sum of a sequence of cubes $(\mathfrak{C})$ and of a set of measure zero. Therefore the set S is measurable, as asserted.

(4.2) ***Theorem.*** *If F is a function of an interval, its two extreme ordinary derivates $\overline{F}$ and $\underline{F}$ and its extreme strong derivates $\overline{F}_s$ and $\underline{F}_s$ are measurable.*

Proof. Let us take first the strong derivates of F, say $\overline{F}_s$. Let a be a finite number and P the set of the points x for which $\overline{F}_s(x) > a$. For any pair of positive integers h and k, let us denote by $P_{h,k}$ the sum of all the intervals I for which $\delta(I) \leqslant 1/k$ and $F(I)/|I| \geqslant a + 1/h$. We see at once that $P = \sum_h \prod_k P_{h,k}$. Now the sets $P_{h,k}$ are measurable on account of Lemma 4.1 and so is the set P. This proves $\overline{F}_s(x)$ to be a measurable function.

Consider next the ordinary upper derivate $\overline{F}$. As before let a be any finite number, and Q the set of the points x at which $\overline{F}(x) > a$. In order that a point x should belong to Q, it is clearly necessary and sufficient that there should exist a positive number α and a sequence $\{I_n\}$ of intervals tending to x such that $\mathrm{r}(I_n) \geqslant \alpha$ and $F(I_n)/|I_n| \geqslant a + \alpha$ for $n = 1, 2, \ldots$. Hence denoting for any pair of positive integers h, k by $Q_{h,k}$ the sum of the intervals I such that $\mathrm{r}(I) \geqslant 1/h$, $\delta(I) \leqslant 1/k$ and $F(I)/|I| \geqslant a + 1/h$, we find easily that $Q = \sum_h \prod_k Q_{h,k}$. Thus, since each set $Q_{h,k}$ is measurable by Lemma 4.1, so is also the set Q. The derivate $\overline{F}(x)$ is therefore measurable.

It follows in particular from Theorem 4.2 that the bilateral extreme derivates of any function of a real variable are measurable. The same is not true of unilateral extreme derivates. Nevertheless, as shown by S. Banach [2] (cf. also H. Auerbach [1]), these derivates are measurable whenever the given function is so. Similarly by a theorem of W. Sierpiński [8], the Dini derivates of a function measurable ($\mathfrak{B}$) are themselves measurable ($\mathfrak{B}$). These two results are included in the following proposition, from which they are obtained by choosing the class $\mathfrak{X}$ to be either $\mathfrak{L}$ or $\mathfrak{B}$.

(4.3) ***Theorem.*** *If $\mathfrak{X}$ is an additive class of sets in $\boldsymbol{R}_1$, which includes the sets measurable ($\mathfrak{B}$), the Dini derivates of any function of a real variable which is finite and measurable ($\mathfrak{X}$), are themselves measurable ($\mathfrak{X}$).*

Proof. If F is any finite function of a real variable, x any point and h, k any pair of positive integers subject to $k > h$, let us write $D_{h,k}(F; x)$ for the upper bound of the ratio $[F(t) - F(x)]/(t - x)$ when $x + 1/k < t < x + 1/h$. At any point x we clearly have

(4.4) $$\overline{F}^+(x) = \lim_h \lim_k D_{h,k}(F; x).$$

Now let a be any finite number and consider the set

(4.5) $$\mathop{\mathrm{E}}_x [D_{h,k}(F; x) > a].$$

We see at once that if the function F is constant on a set E, the set of the points x of E at which $D_{h,k}(F;x) > a$ is open in E (cf. Chap. II, p. 41). Thus the set (4.5), and consequently the expression $D_{h,k}(F;x)$ as function of x, is measurable ($\mathfrak{X}$) whenever the function F is finite, measurable ($\mathfrak{X}$) and assumes at most an enumerable infinity of distinct values.

This being so, let F be any finite function measurable ($\mathfrak{X}$). We can represent it as the limit of a uniformly convergent sequence $\{F_n\}$ of functions measurable ($\mathfrak{X}$) each of which assumes at most an enumerable infinity of distinct values: for instance we may write $F_n(x) = i/n$, when $i/n \leqslant F(x) < (i+1)/n$ for $i = \ldots -2, -1, 0, 1, 2, \ldots$. We then have $D_{h,k}(F;x) = \lim_n D_{h,k}(F_n;x)$, and since by the above the functions $D_{h,k}(F_n;x)$ are measurable ($\mathfrak{X}$) in x, so is $D_{h,k}(F;x)$. It follows at once from (4.4) that the derivate $\overline{F}^+(x)$ is also measurable ($\mathfrak{X}$), and this completes the proof.

§ 5. Lebesgue's Theorem. We shall establish in this § the fundamental theorem of Lebesgue on derivation of additive functions of a set and of additive functions of bounded variation of an interval.

(5.1) ***Lemma.*** *If for a non-negative additive function of a set Φ the inequality $\overline{\mathrm{D}}\Phi(x) \geqslant a$ holds at every point x of a set A, then*

$$\Phi(X) \geqslant a \cdot |A| \tag{5.2}$$

holds for every set $X \supset A$, bounded and measurable ($\mathfrak{B}$).

Proof. Let ε be any positive number and b any number less than a. By Theorems 6.5 and 6.10 of Chap. III, there exists a bounded open set G such that

$$X \subset G \quad \textit{and} \quad \Phi(X) \geqslant \Phi(G) - \varepsilon. \tag{5.3}$$

Let us denote by $\mathfrak{E}$ the family of closed sets $E \subset G$ for each of which $\Phi(E) \geqslant b \cdot |E|$. Since by hypothesis, $\overline{\mathrm{D}}\Phi(x) \geqslant a > b$ at any point $x \in A$, the family $\mathfrak{E}$ covers the set A in the Vitali sense, and by Theorem 3.1, we can extract from it a sequence $\{E_n\}$ of sets no two of which have common points, so as to cover almost entirely the set A. Therefore, on account of (5.3),

$$\Phi(X) \geqslant \Phi(G) - \varepsilon \geqslant \sum_n \Phi(E_n) - \varepsilon \geqslant b \cdot \sum_n |E_n| - \varepsilon \geqslant b \cdot |A| - \varepsilon.$$

In this we make $\varepsilon \to 0$ and $b \to a$, and (5.2) then follows at once.

(5.4) ***Lebesgue's Theorem.*** *An additive function of a set is almost everywhere derivable in the general sense. An additive function of bounded variation of an interval is almost everywhere derivable in the ordinary sense.*

Proof. On account of Theorem 2.1 we may restrict ourselves to non-negative additive functions of a set.

Let Φ be such a function and suppose that $\overline{\mathrm{D}}\Phi(x) > \underline{\mathrm{D}}\Phi(x)$ holds at each point x of a set A of positive measure. For any pair of positive integers h and k let us denote by $A_{h,k}$ the set of the points x of A for which $\overline{\mathrm{D}}\Phi(x) > (h+1)/k > h/k > \underline{\mathrm{D}}\Phi(x)$. We have $A = \sum_{h,k} A_{h,k}$, and therefore there exists a pair of integers h_0 and k_0 such that $|A_{h_0,k_0}| > 0$. Let us denote by B any bounded subset of A_{h_0,k_0} of positive outer measure. Let ε be any positive number and G a bounded open set such that

$$(5.5) \qquad B \subset G \qquad \textit{and} \qquad |G| \leqslant |B| + \varepsilon.$$

Consider the family of all closed sets $E \subset G$ for which $\Phi(E) \leqslant \frac{h_0}{k_0} \cdot |E|$. This family covers the set B in the Vitali sense, and therefore contains a sequence $\{E_n\}$ of sets no two of which have common points, which covers the set B almost entirely. Writing $Q = \sum_n E_n$ we find, on account of (5.5),

$$(5.6) \qquad \Phi(Q) = \sum_n \Phi(E_n) \leqslant \frac{h_0}{k_0} \cdot \sum_n |E_n| \leqslant \frac{h_0}{k_0} \cdot |G| \leqslant \frac{h_0}{k_0} \cdot (|B| + \varepsilon).$$

On the other hand, $\overline{\mathrm{D}}\Phi(x) \geqslant (h_0+1)/k_0$ at each point $x \in B$. Therefore, since all but a subset of measure zero of the set B is contained in the set Q, it follows from Lemma 5.1 that $\Phi(Q) \geqslant \frac{h_0+1}{k_0} \cdot |B|$, and therefore, on account of (5.6) that $(h_0+1) \cdot |B| \leqslant h_0 \cdot (|B| + \varepsilon)$. But this is clearly a contradiction since $|B| > 0$ and ε is an arbitrary positive number.

Thus the function Φ has almost everywhere a general derivative $\mathrm{D}\Phi$. It remains to prove that the latter is almost everywhere finite. Suppose the contrary: there would then exist a sphere S such that $\mathrm{D}\Phi(x) = +\infty$ at any point x of a subset of S of positive measure. We should then have, by Lemma 5.1, $\Phi(S) = +\infty$, which is impossible and completes the proof.

The preceding theorem was proved by H. Lebesgue [I, p. 128] first for continuous functions of a real variable and later [5, p. 408—425] for additive functions of a set in $\boldsymbol{R}_n$. Among the many memoirs devoted to simplifying the proof we may mention: G. Faber [1], W. H. and G. C. Young [1], H. Steinhaus [1], Ch. J. de la Vallée Poussin [1, I; p. 103], A. Rajchman and S. Saks [1], J. Ridder [3] (cf. also the direct proof of Lebesgue's theorem for additive functions of bounded variation of an interval in the first edition of this book). More recently F. Riesz [6; 7] has given an elegant proof of Lebesgue's theorem for functions of a real variable. Finally S. Banach [4, p. 177] has extended the theorem in question to a class of functions of an interval which is slightly wider than that of additive functions of bounded variation. The proof given here applies also without any essential modification to the theorem of Banach.

For an extension of the theorem to certain abstract spaces, see J. A. Clarkson [1] (cf. also S. Bochner [3]).

Another application of Lemma 5.1 is the proof of the following theorem *on term by term derivation of monotone sequences of additive functions*:

(5.7) ***Theorem.*** *If an additive function of a set Φ is the limit of a monotone sequence $\{\Phi_n\}$ of additive functions of a set, then almost everywhere $D\Phi(x) = \lim_n D\Phi_n(x)$.*

In the same way, if an additive function of bounded variation of an interval, F, is the limit of a monotone sequence $\{F_n\}$ of additive functions of bounded variation of an interval, then almost everywhere $F'(x) = \lim_n F'_n(x)$.

Proof. Suppose, to fix the ideas, that the sequence $\{\Phi_n\}$ is non-decreasing and write $\Theta_n = \Phi - \Phi_n$. To establish the first part of the theorem, we need only show that

$$\lim_n \overline{D}\Theta_n(x) = 0 \tag{5.8}$$

almost everywhere.

For this purpose, let A denote the set of the points x at which (5.8) is not satisfied and suppose that $|A| > 0$. For any positive integer k we write A_k for the set of the points x at which $\lim_n \overline{D}\Theta_n(x) \geqslant 1/k$. Since $A = \sum_k A_k$, there is an index $k = k_0$ such that $|A_{k_0}| > 0$. Let B denote any bounded subset of A_{k_0} of positive measure and I an interval containing B. Since the sequence $\{\Theta_n\}$ is non-increasing, so is the sequence $\{\overline{D}\Theta_n\}$ and therefore we must have $\overline{D}\Theta_n(x) \geqslant 1/k_0$ for $n = 1, 2, \ldots$ at any point $x \in B \subset A_{k_0}$. Hence by Lemma 5.1, we find

$\Theta_n(I) \geqslant |B|/k_0$ for every positive integer n, and this is clearly a contradiction since $|B| > 0$ and $\lim_n \Theta_n(I) = \Phi(I) - \lim_n \Phi_n(I) = 0$.

We might prove similarly the second part of the theorem, but actually the latter can be reduced at once to the first part. In fact if we suppose the given sequence $\{F_n\}$ non-decreasing and write $T_n = F - F_n$, then the functions of an interval, T_n, are non-negative and the sequence $\{T_n(I)\}$ converges to 0 in a non-increasing manner for every interval I. The sequence $\{T_n^*\}$ of additive and non-negative functions of a set is then also non-increasing and converges to 0 (cf. Chap. III, Theorem 6.2). Hence, by the first part of our theorem and by Theorem 2.1, we have $\lim_n T_n'(x) = \lim_n \mathrm{D}T_n^*(x) = 0$, and therefore $\lim_n F_n'(x) = F'(x)$, for almost all x, which completes the proof.

For functions of a real variable, Theorem 5.7 may be stated in the following form (*vide* G. Fubini [2]; cf. also L. Tonelli [3] and F. Riesz [6; 7]):

If $F(x) = \sum_n F_n(x)$ *is a convergent series of monotone non-decreasing functions, then the relation* $F'(x) = \sum_n F_n'(x)$ *holds almost everywhere.*

§ 6. Derivation of the indefinite integral. Given a set A, let us write $\mathrm{L}_A(X) = |A \cdot X|$ for every measurable set X. The function L_A of a measurable set, thus defined, is termed *measure-function* for the set A. Considered as function of a measurable set, or as function of an interval, L_A is additive and absolutely continuous; and, if further the set A is measurable, we have $\mathrm{L}_A(X) = \int_X \mathrm{c}_A(x)\,dx$ for every measurable set X, i. e. the function L_A is the indefinite integral of the characteristic function of the set A.

(6.1) ***Theorem.*** *For any set A we have*

$$\mathrm{D}\mathrm{L}_A(x) = \mathrm{c}_A(x) \tag{6.2}$$

at almost all x of A; and if further, the set A is measurable, then (6.2) *holds almost everywhere in the whole space.*

Proof. By Theorem 6.7 of Chap. III the set A can be enclosed in a set $H \in \mathfrak{G}_\delta$ for which the measure-function is the same as for the set A. Let us write $H = \prod_n G_n$, where $\{G_n\}$ is a descending sequence of open sets. We clearly have $DL_{G_n}(x)=1$ at any point $x \epsilon G_n$, and so *a fortiori* at any point $x \epsilon A \subset H \subset G_n$. Hence, remembering that the sequence $\{L_{G_n}\}$ of functions of a set is non-increasing and converges to the function $L_A = L_H$, it follows by Theorem 5.7 that $DL_A(x) = \lim_n DL_{G_n}(x) = 1 = c_A(x)$ almost everywhere in A.

Now suppose the set A measurable. Then $L_A(X) + L_{CA}(X) = |X|$ for every measurable set X, and consequently $DL_A(x) + DL_{CA}(x) = 1$ at any point x at which the two derivatives $DL_A(x)$ and $DL_{CA}(x)$ exist, i. e. almost everywhere by Lebesgue's Theorem 5.4. Now, by what has been proved already, $DL_{CA}(x) = 1$ almost everywhere in CA. Therefore $DL_A(x) = 0 = c_A(x)$ at almost all x of CA and this shows that (6.2) holds almost everywhere in the whole space.

(6.3) ***Theorem.*** *If Φ is the indefinite integral of a summable function f, then*

$$D\Phi(x) = f(x) \tag{6.4}$$

at almost all points x of the space.

Proof. We may clearly assume that f is a non-negative function. If f is the characteristic function of a measurable set, the relation (6.4) holds almost everywhere by the second part of Theorem 6.1. The relation therefore remains valid when f is a finite simple function, i. e. the linear combination of a finite number of characteristic functions. Finally, in the general case, any non-negative summable function f is the limit of a non decreasing sequence $\{f_n\}$ of finite simple measurable functions; therefore, denoting by Φ_n the indefinite integral of f_n, it follows from Theorem 5.7 that $D\Phi(x) = \lim_n D\Phi_n(x) = \lim_n f_n(x) = f(x)$ almost everywhere, and this completes the proof.

§ 7. The Lebesgue decomposition. In this § we shall give for additive functions of a set ($\mathfrak{B}$), a more precise form to the Lebesgue Decomposition Theorem 14.6, Chap. I. We shall prove in fact that the absolutely continuous function which occurs in this theorem is the indefinite integral of the general derivative of the given function. At the same time we shall establish the corresponding decomposition for additive functions of bounded variation.

(7.1) ***Lemma.*** *If Φ is a singular additive function of a set, then* $\mathrm{D}\Phi(x)=0$ *almost everywhere.*

Proof. We may assume (cf. Chap. I, Theorem 13.1 (1°)) that the function Φ is non-negative.

The function Φ being singular, there exists a set E_0 measurable ($\mathfrak{B}$) and of measure zero, such that

(7.2) $\Phi(X\cdot \mathrm{C}E_0)=0$ *for every set X bounded and measurable* ($\mathfrak{B}$).

Suppose that the set of the points x at which $\mathrm{D}\Phi(x)>0$ has positive measure. Then denoting by Q_n the set of the points $x\in \mathrm{C}E_0$ at which $\mathrm{D}\Phi(x)>1/n$, there exists a positive integer N such that $|Q_N|>0$. Consequently, there also exists an interval I such that $|I\cdot Q_N|>0$, and by Lemma 5.1 we find $\Phi(I\cdot \mathrm{C}E_0)\geqslant\Phi(I\cdot Q_N)\geqslant$ $\geqslant|I\cdot Q_N|/N>0$, which clearly contradicts (7.2).

(7.3) ***Theorem.*** *If Φ is an additive function of a set, the derivative $\mathrm{D}\Phi$ is summable, and the function Φ is expressible as the sum of its function of singularities and of the indefinite integral of its general derivative.*

Proof. By Theorem 14.6, Chap. I, we have $\Phi=\Theta+\Psi$ where Θ is a singular additive function of a set and Ψ is the indefinite integral of a summable function f. Hence, making use of Theorem 6.3 and of Lemma 7.1 we find almost everywhere $\mathrm{D}\Phi(x)=\mathrm{D}\Theta(x)+\mathrm{D}\Psi(x)=f(x)$ and this proves the theorem.

We can extend the theorem to additive functions of bounded variation of an interval. We have in fact:

(7.4) ***Theorem.*** *If F is an additive function of bounded variation of an interval, the derivative F' is summable, and the function F is the sum of a singular additive function of an interval and of the indefinite integral of the derivative F'.*

Moreover, if the function F is non-negative, we have for every interval I_0

(7.5) $$F(I_0)\geqslant\int_{I_0}F'(x)\,dx,$$

equality holding only in the case in which the function F is absolutely continuous on I_0.

Proof. We may clearly assume the function F to be non-negative in both parts of the theorem. The corresponding function of a set F^*, together with its function of singularities, will then also be non-negative; and on account of Theorems 7.3 and 2.1 we shall have

$$(7.6)\qquad F^*(X) \geqslant \int_X \mathrm{D}F^*(x)\,dx = \int_X F'(x)\,dx \quad \textit{for every bounded set } X \in \mathfrak{B}.$$

Let us write for any interval I

$$(7.7)\qquad T(I) = F(I) - \int_I F'(x)\,dx.$$

The function of an interval thus defined is clearly non-negative, since by (7.6)

$$F(I) \geqslant F^*(I^\circ) \geqslant \int_{I^\circ} F'(x)\,dx = \int_I F'(x)\,dx$$

for every interval I. Moreover, if we take the derivative of both sides of (7.7) in accordance with Theorem 6.3, we find $\mathrm{D}T^*(x) = T'(x) = 0$ almost everywhere. It therefore follows from Theorem 7.3 that the function of a set T^* — and so by Theorem 12.6, Chap. III, the function of an interval T — are singular. The relation (7.7) therefore provides the required decomposition for the function F.

Finally, since the function T is non-negative, it follows from (7.7) that the inequality (7.5) holds for every interval I_0, and reduces to an equality if, and only if, $T(I) = 0$ for every interval $I \subset I_0$. In other words, in order that there be equality in (7.5) it is necessary and sufficient that the function F be on I_0 the indefinite integral of its derivative, i.e. be absolutely continuous on I_0.

Theorem 7.4 provides a decomposition of an additive function of bounded variation of an interval into two additive functions one of which is absolutely continuous and the other singular. Just as for functions of a set, this decomposition is termed *Lebesgue decomposition* and is uniquely determined for any additive function of bounded variation. For suppose that $G_1 + T_1 = G_2 + T_2$ where G_1 and G_2 are absolutely continuous functions and T_1 and T_2 are singular functions; then $G_2 - G_1 = T_1 - T_2$ and by Theorem 12.1 (2^0, 6^0), Chap. III, this requires $G_1 = G_2$ and $T_1 = T_2$. The absolutely continuous function and the singular function occurring in the Lebesgue decomposition of a function of bounded variation F are called, respectively, the *absolutely continuous part* and the *function of singularities* of the function F.

As a special case of Theorems 7.3 and 7.4, let us mention the following result, in which part 2° includes Lemma 7.1 and its converse.

(7.8) ***Theorem.*** 1° *An additive function of a set, or an additive function of an interval of bounded variation, is absolutely continuous, if, and only if, it is the indefinite integral of its derivative.*

2° *An additive function of a set, or an additive function of an interval of bounded variation, is singular if, and only if, its derivative vanishes almost everywhere.*

Finally, let us mention also an almost immediate consequence of Theorems 7.3 and 7.4:

(7.9) ***Theorem.*** *The derivative of the absolute variation of an additive function of a set, or of an additive function of an interval of bounded variation, is almost everywhere equal to the absolute value of the derivative of the given function.*

Proof. Consider to fix the ideas, an additive function of bounded variation of an interval, F. Let T be the function of singularities of F, and let W and V be the absolute variations of the functions F and T respectively. In virtue of Theorem 7.4 the relation $F(I)=\int_I F'(x)\,dx+T(I)$ holds for every interval I, and hence also

$$W(I)\leqslant\int_I |F'(x)|\,dx+V(I). \tag{7.10}$$

Now the function V is singular together with T, so that its derivative vanishes almost everywhere by Lemma 7.1. Hence taking the derivative of (7.10), we find on account of Theorem 6.3 that $W'(x)\leqslant|F'(x)|$ almost everywhere, and this completes the proof since the opposite inequality is obvious.

§ 8. Rectifiable curves. By a curve in a space $\boldsymbol{R}_m$ we shall mean any system C of m equations $x_i=X_i(t)$ where $i=1,2,\dots,m$ and the $X_i(t)$ are arbitrary finite functions defined on a linear interval or on the whole straight line $\boldsymbol{R}_1$. The variable t will be termed *parameter* of the curve. The point $(X_1(t), X_2(t),\dots,X_m(t))$ will be called *point of the curve* corresponding to the value t of the parameter, and denoted by $\mathrm{p}(C;t)$. If E is a set in $\boldsymbol{R}_1$, the set of the points $\mathrm{p}(C;t)$ for $t\in E$ will be called *graph* of the curve C on E and denoted by $\mathrm{B}(C;E)$ (cf. the similar notation for graphs of functions, Chap. III, p. 88).

For simplicity of wording we consider in the rest of this §, only curves in the plane R_2; we shall suppose also that the functions determining these curves are defined in the whole straight line R_1. But needless to say, these restrictions are not essential for the validity of the proofs that follow.

Let therefore C be a curve in the plane, defined by the equations $x=X(t)$, $y=Y(t)$. Given any two points a and $b>a$, a finite sequence $\tau=\{t_j\}_{j=0,1,\dots,n}$ of points such that $a=t_0\leqslant t_1\leqslant\dots\leqslant t_n=b$ will be called *chain* between the points a and b, and the number

$$\sum_{j=1}^{n}\varrho(p_{j-1},p_j),\qquad \textit{where}\qquad p_j=\mathrm{p}(C;t_j),$$

will be denoted by $\sigma(C;\tau)$. (We may regard this number as the length of the polygon inscribed in the curve C and whose vertices correspond to the values $a=t_0, t_1, \dots, t_n=b$ of the parameter.) The upper bound of the numbers $\sigma(C;\tau)$ when τ is any chain between two fixed points a and b, will be called *length of arc* of the curve C on the interval $I=[a,b]$, and will be denoted by $\mathrm{S}(C;I)$ or $\mathrm{S}(C;a,b)$. If $\mathrm{S}(C;I)\neq\infty$ the curve C is said to be *rectifiable on the interval* I; and if this is the case on every interval we say simply that the curve C is *rectifiable*.

(8.1) *For any curve C we have* $\mathrm{S}(C;a,b)+\mathrm{S}(C;b,c)=\mathrm{S}(C;a,c)$ *whenever* $a<b<c$.

It is enough to prove that $\mathrm{S}(C;a,b)+\mathrm{S}(C;b,c)\geqslant\mathrm{S}(C;a,c)$, since the opposite inequality is obvious. Let $\tau=\{a=t_0,t_1,\dots,t_n=c\}$ be any chain between a and c, and let h be the index for which $t_{h-1}\leqslant b<t_h$. Writing $\tau_1=\{a=t_0,t_1,\dots,t_{h-1},b\}$ and $\tau_2=\{b,t_h,\dots,t_n=c\}$, we have $\sigma(C;\tau)\leqslant\sigma(C;\tau_1)+\sigma(C;\tau_2)\leqslant\mathrm{S}(C;a,b)+\mathrm{S}(C;b,c)$, and so $\mathrm{S}(C;a,c)\leqslant\mathrm{S}(C;a,b)+\mathrm{S}(C;b,c)$.

It follows from (8.1) that if a curve C is rectifiable, the length of arc $\mathrm{S}(C;I)$ is an additive function of the interval I. We shall call this function *length of the curve C*. Any function of a real variable that corresponds to this function of an interval, i.e. any function $S(t)$ such that $S(b)-S(a)=\mathrm{S}(C;a,b)$ for every interval $[a,b]$, will also be termed *length of the curve C*.

(8.2) ***Jordan's Theorem.*** *If C is a curve given by the equations $x=X(t)$, $y=Y(t)$; we have*

$$\text{(8.3)}\qquad \begin{gathered} \mathrm{W}(X;I)\leqslant \mathrm{S}(C;I), \qquad \mathrm{W}(Y;I)\leqslant \mathrm{S}(C;I), \\ \mathrm{W}(X;I)+\mathrm{W}(Y;I)\geqslant \mathrm{S}(C;I) \end{gathered}$$

for any interval I; and therefore, in order that the curve C be rectifiable on an interval I_0, it is necessary and sufficient that the functions X and Y be of bounded variation on I_0.

Proof. Given an interval $I=[a,b]$, we easily find that for any chain $\tau=\{a=t_0, t_1, \dots, t_n=b\}$ between the points a and b,

$$\sum_{j=1}^{n}|X(t_j)-X(t_{j-1})|\leqslant\sigma(C;\tau), \qquad \sum_{j=1}^{n}|Y(t_j)-Y(t_{j-1})|\leqslant\sigma(C;\tau),$$

$$\sigma(C;\tau)\leqslant\sum_{j=1}^{n}|X(t_j)-X(t_{j-1})|+\sum_{j=1}^{n}|Y(t_j)-Y(t_{j-1})|\leqslant \mathrm{W}(X;I)+\mathrm{W}(Y;I),$$

from which the inequalities (8.3) follow at once.

(8.4) ***Theorem.*** *If C is a rectifiable curve given by the equations $x=X(t)$, $y=Y(t)$, and the function $S(t)$ is its length, then*

(i) *in order that $S(t)$ be continuous at a point [absolutely continuous on an interval] it is necessary and sufficient that the two functions $X(t)$ and $Y(t)$ should both be so;*

(ii) *we have $\Lambda\{\mathrm{B}(C;E)\}\leqslant|S[E]|$ for any linear set E (i.e. on any set E the length of the graph of the curve C does not exceed the measure of the set of values taken by the function $S(t)$ for $t\in E$);*

(iii) *$[S'(t)]^2=[X'(t)]^2+[Y'(t)]^2$ for almost every t;*

(iv) *$\mathrm{S}(C;a,b)\geqslant\int_a^b\sqrt{[X'(t)]^2+[Y'(t)]^2}\,dt$ for every interval $[a,b]$,*

and the sign of equality holds if, and only if, both the functions $X(t)$ and $Y(t)$ are absolutely continuous on $[a,b]$.

Proof. *re* (i): This part of the theorem is an immediate consequence of the relations (8.3), since by Theorems 4.8 and 12.1 (1^0) of Chap. III, a function of bounded variation is continuous at a point [absolutely continuous on an interval] if, and only if, its absolute variation is so.

re (ii). Let ε be any positive number and let (I_n) be a sequence of intervals such that

(8.5) $S[E]\subset\sum_n I_n$ and (8.6) $\sum_n |I_n|\leqslant|S[E]|+\varepsilon$.

We may clearly assume that no interval I_n has a diameter exceeding ε.

This being so, we write $\widetilde{E}=\mathrm{B}(C;E)$ and we denote by $\widetilde{E}_n$ the set of the points $\mathrm{p}(C;t)$ of the curve C for each of which $S(t)\in I_n$. It is easy to see, on account of (8.5), that $\widetilde{E}\subset\sum_n \widetilde{E}_n$. On the other hand $\delta(\widetilde{E}_n)\leqslant\delta(I_n)=|I_n|\leqslant\varepsilon$ for any n, and it follows from (8.6) (cf. Chap. II, § 8) that $\Lambda^{(\varepsilon)}(\widetilde{E})\leqslant|S[E]|+\varepsilon$, and hence by making ε tend to zero, that $\Lambda(\widetilde{E})\leqslant|S[E]|$, as asserted.

re (iii): Let $I_0=[a_0,b_0]$ be any interval. We shall show successively that both the relations

(8.7) $[S'(t)]^2\geqslant[X'(t)]^2+[Y'(t)]^2$ and (8.8) $[S'(t)]^2\leqslant[X'(t)]^2+[Y'(t)]^2$

hold almost everywhere in I_0; here the derivatives $S'(t)$, $X'(t)$ and $Y'(t)$ exist almost everywhere on account of Theorem 8.2 and of Lebesgue's Theorem 5.4.

We have $S(t+h)-S(t)\geqslant\{[X(t+h)-X(t)]^2+[Y(t+h)-Y(t)]^2\}^{1/2}$ for any point t and any $h>0$, and if we divide both sides by h and make $h\to 0$, this implies the relation (8.7) at any point t for which all three functions are derivable at the same time, i. e. almost everywhere.

Now let A denote the set of the points $t\in I_0$ at which the three derivatives $X'(t)$, $Y'(t)$ and $S'(t)$ exist without satisfying the inequality (8.8); and for any positive integer n, let A_n denote the set of the points $t\in A$ for each of which the inequality

$$S(I)/|I|\geqslant\{[X(I)/|I|]^2+[Y(I)/|I|]^2\}^{1/2}+1/n$$

holds for all the intervals I containing t, whose diameters are less than $1/n$. Clearly $A=\sum_n A_n$.

Keeping n fixed for the moment, let ε be any positive number. There exists a chain $\tau=\{a_0=t_0,t_1,\dots,t_p=b_0\}$ such that $t_k-t_{k-1}<1/n$ for $k=1,2,\dots,p$, and such that $\mathrm{S}(C;I_0)\leqslant\sigma(C;\tau)+\varepsilon$. Consequently, writing for brevity $J_k=[t_{k-1},t_k]$, $p_k=\mathrm{p}(C;t_k)$, $\varrho_k=\varrho(p_{k-1},p_k)$, we have

(8.9) $S(J_k)\geqslant\varrho_k+|J_k|/n$ *for* $k=1,2,\dots,p$, *whenever* $J_k\cdot A_n\neq 0$,

and on the other hand

(8.10) $$\sum_{k=1}^{p}S(J_k)\leqslant\sum_{k=1}^{p}\varrho_k+\varepsilon.$$

Therefore if $\sum_k^{(n)}$ stands for a summation over all the indices k for which $J_k \cdot A_n \neq 0$, we find on account of (8.9) and (8.10) that

$$|A_n| \leqslant \sum_k^{(n)} |J_k| \leqslant n \cdot \sum_k^{(n)} [S(J_k) - \varrho_k] \leqslant n \cdot \sum_{k=1}^{p} [S(J_k) - \varrho_k] \leqslant n\varepsilon.$$

Now since ε is an arbitrary positive number, it follows that $|A_n| = 0$ for any n, and therefore also that $|A| = 0$. Thus the inequality (8.8) holds almost everywhere, as well as the inequality (8.7), and this completes the proof of part (iii) of the theorem.

Finally, since $\mathrm{S}(C; a, b) = S(b) - S(a)$, part (iv) reduces on account of (i) and (iii) to an immediate consequence of Theorem 7.4.

Theorem 8.4 (in particular its parts (iii) and (iv)) is due to L. Tonelli [1; 4]; cf. also F. Riesz [6; 7].

As regards part (ii) of the theorem, it may be observed that in the case in which the curve C has no multiple points (i. e. when every point of the curve corresponds to a single value of the parameter) the inequality $\Lambda\{\mathrm{B}(C; E)\} \leqslant |S[E]|$ can easily be shown to reduce to an equality.

As proved by T. Ważewski [1], any bounded continuum P of finite length may be regarded as the set of the points of a curve C on the interval [0, 1], such that $\mathrm{S}(C; 0,1)$ $2 \cdot \Lambda(P)$.

§ 9. De la Vallée Poussin's theorem.

With the help of the results established in the preceding § we can complete further, for continuous functions of bounded variation of a real variable, the decomposition formula of Lebesgue.

We shall begin with the following theorem, which itself completes, in part at any rate, the second half of Lebesgue's Theorem 5.4.

(9.1) ***Theorem.*** *If $F(x)$ is a function of bounded variation and $W(x)$ denotes its absolute variation, then for the set N of the points at which the function $F(x)$ is continuous but has no derivative finite or infinite, we have*

(9.2) $|F^*(N)| = W^*(N) = |N| = 0$ *and* (9.3) $\Lambda\{\mathrm{B}(F; N)\} = 0$.

Proof. Consider the curve C: $x = x$, $y = F(x)$. Let $S(x)$ be the length of this curve and let E be the set of the values assumed by the function $S(x)$. For any $s \in E$, denote by $X(s)$ the value of x for which $S(x) = s$ and write $Y(s) = F(X(s))$. Since (cf. Theorem 8.2) $|X(s_2) - X(s_1)| \leqslant |s_2 - s_1|$ and $|Y(s_2) - Y(s_1)| \leqslant |s_2 - s_1|$ for any pair of points s_1, s_2 of E, the functions $X(s)$ and $Y(s)$ are continuous on the set E, and moreover may be continued on to the closure $\bar{E}$ of this set by continuity. If now $[a, b]$ is an interval contiguous to $\bar{E}$, the function $X(s)$ assumes equal values at the ends of this interval, and the point $x=X(a)=X(b)$ is a point of discontinuity of the function $F(x)$. We shall complete further the definition of the functions $X(s)$ and $Y(s)$ on the whole straight line $\boldsymbol{R}_1$ so as to make the former constant and the second linear, on each interval contiguous to $\bar{E}$.

This being so, consider the curve C_1 given by the equations $x=X(s)$, $y=Y(s)$. We verify easily that the parameter s of this curve is its length. (Actually we see easily that the graph of the curve C_1 is derived from that of the curve C by adding to the latter at most an enumerable infinity of segments situated on the lines $x=c_i$ where c_i are the points of discontinuity of the function F.) By Theorem 8.4 (iii), we therefore have $[X'(s)]^2+[Y'(s)]^2=1$ for almost all s, and therefore the set H of the points s for which either one of the derivatives $X'(s)$ and $Y'(s)$ does not exist, or both exist and vanish, is of measure zero.

Now we see at once that if $s \in E-H$, then at the point $x=X(s)$, the derivative $F'(x)$ exists (with the value $Y'(s)/X'(s)$ if $X'(s)\neq 0$, or with the value $\pm\infty$ if $X'(s)=0$ and $Y'(s)\gtrless 0$). Therefore $N \subset X[E \cdot H]$, or what amounts to the same, $S[N] \subset E \cdot H$, and hence $|S[N]| \leqslant |H|=0$.

From this we derive at once with the help of Theorem 8.4 (ii) the relation (9.3), since $\mathrm{B}(F; N)=\mathrm{B}(C; N)$. Finally, the function $S(x)$ is continuous (cf. Theorem 8.4 (i)) at any point at which the function $F(x)$ is continuous, and so at any point of the set N, and therefore it follows from Theorem 13.3, Chap. III, and from Theorem 8.2, that $|F^*(N)| \leqslant W^*(N) \leqslant S^*(N)=|S[N]|=0$; this completes the proof.

(9.4) ***Lemma.*** *If $F(x)$ is a function of bounded variation, then*

(i) $F^*(A) \geqslant k \cdot |A|$ *for any bounded set A and any finite number k whenever the inequality $F'(x) \geqslant k$ holds at every point x of A (and the assertion obtained by changing the direction of both inequalities is then evidently also true),*

(ii) $F^*(B)=0$ *for any bounded set B of measure zero throughout which the derivative $F'(x)$ exists and is finite.*

Proof. *re* (i). Let ε be any positive number. Denote, for any positive integer n, by $A^{(n)}$ the set of the points $x \in A$ such that $F(I) \geqslant (k-\varepsilon)\cdot|I|$ holds whenever I is an interval containing x and of diameter less than $1/n$. Clearly $A = \lim\limits_{n} A^{(n)}$.

Keeping the index n fixed for the moment, let us denote by $G^{(n)}$ a bounded open set containing $A^{(n)}$, such that (cf. Theorem 6.9, Chap. III)

$$(9.5) \qquad |F^*(X)-F^*(A^{(n)})|<\varepsilon \quad \textit{whenever} \quad A^{(n)}\subset X\subset G^{(n)},$$

and let us represent $G^{(n)}$ as the sum of a sequence $\{I_p^{(n)}\}_{p=1,2,\dots}$ of non-overlapping intervals. We may clearly suppose that all the intervals $I_p^{(n)}$ are of diameter less than $1/n$ and that their extremities are not points of discontinuity of $F(x)$. So that if $\sum\limits_p^{(n)}$ stands for summation over the indices p for which $I_p^{(n)}\cdot A^{(n)} \neq 0$, and $X^{(n)}$ denotes the sum of the intervals $I_p^{(n)}$ corresponding to these indices, we find $F^*(X^{(n)})=\sum\limits_p^{(n)} F(I_p^{(n)}) \geqslant (k-\varepsilon)\cdot\sum\limits_p^{(n)}|I_p^{(n)}| \geqslant (k-\varepsilon)\cdot|A^{(n)}|$, and hence on account of (9.5), $F^*(A^{(n)}) \geqslant (k-\varepsilon)\cdot|A^{(n)}|-\varepsilon$. Making $\varepsilon\to 0$ and $n\to\infty$, we obtain in the limit $F^*(A)\geqslant k\cdot|A|$.

re (ii). Let $B^{(n)}$ denote the set of the points $x \in B$ for which $F'(x)\geqslant -n$. By (i) we have $F^*(B^{(n)})\geqslant -n\cdot|B^{(n)}|=0$ for any positive integer n, and so $F^*(B)\geqslant 0$. By symmetry we must have also $F^*(B)\leqslant 0$, and therefore $F^*(B)=0$.

(9.6) ***De la Vallée Poussin's Decomposition Theorem.*** *If $F(x)$ is a function of bounded variation with $W(x)$ for its absolute variation, and if $E_{+\infty}$ and $E_{-\infty}$ denote the sets in which $F(x)$ has a derivative equal to $+\infty$ and to $-\infty$ respectively, then*

(i) *for any bounded set X measurable ($\mathfrak{B}$) at each point of which the function $F(x)$ is continuous, we have the relations:*

$$(9.7) \qquad F^*(X)=F^*(X\cdot E_{+\infty})+F^*(X\cdot E_{-\infty})+\int_X F'(x)\,dx,$$

$$(9.8) \qquad W^*(X)=F^*(X\cdot E_{+\infty})+|F^*(X\cdot E_{-\infty})|+\int_X |F'(x)|\,dx;$$

(ii) *the two derivatives $F'(x)$ and $W'(x)$ exist and fulfil the relation $W'(x)=|F'(x)|$ at any point x of continuity of F, except at most at the points of a set N such that $W^*(N)=|N|=0$ (i. e. a set which is at the same time of measure* (L) *zero and of measure* (W) *zero).*

Proof. *re* (i). On account of Theorem 7.8 there exists a set A of measure zero such that for any set X bounded and measurable ($\mathfrak{B}$)

$$F^*(X)=F^*(X\cdot A)+\int_X F'(x)\,dx. \tag{9.9}$$

Supposing further that the function F is continuous at every point of X, we may assume, in virtue of Theorem 9.1, that the function $F(x)$ has everywhere in A, a derivative, finite or infinite. Moreover since by Lemma 9.4 (ii) the function $F^*(X)$ vanishes for any bounded subset of $A-(E_{+\infty}+E_{-\infty})$, we may assume that $A\subset E_{+\infty}+E_{-\infty}$. Finally, we obtain directly from (9.9) that $F^*(X)$ vanishes when $X\subset CA$ and $|X|=0$. We may therefore choose simply $A=E_{+\infty}+E_{-\infty}$ and formula (9.9) becomes (9.7).

Formula (9.8) is, by Theorem 13.2, Chap. III, an immediate consequence of (9.7), since Lemma 9.4 (i) shows that $F^*(X\cdot E_{+\infty})\geqslant 0$ and $F^*(X\cdot E_{-\infty})\leqslant 0$ for every set X bounded and measurable ($\mathfrak{B}$).

re (ii). Let N be the set of the points x at which the function $F(x)$ is continuous and either one at least of the derivatives $F'(x)$ and $W'(x)$ does not exist, or both exist but do not satisfy the relation $W'(x)=|F'(x)|$. We then have $N\cdot E_{+\infty}=N\cdot E_{-\infty}=0$, since evidently $W'(x)=+\infty=|F'(x)|$ at any point where $F'(x)=\pm\infty$. Therefore, since the set N is further, by Theorem 7.9, of measure (L) zero, it follows from formula (9.8) that $W^*(N)=0$ and this completes the proof.

Let us mention an immediate consequence of Theorem 9.6. *In order that a continuous function of bounded variation $F(x)$ be absolutely continuous, it is necessary and sufficient that the function of a set $F^*(X)$ should vanish identically on the set of the points at which $F(x)$ has an infinite derivative. In particular therefore, any continuous function of bounded variation which is not absolutely continuous has an infinite derivative on a non-enumerable set.*

Let us remark further that the theorems of this § cannot be extended directly to additive functions of an interval in the plane. Thus if $F(I)$ denotes the continuous singular function of an interval in R_2, which for any interval I equals the length of the segment of the line $x=y$ contained in I, we have $F(x)=0$ for every point x, so that $F'(x)=\infty$ does not hold at any point.

§ 10. Points of density for a set. Given a set E in a space R_m, the strong upper and lower derivates of the measure-function of E (cf. § 6, p. 117) at a point x will be called respectively the *outer upper* and *outer lower density* of E at x. The points at which these two densities are equal to 1 are termed *points of outer density*, and the points at which they are equal to 0, *points of dispersion*, for the set E.

If the set E is measurable we suppress the word "outer" in these expressions. We see further, that if the set E is measurable, any point of density for E is a point of dispersion for CE, and vice-versa.

We shall show in this § (cf. below Theorem 10.2) that almost all points of any set E are points of outer density for E, or what amounts to the same that

(10.1) *For almost all points x of E, if $\{I_n\}$ is any sequence of intervals tending to x (in the sense of § 2, p. 106), we have* $|E \cdot I_n|/|I_n| \to 1$.

This proposition presents an obvious analogy to Theorem 6.1 and it is in the form (6.1) that the "density theorem" is often stated and proved either with the help of Vitali's Covering Theorem or by more or less equivalent means (*vide*, for instance, E. W. Hobson [I], Ch. J. de la Vallée Poussin [I, p. 71] and W. Sierpiński [10]). Theorem 10.2 will be however, so to speak, independent of Vitali's theorem, because the sequences of intervals occurring in (10.1) are not supposed regular.

Also, Theorem 10.2 will be more precise than Theorem 6.1, because at any point x of outer density for a set E we have *a fortiori* $\mathrm{DL}_E(x)=1$, and indeed, at any x the relations $\mathrm{L}'_E(x)=1$ and $\mathrm{DL}_E(x)=1$ are equivalent. To see this it is enough to show that the former of these relations implies the latter, the converse being obvious from Theorem 2.1. We may assume moreover, on account of Theorem 6.7, Chap. III, that the set E is measurable.

Let therefore x_0 be a point such that $\mathrm{L}'_E(x_0)=1$ and let $\{X_n\}$ be a regular sequence of measurable sets tending to x_0. Then there exists a sequence $\{J_n\}$ of cubes such that $X_n \subset J_n$ and $|X_n|/|J_n|>\alpha$, where $n=1, 2, \ldots$ and α is a fixed positive number. Since by hypothesis, $|E \cdot J_n|/|J_n| \to 1$, and so $|CE \cdot J_n|/|J_n| \to 0$, it follows that $|CE \cdot X_n|/|X_n| \to 0$, or what amounts to the same that $|E \cdot X_n|/|X_n| \to 1$. Therefore $\mathrm{DL}_E(x_0)=1$.

It is, of course, only for spaces $\boldsymbol{R}_m$ of dimension number $m \geqslant 2$ that Theorem 10.2 will differ from Theorem 6.1. The two statements are equivalent for $\boldsymbol{R}_1$.

For the various proofs of Theorem 10.2 *vide* F. Riesz [8] and H. Busemann and W. Feller [1]. In the second of these memoirs will be found a general discussion of the different forms of "density theorems".

It is of interest to observe that the proposition (10.1) ceases to be true even for closed sets E, if the intervals I_n are replaced by arbitrary rectangles with sides not necessarily parallel to the axes of coordinates. This remarkable fact has been established by O. Nikodym and A. Zygmund (*vide* O. Nikodym [1, p. 167]) and by H. Busemann and W. Feller [1, p. 243].

(10.2) ***Density Theorem.*** *Almost all the points of an arbitrary set E are points of outer density for E; and if further the set E is measurable, almost all the points of CE are points of dispersion for E.*

Proof. For simplicity of notation, we shall state the proof for sets which lie in the plane; the corresponding discussion in any space $\boldsymbol{R}_m$ is however essentially the same (except that in $\boldsymbol{R}_1$, as already remarked, the theorem reduces to Theorem 6.1).

By Theorem 6.7, Chap. III, any set can be enclosed in a measurable set having the same measure-function. On the other hand any measurable set is the sum of a set of zero measure and of a sequence of bounded closed sets. We may therefore suppose that the set considered is bounded and closed.

Let ε be any positive number. We shall begin by defining a positive number σ and a closed subset A of E such that $|E-A|<\varepsilon$ and that, for any point (ξ,η) in the plane,

$$\text{(i)} \qquad \begin{gathered} |\underset{x}{\mathrm{E}}[(x,\eta)\in E;\ a\leqslant x\leqslant b]|\geqslant(1-\varepsilon)(b-a) \\ \textit{whenever}\quad (\xi,\eta)\in A,\quad a\leqslant\xi\leqslant b \quad \textit{and} \quad b-a<\sigma. \end{gathered}$$

To do this, let us write for brevity, when Q is any set in the plane, $Q^{[\eta]}=\underset{x}{\mathrm{E}}[(x,\eta)\in Q]$, and let us denote, for any positive integer n, by A_n the set of the points (ξ,η) of E such that $|E^{[\eta]}\cdot I|\geqslant(1-\varepsilon)\cdot|I|$ whenever I is a linear interval containing ξ and of diameter less than $1/n$. The sequence $\{A_n\}$ is evidently ascending. Let us write

$$\text{(10.3)} \qquad N=E-\lim_n A_n.$$

For any η, if ξ is a point of the set $N^{[\eta]}$, there will then exist, for each positive integer n, a linear interval I such that $\xi\in I$, $\delta(I)<1/n$ and $|N^{[\eta]}\cdot I|\leqslant|E^{[\eta]}\cdot I|<(1-\varepsilon)\cdot|I|$. Therefore the lower derivate of the measure-function for the linear set $N^{[\eta]}$ cannot exceed $1-\varepsilon$ at any point of this set, whence by Theorem 6.1,

$$\text{(10.4)} \qquad |N^{[\eta]}|=|\underset{x}{\mathrm{E}}[(x,\eta)\in N]|=0 \quad \textit{for every real number } \eta.$$

Let us now remark that the sets A_n are closed. For, keeping for a moment an index n fixed, let (ξ_0,η_0) be the limit of a sequence $\{(\xi_k,\eta_k)\}_{k=1,2,\ldots}$ of points of A_n. Let I_0 be a linear interval such that $\xi_0\in I_0$ and $\delta(I_0)<1/n$, and let I be any linear interval containing I_0 in its interior, whose diameter is less than $1/n$. Then for any sufficiently large k, $\xi_k\in I$ and therefore $|E^{[\eta_k]}\cdot I|\geqslant(1-\varepsilon)\cdot|I|$. On the other hand, the set E being closed, we easily see that $E^{[\eta_0]}\supset\limsup_k E^{[\eta_k]}$; so that $|E^{[\eta_0]}\cdot I|\geqslant\limsup_k|E^{[\eta_k]}\cdot I|\geqslant(1-\varepsilon)\cdot|I|$, and therefore also $|E^{[\eta_0]}\cdot I_0|\geqslant(1-\varepsilon)\cdot|I_0|$. Hence $(\xi_0,\eta_0)\in A_n$, i.e. each set A_n is closed.

It follows, according to (10.3), that the set N is measurable.

Therefore, applying Fubini's theorem in the form (8.6), Chap. III, we conclude, on account of (10.4), that the plane set N is of measure zero. Consequently $|E-A_{n_0}|<\varepsilon$ for a sufficiently large index n_0, and writing $\sigma=1/n_0$ and $A=A_{n_0}$ we find that the inequality $|E-A|<\varepsilon$ and condition (i) are both satisfied.

In exactly the same way, but replacing the set E by A and interchanging the rôle of the coordinates x and y, we determine now a positive number $\sigma_1<\sigma$ and a closed subset B of A such that $|A-B|<\varepsilon$ and that, for any point (ξ,η) in the plane

(ii)
$$|\underset{y}{\mathrm{E}}[(\xi,y)\in A;\ a\leqslant y\leqslant b]|\geqslant(1-\varepsilon)(b-a)$$
$$whenever\quad (\xi,\eta)\in B,\quad a\leqslant\eta\leqslant b\quad and\quad b-a<\sigma_1.$$

This being so, let (ξ_0,η_0) be any point of B. Let $J=[\alpha_1,\beta_1;\ \alpha_2,\beta_2]$ denote any interval such that $(\xi_0,\eta_0)\in J$ and $\delta(J)<\sigma_1<\sigma$. By Fubini's theorem (in the form (8.6), Chap. III) we have

$$|E\cdot J|=\int_{\alpha_2}^{\beta_2}|\underset{x}{\mathrm{E}}[(x,y)\in E;\ \alpha_1\leqslant x\leqslant\beta_1]|\,dy. \tag{10.5}$$

Since $(\xi_0,\eta_0)\in B$ and $\alpha_2\leqslant\eta_0\leqslant\beta_2$, it follows from (ii) that the set of the y such that $(\xi_0,y)\in A$ and $\alpha_2\leqslant y\leqslant\beta_2$ is of measure at least equal to $(1-\varepsilon)(\beta_2-\alpha_2)$. On the other hand, since $\alpha_1\leqslant\xi_0\leqslant\beta_1$, it follows from (i) that $|\underset{x}{\mathrm{E}}[(x,y)\in E;\ \alpha_1\leqslant x\leqslant\beta_1]|\geqslant(1-\varepsilon)(\beta_1-\alpha_1)$ whenever $(\xi_0,y)\in A$. Hence, formula (10.5) gives

$$|E\cdot J|\geqslant(1-\varepsilon)^2(\beta_1-\alpha_1)(\beta_2-\alpha_2)=(1-\varepsilon)^2\cdot|J|,$$

i. e. the lower density of E is at least equal to $(1-\varepsilon)^2$ at any point (ξ_0,η_0) of B. Therefore, since $|E-B|\leqslant|E-A|+|A-B|\leqslant2\varepsilon$ and since ε is an arbitrary positive number, the lower density of E is exactly equal to 1 at almost all the points of the set E, i. e. almost all points of this set are points of density for it.

The second part of the theorem is an immediate consequence of the first part. In fact, if the set E is measurable, so is the set CE, and almost all points of CE, since they are points of density for CE, are points of dispersion for E.

In connection with the definition of points of density, Denjoy introduced the important notion of approximate continuity of a function. We call a function of a point $f(x)$ (in any space R_m), *approximately continuous* at a point x_0, if $f(x_0) \neq \infty$ and $f(x) \to f(x_0)$ as x tends to x_0 on a measurable set E for which x_0 is a point of density.

(10.6) ***Theorem.*** *If f is a measurable function almost everywhere finite on a set E, then the function f is approximately continuous at almost all points of E.*

Proof. On account of Lusin's theorem (Chap. III, § 7), given any $\varepsilon > 0$, we can represent the set E as the sum of a closed set F on which the function f is continuous and of a set of measure less than ε. The function f is clearly approximately continuous at any point of density for the set F, and so, by Theorem 10.2, at almost all points of F. This implies, as ε is an arbitrary positive number, that the function f is aproximately continuous at almost all points of the set E itself.

Theorem 10.6 is due to A. Denjoy [5] (cf. also W. Sierpiński [6; 9]). It is easy to see that the converse holds also, i. e. that *every function which is approximately continuous at almost all the points of a measurable set E is measurable on E* (*vide* W. Stepanoff [2] and E. Kamke [1]).

Let us mention also the following theorem, an almost immediate consequence of Theorem 10.6, which completes, in part, Theorem 2.2 on derivation of an indefinite integral:

(10.7) ***Theorem.*** *If Φ is the indefinite integral of a bounded measurable function f, then $\Phi'_s(x)=f(x)$ at almost all points x, and in fact, at any point x at which the function f is approximately continuous.*

Proof. Let x_0 be a point at which the function f is approximately continuous and let E be a measurable set for which x_0 is a point of density, while $f(x) \to f(x_0)$ as x tends to x_0 on the set E. We may suppose (by subtracting, if necessary, a constant from $f(x)$) that $f(x_0)=0$. Therefore, given any positive number ε, we have for any interval I of sufficiently small diameter containing x_0, (i) $|I\cdot CE| \leqslant \varepsilon\cdot|I|$ and (ii) $|f(x)| < \varepsilon$ for every $x \in I\cdot E$. Denoting by M the upper bound of $|f(x)|$, conditions (i) and (ii) imply $|\Phi(I)| \leqslant |\Phi(I\cdot CE)| + |\Phi(I\cdot E)| \leqslant M\varepsilon\cdot|I| + \varepsilon\cdot|I| \leqslant \varepsilon\cdot(M+1)\cdot|I|$, whence $\Phi'_s(x_0)=0=f(x_0)$.

If Φ is the indefinite integral of a function f which is summable but unbounded, it may happen that the relation $\Phi'_s(x)=f(x)$ is not fulfilled at any point. In virtue of Theorem 6.3, this relation clearly holds at almost all points at which the strong derivative $\Phi'_s(x)$ exists; but if the function f is unbounded, its indefinite integral Φ may have no finite strong derivative at any point (cf. on this point Busemann and Feller [1, p. 256]; the result of Banach and Bohr mentioned above, p. 112, follows as a particular case).

Nevertheless, the result contained in Theorem 10.7 may be generalized considerably. In fact, according to a theorem of B. Jessen, J. Marcinkiewicz and A. Zygmund [1] (see below § 13) *the indefinite integral of a function f in a space $\boldsymbol{R}_m$ is almost everywhere derivable in the strong sense whenever the function* $|f|\cdot(\log^+|f|)^{m-1}$ *is summable* (in a less general form, for functions f of which the power $p>1$ is summable, this theorem was established a little earlier by A. Zygmund [1]). On the other hand however, *given an arbitrary function $\sigma(t)$ positive for $t>0$ and such that* $\liminf_{t\to+\infty} \sigma(t)=0$, *there always exists a function $f(x)$ in $\boldsymbol{R}_m$ such that the function* $\sigma(|f|)\cdot|f|\cdot(\log^+|f|)^{m-1}$ *is summable and such that the indefinite integral of f is not derivable in the strong sense (has the strong upper derivate $+\infty$) at any point of $\boldsymbol{R}_m$.*

*** § 11. Ward's theorems on derivation of additive functions of an interval.** In the preceding §§ of this Chapter, we have treated the Lebesgue theory of derivation of additive functions of an interval of bounded variation. As regards functions of a real variable, this theory has been extended to arbitrary functions by Montel, Lusin and especially by Denjoy. Recently Denjoy's theorems, which already belong to the classical results of the theory, have been generalized still further. On the one hand they have been given a geometrical form by which they become theorems on certain metrical properties of sets, and in this form an account will be given of them in Chapter IX. On the other hand, recent researches of Besicovitch and Ward have made it possible to extend an essential part of the Denjoy results, particularly the relations between the extreme bilateral derivates, to additive functions of an interval in a space $\boldsymbol{R}_m$ of any number of dimensions. These researches will form the subject of the present §.

It was A. S. Besicovitch [5] who started these researches, by establishing between the extreme strong and ordinary derivates of absolutely continuous functions of an interval, relations analogous to those proved by Denjoy for derivates of functions of a single variable. A. J. Ward [2; 5] has extended this result to quite arbitrary additive functions of an interval. Of the two theorems of Ward (*vide*, below, Theorems 11.15 and 11.21) one concerns only ordinary derivates, while the other applies also to strong derivates. It is the latter that generalizes the result of Besicovitch; this second theorem is one which can be proved fairly simply for functions of an interval in the plane; it is rather curious that it requires much more delicate methods in an arbitrary space $\boldsymbol{R}_m$.

We shall make use in this § of some auxiliary notations. If F is an additive function of an interval and $\alpha \leqslant 1$ is a positive number, $\overline{F}_{(\alpha)}(x)$ and $\underline{F}_{(\alpha)}(x)$ will denote at any point x the upper and lower limit of the ratio $F(I)/|I|$ where I is any interval containing x, which is subject to the condition $\mathrm{r}(I) \geqslant \alpha$, and which has diameter tending to zero. We see at once that at any point x, $\overline{F}_{(\alpha)}(x)$ and $\underline{F}_{(\alpha)}(x)$ tend to $\overline{F}(x)$ and $\underline{F}(x)$ respectively as $\alpha \to 0$.

We shall suppose fixed a Euclidean space $\boldsymbol{R}_m$, and in it we define a regular sequence of nets of cubes $\{\mathfrak{Q}_k\}_{k=1,2,\ldots}$, denoting by $\{\mathfrak{Q}_k\}$ the family of all the cubes of the form

$$[p_1 2^{-k}, (p_1+1) 2^{-k};\ p_2 2^{-k}, (p_2+1) 2^{-k}; \ldots;\ p_m 2^{-k}, (p_m+1) 2^{-k}]$$

where $p_1, p_2, \ldots, p_m$ are arbitrary integers.

(11.1) *Lemma. Given an additive function of an interval G, and positive numbers $\alpha \leqslant 2^{-m}$ and a, suppose that the inequalities $0 < \underline{G}_{(\alpha)}(x) < a$ hold at every point x of a set E having positive outer measure; then there exists for each $\varepsilon > 0$, a cube Q which belongs to one of the nets $\mathfrak{Q}_k$ and for which we have*

(11.2) $\delta(Q) < \varepsilon, \quad |E \cdot Q| > (1-\varepsilon) \cdot |Q| \quad$ *and* $\quad G(Q) < 8^m \cdot \alpha^{-m} \cdot a \cdot |Q|.$

Proof. By replacing, if necessary, the set E by a suitable subset of E having positive outer measure, we may suppose that there exists a positive number σ such that for every interval I,

(11.3) $G(I) > 0 \quad$ *whenever* $\quad I \cdot E \neq 0, \quad \mathrm{r}(I) \geqslant \alpha \quad$ *and* $\quad \delta(I) < \sigma.$

We may further clearly assume that σ is less than both ε and $\alpha^m/8^m$.

This being so, let $x_0 \in E$ be a point of outer density for the set E (cf. § 10). Since $\underline{G}_{(\alpha)}(x_0) < a$, we can determine an interval $J = [a_1, b_1; \ldots; a_m, b_m]$ containing x_0 and such that

(11.4) $\delta(J) < \sigma, \quad \mathrm{r}(J) \geqslant \alpha, \quad |E \cdot J| > (1-\sigma^2) \cdot |J| \quad$ *and* $\quad G(J) < a \cdot |J|.$

It follows in particular that

(11.5) $|E \cdot I| > (1-\sigma) \cdot |I| \quad$ *for any interval* $\quad I \subset J \quad$ *such that* $\quad |I| > \sigma \cdot |J|.$

Let l be the smallest of the edges of J. Since $\mathrm{r}(J) \geqslant \alpha$, no edge of J can exceed l/α, and therefore we have $|J| \leqslant l^m/\alpha^m$. Finally let k be the positive integer given by

(11.6) $$1/2^k < l/4 \leqslant 1/2^{k-1},$$

and let $Q=[a'_1, b'_1; \dots; a'_m, b'_m]$ be a cube which belongs to the net $\mathfrak{Q}_k$ and which contains the centre of the interval J. By (11.6) we find that $Q \subset J$ and that $a'_i - a_i \geqslant l/4$, $b_i - b'_i \geqslant l/4$ and $b'_i - a'_i = 1/2^k \geqslant l/8$. It follows easily that the figure $J \ominus Q$ can be subdivided into a finite number of non-overlapping intervals with no edge smaller than $l/8$.

Now any such interval can clearly be further subdivided into a finite number of non-overlapping subintervals whose edges all lie between $l/8$ and $l/4$. We thus obtain a subdivision of the figure $J \ominus Q$ into a finite number of non-overlapping intervals, whose parameters of regularity are greater than, or equal to, $2^{-m} \geqslant \alpha$, and whose volumes are greater than, or equal to, $8^{-m} l^m \geqslant 8^{-m} \alpha^m \cdot |J| > \sigma \cdot |J|$. It therefore follows from (11.5) and (11.3) that

(11.7) $$G(J \ominus Q) > 0.$$

Similarly, it follows from (11.6) that $|Q| = 2^{-km} \geqslant 8^{-m} l^m \geqslant 8^{-m} \alpha^m \cdot |J| > \sigma \cdot |J|$, whence by (11.5) we derive at once the second of the relations (11.2); at the same time, by the relations (11.7) and (11.4), $G(Q) < G(J) < a \cdot |J| \leqslant 8^m \alpha^{-m} a \cdot |Q|$, and this gives the third of the relations (11.2) and completes the proof.

(11.8) ***Lemma.*** *Let G be an additive function of an interval in $\boldsymbol{R}_m$, E a set in $\boldsymbol{R}_m$, Q a cube belonging to one of the nets $\mathfrak{Q}_k$, and $\alpha > 0$, $\varepsilon > 0$ and b arbitrary fixed numbers. Suppose that*

(i) $|E \cdot Q| > (1-\varepsilon) \cdot |Q|$,

(ii) $G(I) > 0$ *for every interval I such that $I \subset Q$, $I \cdot E \neq 0$ and* $\mathrm{r}(I) \geqslant 2^{-m}$,

(iii) $\overline{G}_{(\alpha)}(x) > b$ *at any point $x \in E$;*

then $G(Q) > 12^{-m} \cdot \alpha^m b \cdot (1 - 2^m \varepsilon) \cdot |Q|$.

Proof. We may clearly assume that the set E is contained in the interior of Q and that every point of the set is a point of density.

This being so, we shall begin by establishing the following result:

(11.9) *Given any $\eta > 0$, we can associate with any point $x \in E$ a cube P, belonging to one of the nets $\mathfrak{Q}_k$, and a cube $J \supset P$, such that* (a) $G(P) > \alpha^m \cdot 12^{-m} \cdot b \cdot |P|$ *and* (b) $x \in J$, $\delta(J) < \eta$ *and* $|J| = 3^m \cdot |P|$.

For this purpose, let us associate with the point x an interval S such that $x \in S$, $\delta(S) \leqslant 1/4$, $\mathrm{r}(S) \geqslant \alpha$ and $G(S) > b \cdot |S|$. Let h denote the largest edge of S, and let k_1 be the positive integer satisfying the inequality $1/2^{k_1} > 2h \geqslant 1/2^{k_1+1}$. Let S_1 be a cube of the net $\mathfrak{Q}_{k_1}$ having points in common with S, and let J denote the cube formed by the 3^m cubes of the same net (including the cube S_1 itself) which have points in common with S_1.

The cube J clearly contains the interval S, and since no edge of S can be less than αh, we find that

$$(11.10) \qquad |J| = 3^m \cdot 2^{-mk_1} = 6^m \cdot 2^{-m(k_1+1)} \leqslant 12^m \cdot h^m \leqslant 12^m \cdot \alpha^{-m} \cdot |S|.$$

On the other hand, since $2^{-k_1} - h > 2^{-(k_1+1)}$ and $\alpha h \geqslant \alpha \cdot 2^{-(k_1+2)}$, the figure $J \ominus S$ can be subdivided into a finite number of non-overlapping intervals with edges greater than, or equal to, $\alpha \cdot 2^{-(k_1+2)}$, and therefore, as in the proof of Lemma 11.1, into a finite number of non-overlapping intervals whose edges have lengths between $\alpha \cdot 2^{-(k_1+2)}$ and $\alpha \cdot 2^{-(k_1+1)}$. Therefore, denoting by I any interval of this subdivision, we find $\mathrm{r}(I) \geqslant 2^{-m}$ and $|I| \geqslant \alpha^m \cdot 2^{-m(k_1+2)} = 12^{-m}\, \alpha^m \cdot |J|$. Consequently, by supposing the interval S, and *a fortiori* the cube J, sufficiently small, we may assume that $\delta(J) < \eta$ and that each of the intervals of the subdivision in question contains points of E. It follows, by condition (ii) of our lemma, that $G(J \ominus S) > 0$, and so, by (11.10), that $G(J) > G(S) > b \cdot |S| \geqslant 12^{-m} \cdot \alpha^m \cdot b \cdot |J|$. Thus among the 3^m cubes of the net $\mathfrak{Q}_{k_1}$ which make up the cube J, there is one at least, P say, such that $G(P) > 12^{-m} \cdot \alpha^m \cdot b \cdot |P|$, and the cubes P and $J \supset P$, thus defined, clearly satisfy the conditions (a) and (b) of (11.9).

It now follows, on account of (11.9) and condition (i) of the lemma, that (with the help of Vitali's theorem in the form (3.8)) we can determine in Q a finite system of non-overlapping intervals $P_1, P_2, \dots, P_n$ belonging to the nets $\mathfrak{Q}_k$, such that:

$$(11.11) \qquad G(P_i) > 12^{-m} \cdot \alpha^m\, b \cdot |P_i| \quad \textit{and} \quad P_i \cdot E \neq 0 \quad \textit{for} \quad i = 1, 2, \dots\, n,$$

$$(11.12) \qquad \sum_{i=1}^{n} |P_i| > (1 - \varepsilon) \cdot |Q|.$$

Among the cubes of the nets $\mathfrak{Q}_k$, we shall consider specially two classes of cubes. A cube of a net $\mathfrak{Q}_k$ contained in Q will be said to be of the first class if it is one of the cubes $P_1, P_2, \dots, P_n$; and of the second class if it contains points of E and if further among the 2^m cubes ($\mathfrak{Q}_{k+1}$) composing it, there exists at least one which does not overlap with any cube P_i. Since the number of cubes P_i is finite, there exists a net $\mathfrak{Q}_K$ such that no cube of this net contains cubes of the first class. Let $\mathfrak{A}$ be the set of all the cubes of the first or second class contained in Q and belonging to the nets $\mathfrak{Q}_k$ for $k \leqslant K$.

The set of these cubes covers the whole cube Q. For if not, there would certainly exist in the net $\mathfrak{Q}_K$ a cube $I_0 \subset Q$ not contained in any cube ($\mathfrak{A}$). Now, since I_0 contains no cube of the first class, I_0 would not contain any point of the set E; and since, by hypothesis, I_0 is not contained in any cube of the first or second class, we could, starting with I_0, form in Q a finite ascending sequence of cubes without points in common with E and which belong respectively to the nets $\mathfrak{Q}_K, \mathfrak{Q}_{K-1}, \dots, \mathfrak{Q}_{k_0}$, where $\mathfrak{Q}_{k_0}$ is the net containing the cube Q. But the last term of this sequence of cubes is evidently the cube Q itself, and we arrive at a contradiction since $E \subset Q$.

Let us now remark that since all the cubes ($\mathfrak{A}$) belong to the nets of the regular sequence $\{\mathfrak{Q}_k\}$, it follows that, of any two overlapping cubes ($\mathfrak{A}$), one is always contained in the other. Hence, we can replace the system of cubes $\mathfrak{A}$ by another system $\mathfrak{A}_1 \subset \mathfrak{A}$ which also covers Q, and which, this time, consists of non-overlapping cubes. Let A be the sum of the cubes ($\mathfrak{A}_1$) of the first class. On account of (11.11) we have

$$G(A) \geqslant 12^{-m} \cdot a^m \cdot b \cdot |A|. \tag{11.13}$$

Moreover, since the figure $Q \ominus A$ is formed of a finite number of cubes of the second class which do not overlap, it follows from condition (ii) of the lemma that

$$G(Q \ominus A) \geqslant 0. \tag{11.14}$$

Finally, in each cube I of the second class, there is always a cube which is contained in $Q \ominus \sum_{i=1}^{n} P_i$ and whose volume is $2^{-m} \cdot |I|$. It therefore follows from (11.12) that $|Q \ominus A| < 2^m \cdot \varepsilon \cdot |Q|$, and in virtue of (11.14) and (11.13) we find

$$G(Q) \geqslant G(A) \geqslant 12^{-m} \cdot a^m \cdot b \cdot |A| > 12^{-m} \cdot a^m \cdot b \cdot (1 - 2^m \varepsilon) \cdot |Q|,$$

which completes the proof.

(11.15) ***Theorem.*** *Any additive function of an interval F is derivable at almost all the points x at which either $\underline{F}(x) > -\infty$, or $\overline{F}(x) < +\infty$.*

Proof. Consider the set of the points x at which $\underline{F}(x) > -\infty$ and suppose, if possible, that the set A of the points x at which $\overline{F}(x) > \underline{F}(x) > -\infty$ is of positive measure. We could then determine a number $\alpha > 0$, and a set $B \subset A$ of positive outer measure, such that $\underline{F}_{(\alpha)}(x) \neq \infty$ and $\overline{F}_{(\alpha)}(x) - \underline{F}_{(\alpha)}(x) > \alpha$ at every point x of B. We may clearly assume that $\alpha \leqslant 2^{-m}$.

Let ε be any positive number. Let us denote for any integer p by B_p the set of the points x of B at which $p\varepsilon < \underline{F}_{(\alpha)}(x) \leqslant (p+1)\,\varepsilon$, and let p_0 be an integer such that $|B_{p_0}| > 0$. We can determine a number $\sigma > 0$ and a set $E \subset B_{p_0}$, whose measure is not zero, so as to have $F(I) > p_0\,\varepsilon \cdot |I|$ whenever the interval I is subject to the conditions $\delta(I) < \sigma$, $\mathrm{r}(I) \geqslant \alpha$ and $E \cdot I \neq 0$.

Now write $G(I) = F(I) - p_0\,\varepsilon \cdot |I|$ (where I denotes any interval). Thus defined, the function G clearly fulfils the conditions:

1° $0 < \underline{G}_{(\alpha)}(x) < 2\varepsilon$ and $\overline{G}_{(\alpha)}(x) > \alpha$ at any point $x \in E$,

2° $G(I) > 0$ for any interval I such that $\delta(I) < \sigma$, $\mathrm{r}(I) \geqslant \alpha$ and $E \cdot I \neq 0$.

By Lemma 11.1 we can therefore determine a cube Q, belonging to one of the nets $\mathfrak{Q}_k$, so as to have $\delta(Q) < \sigma$, $|E \cdot Q| > (1-\varepsilon) \cdot |Q|$ and $G(Q) \leqslant 8^m \alpha^{-m} \cdot 2\varepsilon \cdot |Q|$. From the first two of these relations and from conditions 1° and 2°, it follows, on account of Lemma 11.8, that $G(Q) > 12^{-m} \alpha^{m+1} \cdot (1-2^m \varepsilon) |Q|$. Thus $12^{-m} \alpha^{m+1} \cdot (1-2^m \varepsilon) \leqslant 8^m \alpha^{-m} \cdot 2\varepsilon$ for every $\varepsilon > 0$, and this is clearly impossible. We arrive at a contradiction and this shows that $|A| = 0$, i. e. that $\underline{F}(x) = \overline{F}(x)$ for almost all x for which $\underline{F}(x) > -\infty$.

It remains to be shown that the set of the points x at which the derivative $F'(x)$ is infinite, is of measure zero. Suppose then, if possible, that $F'(x) = +\infty$ at each point x of a set M of positive measure. We may clearly assume that there exists a number $\eta > 0$ such that $F(I) > 0$ whenever I is an interval containing points of M and subject to the conditions $\delta(I) < \eta$ and $\mathrm{r}(I) \geqslant 2^{-m}$. Therefore, denoting by R any cube which belongs to one of the nets $\mathfrak{Q}_k$ and which satisfies the relations $|M \cdot R| > (1-2^{-(m+1)}) \cdot |R|$ and $\delta(R) < \eta$, we find easily from Lemma 11.8 that $F(R) > 2^{-1} \cdot 12^{-m} \cdot b \cdot |R|$ for every finite number b. We thus again arrive at a contradiction and this completes the proof.

It should be remarked that for the validity of Lemma 11.1 it is enough to suppose merely that $\alpha<1$ (instead of $\alpha\leqslant 2^{-m}$). Similarly in condition (ii) of Lemma 11.8, the inequality $\mathrm{r}(I)\geqslant 2^{-m}$ may be replaced by $\mathrm{r}(I)\geqslant\alpha$. The proofs of the lemmas remain essentially the same; we need only observe that if I is an interval whose parameter of regularity is greater than, or equal to 2^{-m}, and if $\alpha<1$ is a positive number, the interval I can always be subdivided into a finite number of non-overlapping subintervals I_j, where $j=1, 2, \ldots$, such that $\mathrm{r}(I_j)\geqslant\alpha$ and $|I_j|\geqslant k_\alpha\cdot|I|$, where k_α is a constant depending only on α.

We can now easily see that Theorem 11.15 may be stated in a slightly more general form as follows: *any additive function of an interval F is derivable at almost all the points x at which either $\underline{F}_{(\alpha)}(x)>-\infty$ or $\overline{F}_{(\alpha)}(x)<+\infty$, where α is any positive number less than* 1. The question whether the condition $\alpha<1$ is necessary here, does not seem to have been solved yet completely. It may however easily be proved (by the method of nets used in the proof of Lemma 11.8) that *for any additive function F, the set of the points x for which either $\overline{F}_{(1)}(x)=-\infty$ or $\underline{F}_{(1)}(x)=+\infty$ is of measure zero.* For a discussion of these questions, *vide* the memoir of A. J. Ward [5].

We shall now proceed to prove the second theorem of Ward, in which the ordinary extreme derivates $\underline{F}(x)$ and $\overline{F}(x)$ of Theorem 11.15 are replaced by the strong derivates $\underline{F}_s(x)$ and $\overline{F}_s(x)$. It should be remarked however, that we cannot at the same time replace, in the assertion of Theorem 11.15, derivability in the ordinary sense by derivability in the strong sense: in fact, in general, a non-negative function, even when it is absolutely continuous, may yet have a strong upper derivate which is everywhere infinite (see p. 133 above).

We shall begin by proving the following lemma which is similar to Lemma 11.1.

(11.16) ***Lemma.*** *If G is an additive function of an interval in $\boldsymbol{R}_m$ and if for some fixed number a we have $0<\underline{G}_s(x)<a$ at every point of a set E of positive outer measure, then given any $\varepsilon>0$ there exists an interval Q such that*

$$(11.17)\qquad \delta(Q)<\varepsilon,\quad \mathrm{r}(Q)>2^{-m},\quad E\cdot Q\neq 0 \quad \textit{and} \quad G(Q)<3^m\cdot a\cdot|Q|.$$

Proof. Let us write for brevity $\gamma=1/3^m$. We may suppose (by replacing, if necessary, the set E by a subset of positive outer measure) that $G(I)>0$ for every interval I containing points of E, which has diameter less than a positive number $\sigma<\varepsilon$. Let $x_0\in E$ be a point of outer density for E and let $J=[a_1, b_1; a_2, b_2; \ldots ; a_m, b_m]$ be an interval containing x_0 such that

(11.18) $\delta(J) < \sigma, \ |E\cdot J| > (1-\gamma)\cdot|J| \text{ and } G(J) < a\cdot|J|.$

Let us denote by l the smallest edge of J and by n_1 the positive integer satisfying the inequality

(11.19) $$n_1 l \leqslant b_1 - a_1 < (n_1+1)\, l.$$

Writing $d_1 = (b_1 - a_1)/n_1$, let us subdivide the interval J into n_1 equal non-overlapping subintervals

$$J_i = [a_1 + (i-1)\, d_1,\ a_1 + i\, d_1;\ a_2, b_2;\ \dots;\ a_m, b_m]$$

where $i = 1, 2, \dots, n_1$. We shall call an interval J_i of the first kind if $|E\cdot J_i| > (1-3\gamma)\cdot|J_i|$, and of the second kind in the opposite case. Denoting by $\sum_i'$ a summation over the indices i corresponding to intervals of the second kind, we see easily, on account of the second of the relations (11.18), that $\sum_i' 3\gamma\cdot|J_i| < \gamma\cdot|J| = \sum_{i=1}^{n_1} \gamma\cdot|J_i|$. Hence, if p and q are the number of intervals J_i of the first and second kind respectively, we find $3q < n_1 = p+q$. Now let us subdivide the interval J into a finite number of non-overlapping subintervals, in such a manner that each of these is the sum of a certain number of intervals J_i among which exactly one is of the first kind. Since $2q < p$, the intervals of this subdivision include some which coincide with certain intervals J_i of the first kind, and their number is at least equal to $p - q > n_1/3$. Thus if we denote their sum by A, we find

(11.20) $$|A| > |J|/3.$$

On the other hand, the figure $J \ominus A$ consists of a finite number of non-overlapping intervals each of which contains an interval J_i of the first kind, and therefore points of E. Consequently, $G(J\ominus A) > 0$, and, on account of (11.18) and (11.20)

$$G(A) < G(J) < a\cdot|J| < 3a\cdot|A|.$$

It follows that among the intervals J_i of the first kind of which the figure A is formed, there exists one at least, J_{i_0} say, such that $G(J_{i_0}) < 3a\cdot J_{i_0}$.

Let us write, for brevity, $a_1^0 = a_1 + (i_0 - 1)\, d_1$, $b_1^0 = a_1 + i_0\, d_1$ and $J^{(1)} = J_{i_0} = [a_1^0, b_1^0;\ a_2, b_2;\ \dots;\ a_m, b_m]$. By the above, $J^{(1)} \subset J$, $G(J^{(1)}) < 3a\cdot|J^{(1)}|$ and, since $J^{(1)}$ coincides with an interval J_i of the first kind, $|E\cdot J^{(1)}| > (1-3\gamma)\cdot|J^{(1)}|$; finally by (11.19), $l \leqslant b_1^0 - a_1^0 = d_1 \leqslant 2l$.

If we now operate on $J^{(1)}$ just as we formerly did on J (except that we replace γ by 3γ, a by $3a$ and the linear interval $[a_1, b_1]$ by $[a_2, b_2]$), we obtain an interval $J^{(2)}=[a_1^0, b_1^0; a_2^0, b_2^0; a_3, b_3; \dots; a_m, b_m]\subset J^{(1)}$ such that $G(J^{(2)})<3^2\cdot a\cdot|J^{(2)}|$, $|E\cdot J^{(2)}|>(1-3^2\gamma)\cdot|J^{(2)}|$ and $l\leqslant b_j^0-a_j^0\leqslant 2l$ for $j=1,2$.

Proceeding in this way m times, we obtain after m operations an interval $J^{(m)}=[a_1^0, b_1^0; a_2^0, b_2^0; \dots; a_m^0, b_m^0]\subset J$ such that $G(J^{(m)})<3^m a\cdot|J^{(m)}|$, $|E\cdot J^{(m)}|>(1-3^m\gamma)\cdot|J^{(m)}|$ and $l\leqslant b_j^0-a_j^0\leqslant 2l$ for $j=1,2,\dots,m$. It follows that $\mathrm{r}(J^{(m)})\geqslant 2^{-m}$, and if we write $Q=J^{(m)}$ and substitute $\gamma=3^{-m}$, we find at once that the interval Q fulfils the conditions (11.17).

(11.21) ***Theorem.*** *If F is an additive function of an interval, we have $F'(x)=\underline{F}_s(x)\neq\infty$ $[F'(x)=\overline{F}_s(x)\neq\infty]$ at almost all the points at which $\underline{F}_s(x)>-\infty$ $[\overline{F}_s(x)<+\infty]$.*

Thus, in particular, the function F is derivable in the strong sense at almost all the points at which both the extreme strong derivates $\underline{F}_s(x)$ and $\overline{F}_s(x)$ are finite.

Proof. Since $\underline{F}(x)\geqslant\underline{F}_s(x)$ holds for all x, the function F is, by Theorem 11.15, derivable (in the ordinary sense) at almost all the points x for which $\underline{F}_s(x)>-\infty$, and we have only to show further that at almost all these points $F'(x)=\underline{F}_s(x)$. Suppose therefore that the set of the points x for which $F'(x)>\underline{F}_s(x)>-\infty$ is of positive measure. We could then determine a number $\alpha>0$ and a set B of positive measure such that $F'(x)-\underline{F}_s(x)>\alpha$ at every point $x\in B$.

For brevity, write $\varepsilon=\alpha\cdot 3^{-(m+1)}$, and let B_p denote the set of the points $x\in B$ for which $p\varepsilon<\underline{F}_s(x)\leqslant(p+1)\cdot\varepsilon$. Let p_0 be an integer such that $|B_{p_0}|>0$, and write $G(I)=F(I)-p_0\varepsilon\cdot|I|$ (where I is any interval). Since $G'(x)>\underline{G}_s(x)+\alpha>\alpha$ at every point $x\in B_{p_0}$, we can determine a positive number σ and a set $E\subset B_{p_0}$ of positive measure, such that $G(Q)>\alpha\cdot|Q|$ whenever Q is an interval satisfying the conditions

$$(11.22)\qquad \delta(Q)<\sigma,\quad \mathrm{r}(Q)>2^{-m}\quad \textit{and}\quad E\cdot Q\neq 0.$$

But since $0<\underline{G}_s(x)<2\varepsilon$ at every point $x\in E\subset B_{p_0}$, there exists by Lemma 11.16, an interval Q subject to the conditions (11.22) and such that $G(Q)<3^m\cdot 2\varepsilon\cdot|Q|<\alpha\cdot|Q|$. We thus arrive at a contradiction and this proves the theorem.

§ 12. A theorem of Hardy Littlewood. The theorem of Jessen, Marcinkiewicz and Zygmund concerning strong derivation of indefinite integrals, which was mentioned in § 10, p. 133, is connected with an important inequality due to G. H. Hardy and J. E. Littlewood [2]. This inequality, which was established in connection with certain problems of the theory of trigonometrical series, thus obtains a new and interesting application.

We reproduce in this § the elegant proof given by F. Riesz [5] (cf. also A. Zygmund [I, pp. 241—245]) for this inequality. Although simpler than the other proofs, it requires nevertheless some rather delicate considerations. Certain parts of the argument have been touched up in accordance with suggestions communicated to the author by Zygmund.

The reasonings of this § concern functions of a real variable.

(12.1) ***F. Riesz's lemma.*** *Let $F(x)$ be a continuous function on an interval $[a, b]$ and k a finite number. Let E be the set of the points x, interior to the interval $[a, b]$, for each of which the inequality $F(x)-F(u) > k\cdot(x-u)$ is fulfilled by at least one point u subject to $a < u < x$.*

Then the set E is either empty, or else expressible as the sum of a sequence $\{(a_n, b_n)\}$ of open non-overlapping intervals such that $F(b_n)-F(a_n) \geqslant k\cdot(b_n-a_n)$.

Proof. By subtracting from $F(x)$ the linear function kx, we may suppose that $k=0$. Then E is the set of all the points x of the open interval (a, b), for each of which there exists a point u such that $F(u) < F(x)$ and $a < u < x$. Since the function F is continuous, the set E is clearly open, — and, unless empty, it is therefore expressible as the sum of a sequence $\{(a_n, b_n)\}$ of non-overlapping open intervals. We have to prove $F(a_n) \leqslant F(b_n)$ for each n.

To see this, let us fix an index n and suppose that $F(a_n) > F(b_n)$. Let h be any number such that

(12.2) $$F(a_n) > h > F(b_n),$$

and let x_0 be the lower bound of the points x of the interval $[a_n, b_n]$ for which $F(x)=h$. By (12.2) the point x_0 belongs to the open interval (a_n, b_n), and so to the set E; thus there exists a point y such that $F(y) < F(x_0) = h < F(a_n)$ and $a < y < x_0$. This last relation implies $a < y < a_n$, since, by (12.2) and by the definition of the point

x_0, the inequality $F(y) < h$ cannot hold for any y of the interval $[a_n, x_0]$. Thus $F(y) < F(a_n)$ and $a < y < a_n$, and consequently $a_n \in E$; but this is clearly contradictory, since a_n is an end-point of one of the non-overlapping open intervals which constitute the set E.

Besides the results treated in this §, many other applications of Lemma 12.1 are given by F. Riesz [6; 7; 8], particularly in the theory of derivation of functions of a real variable. Cf. also S. Izumi [1]. The lemma might also have been used in the considerations of § 9 (instead of appealing to the theorems of § 8 on rectifiable curves).

To shorten our notations we shall restrict ourselves in the rest of this § to functions defined in the open interval (0, 1); and we shall agree to write $\mathrm{E}[f > a]$ for $\underset{x}{\mathrm{E}}[f(x) > a;\ 0 < x < 1]$. The symbols $\mathrm{E}[f \geqslant a]$, $\mathrm{E}[b > f > a]$ and so on, will have similar meanings.

Two measurable functions g and h in (0, 1) will be called (in accordance with the terminology of F. Riesz) *equi-measurable* if $|\mathrm{E}[g > a]| = |\mathrm{E}[h > a]|$ for every finite number a. We see at once that we then also have

$$|\mathrm{E}[g \geqslant a]| = |\mathrm{E}[h \geqslant a]|, \quad \mathrm{E}|[b > g \geqslant a]| = |\mathrm{E}[b > h \geqslant a]|, \quad \text{etc.}$$

(12.3) *If two non-negative measurable functions g and h in the interval* (0, 1) *are equi-measurable, their definite integrals over this interval are equal.*

To see this, let us associate with the function g a non-decreasing sequence $\{g_n\}$ of simple functions by writing $g_n(x) = (k-1)/2^n$ when $(k-1)/2^n \leqslant g(x) < k/2^n$ and $k = 1, 2, \dots, 2^n \cdot n$, and $g_n(x) = n$ when $g(x) \geqslant n$. Similarly with g replaced by h, we define the sequence $\{h_n\}$ converging to the function h. If we calculate directly the integrals of the functions g_n and h_n over (0, 1) by formula 10.1 of Chap. I, p. 20, we see at once from the fact that the given functions g and h are equi-measurable that $\int_0^1 g_n(x)\,dx = \int_0^1 h_n(x)\,dx$. Making $n \to \infty$, this gives $\int_0^1 g(x)\,dx = \int_0^1 h(x)\,dx$ as asserted.

If f is a continuous function in (0, 1) which is not constant on any set of positive measure, and if m and M denote the lower and upper bound of f respectively, the function $g(y) = |\mathrm{E}[f > y]|$ is evidently continuous and decreases from 1 to 0 in the open interval

(m, M). Its inverse function is therefore continuous and decreasing in $(0, 1)$ and, as we easily verify, equi-measurable with the given function.

We shall extend this process with suitable modifications, to arbitrary measurable functions finite almost everywhere in $(0, 1)$.

With any such a function $f(x)$, we associate the function $f^{\alpha}(x)$ defined for each x of $(0, 1)$ as the upper bound of the numbers y for which $|E[f>y]|>x$. The function $f^{\alpha}(x)$ is clearly finite and non-increasing in $(0, 1)$. To show that this function is equi-measurable with $f(x)$, let y_0 be any finite number, and let x_0 denote the upper bound of the set $E[f^{\alpha}>y_0]$, or else $x_0=0$ if this set is empty. Then since $|E[f^{\alpha}>y_0]|=x_0$, it has to be proved that $|E[f>y_0]|=x_0$.

We have, in the first place, $f^{\alpha}(x_0+\varepsilon)\leqslant y_0$ for every $\varepsilon>0$ (provided, of course, that $x_0+\varepsilon<1$), so that $|E[f>y_0+\varepsilon]|\leqslant x_0+\varepsilon$, and therefore $|E[f>y_0]|\leqslant x_0$. On the other hand, $f^{\alpha}(x_0-\varepsilon)>y_0$ for every $\varepsilon>0$ (provided that $x_0-\varepsilon>0$), so that $|E[f>y_0]|>x_0-\varepsilon$, whence $|E[f>y_0]|\geqslant x_0$, and finally $|E[f>y_0]|=x_0=E[f^{\alpha}>y_0]$.

We shall further define, in connection with any summable function $f(x)$, three functions $f^{\beta_1}(x)$, $f^{\beta_2}(x)$ and $f^{\beta}(x)$. At any point x of $(0, 1)$ we shall denote by $f^{\beta_1}(x)$ the upper bound of the mean values of f on the intervals (u, x) contained in $(0, x)$, i.e. the upper bound of the numbers $\dfrac{1}{x-u}\displaystyle\int_u^x f(t)\,dt$ for $0<u<x$. Similarly, $f^{\beta_2}(x)$ will denote the upper bound of the means $\dfrac{1}{v-x}\displaystyle\int_x^v f(t)\,dt$ for $x<v<1$. Finally, $f^{\beta}(x)$ will denote the larger of the two numbers $f^{\beta_1}(x)$ and $f^{\beta_2}(x)$, or what comes to the same, the upper bound of the means $\dfrac{1}{v-u}\displaystyle\int_u^v f(t)\,dt$ where u and v are subject to the condition $0<u<x<v<1$.

(12.4) ***Lemma.*** *If $f(x)$ is a non-negative measurable function in the open interval* $(0, 1)$ *and if E is a set contained in this interval, then*

$$\int_E f(x)\,dx\leqslant\int_0^{|E|} f^{\alpha}(x)\,dx.$$

Proof. Let f_1 be the function equal to f on the set E and to 0 elsewhere. We evidently have $f_1^\alpha(x) \leqslant f^\alpha(x)$ at each point x of the interval (0,1). Furthermore $f_1^\alpha(x)=0$ as soon as $x>|E|$. Therefore on account of (12.3) we find $\int_E f(x)\,dx = \int_0^1 f_1(x)\,dx = \int_0^1 f_1^\alpha(x)\,dx \leqslant \int_0^{|E|} f^\alpha(x)\,dx$.

(12.5) ***Lemma.*** *If $f(x)$ is a non-negative summable function in the interval* (0,1), *then for each point x of the interval, we have* $f^{\beta_1\alpha}(x) \leqslant \frac{1}{x}\int_0^x f^\alpha(t)\,dt$.

Proof. Let x_0 be any point in (0,1), let $y_0 = f^{\beta_1\alpha}(x_0)$, and let ε denote an arbitrary positive number. We write $A = \mathrm{E}[f^{\beta_1\alpha} > y_0 - \varepsilon]$ and $B = \mathrm{E}[f^{\beta_1} > y_0 - \varepsilon]$. Then since the function $f^{\beta_1\alpha}$ is non-increasing, we have $|A| \geqslant x_0$ and therefore, remembering that the functions $f^{\beta_1\alpha}$ and f^{β_1} are equi-measurable, $|B| = |A| \geqslant x_0$.

Now B is the set of the points x for each of which there exists a point u subject to the conditions $\int_u^x f(t)\,dt > (y_0-\varepsilon)\cdot(x-u)$ and $0<u<x$. Therefore, applying F. Riesz's Lemma 12.1 to the indefinite integral of f, we find easily that B is an open set and that $\int_B f(t)\,dt \geqslant (y_0-\varepsilon)\cdot|B|$. It follows by Lemma 12.4 that

$$y_0 - \varepsilon \leqslant \frac{1}{|B|}\int_B f(t)\,dt \leqslant \frac{1}{|B|}\int_0^{|B|} f^\alpha(t)\,dt. \tag{12.6}$$

Now since $|B| \geqslant x_0$ and since the function f^α is non-increasing, the last term of (12.6) cannot exceed $\frac{1}{x_0}\int_0^{x_0} f^\alpha(t)\,dt$; and since ε is an arbitrary positive number, we must have $f^{\beta_1\alpha}(x_0) = y_0 \leqslant \frac{1}{x_0}\int_0^{x_0} f^\alpha(t)dt$. This completes the proof.

(12.7) ***Theorem of Hardy-Littlewood.*** *If $f(x)$ is a non-negative summable function in* (0, 1) *and ε is a positive number, then*

$$\int_0^1 f^\beta(x)\,dx \leqslant A\cdot\int_0^1 f(x)\cdot\log^+ f(x)\,dx + B\cdot\int_0^1 f(x)\,dx + \varepsilon, \tag{12.8}$$

where A and B are constants depending on ε, but not on f.

Proof. We first evaluate the integral of f^{β_1} over $(0,1)$. According to (12.3) and Lemma 12.5 we have

$$\int_0^1 f^{\beta_1}(x)\,dx = \int_0^1 f^{\beta_1\alpha}(x)\,dx \leqslant \int_0^1 \left[\int_0^x \frac{f^\alpha(y)}{x}\,dy\right] dx.$$

In virtue of Fubini's theorem the last member of this inequality is the surface integral of the function $f^\alpha(y)/x$ over the triangle $0 \leqslant x \leqslant 1$, $0 \leqslant y \leqslant x$. Therefore inverting the order of integration in this member, we find

$$(12.9)\qquad \int_0^1 f^{\beta_1}(x)\,dx \leqslant \int_0^1 \left[\int_y^1 \frac{dx}{x}\right] f^\alpha(y)\,dy = \int_0^1 f^\alpha(y)\cdot|\log y|\,dy.$$

Let now $\eta < 1$ be a positive number such that $\int_0^\eta |\log y|/\sqrt{y}\,dy < \varepsilon/2$. Let us denote by E_1 the set of the points y of the interval $(0, \eta)$ at which $f^\alpha(y) \leqslant 1/\sqrt{y}$, and by E_2, the set of the remaining points of this interval. We find

$$(12.10)\qquad \int_0^1 f^\alpha(y)\cdot|\log y|\,dy \leqslant \int_{E_1} \frac{|\log y|}{\sqrt{y}}\,dy + 2\int_{E_2} f^\alpha(y)\cdot\log f^\alpha(y)\,dy +$$
$$+ |\log \eta|\cdot\int_\eta^1 f^\alpha(y)\,dy \leqslant 2\int_0^1 f^\alpha(y)\cdot\log^+ f^\alpha(y)\,dy + |\log \eta|\cdot\int_0^1 f^\alpha(y)\,dy + \varepsilon/2.$$

Further, since the functions f and f^α are equi-measurable, so are the functions $f\cdot\log^+ f$ and $f^\alpha\cdot\log^+ f^\alpha$, and it therefore follows from (12.9) and (12.10) that

$$(12.11)\qquad \int_0^1 f^{\beta_1}(x)\,dx \leqslant 2\int_0^1 f(x)\cdot\log^+ f(x)\,dx + |\log \eta|\cdot\int_0^1 f(x)\,dx + \varepsilon/2.$$

A similar inequality clearly holds when on the left-hand side of (12.11) f^{β_1} is replaced by f^{β_2}, and on adding the two inequalities we find $\int_0^1 f^\beta(x)\,dx \leqslant \int_0^1 f^{\beta_1}(x)\,dx + \int_0^1 f^{\beta_2}(x)\,dx \leqslant 4\int_0^1 f(x)\cdot\log^+ f(x)\,dx +$
$+ |2\log \eta|\cdot\int_0^1 f(x)\,dx + \varepsilon$; this gives (12.8) with $A = 4$ and with $B = 2|\log \eta|$.

***§ 13. Strong derivation of the indefinite integral.** We proceed to prove the theorem of Jessen, Marcinkiewicz and Zygmund. We shall give the proof for the case of the plane; its extension to spaces $\boldsymbol{R}_m$ of any number of dimensions (cf. § 10, p. 133) presents no fresh difficulties and is effected by means of the well-known inequality of Jensen.

We shall begin with some auxiliary remarks. Suppose given a non-negative function $f(x, y)$ summable over the open square $J_0=(0, 1; 0, 1)$. By Fubini's theorem, the function $f(x, y)$ is summable in x over $(0, 1)$ for almost all y of $(0, 1)$. Denote by H the set of these values of y. For any $y \in H$ and for any x of the interval $(0, 1)$, we shall denote (cf. § 12, p. 144) by $f^{\beta}(x, y)$ the upper bound of the mean $\dfrac{1}{v-u}\displaystyle\int_u^v f(t, y)\,dt$ for $0<u<x<v<1$; and whenever $y \in CH$, we shall write, for definiteness, $f^{\beta}(x, y)=0$ identically in x. We shall prove that the function $f^{\beta}(x, y)$ thus associated with any function $f(x, y)$ which is summable over the open square $J_0=(0,1; 0,1)$, is measurable.

For this purpose, let a and b denote two positive numbers, and write $g_{a,b}(x, y)=\displaystyle\int_{x-a}^{x+b} f(t, y)\,dt$ when $y \in H$ and $0\leqslant x-a<x+b\leqslant 1$, and $g_{a,b}(x, y)=0$ elsewhere in J_0. We shall begin by showing that each of the functions $g_{a,b}(x, y)$ is measurable. By Lusin's theorem, or more directly by the theorem of Vitali-Carathéodory (Chap. III, § 7), the function f is equal almost everywhere to the limit of a non-decreasing sequence $\{f^{(n)}\}$ of non-negative, bounded, upper semi-continuous functions. Now, let us put $g_{a,b}^{(n)}(x, y)=\displaystyle\int_{x-a}^{x+b} f^{(n)}(t, y)\,dt$ when $0\leqslant x-a<x+b\leqslant 1$, and $g_{a,b}^{(n)}(x, y)=0$ elsewhere. As is easy to show (e. g. by means of Theorem 12.11, Chap. I), each of the functions $g_{a,b}^{(n)}(x, y)$ is then also upper semi-continuous, and since, as we readily see, $g_{a,b}(x, y)=\lim\limits_n g_{a,b}^{(n)}(x, y)$ almost everywhere, the function $g_{a,b}(x, y)$ is measurable.

Finally, with the same notation as above, if $\{u_p\}$ is the sequence of rational numbers of the interval $(0, 1)$ we have

$$f^{\beta}(x, y)=\underset{p,q}{\text{upper bound}}\; g_{u_p,u_q}(x, y)/(u_p-u_q)$$

at any point (x, y) of J_0. Thus the function $f^\beta(x, y)$ is also measurable, and this proves our assertion.

(13.1) ***Theorem.*** *If $f(x, y)$ is a measurable function in the plane $\boldsymbol{R}_2$ and if the function $f \log^+ |f|$ is summable, then the indefinite integral of f is almost everywhere derivable in the strong sense.*

Proof. Clearly we need only consider the function f in the open square $J_0=(0, 1; 0, 1)$; and we may also suppose that this function is non-negative.

We write $g_n(x, y)=f(x, y)$ wherever $f(x, y)\leqslant n$, and $g_n(x, y)=n$ wherever $f(x, y)>n$; we write further $h_n(x, y)=f(x, y)-g_n(x, y)$ and we denote by σ an arbitrary positive number. The functions $h_n^\beta(x, y)$ are measurable and non-negative; so that by Theorem 12.7 of Hardy-Littlewood,

$$\iint_{J_0} h_n^\beta(x, y)\, dxdy \leqslant \tag{13.2}$$
$$\leqslant A \iint_{J_0} h_n(x, y)\cdot\log^+ h_n(x,y)\, dxdy + B \iint_{J_0} h_n(x, y)\, dxdy + \tfrac{1}{2}\sigma^2,$$

where A and B are finite constants depending only on σ. And since the integrals on the right-hand side of (13.2) tend to 0 as $n\to\infty$, there exists a positive integer N such that the left-hand side of (13.2) becomes less than σ^2 for $n=N$. Therefore, writing for brevity $h(x, y)=h_N(x, y)$ and $g(x, y)=g_N(x, y)$, we have

$$\iint_{J_0} h^\beta(x, y)\, dxdy < \sigma^2, \tag{13.3}$$

so that in particular the function $h^\beta(x, y)$, besides being measurable and non-negative, is summable on J_0.

Now denote by E the set of the points (x_0, y_0) of J_0 such that 1^0 $\int_0^1 h^\beta(x_0, t)\, dt<+\infty$, and 2^0 the indefinite integral $\int_0^y h^\beta(x_0, t)\, dt$ has at the point $y=y_0$ the derivative $h^\beta(x_0, y_0)$ with respect to y. Since, by Theorem 6.3, condition 2^0 is fulfilled for almost all y_0 of $(0, 1)$ provided that condition 1^0 is satisfied, it follows at once from Fubini's theorem in the form (8.6), Chap. III (cf. also Theorem 6.7, Chap. III) that $|E|=|J_0|=1$.

Let us write F, H and G for the indefinite integrals of the functions f, h and g, respectively, in J_0. Let (x_0, y_0) be a point of the set E and $I=[x_0-u_1, x_0+u_2; y_0-v_1, y_0+v_2]$ any interval containing (x_0, y_0) and contained in J_0. We have

$$\frac{H(I)}{|I|} = \frac{1}{v_2+v_1} \int_{-v_1}^{v_2} \left[\frac{1}{u_2+u_1} \int_{-u_1}^{u_2} h(x_0+u,\, y_0+v)\, du \right] dv \leqslant$$

$$\leqslant \frac{1}{v_2+v_1} \int_{-v_1}^{v_2} h^{\beta}(x_0,\, y_0+v)\, dv,$$

whence making $\delta(I) \to 0$ we obtain $\overline{H}_s(x_0, y_0) \leqslant h^{\beta}(x_0, y_0)$. Thus, since (x_0, y_0) is an arbitrary point of the set $E \subset J_0$ of outer measure 1, and since the extreme derivate $\overline{H}_s(x_0, y_0)$ is measurable (cf. Theorem 4.2), it follows from (13.3) that $0 \leqslant \underline{H}_s(x, y) \leqslant \overline{H}_s(x, y) \leqslant \sigma$ at every point (x, y) of J_0, except at most a set of measure less than σ. On the other hand, since the function $g = g_N$ is bounded, its indefinite integral G is, by Theorem 10.7, derivable in the strong sense almost everywhere. Therefore $\overline{F}_s(x, y) - \underline{F}_s(x, y) \leqslant \sigma$ at all but a subset of measure σ of the points of J_0; and so finally, since σ is an arbitrary positive number, $\overline{F}_s(x, y) = \underline{F}_s(x, y)$ almost everywhere in J_0, which completes the proof.

By Ward's Theorem 11.21, to prove that the non-negative function F is almost everywhere derivable in the strong sense, it is enough to show that $\overline{F}_s(x) < +\infty$ almost everywhere. Hence by using Theorem 11.21, the proof of Theorem 13.1 might be slightly shortened.

***§ 14. Symmetrical derivates.** If Φ is an additive function of a set in a space R_m, we shall denote by $\overline{\mathrm{D}}_{\mathrm{sym}}\, \Phi(x)$ the *upper*, and by $\underline{\mathrm{D}}_{\mathrm{sym}}\, \Phi(x)$ the *lower*, *symmetrical derivate* of Φ at a point x, these being defined respectively as the upper, and as the lower, limit of the ratio $\Phi(S)/|S|$ where S represents a closed sphere of centre x and of radius tending to zero. It is obvious that, for any point x whatsoever $\overline{\mathrm{D}}\Phi(x) \geqslant \overline{\mathrm{D}}_{\mathrm{sym}}\, \Phi(x) \geqslant \underline{\mathrm{D}}_{\mathrm{sym}}\, \Phi(x) \geqslant \underline{\mathrm{D}}\Phi(x)$.

Following A. J. Ward [5], we shall establish a decomposition theorem in terms of symmetrical derivates, which is similar to Theorem 9.6. We shall begin by the following "covering theorem":

(14.1) ***Theorem.*** *If Φ is an additive function of a set in R_m and E a bounded set measurable ($\mathfrak{B}$), contained in an open set G, then for any $\varepsilon > 0$ there exists in G an enumerable sequence of closed spheres $\{S_k\}$ such that* (i) *the centre of each S_k belongs to E and the radius is less than ε,* (ii) *$S_i \cdot S_j = 0$ whenever $i \neq j$, and* (iii) *the spheres S_k cover together the whole of the set E, with the possible exception of a subset on which the function Φ vanishes identically.*

Proof. We can clearly assume (by replacing, if necessary), the function Φ by its absolute variation) that the function Φ is monotone non-negative.

a) We shall first prove that, with the hypotheses of the theorem, there always exists in G a finite system of equal spheres $\{S_k\}$ which sasisfy the conditions (i) and (ii) and cover the set E except perhaps for a set $T \subset E$ such that

$$(14.2) \qquad \Phi(T) \leqslant (1-1/4^{m+1}\, m^m)\cdot\Phi(E).$$

To see this, let A be a subset of E, measurable ($\mathfrak{B}$), such that $\Phi(A) \geqslant \frac{1}{2}\Phi(E)$ and $\varrho(A, CG) > 0$. Let n_0 be a positive integer such that $m/n_0 < \varrho(A, CG)$ and $m/n_0 < \varepsilon$.

Denote by $\mathfrak{P}$ the net in the space $\boldsymbol{R}_m$, which consists of the cubes of the form $[p_1/n_0, (p_1+1)/n_0;\ p_2/n_0, (p_2+1)/n_0; \dots, p_m/n_0, (p_m+1)\, n_0]$ where $p_1, p_2, \dots, p_m$ are arbitrary integers. We can clearly subdivide the net $\mathfrak{P}$ into $(4m)^m$ families of cubes, $\mathfrak{P}_1, \mathfrak{P}_2, \dots, \mathfrak{P}_{(4m)^m}$ say, such that the distance between any two cubes belonging to the same family is not less than $(4m-1)/n_0$. Denote, for each $k=1, 2, \dots, (4m)^m$, by A_k the part of the set A covered by the cubes of the family $\mathfrak{P}_k$. Then there exists a positive integer $k_0 \leqslant (4m)^m$ such that

$$(14.3) \qquad \Phi(A_{k_0}) \geqslant \Phi(A)/(4m)^m \geqslant \Phi(E)/4^{m+1}\, m^m$$

Now let $P_1, P_2, \dots, P_r$ be those cubes of $\mathfrak{P}_{k_0}$ which contain points of A_{k_0}. With each P_i we can associate a closed sphere S_i, of radius m/n_0, whose centre belongs to $A_{k_0}\cdot P_i$. The system of spheres $S_1, S_2, \dots, S_r$ thus defined is contained in G and clearly satisfies the conditions (i) and (ii) of the theorem. Again, since $P_i \subset S_i$ for every $i=1, 2, \dots, r$, the spheres S_i cover the whole of the set E with the possible exception of the points of the set $T=E-A_{k_0}$, which, in virtue of (14.3), fulfils the condition (14.2)

b) We now pass on to the proof of the assertion of the theorem. By what has already been proved, we can define by induction a sequence $\{\mathfrak{S}_n\}_{n=1,2,\dots}$ of finite systems of closed spheres with centres in E and radii less than ε, subject to the following two conditions: 1° If B_0 denotes the empty set and B_n, for $n \geqslant 1$, the sum of the spheres belonging to $\mathfrak{S}_1 + \mathfrak{S}_2 + \dots + \mathfrak{S}_n$, then the system $\mathfrak{S}_{n+1}$, where $n \geqslant 0$, consists of a finite number of closed spheres, contained in the open set $G-B_n$, no two of which have common points; 2° $\Phi(E-B_{n+1}) \leqslant (1-h_m)\ \Phi(E-B_n)$ where $h_m = 1/4^{m+1}\, m^m$ and $n=0, 1, \dots$ Now, arranging the spheres belonging to the family

$\mathfrak{S}_1+\mathfrak{S}_2+\ldots+\mathfrak{S}_n+\ldots$ in a sequence $\{S_i\}$, we see at once that the latter fulfils conditions (i) and (ii) of the theorem. On the other hand, by 2° we have $\Phi(E-B_n)\leqslant(1-h_m)^n\cdot\Phi(E)$ for each n; whence, denoting by B the sum of all the spheres S_i, it follows that $\Phi(E-B)=0$, which establishes condition (iii) and completes the proof.

Theorem 14.1 may be established in a slightly more general form: *Given a bounded set E measurable ($\mathfrak{B}$), a sequence of positive numbers $\{r_n\}$ converging to 0 and a family of closed sets $\mathfrak{A}$, suppose that with each point x of E there are associated two finite numbers $\alpha=\alpha(x)$, $N=N(x)$, and a sequence $\{A_n(x)\}$ of sets ($\mathfrak{A}$) such that $\mathrm{S}(x;r_n)\subset A_n(x)\subset \mathrm{S}(x;\alpha r_n)$ for $n\geqslant N(x)$.*

Then, for any sequence $\{\Phi_n\}$ of additive functions of a set, we can extract from $\mathfrak{A}$ a sequence of sets $\{A_i=A_{n_i}(x_i)\}$ such that (i) $x_i\in E$ *for* $i=1,2,\ldots$, (ii) $A_i\cdot A_j=0$ *whenever* $i\neq j$, *and* (iii) *the sets A_i cover the whole of the set E, with the exception at most of a set of measure zero on which all the functions Φ_n vanish identically.*

(14.4) ***Lemma.*** *If Φ is an additive function of a set in $\boldsymbol{R}_m$, and if $\underline{\mathrm{D}}_{\mathrm{sym}}\Phi(x)>0$ at each point x of a bounded set X measurable ($\mathfrak{B}$), then $\Phi(X)\geqslant 0$.*

Proof. Let us denote, for every positive integer n, by X_n the set of the points $x\in X$ such that $\Phi(S)\geqslant 0$ whenever S is a closed sphere of centre x and radius less than $1/n$. Each set X_n is evidently measurable ($\mathfrak{B}$), in fact closed in X. Hence, for any $\varepsilon>0$, we can associate with each X_n an open set $G_n\supset X_n$ such that $\mathrm{W}(\Phi;G_n-X_n)\leqslant\varepsilon$ (cf. Theorems 6.9 and 6.10, Chap. III). Next, keeping n fixed for the moment, we can (on account of Theorem 14.1) define in G_n a sequence $\{S_k\}$ of closed spheres with centres in X_n and radii less than $1/n$, such that (i) $S_i\cdot S_j=0$ whenever $i\neq j$, and (ii) the spheres S_k cover the whole of the set X_n with the exception at most of a set T on which the function Φ vanishes identically. Since $\Phi(S_k)\geqslant 0$ for every k, we find by (i) and (ii) that $\Phi(X_n)\geqslant -[\mathrm{W}(\Phi;T)+\mathrm{W}(\Phi;G_n-X_n)]\geqslant-\varepsilon$. Hence, as $X=\lim_n X_n$ and ε is an arbitrary positive number, it follows that $\Phi(X)\geqslant 0$, which completes the proof.

(14.5). ***Theorem.*** *If Φ is an additive function of a set in $\boldsymbol{R}_m$, and if A_∞ denotes the set of x at which one at least of the derivates $\overline{\mathrm{D}}_{\mathrm{sym}}\Phi(x)$ and $\underline{\mathrm{D}}_{\mathrm{sym}}\Phi(x)$ is infinite, then for any bounded set X measurable ($\mathfrak{B}$), we have*

(14.6) $$\Phi(X)=\Phi(X\cdot A_\infty)+\int_X \mathrm{D}\Phi(x)\,dx.$$

Consequently, if $\underline{\mathrm{D}}_{\mathrm{sym}}\Phi(x)>-\infty$ at every point x and $\mathrm{D}\Phi(x)\geqslant 0$ at almost every point x of a bounded set X measurable ($\mathfrak{B}$), then $\Phi(X)\geqslant 0$.

Proof. We firstly remark that if $-\infty<\underline{\mathrm{D}}_{\mathrm{sym}}\Phi(x)$ at each point x of a bounded set Q measurable ($\mathfrak{B}$) and of measure zero, then $\Phi(Q)\geqslant 0$. In fact, denoting for each positive integer n by Q_n the set of the points x of Q at which $-n<\underline{\mathrm{D}}_{\mathrm{sym}}\Phi(x)$, and writing $\Phi_n(X)=\Phi(X)+n\cdot|X|$, we obtain $\underline{\mathrm{D}}_{\mathrm{sym}}\Phi_n(x)>0$ at every point $x\in Q_n$. Hence, by Lemma 14.4, we must have $\Phi(Q_n)=\Phi_n(Q_n)\geqslant 0$, and making $n\to\infty$ we find $\Phi(Q)\geqslant 0$. By symmetry we also have $\Phi(Q)\leqslant 0$ whenever Q is a bounded set measurable ($\mathfrak{B}$) of measure zero, such that $\overline{\mathrm{D}}\Phi(x)<+\infty$ at each point x of Q.

We pass on to the proof of formula (14.6). By Theorem 7.3, there exists a set A, measurable ($\mathfrak{B}$) and of measure zero, such that the relation

$$\Phi(X)=\Phi(X\cdot A)+\int_X \mathrm{D}\Phi(x)\,dx \tag{14.7}$$

holds whenever X is a bounded set measurable ($\mathfrak{B}$). Since the set A_∞ is of measure zero, we see at once from the equation (14.7) that the function Φ must vanish identically for all the subsets of $A_\infty - A$, which are bounded and measurable ($\mathfrak{B}$). On the other hand, by what has just been proved, the function vanishes also for all subsets of $A - A_\infty$. Hence the set A_∞ may be taken in place of the set A in (14.7) and this gives (14.6). Finally, if $\underline{\mathrm{D}}_{\mathrm{sym}}\Phi(x)>-\infty$ at every point x of a bounded set X measurable ($\mathfrak{B}$), then $\Phi(X\cdot A_\infty)\geqslant 0$ and the second part of the theorem follows at once from the first.

Let us mention the following consequence of Theorem 14.5: *If at each point x both the symmetrical derivates of a given additive function of a set are finite, the latter is absolutely continuous.* For ordinary derivates the corresponding proposition has long been known (cf. H. Lebesgue [5, p. 423]) and is moreover included in Theorem 15.7 of this chapter, as well as in Theorem 2.1 of Chap. VI.

***§ 15. Derivation in abstract spaces.** With certain hypotheses, a process of derivation may be defined for additive functions of a set in any separable metrical space, and for such a process, theorems similar to those of §§ 7 and 9 may be established.

(15.1) ***Lemma.*** *If Φ is an additive function of a set ($\mathfrak{B}$) on a metrical space M, then given any set X measurable ($\mathfrak{B}$) and any $\varepsilon>0$, there exists an open set G such that*

$$\mathrm{W}(\Phi;\,G-X)<\varepsilon \quad \textit{and} \quad \mathrm{W}(\Phi;\,X-G)<\varepsilon. \tag{15.2}$$

Proof. Let $\mathfrak{B}_0$ denote the class of the sets X measurable $(\mathfrak{B})$ for each of which there exists, however we choose $\varepsilon>0$, an open set G satisfying the relations (15.2). Since any closed set F is the limit of a descending sequence of open sets, we observe easily (cf. Theorems 5.1 and 6.4, Chap. I) that there exists for each $\varepsilon>0$ an open set $G\supset F$ such that $\mathrm{W}(\Phi;\, G-F)<\varepsilon$. The class $\mathfrak{B}_0$ thus includes all closed sets; to prove that $\mathfrak{B}=\mathfrak{B}_0$, it suffices, therefore, to show that the class $\mathfrak{B}_0$ is additive.

To do this, we choose $\varepsilon>0$ and denote by X the sum of a sequence $\{X_n\}_{n=1,2,\dots}$ of sets $(\mathfrak{B}_0)$. To each set X_n there corresponds an open set G_n such that $\mathrm{W}(\Phi;\, G_n-X_n)<\varepsilon/2^n$ and $\mathrm{W}(\Phi;\, X_n-G_n)<\varepsilon/2^n$. Writing $G=\sum_n G_n$, we clearly find that the inequalities (15.2) are satisfied. Therefore $X\in\mathfrak{B}_0$.

Again, suppose that $\varepsilon>0$ and that $X=\mathrm{C}Y$, where $Y\in\mathfrak{B}_0$. There will then exist an open set H such that $\mathrm{W}(\Phi;\, Y-H)<\varepsilon/2$ and $\mathrm{W}(\Phi;\, H-Y)<\varepsilon$. Consequently writing $P=\mathrm{C}H$, we find that

$$(15.3)\qquad \mathrm{W}(\Phi;\, P-X)<\varepsilon/2 \qquad \textit{and} \qquad \mathrm{W}(\Phi;\, X-P)<\varepsilon.$$

But since the set P is closed, there exists an open set G such that $G\supset P$ and $\mathrm{W}(\Phi;\, G-P)<\varepsilon/2$; and this implies, on account of (15.3), the inequalities (15.2) and so completes the proof.

We shall call *net* in a metrical space $\boldsymbol{M}$ any finite or enumerable family of sets measurable $(\mathfrak{B})$ no two of which have common points and which together cover the space $\boldsymbol{M}$. The sets constituting a net will be called its *meshes*. A sequence $\{\mathfrak{M}_n\}$ of nets will be termed *regular*, if each mesh of $\mathfrak{M}_{n+1}$ (where $n>0$) is contained in a mesh of $\mathfrak{M}_n$ and if further $\Delta(\mathfrak{M}_n)\to 0$ as $n\to\infty$ (where $\Delta(\mathfrak{M}_n)$ denotes the characteristic number of $\mathfrak{M}_n$; cf. Chap. II, p. 40). It is easy to see that in order that there exist a regular sequence of nets in a metrical space, it is necessary and sufficient that this space be separable.

In the rest of this § we shall keep fixed a separable metrical space $\boldsymbol{M}$ and we shall suppose given in $\boldsymbol{M}$ a regular sequence $\mathfrak{M}=\{\mathfrak{M}_n\}$ of nets and a measure μ which is defined for the sets measurable $(\mathfrak{B})$ and which is subject to the condition $\mu(\boldsymbol{M})<+\infty$. Let Φ be an additive function of a set $(\mathfrak{B})$ on $\boldsymbol{M}$. For $x\in M$, where M is any mesh of a net $\mathfrak{M}_n$, let us write

$$d_n(x)=\begin{cases} \Phi(M)/\mu(M) & \textit{when} \quad \mu(M)\neq 0, \\ +\infty & \textit{when} \quad \mu(M)=0 \quad \textit{and} \quad \Phi(M)\geqslant 0, \\ -\infty & \textit{when} \quad \mu(M)=0 \quad \textit{and} \quad \Phi(M)<0. \end{cases}$$

The functions $d_n(x)$ are thus defined on the whole space M and are measurable ($\mathfrak{B}$). Let us write $(\mu, \mathfrak{M})\overline{\mathrm{D}}\Phi(x) = \limsup_n d_n(x)$. The number $(\mu, \mathfrak{M})\overline{\mathrm{D}}\Phi(x)$ thus defined will be called *upper derivate of the function Φ at the point x with respect to the measure μ and the regular sequence of nets $\mathfrak{M}$*. Considered as a function of x, this upper derivate is clearly measurable ($\mathfrak{B}$). Similarly we define the lower derivate $(\mu, \mathfrak{M})\underline{\mathrm{D}}\Phi(x)$. If at a point x the two numbers $(\mu, \mathfrak{M})\overline{\mathrm{D}}\Phi(x)$ and $(\mu, \mathfrak{M})\underline{\mathrm{D}}\Phi(x)$ are equal, their common value will be written $(\mu, \mathfrak{M})\mathrm{D}\Phi(x)$ and called *derivative of the function Φ at x with respect to the measure μ and the regular sequence of nets $\mathfrak{M}$*. For the rest of this §, a measure μ and a regular sequence of nets $\mathfrak{M}$ will be kept fixed in the space M.

(15.4) ***Lemma.*** *Let Φ be an additive function of a set ($\mathfrak{B}$) on the space M. Then*

(i) *if the inequality $(\mu, \mathfrak{M})\overline{\mathrm{D}}\Phi(x) \geqslant k$, where k is a finite number, holds at every point x of a set A measurable ($\mathfrak{B}$), we have $\Phi(A) \geqslant k \cdot \mu(A)$;*

(ii) *if at each point x of a set B measurable ($\mathfrak{B}$) and of measure (μ) zero, the derivative $(\mu, \mathfrak{M})\mathrm{D}\Phi(x)$ either does not exist or else exists and is finite, $\Phi(B) = 0$.*

Proof. *re* (i). By subtracting from the function Φ the function $k \cdot \mu$, we may assume that $k = 0$. Let ε be any positive number. By Lemma 15.1 there exists an open set G such that

$$\text{(15.5)} \qquad \mathrm{W}(\Phi; G - A) < \varepsilon \quad \textit{and} \quad \mathrm{W}(\Phi; A - G) < \varepsilon.$$

Let $\widetilde{\mathfrak{M}}_1$ be the set of the meshes M of the net $\mathfrak{M}_1$ such that

$$\text{(15.6)} \qquad M \subset G \quad \textit{and} \quad \Phi(M) \geqslant -\varepsilon \cdot \mu(M),$$

and generally, for $n \geqslant 1$, let $\widetilde{\mathfrak{M}}_{n+1}$ be the set of the meshes M of the net $\mathfrak{M}_{n+1}$ which fulfil the conditions (15.6) and are not contained in any of the meshes of $\widetilde{\mathfrak{M}}_1 + \widetilde{\mathfrak{M}}_2 + \ldots + \widetilde{\mathfrak{M}}_n$. By arranging the sets belonging to $\widetilde{\mathfrak{M}}_1 + \widetilde{\mathfrak{M}}_2 + \ldots + \widetilde{\mathfrak{M}}_n + \ldots$ in a sequence $\{M_k\}$, we have $\Phi(M_k) > -\varepsilon \cdot \mu(M_k)$ for $k = 1, 2, \ldots$, and $A \cdot G \subset \sum_k M_k$. Since the sets M_k are measurable ($\mathfrak{B}$) and no two of them have common points, it therefore follows from (15.5) that $\Phi(A) = \Phi(A \cdot G) + \Phi(A - G) \geqslant \Phi(\sum_k M_k) - 2\varepsilon \geqslant$ $\geqslant -\varepsilon \cdot \sum_k \mu(M_k) - 2\varepsilon \geqslant -\varepsilon \cdot [\mu(G) + 2]$, and so that $\Phi(A) \geqslant 0$.

re (ii). Denote, for any positive integer n, by B_n the set of the points x of B at which $\overline{\mathrm{D}}\Phi(x)\geqslant -n$. On account of (i) we have $\Phi(B_n)\geqslant -n\cdot\mu(B_n)=0$ for each n, and, since $B=\lim_n B_n$, this gives $\Phi(B)\geqslant 0$. By symmetry $\Phi(B)\leqslant 0$, and so finally $\Phi(B)=0$.

(15.7) ***Theorem.*** *If Φ is a function of a set $(\mathfrak{B})$, which is additive on the space M, the derivative $(\mu, \mathfrak{M})\mathrm{D}\Phi(x)$ exists almost everywhere and is integrable $(\mathfrak{B}, \mu)$ on M; moreover, if $E_{+\infty}$ and $E_{-\infty}$ denote the sets of the points at which $(\mu, \mathfrak{M})\mathrm{D}\Phi(x)=+\infty$ and $(\mu, \mathfrak{M})\mathrm{D}\Phi(x)=-\infty$ respectively, we have*

(15.8) $$\Phi(X)=\Phi(X\cdot E_{+\infty})+\Phi(X\cdot E_{-\infty})+\int_X (\mu, \mathfrak{M})\mathrm{D}\Phi(x)\,d\mu(x)$$

and

(15.9) $$\mathrm{W}(\Phi; X)=\Phi(X\cdot E_{+\infty})+|\Phi(X\cdot E_{-\infty})|+\int_X |(\mu, \mathfrak{M})\mathrm{D}\Phi(x)|\,d\mu(x)$$

for every set X measurable $(\mathfrak{B})$.

Proof. By Theorem 14.6, Chap. I, there exist a function of a point f integrable $(\mathfrak{B}, \mu)$ on M and an additive function of a set Θ singular $(\mathfrak{B}, \mu)$ on M such that

(15.10) $$\Phi(X)=\Theta(X)+\int_X f(x)\,d\mu(x) \quad \textit{for every set } X\in\mathfrak{B}.$$

Let E be a set measurable $(\mathfrak{B})$ such that $\mu(E)=0$ and that the function Θ vanishes identically on CE. Writing, for brevity, D, $\overline{D}$ and $\underline{D}$ in place of $(\mu,\mathfrak{M})\mathrm{D}$, $(\mu, \mathfrak{M})\overline{\mathrm{D}}$ and $(\mu,\mathfrak{M})\underline{\mathrm{D}}$ respectively, let us denote for any pair of integers $n>0$ and k, by $P_{n,k}$ the set of the points x at which $\overline{D}\Phi(x)\geqslant(k+1)/n>k/n\geqslant f(x)$. If we substitute $P_{n,k}\cdot CE$ for X in (15.10), we find on account of Lemma 15.4 (i) that

$$\Phi(P_{n,k}\cdot CE)\geqslant\frac{k+1}{n}\mu(P_{n,k}\cdot CE)\geqslant\frac{k}{n}\cdot\mu(P_{n,k}\cdot CE)\geqslant\int_{P_{n,k}\cdot CE} f(x)d\mu(x)=\Phi(P_{n,k}\cdot CE),$$

and so that $\mu(P_{n,k})=\mu(P_{n,k}\cdot CE)=0$. Therefore $\overline{D}\Phi(x)\leqslant f(x)$ at almost all points x. By symmetry $\underline{D}\Phi(x)\geqslant f(x)$ must also hold almost everywhere in M. Therefore the derivative $D\Phi(x)$ exists and equals $f(x)$ at almost all the points x of M, and the identity (15.10) takes the form

(15.11) $$\Phi(X)=\Theta(X)+\int_X D\Phi d\mu=\Phi(E\cdot X)+\int_X D\Phi d\mu \quad \textit{for every set } X\in\mathfrak{B}.$$

Moreover, since $D\Phi(x)=f(x)\neq\infty$ almost everywhere, the set $E_{+\infty}+E_{-\infty}$ is of measure (μ) zero, and it follows directly from (15.11) that the function Φ vanishes identically on the set $(E_{+\infty}+E_{-\infty})-E$.

On the other hand, by Lemma 15.4 (ii), Φ vanishes identically on $E-(E_{+\infty}+E_{-\infty})$. Therefore in (15.11) the set E may be replaced by the set $E_{+\infty}+E_{-\infty}$, and the relation (15.11) becomes the required formula (15.8). Finally, since by Lemma 15.4 (i) the function Φ is non-negative for the subsets ($\mathfrak{B}$) of $E_{+\infty}$ and non-positive for the subsets ($\mathfrak{B}$) of $E_{-\infty}$, formula (15.9) follows at once from formula (15.8).

Let us mention specially the following corollary of Theorem 15.7:

(15.12) ***Theorem.*** *Suppose given in the space $\boldsymbol{M}$ two regular sequences of nets $\mathfrak{N}$ and $\mathfrak{P}$, and, as before, a measure μ defined for the sets ($\mathfrak{B}$) and subject to the condition $\mu(\boldsymbol{M})<+\infty$. Then for every function Φ of a set ($\mathfrak{B}$), which is additive on $\boldsymbol{M}$, we have almost everywhere $(\mu,\mathfrak{N})\mathrm{D}\Phi(x)=(\mu,\mathfrak{P})\mathrm{D}\Phi(x)$; moreover, if E denotes the set of the points x at which either one at least of the derivatives $(\mu,\mathfrak{N})\mathrm{D}\Phi(x)$ and $(\mu,\mathfrak{P})\mathrm{D}\Phi(x)$ does not exist, or else both exist but have different values, then the function Φ vanishes identically on E, i. e. $\mathrm{W}(\Phi;E)=0$.*

In fact, if we write, for brevity, D_1 and D_2 in place of $(\mu,\mathfrak{N})\mathrm{D}$ and $(\mu,\mathfrak{P})\mathrm{D}$ respectively, and if we denote by Θ the function of singularities of Φ, we have by the previous theorem

$$\Phi(X)=\Theta(X)+\int_X D_1\Phi(x)\,d\mu(x)=\Theta(X)+\int_X D_2\Phi(x)\,d\mu(x)$$

for every set X measurable ($\mathfrak{B}$). Equating the two integrals which occur in this relation, we obtain almost everywhere $D_1\Phi(x)=D_2\Phi(x)$.

Now the set E of the points at which this relation does not hold, may be expressed as the sum of three sets A_1, A_2 and A_3, where A_1 is the set of the points $x\in E$ at which one at least of the derivatives $D_1\Phi(x)$ and $D_2\Phi(x)$ does not exist, or else exists and is finite, A_2 the set of the points x at which $D_1\Phi(x)=+\infty$ and $D_2\Phi(x)=-\infty$, and A_3 the set of the points x at which $D_1\Phi(x)=-\infty$ and $D_2\Phi(x)=+\infty$. It follows directly from Lemma 15.4 (ii) that the function Φ vanishes identically on A_1. In the same way, it follows from part (i) of this lemma that we have simultaneously $\Phi(X)\geqslant 0$ and $\Phi(X)\leqslant 0$, and so $\Phi(X)=0$, for every subset X measurable ($\mathfrak{B}$) of A_2 or of A_3. Consequently $\mathrm{W}(\Phi;E)=0$, and this completes the proof.

Theorem 15.7, which corresponds, to a certain extent, to Theorem 9.6, was first proved by Ch. J. de la Vallée Poussin [1; cf. also I, p. 103] for derivation with respect to the Lebesgue measure, and with respect to the regular sequences of nets of half open intervals in Euclidean spaces. Strictly, the Lebesgue measure does not fulfil the condition which we laid down for the measure μ, since Euclidean space has infinite Lebesgue measure. Nevertheless it is easy to see that for the validity of Theorem 15.7 (as well as for that of the other propositions of this §) it suffices to suppose only that the meshes of the nets considered have finite measure.

For the derivation of additive functions of a set in abstract spaces, see also R. de Possel [1].

*§ 16. **Torus space.** As an example and an application of the results of the preceding §, we shall discuss in this § a metrical space which, from the point of view of the theory of measure and integration, may be considered as one of the nearest generalizations of Euclidean spaces. This space, called torus space of an infinite number of dimensions, occurs in a more or less explicit form in the important researches of H. Steinhaus [2], of P. J. Daniell [2; 3], and of other authors, in connection with certain problems of probability; but the first systematic study of this space is due to B. Jessen [2].

Following Jessen, we shall call *torus space* Q_ω the metrical space whose elements are the infinite sequences of real numbers $\xi=(x_1, x_2, \ldots, x_n, \ldots)$ where $0 \leqslant x_n < 1$ for $n=1, 2, \ldots$, the distance $\varrho(\xi, \eta)$ of two points $\xi=(x_1, x_2, \ldots, x_n, \ldots)$ and $\eta=(y_1, y_2, \ldots, y_n, \ldots)$ in Q_ω being defined by the formula $\varrho(\xi, \eta)=\sum_n |y_n - x_n|/2^n$. By Q_m, where m is any positive integer, we shall denote the half open cube $[0, 1; 0, 1; \ldots; 0, 1)$ in the Euclidean space R_m. If $\xi=(x_1, x_2, \ldots, x_n, \ldots)$ is a point of Q_ω, we shall denote, for any positive integer m, by ξ'_m the point $(x_1, x_2, \ldots, x_m)$ of Q_m, and by ξ''_m the point $(x_{m+1}, x_{m+2}, \ldots)$ of Q_ω, and we shall write $\xi=(\xi'_m, \xi''_m)$. According to this notation, (ξ, η) is a point of Q_ω whenever $\xi \epsilon Q_m$ (where m is any positive integer) and $\eta \epsilon Q_\omega$. So that, if $A \subset Q_m$ and $B \subset Q_\omega$, the set $A \times B$ (cf. Chap. III, §§ 8, 9) lies in the space Q_ω; and in particular $Q_m \times Q_\omega = Q_\omega$.

We shall call *closed interval*, or simply *interval*, in the space Q_ω, any set of the form $I \times Q_\omega$, where I is a closed subinterval of Q_m for some value of $m=1, 2, \ldots$. Similarly, taking I to be an interval which is half open (on the left or on the right) in Q_m, we define in the space Q_ω the *half open intervals (on the left or on the right)*.

Every (closed) interval J in Q_ω has only one expression of the form $I \times Q_\omega$ where I is an interval in a space Q_m. (It is to be remarked that the space Q_ω itself is not a closed interval in the sense of the definitions given above.) By the *volume* of the interval $J=I \times Q_\omega$ we shall mean the volume of the interval I in $Q_m \subset R_m$ (cf. Chap. III, § 2). Just as in Euclidean spaces, the volume of an interval J in Q_ω will be denoted by $|J|$ or $L_\omega(J)$. Again, as in Euclidean spaces (cf. Chap. III, § 5), we shall extend the notion of volume in the space Q_ω by defining for every set E in this space the *outer measure* $L^*_\omega(E)$ of the set E as the lower bound of the sums $\sum_k |J_k|$ where $\{J_k\}$ is any sequence of intervals such that $E \subset \sum_k J^\circ_k$. Thus defined, the outer measure evidently fulfils the three conditions of Carathéodory (cf. Chap. II, § 4) and determines, first the class of sets measurable ($\mathfrak{L}_{L_\omega^*}$), and then the class of functions measurable ($\mathfrak{L}_{L_\omega^*}$). For brevity, the sets and the functions belonging respectively to these classes, will simply be termed *measurable*. Also by the *measure* of a set E in the space Q_ω we shall always mean its measure (L_ω^*).

It is easily shown, with the help of Borel's Covering Theorem, that the measure of any closed interval coincides with its volume (cf. Chap. III, § 5, p. 65), so that we can, without ambiguity, write $|E|$ or $L_\omega(E)$ (omitting the asterisk) to denote the outer measure of any set E in Q_ω. We also see that the boundary of any closed interval is of measure zero. Finally, we remark that the whole space Q_ω is of measure 1.

We shall now define in Q_ω a regular sequence of nets (cf. § 15, p. 153) of intervals half open on the right. We shall, in fact, denote for any positive integer m, by $\mathfrak{Q}^{(m)}$ the finite system of 2^{m^2} intervals half open on the right

$$[k_1/2^m, (k_1+1)/2^m; k_2/2^m, (k_2+1)/2^m; \dots; k_m/2^m, (k_m+1)/2^m) \times Q_\omega$$

where the k_i are arbitrary non-negative integers less than 2^m. We see at once that each system $\mathfrak{Q}^{(m)}$ is a net in Q_ω. To see that the sequence of these nets is regular, we observe in the first place that each interval of $\mathfrak{Q}^{(m+1)}$ is contained in one of the intervals of $\mathfrak{Q}^{(m)}$. On the other hand, no interval of the net $\mathfrak{Q}^{(m)}$ can have a diameter exceeding the number $\sum_{k=1}^{m} 1/2^{m+k} + \sum_{k=m+1}^{\infty} 1/2^k \leqslant 1/2^{m-1}$, so that the characteristic number $\Delta(\mathfrak{Q}^{(m)})$ of the net $\mathfrak{Q}^{(m)}$ tends to zero as $m \to \infty$.

If x and y are two real numbers, $x \dot{+} y$ will denote the number $x+y-[x+y]$, where, as usual, $[x+y]$ stands for the largest integer not exceeding $x+y$. If $\xi=(x_1, x_2, \dots, x_n, \dots)$ and $\eta=(y_1, y_2, \dots, y_n, \dots)$ are two points of Q_ω, we shall write $\xi \dot{+} \eta$ for $(x_1 \dot{+} y_1, x_2 \dot{+} y_2, \dots, x_n \dot{+} y_n, \dots)$. The point $\xi \dot{+} \eta$ clearly belongs to Q_ω.

We shall call *translation by the vector* a, where a is a point of Q_ω, the transformation which makes correspond to each point ξ of Q_ω the point $\xi \dot{+} a$. The translation by the vector a will be termed of order m, if all, except at most the first m, coordinates of a vanish.

A function f in Q_ω will be termed *cylindrical of order* m, if $f(\xi)$ does not depend on the first m coordinates of the point ξ, i. e. if

$f(\xi)=f(\xi \dot{+} a)$ identically in ξ, for every point a whose coordinates, except perhaps the first m, all vanish. A set E in Q_ω will be termed *cylindrical of order m*, if its characteristic function is so, or, what amounts to the same, if $E=Q_m \times A$ where A is a set in Q_ω.

(16.1) ***Theorem.*** *A function which is measurable on Q_ω and cylindrical of every finite order, is constant almost everywhere, i. e. $f(\xi)=c$ for almost all points ξ of Q_ω, where c is a constant.*

Proof. Suppose first that the function f is bounded, and therefore integrable, on Q_ω. Denoting by Φ the indefinite integral of f, let us define, for each value of m and for each mesh Q of the net $\mathfrak{Q}^{(m)}$, $f^{(m)}(\xi)=\Phi(Q)/\mathrm{L}_\omega(Q)$ whenever $\xi \in Q$. For every pair of meshes Q_1 and Q_2 of the same net $\mathfrak{Q}^{(m)}$, there always exists a translation of order m which transforms Q_1 into Q_2; therefore, since the function f is cylindrical of order m, it follows that $\Phi(Q_1)=\Phi(Q_2)$; and since further $\mathrm{L}_\omega(Q_1)=\mathrm{L}_\omega(Q_2)$, each of the functions $f^{(m)}(\xi)$ is constant on Q_ω. On the other hand, we deduce from Theorem 15.7 that $f(\xi)=\lim_m f^{(m)}(\xi)$ almost everywhere in Q_ω, i. e. that the function is almost everywhere identical with a constant.

Now let f be any measurable function which is cylindrical of every finite order. Let us write $f_n(\xi)=f(\xi)$ when $|f(\xi)|\leqslant n$ and $f(\xi)=n$ when $|f(\xi)|>n$. Each of the functions $f_n(\xi)$ is bounded and cylindrical of every finite order, so that by what has just been proved, each of these functions is constant almost everywhere. Therefore the same is true of the function $f(\xi)=\lim_n f_n(\xi)$ and this completes the proof.

The fundamental properties of our measure in the space Q_ω may be established by methods similar to those used in Euclidean spaces. To illustrate this, let us enumerate some of these properties.

Given any measurable set E and any $\varepsilon>0$, there exists a closed set F and an open set G such that $F\subset E\subset G$ and such that $|G-E|<\varepsilon$ and $|E-F|<\varepsilon$ (cf. Theorem 6.6, Chap. III).

From this we may deduce next Lusin's theorem (cf. Theorem 7.1, Chap. III): *If f is a finite function measurable on a set E, there exists for each $\varepsilon>0$, a closed set $F\subset E$ such that the function f is continuous on F and that $|E-F|<\varepsilon$*; and its immediate corollary: *any function which is measurable in Q_ω, is equal almost everywhere in Q_ω to a function measurable* $(\mathfrak{B})$. Finally Fubini's theorem (cf. Chap. III, § 8) may be stated as follows for the space Q_ω:

(16.2) **Theorem.** *If f is a non negative measurable function in the space Q_ω, then for any positive integer m,*

(i) *the definite integral* $\int_{Q_\omega} f(\xi, \eta) d\mathrm{L}_\omega(\eta)$ *exists for every* $\xi \in Q_m$, *except at most for those of a set of measure* (L_m) *zero,*

(ii) *the definite integral* $\int_{Q_m} f(\xi, \eta) d\mathrm{L}_m(\xi)$ *exists for every* $\eta \in Q_\omega$, *except at most for those of a set of measure* (L_ω) *zero,*

(iii) $$\int_{Q_\omega} f(\zeta) d\mathrm{L}_\omega(\zeta) = \int_{Q_m}\Big[\int_{Q_\omega} f(\xi,\eta) d\mathrm{L}_\omega(\eta)\Big] d\mathrm{L}_m(\xi) = \int_{Q_\omega}\Big[\int_{Q_m} f(\xi,\eta) d\mathrm{L}_m(\xi)\Big] d\mathrm{L}_\omega(\eta).$$

Proof. We begin by verifying this directly when f is the characteristic function of a closed interval, or of a half open interval, and then successively when f is the characteristic function of an open set, of a set $(\mathfrak{G}_\delta)$, of a set of measure zero, and finally of any measurable set. It follows at once that the theorem is valid in the case where f is a simple function, and then, by passage to the limit, in the general case where f is any non-negative measurable function.

The line of argument that we have sketched, does not differ substantially in any way from the proof of Fubini's theorem for Euclidean spaces, and is even in a sense simpler than the latter, since in proving Theorem 8.1 of Chap. III we had to allow for the possibility of there being hyperplanes of discontinuity of the functions U and V.

In the space Q_ω there is, however, as shown by B. Jessen [2, p. 273], another theorem of the Fubini type, whose proof requires new methods. This theorem allows integration over the space Q_ω to be, so to speak, reduced to integrations over the cubes Q_m in Euclidean spaces, whereas each of the three members of the relation (iii) of Theorem 16.2 contains an integration extended over the space Q_ω.

(16.3) ***Jessen's theorem.*** *If f is a non-negative measurable function in the space Q_ω, the integral*

(16.4) $$f_m(\zeta) = \int_{Q_m} f(\xi, \zeta''_m) d\mathrm{L}_m(\xi), \quad \textit{where } m = 1, 2, \dots,$$

exists, and we have

(16.5) $$\lim_m f_m(\zeta) = \int_{Q_\omega} f(\xi) d\mathrm{L}_\omega(\xi),$$

for almost all ζ in Q_ω.

Proof. Let us first remark that if Q is a set of measure zero in Q_ω, it follows from Theorem 16.2, applied to the characteristic function of Q, that for any m whatever, the set $\underset{\xi}{\mathrm{E}}[(\xi, \eta) \epsilon Q;\ \xi \epsilon Q_m]$ is of measure (L_m) zero for almost all η of Q_ω. Hence (with the notation adopted p. 157) we also have $\mathrm{L}_m\{\underset{\xi}{\mathrm{E}}[(\xi, \zeta''_m) \epsilon Q]\} = 0$ for almost all ζ of Q_ω. It follows that if g and h are two non-negative measurable functions which are almost everywhere equal in Q_ω, the integrals $\int_{Q_m} g(\xi, \zeta''_m)\, d\mathrm{L}_m(\xi)$ and $\int_{Q_m} h(\xi, \zeta''_m)\, d\mathrm{L}_m(\xi)$ are equal for almost all the ζ of Q_ω, whatever m may be. We may therefore, without loss of generality, assume in the proof of Theorem 16.3 that the given function f is measurable ($\mathfrak{B}$); for any measurable function is almost everywhere equal to a function measurable ($\mathfrak{B}$).

The integral in the formula (16.4) then clearly exists for every ζ, and moreover it follows directly from this formula that the function $f_m(\zeta)$ is cylindrical of order m. The upper and lower limits of the sequence $\{f_m(\zeta)\}$ are thus cylindrical of every finite order and by Theorem 16.1 we may write almost everywhere in Q_ω

$$\liminf_m f_m(\zeta) = A \qquad \textit{and} \qquad \limsup_m f_m(\zeta) = B$$

where A and B are constants. It remains to be proved that $A = M = B$, where M denotes the integral on the right-hand side of (16.5).

We shall prove in the first place that $A \geqslant M$. For this purpose, let A' be any number exceeding A (if $A = +\infty$ our assertion is obvious), and write

$$(16.6)\quad P_k = \underset{\zeta}{\mathrm{E}}[f_k(\zeta) \leqslant A'], \qquad S_m = \sum_{k=1}^{m} P_k \qquad \textit{and} \qquad S = \lim_m S_m.$$

The set S coincides, except for a set of measure zero, with the whole space Q_ω. Keeping an index m fixed, let us evaluate the integral of f_m over S_m. Writing $R_m = P_m$, $R_{m-1} = P_{m-1} \cdot CP_m, \ldots, R_1 = P_1 \cdot CP_2 \cdot \ldots \cdot CP_m$, we have

$$(16.7)\quad S_m = \sum_{k=1}^{m} R_k \qquad \text{and} \qquad (16.8)\quad R_i \cdot R_j = 0 \quad \textit{whenever } 1 \leqslant i < j \leqslant m.$$

On the other hand, since every function f_k is cylindrical of order k, so are the sets P_k and CP_k and therefore the sets R_k for $k = 1, 2, \ldots, m$. We may thus write (cf. above p. 159) $R_k = Q_k \times \widetilde{R}_k$ where $\widetilde{R}_k \subset Q_\omega$. According to (16.6), we have $f_k(\zeta) \leqslant A'$ for every $\zeta \epsilon R_k \subset P_k$ where $k = 1, 2, \ldots, m$, or, what amounts to the same by formula (16.4),

$\int_{Q_k} f(\xi, \eta)\, d\mathrm{L}_k(\xi) \leqslant A'$ for every $\eta \in \tilde{R}_k$. Therefore, on account of Theorem 16.2, we obtain for $k=1, 2, \ldots, m$,

$$\int_{R_k} f(\zeta)\, d\mathrm{L}_\omega(\zeta) = \int_{\tilde{R}_k} \Big[\int_{Q_k} f(\xi, \eta)\, d\mathrm{L}_k(\xi) \Big]\, d\mathrm{L}_\omega(\eta) \leqslant A' \cdot \mathrm{L}_\omega(\tilde{R}_k) = A' \cdot \mathrm{L}_\omega(R_k),$$

whence it follows by (16.7) and (16.8) that $\int_{S_m} f(\zeta) d\mathrm{L}_\omega(\zeta) \leqslant A' \cdot \mathrm{L}_\omega(S_m) \leqslant A'$.

Making $m \to \infty$, we obtain in the limit $M = \int_{Q_\omega} f(\zeta)\, d\mathrm{L}_\omega(\zeta) \leqslant A'$ and so $M \leqslant A$.

By symmetry $M \geqslant B$ and, since it is clear that $A \leqslant B$, this requires $A = M = B$ and completes the proof.

CHAPTER V.

Area of a surface $z = F(x, y)$.

§ 1. Preliminary remarks. We saw (cf. Chap. IV, § 8) that the Lebesgue theory enables us to solve completely the elementary problems concerning the length of a curved line and the expression of this length by an integral. However, similar problems concerning curved surfaces involve difficulties of a much more serious kind. Certain classical treatises on the differential and integral calculus, even in the second half of the XIX-th century, contain an inaccurate definition of the area of a surface. By analogy with the definition of length of a curve, the authors attempted to define the area of a surface as the limit of the areas of polyhedra inscribed in the surface and tending to it. H. A. Schwarz [I, p. 309] (cf. also M. Fréchet [3]) was the first to remark that such a limit may not exist and that it is possible to choose a sequence of inscribed polyhedra whose areas tend to any number not less than the actual area of the surface. About the same time Peano and Hermite subjected the old definition to similar criticisms and proposed new definitions based on quite different ideas. It was H. Lebesgue who first returned in his Thesis [1] to the old method, in a modified form that may be roughly described as follows: the area of a surface is the lower limit of the areas of polyhedra tending uniformly to the surface in question (without, however, being necessarily inscribed in the latter).

Nevertheless, in the more general case in which the surface is given parametrically, this definition requires various additional notions and considerations (cf. T. Radò [I; 1; 4]; also E. J. McShane [1], C. B. Morrey [1] and T. Radò [5]) and the results obtained are far from being as complete as those available for curves. The difficulties that arise belong to Geometry and

Topology rather than to the Theory of functions of a real variable. (For the special case in which the functions $x=X(u, v)$, $y=Y(u, v)$ and $z=Z(u, v)$ which define the surface parametrically fulfil the Lipschitz condition *vide* T. Radò [4] and H. Rademacher [4]).

We shall therefore restrict ourselves to the case of continuous surfaces of the form $z=F(x, y)$. The most elegant and the most complete results concerning these surfaces are due to L. Tonelli [5; 6; 7]; they will be given in § 8 and are the principal object of this chapter.

Tonelli's theory is based on the definition of area proposed by Lebesgue. As regards the modern work on area of surfaces based on other definitions, we should mention: W. H. Young [4], J. C. Burkill [3], S. Banach [5], A. Kolmogoroff [3] and J. Schauder [1].

T. Radò [1, pp. 154—169; 2] has developed further the methods of Tonelli by means of older ideas due to de Geöcze and with the help of certain functionals introduced by the latter. The principal result of Radò (*vide* Theorem 7.3), applications of which will be discussed below, enables us to define the area of a surface as the limit of certain simple expressions, whereas the Lebesgue definition only enables us to obtain it as a lower limit. Another expression is due to L. C. Young (*vide* below § 8) and constitutes a direct generalization of the classical formula for the area of a surface.

Except where the contrary is expressly stated, the reasoning of this chapter will be formulated for functions of two real variables. The extension to spaces of any number of dimensions offers no difficulty.

§ 2. Area of a surface. By a *continuous surface* on a plane interval I_0, we shall mean any equation of the form $z=F(x, y)$, where F is a continuous function on I_0.

A continuous surface $z=P(x, y)$ on an interval I_0 is termed *polyhedron* if there exists a decomposition of I_0 into a finite number of non-overlapping triangles $T_1, T_2, \dots, T_n$ such that the function P is linear on each of these triangles, i. e. such that $P(x, y)=a_i x+b_i y+c_i$ for $(x, y) \in T_i$, where $i=1, 2, \dots, n$ and a_i, b_i, c_i are constant coefficients. We shall call, respectively, *faces* and *vertices* of the polyhedron $z=P(x, y)$, the parts and the points of the graph (cf. Chap. III, § 10) of the function P, which correspond to the triangles T_i, and to the vertices of the T_i. The sum of the areas of the faces in the sense of elementary Geometry, i.e. the number $\sum_i |T_i| \cdot (a_i^2+b_i^2+1)^{\frac{1}{2}} = \int\int_{I_0} [(\partial P/\partial x)^2 + (\partial P/\partial y)^2 + 1]^{\frac{1}{2}} dx\, dy$, will be called *elementary area* of the polyhedron $z=P(x, y)$ on I_0 and denoted by $\mathrm{S}_0(P; I_0)$.

Given any continuous surface $z=F(x, y)$ on an interval I_0, we shall term its *area* on I_0, and denote by $\mathrm{S}(F; I_0)$, the lower limit of the elementary areas of polyhedra tending uniformly to this surface, i.e. the lower bound of all the numbers s for each of which there exists, given any $\varepsilon > 0$, a polyhedron $z=P(x, y)$ on I_0 such that 1° $|P(x, y) - F(x, y)| < \varepsilon$ at every point $(x, y) \epsilon I_0$ and 2° $\mathrm{S}_0(P; I_0) \leqslant s$.

We might verify here that for polyhedra the elementary area agrees with the area according to the general definition just given. As, however, this is an easy consequence of the theorems given further on (*vide* p. 181), a special proof is unnecessary at this point. It should be remarked that, in accordance with the definition adopted, the area of a surface may be either finite or infinite.

The following theorem is an immediate consequence of the definition.

(2.1) ***Theorem.*** *For any sequence of continuous functions* $\{F_n\}$ *which converges uniformly on an interval* I_0 *to a function* F, *we have* $\liminf_n \mathrm{S}(F_n; I_0) \geqslant \mathrm{S}(F; I_0)$.

§ 3. The Burkill integral. Instead of treating the theory of area of surfaces by itself, it is more convenient to associate it with certain differential properties of functions of an interval. However, the functions of an interval occurring in the theory of area are not in general additive, and in consequence we shall have to complete in some minor points the theory of functions of an interval, developed in the two preceding chapters.

We shall begin with some subsidiary definitions. To simplify the wording we shall understand in the sequel by *subdivision* of a figure R_0 any finite system of non-overlapping intervals $I_1, I_2, \ldots, I_n$ such that $R_0 = \sum_k I_k$. Given any function of an interval U and given a finite system of intervals $\mathfrak{J} = \{I_k\}$, we shall write, for brevity, $U(\mathfrak{J})$ in place of $\sum_k U(I_k)$. In particular therefore, $\mathrm{L}(\mathfrak{J})$ will denote the sum of the areas of the intervals belonging to the system $\mathfrak{J}$.

We call *upper* and *lower integral* in the sense of Burkill of a function of an interval $U(I)$ over a figure R_0, and we denote by $\overline{\int\limits_{R_0}} U$ and $\underline{\int\limits_{R_0}} U$ respectively, the upper and the lower limit of the numbers $U(\mathfrak{J})$ for arbitrary subdivisions $\mathfrak{J}$ of R_0, whose characteristic numbers $\Delta(\mathfrak{J})$ tend to zero (cf. Chap. II, p. 40). When these integrals are equal, their common value is called the *Burkill definite integral* (or simply the *integral*) of the function U over R_0 and is denoted by $\int\limits_{R_0} U$. If this integral exists and is finite, the function U is said to be *integrable* on R_0 (in the sense of Burkill). If the function U is integrable on every figure R (in the whole plane or in a figure R_0) its integral $\int\limits_R U$ considered as a function of the figure R is called *indefinite integral* of U (in the whole plane or on R_0)

(3.1) **Theorem** 1° *If U is a function of an interval and R_1, R_2 are non-overlapping figures, we have*

$$(3.2) \qquad \overline{\int\limits_{R_1+R_2}} U \geqslant \overline{\int\limits_{R_1}} U + \overline{\int\limits_{R_2}} U \quad \text{and} \quad \underline{\int\limits_{R_1+R_2}} U \leqslant \underline{\int\limits_{R_1}} U + \underline{\int\limits_{R_2}} U,$$

provided that both integrals of U over R_1+R_2 are finite.

2° *Any function of an interval U which is integrable on a figure R_0, is equally so on every figure $R \subset R_0$ and its indefinite integral on R_0 is an additive function of a figure.*

Proof. Part 1° of the theorem is a direct consequence of the definition of the Burkill integrals, and part 2° follows at once from the formulae (3.2) when we subtract the second of these formulae from the first.

If U is a function of an interval on a figure R, we shall call *variation of U on R at a set D* the upper limit of $|U(\mathfrak{J})|$ as $\Delta(\mathfrak{J}) \to 0$, where $\mathfrak{J}$ denotes any finite system of non-overlapping intervals contained in R and possessing common points with D. The following analogue of Theorem 4.1, Chap. III, may be noted.

(3.3) **Theorem.** *Given on a figure R_0 a function of an interval U such that $\overline{\int\limits_{R_0}} |U| < +\infty$, there can be at most an enumerable infinity of straight lines D, which are parallel to the coordinate axes and at which the variation of U on R_0 is not zero.*

In fact, the number of straight lines which are parallel to the axis of x or of y, and at which the variation of U on R_0 exceeds a positive number ε, cannot be greater than $2\varepsilon^{-1} \cdot \overline{\int_{R_0}} |U| < +\infty$.

(3.4) **Lemma.** *Given a function of an interval U integrable on a figure R_0, there exists, for each $\varepsilon > 0$, an $\eta > 0$ such that for every system $\mathfrak{I} = \{I_1, I_2, \ldots, I_p\}$ of non-overlapping intervals situated in R_0, the inequality $\Delta(\mathfrak{I}) < \eta$ implies the inequality*

$$(3.5) \qquad \left| \sum_{k=1}^{p} \left[U(I_k) - \int_{I_k} U \right] \right| < \varepsilon.$$

Proof. Let $\eta > 0$ be a number such that, for every subdivision $\mathfrak{T}$ of R_0, $\Delta(\mathfrak{T}) < \eta$ implies $|U(\mathfrak{T}) - \int_{R_0} U| < \varepsilon/2$, and let $\mathfrak{I} = \{I_1, I_2, \ldots, I_p\}$ be any finite system of non-overlapping intervals situated in R_0, such that $\Delta(\mathfrak{I}) < \eta$. Let $R_1 = R_0 \ominus \sum_{k=1}^{p} I_k$. By Theorem 3.1, the function U is integrable on R_1. It follows that there exists a subdivision $\mathfrak{I}_1$ of R_1 such that

$$(3.6) \qquad \Delta(\mathfrak{I}_1) < \eta \quad and \quad |U(\mathfrak{I}_1) - \int_{R_1} U| < \varepsilon/2.$$

Now $\mathfrak{I} + \mathfrak{I}_1$ clearly constitutes a subdivision of R_0 such that $\Delta(\mathfrak{I} + \mathfrak{I}_1) < \eta$. We therefore have $|U(\mathfrak{I} + \mathfrak{I}_1) - \int_{R_0} U| < \varepsilon/2$, and we need only subtract the second of the relations (3.6) from it to obtain (3.5).

If R_0 is a fixed figure, then to any $\eta > 0$ there corresponds a positive integer p such that every interval $I \subset R_0$ may be subdivided in p subintervals of diameter less than η. Hence applying Lemma 3.4, we obtain at once the following

(3.7) **Theorem.** *If a function of an interval $U(I)$ which is integrable on a figure R_0, is continuous, then the same is true of its indefinite integral $B(R) = \int_R U$.*

(3.8) **Theorem.** *If U is a function of an interval which is integrable on a figure R_0 and if B is its indefinite integral, then $\overline{B}(x, y) = \overline{U}(x, y)$ and $\underline{B}(x, y) = \underline{U}(x, y)$ at almost all points $(x, y) \epsilon R_0$.*

In particular therefore, if one of the functions U and B is almost everywhere derivable in R_0, the same is true of the other and the derivatives of U and of B are almost everywhere equal.

Proof. Suppose that the set of the points (x, y) at which $\overline{U}(x, y) > \overline{B}(x, y)$ has positive measure. We could then determine a set $E \subset R_0$ of positive outer measure and a number $a > 0$, such that $\overline{U}(x, y) - \overline{B}(x, y) > a$ at each point (x, y) of E. Therefore, on account of Vitali's Covering Theorem (Chap. IV, Theorem 3.1), we could determine in R_0, for any $\eta > 0$, a finite system of non-overlapping intervals $\mathfrak{J} = \{I_k\}_{k=1,2,\dots,n}$ such that $\Delta(\mathfrak{J}) < \eta$, $L(\mathfrak{J}) > |E|/2$, and $U(I_k) - B(I_k) > a \cdot |I_k|$ for $k = 1, 2, \dots, n$. Now it follows from the last two relations that $U(\mathfrak{J}) - B(\mathfrak{J}) > a \cdot |E|/2$, which contradicts Lemma 3.4. Hence, $\overline{U}(x, y) \leqslant \overline{B}(x, y)$ almost everywhere in R_0. In the same way we prove that the opposite inequality holds also almost everywhere in R_0, and this completes the proof.

(3.9) ***Theorem.*** *Suppose that U is a continuous function of an interval on a figure R_0 and that* (i) $\overline{\int_{R_0}} |U| < +\infty$ *and* (ii) $U(I) \leqslant U(\mathfrak{S})$ *for every interval $I \subset R_0$ and every subdivision $\mathfrak{S}$ of I. Then the function U is integrable on R_0.*

Proof. Given a number $\varepsilon > 0$, let $\mathfrak{T} = \{J_i\}_{i=1,2,\dots,p}$ be a subdivision of R_0 such that

$$U(\mathfrak{T}) > \overline{\int_{R_0}} U - \varepsilon. \tag{3.10}$$

Let us denote by $D_1, D_2, \dots, D_r$ the sides of the intervals $(\mathfrak{T})$ which do not belong to the boundary of R_0. By Theorem 3.3 it may be assumed, in view of the continuity of the function U and of condition (ii), that the variation of U on R_0 vanishes at each side D_i. It follows that there exists an $\eta > 0$ such that, given any finite system $\mathfrak{S}$ of non-overlapping intervals situated in R_0 and having points in common with the sides D_i, the inequality $\Delta(\mathfrak{S}) < \eta$ implies $|U(\mathfrak{S})| < \varepsilon$. We can clearly assume that η does not exceed the length of any side of the intervals $(\mathfrak{T})$.

This being so, consider an arbitrary subdivision $\mathfrak{J} = \{I_1, I_2, \dots, I_n\}$ of R_0 such that $\Delta(\mathfrak{J}) < \eta$. By numbering the intervals of $\mathfrak{J}$ suitably, we may evidently suppose that $I_1, I_2, \dots, I_q$ are those having points in common with the sides D_i, while the remaining intervals of $\mathfrak{J}$ (if any) have none. Finally, let us agree to write $U(J_i \odot I_k) = 0$ when $J_i \odot I_k = 0$. Then $|\sum_{k=1}^{q} U(I_k)| < \varepsilon$ and $|\sum_{i=1}^{p} \sum_{k=1}^{q} U(J_i \odot I_k)| < \varepsilon$, so that, by (3.10) and by condition (ii) of the theorem, we have $\overline{\int_{R_0}} U - \varepsilon < U(\mathfrak{T}) \leqslant U(\mathfrak{Z}) - \sum_{k=1}^{q} U(I_k) + \sum_{i=1}^{p} \sum_{k=1}^{q} U(J_i \odot I_k) < U(\mathfrak{Z}) + 2\varepsilon$. It follows that $\overline{\int_{R_0}} U \leqslant \underline{\int_{R_0}} U + 3\varepsilon$, and so, that $\overline{\int_{R_0}} U = \underline{\int_{R_0}} U$.

In connection with this §, *vide* J. C. Burkill [2; 3; 4], R. C. Young [2] and F. Riesz [6; 7].

§ 4. Bounded variation and absolute continuity for functions of two variables. Given a function $F(x, y)$ continuous on an interval $I = [a_1, b_1; a_2, b_2]$, let us denote for any value x subject to $a_1 \leqslant x \leqslant b_1$, by $W_1(F; x; a_2, b_2)$ the absolute variation of the function $F(x, y)$ with respect to the variable y on the interval $[a_2, b_2]$, and for any value y subject to $a_2 \leqslant y \leqslant b_2$, by $W_2(F; y; a_1, b_1)$ that of the function $F(x, y)$ with respect to x on $[a_1, b_1]$. Denoting by J_1 and J_2 respectively the linear intervals $[a_1, b_1]$ and $[a_2, b_2]$ we shall also write $W_1(F; x; J_2)$ for $W_1(F; x; a_2, b_2)$ and $W_2(F; y; J_1)$ for $W_2(F; y; a_1, b_1)$.

By continuity of the function F, the non-negative expressions $W_1(F; x; J_2)$ and $W_2(F; y; J_1)$ are, as is easily seen, lower semi-continuous functions of the variables x and y respectively. When the integrals $\int_{a_1}^{b_1} W_1(F; x; J_2)\,dx$ and $\int_{a_2}^{b_2} W_2(F; y; J_1)\,dy$ are both finite, the function F is said to be *of bounded variation* on I in the Tonelli sense. It follows at once that any function of bounded variation of two variables x, y is of bounded variation with respect to x for almost every value of y and with respect to y for almost every value of x.

A continuous function $F(x, y)$ will be termed *absolutely continuous* on an interval $I = [a_1, b_1; a_2, b_2]$ in the Tonelli sense, if it is of bounded variation on I and moreover, absolutely continuous with respect to x for almost every value of y in $[a_2, b_2]$, and absolutely continuous with respect to y for almost every value of x in $[a_1, b_1]$.

We say that a function $F(x, y)$ fulfils the *Lipschitz condition* on I, if there exists a finite constant N such that $|F(x', y') - F(x'', y'')| \leqslant N \cdot (|x' - x''| + |y' - y''|)$ for every pair of points (x', y') and (x'', y'') of I.

Any function which fulfils the Lipschitz condition on an interval I is evidently absolutely continuous on I. In particular polyhedra and also functions of two variables with continuous partial derivatives, are always absolutely continuous functions.

A function F which is continuous and of bounded variation [absolutely continuous, or subject to the Lipschitz condition] on an interval $I_0=[a_1,b_1;\, a_2,b_2]$ can easily be continued, even so as to be periodic, over the whole plane in such a manner as to remain continuous and of bounded variation [absolutely continuous, or subject to the Lipschitz condition] on every interval. In fact, denoting by I_1 one of the intervals congruent to I_0 with a common side parallel to the axis of x, let us continue the function F from the interval I_0 on to the interval I_1 by symmetry relative to the common side of these intervals. Let us further continue similarly the function F from the interval I_0+I_1 on to an interval I_2 congruent to I_0+I_1 which has with the latter a common side parallel to the axis of y. The function F is then defined on the interval $I_0+I_1+I_2$ whose sides are respectively of lengths $2\cdot(b_1-a_1)$ and $2\cdot(b_2-a_2)$. Writing $u=2\cdot(b_1-a_1)$ and $v=2\cdot(b_2-a_2)$, and continuing the function F from the interval $I_0+I_1+I_2$ on to the rest of the plane by the periodicity condition $F(x+u,y)=F(x,y+v)=F(x,y)$, we see easily that the continuation obtained for the function F has the properties required.

Besides the definition of Tonelli several other definitions have been given of conditions under which a function of two variables is said to be of bounded variation. For a discussion of these definitions see C. R. Adams and J. A. Clarkson [1; 2]. Throughout this chapter, use is made of Tonelli's concept only.

We shall subsequently make use of the following theorem concerning the partial derivates of any continuous function:

(4.1) ***Theorem.*** *Given a continuous function $F(x,y)$, its partial Dini derivates, $\overline{F}_x^+, \overline{F}_x^-, \underline{F}_x^+, \underline{F}_x^-$ and $\overline{F}_y^+, \overline{F}_y^-, \underline{F}_y^+, \underline{F}_y^-$, are functions measurable* ($\mathfrak{B}$).

Proof. It will suffice to prove this for any one of these derivates, say $\overline{F}_x^+$.

Given an arbitrary real number a, consider the set

$$E=\underset{(x,y)}{\mathrm{E}}\,[\overline{F}_x^+(x,y)<a],$$

and denote by E_n the set of all the points (x,y) such that for every h the inequality $0<h\leqslant 1/n$ implies $[F(x+h,y)-F(x,y)]/h\leqslant a-1/n$.

We find that $E = \sum_n E_n$ and, since by continuity of the function F each of the sets E_n is closed, E is a set $(\mathfrak{F}_\sigma)$, so that the derivate $\overline{F}_x^+$ is a function measurable $(\mathfrak{B})$.

Theorem 4.1 may be compared with Theorems 4.2 and 4.3 of Chap. IV concerning measurability of the derivates of functions of one real variable. Nevertheless it is to be remarked that contrary to what occurs for functions of one variable, the partial Dini derivates of a function measurable $(\mathfrak{B})$ need not in general be measurable $(\mathfrak{B})$, although they are still measurable $(\mathfrak{L})$ (the proof of this requires, however, the theory of analytic sets; *vide* F. Hausdorff [II, p. 274], M. Neubauer [1] and A. E. Currier [1]). On the other hand, a function of two variables may be measurable $(\mathfrak{L})$ without its partial Dini derivates being so.

§ 5. The expressions of de Geöcze. We shall make correspond to any function $F(x, y)$ which is continuous on an interval $I = [a_1, b_1; a_2, b_2]$, the following expressions introduced by Z. de Geöcze [1] into the theory of areas of surfaces:

$$\mathrm{G}_1(F; I) = \int_{a_1}^{b_1} |F(x, b_2) - F(x, a_2)|\, dx, \quad \mathrm{G}_2(F; I) = \int_{a_2}^{b_2} |F(b_1, y) - F(a_1, y)|\, dy,$$

$$\mathrm{G}(F; I) = \{[\mathrm{G}_1(F; I)]^2 + [\mathrm{G}_2(F; I)]^2 + |I|^2\}^{1/2}$$

While studying the fundamental properties of these expressions, we shall often find the following two inequalities useful:

$$\text{(5.1)} \qquad \Big[\Big(\sum_{i=1}^n x_i\Big)^2 + \Big(\sum_{i=1}^n y_i\Big)^2 + \Big(\sum_{i=1}^n z_i\Big)^2\Big]^{1/2} \leqslant \sum_{i=1}^n (x_i^2 + y_i^2 + z_i^2)^{1/2}$$

for any three sequences $\{x_i\}$, $\{y_i\}$ *and* $\{z_i\}$ *of real numbers;*

$$\text{(5.2)} \qquad \Big[\Big(\int_E x\, dt\Big)^2 + \Big(\int_E y\, dt\Big)^2 + \Big(\int_E z\, dt\Big)^2\Big]^{1/2} \leqslant \int_E (x^2 + y^2 + z^2)^{1/2}\, dt$$

for any measurable set E *in a space* $\boldsymbol{R}_m$ *and any three non-negative functions* $x(t)$, $y(t)$ *and* $z(t)$, *measurable on* E.

The inequality (5.1) is easily deduced by induction from the case $n = 2$ which can be verified directly. The inequality (5.2), in the special case in which the functions $x(t)$, $y(t)$, $z(t)$ are simple, is an obvious consequence of (5.1); and we pass at once to the general case with the help of Theorems 7.4 and 12.6 of Chapter I.

(5.3) ***Theorem.*** *The expressions of de Geöcze* $G_1(I)=\mathrm{G}_1(F; I)$, $G_2(I)=\mathrm{G}_2(F; I)$ *and* $G(I)=\mathrm{G}(F; I)$, *associated with a continuous function* $F(x, y)$, *are continuous functions of the interval* I *and their integrals over any interval exist (finite or infinite); these integrals over any interval* $I_0=[a_1, b_1; a_2, b_2]$ *fulfil the following relations:*

$$(5.4)\quad \int_{I_0} G_1=\int_{a_1}^{b_1} \mathrm{W}_1(F; x; a_2, b_2)\,dx \quad \text{and} \quad \int_{I_0} G_2=\int_{a_2}^{b_2} \mathrm{W}_2(F; y; a_1, b_1)\,dy$$

$$(5.5)\quad G_1(I_0)\leqslant\int_{I_0} G_1,\quad G_2(I_0)\leqslant\int_{I_0} G_2 \quad \text{and} \quad G(I_0)\leqslant\int_{I_0} G,$$

$$(5.6)\quad \int_{I_0} G_i\leqslant\int_{I_0} G\leqslant\int_{I_0} G_1+\int_{I_0} G_2+|I_0| \quad \text{where } i=1, 2.$$

Proof. Given an arbitrary $\varepsilon>0$, let $\eta<\varepsilon$ be a positive number such that, for any pair of the points (x, y_1) and (x, y_2) in I_0,

$$(5.7)\qquad |y_2-y_1|<\eta \quad \text{implies} \quad |F(x, y_2)-F(x, y_1)|<\varepsilon.$$

Let M denote the upper bound of $F(x, y)$ on I_0 and consider in I_0 an interval $I=[\alpha_1, \beta_1; \alpha_2, \beta_2]$ such that $|I|<\eta^2$. We then have either $\beta_1-\alpha_1<\eta$ or $\beta_2-\alpha_2<\eta$. In the former case, we find $G_1(I)\leqslant(\beta_1-\alpha_1)\cdot 2M<2M\eta\leqslant 2M\varepsilon$, and in the latter we derive from (5.7), $G_1(I)\leqslant(\beta_1-\alpha_1)\cdot\varepsilon\leqslant(b_1-a_1)\cdot\varepsilon$, so that in both cases $G_1(I)\leqslant(2M+b_1-a_1)\cdot\varepsilon$. The function $G_1(I)$ is therefore continuous. The same is of course true of $G_2(I)$ and the continuity of these two functions at once implies that of $G(I)$.

This being so, we shall show that the functions G_1 and G_2 are integrable and, at the same time, we shall deduce the formulae (5.4).

Let $\{\mathfrak{J}_n\}$ be a sequence of subdivisions of I_0 such that $\lim_n \Delta(\mathfrak{J}_n)=0$ and $\lim_n G_1(\mathfrak{J}_n)=\underline{\int_{I_0}} G_1$; and denote, for any positive integer n and any $\xi\in[a_1, b_1]$, by $V_n(\xi)$ the sum of the absolute increments of the function $F(\xi, y)$ on the linear intervals cut off on the line $x=\xi$ by the rectangles of the subdivision $\mathfrak{J}_n$. We then have, on the one hand,

$$(5.8)\qquad G_1(\mathfrak{J}_n)=\int_{a_1}^{b_1} V_n(\xi)\,d\xi \quad \text{for} \quad n=1, 2, \ldots,$$

and on the other hand, on account of continuity of the function F, $\lim_n V_n(\xi)=\mathrm{W}_1(F; \xi; a_2, b_2)$ for any $\xi\in[a_1, b_1]$. Therefore, in virtue of

Fatou's Lemma (Chap. I, Theorem 12.10) and by (5.8), we obtain $\underline{\int_{I_0}} G_1 \geqslant \int_{a_1}^{b_1} \mathrm{W}_1(F; \xi; a_2, b_2)\, d\xi$. But since $G_1(\mathfrak{J}) \leqslant \int_{a_1}^{b_1} \mathrm{W}_1(F; \xi; a_2, b_2)\, d\xi$ for every subdivision $\mathfrak{J}$ of I_0, we have also $\overline{\int_{I_0}} G_1 \leqslant \int_{a_1}^{b_1} \mathrm{W}_1(F; \xi; a_2, b_2)\, d\xi$. Therefore the function G_1 has a unique integral over I_0 and this integral fulfils the first of the relations (5.4). The existence of the integral $\int_{I_0} G_2$ and the validity of the second of these relations are deduced by symmetry.

Let us pass on now to the function G. We first remark that the integral $\int_{I_0} G$ clearly exists in the case in which one at least of the integrals $\int_{I_0} G_1$ and $\int_{I_0} G_2$ is infinite, and is then also infinite on account of the relations

(5.9) $\qquad G_1(I) \leqslant G(I)$ *and* $G_2(I) \leqslant G(I)$ *for any interval* I.

In the remaining case, the two integrals in question being finite, the evident inequality $G(I) \leqslant G_1(I) + G_2(I) + |I|$ yields

(5.10) $$\overline{\int_{I_0}} G \leqslant \int_{I_0} G_1 + \int_{I_0} G_2 + |I_0| < +\infty;$$

and on the other hand, for every subdivision $\mathfrak{J}$ of any interval I the equally obvious relations

(5.11) $$G_1(I) \leqslant G_1(\mathfrak{J}) \quad \textit{and} \quad G_2(I) \leqslant G_2(\mathfrak{J})$$

lead, in view of the inequality (5.1), to

(5.12) $$G(I) \leqslant G(\mathfrak{J}).$$

Now, continuity of the function G being already established, the formulae (5.10) and (5.12) imply, by Theorem 3.9, that this function has over I_0 a unique integral.

To complete the proof we need only remark that the formulae (5.11) and (5.12) imply at once the formulae (5.5) and finally that formula (5.6) follows directly from (5.9) and (5.10).

As a corollary of Theorem 5.3, and more particularly as a consequence of the formulae (5.4) and (5.6), we have:

(5.13) ***Theorem.*** *In order that the function of an interval* $G(I)=G(F;I)$, *associated with a continuous function* $F(x,y)$, *be integrable on an interval* I_0 (*i. e. in order that* $\int_{I_0} G<+\infty$), *it is necessary and sufficient that the function* $F(x,y)$ *be of bounded variation on* I_0.

§ 6. Integrals of the expressions of de Geöcze. Given a continuous function $F(x,y)$, we shall denote, for any interval I_0, by $\mathrm{H}_1(F;I_0)$, $\mathrm{H}_2(F;I_0)$ and $\mathrm{H}(F;I_0)$ respectively, the integrals of the functions of an interval $G_1(I)=\mathrm{G}_1(F;I)$, $G_2(I)=\mathrm{G}_2(F;I)$ and $G(I)=\mathrm{G}(F;I)$ over the interval I_0. All these integrals exist on account of Theorem 5.3 and their importance in the theory of area of surfaces is due to the fact that, as will be shown in the next §, the number $\mathrm{H}(F;I_0)$ coincides with the area of the surface $z=F(x,y)$ on I_0.

(6.1) ***Theorem.*** *For any function* $F(x,y)$ *which is continuous and of bounded variation, the expressions* $H_1(I)=\mathrm{H}_1(F;I)$, $H_2(I)=\mathrm{H}_2(F;I)$ *and* $H(I)=\mathrm{H}(F;I)$ *are additive, continuous, and non-negative functions of the interval* I, *and we have at almost all points* (x,y) *of the plane*

$$(6.2)\qquad \begin{aligned} &H_1'(x,y)=|F_y'(x,y)|, \qquad H_2'(x,y)=|F_x'(x,y)|,\\ &H'(x,y)=\{[F_x'(x,y)]^2+[F_y'(x,y)]^2+1\}^{\frac{1}{2}}. \end{aligned}$$

Proof. Additivity and continuity of the functions in question follow at once from Theorems 3.1 and 3.7 on account of Theorem 5.3. We have therefore only to establish the relations (6.2). Now, for any interval $I=[a_1,b_1;a_2,b_2]$ we have according to Theorem 5.3 and Theorem 7.4 of Chap. IV, the following relation (in which the transformation is effected in accordance with Fubini's Theorem 8.1, Chap. III, rendered applicable to the partial derivates of the function $F(x,y)$ by Theorem 4.1):

$$H_1(I)=\int_{a_1}^{b_1} \mathrm{W}_1(F;x;a_2,b_2)\,dx \geqslant \int_{a_1}^{b_1}\Big[\int_{a_2}^{b_2}|F_y'(x,y)|\,dy\Big]dx=\int\int_I |F_y'(x,y)|\,dx\,dy;$$

whence

$$(6.3)\qquad H_1'(x,y)\geqslant |F_y'(x,y)| \quad \textit{for almost every point } (x,y).$$

Let us now denote by $\{J_n\}$ the sequence of the linear intervals with rational extremities. In view of Theorem 7.4, Chap. IV, we have for $n=1, 2, \ldots$ and for every linear interval J,

$$\int_J \mathrm{W}_1(F; x; J_n)\, dx = H_1(J\times J_n) \geqslant \iint_{J\times J_n} H_1'(x, y)\, dx\, dy = \int_J \Big[\int_{J_n} H_1'(x, y)\, dy\Big]\, dx,$$

and consequently, for each positive integer n, the inequality $\mathrm{W}_1(F; x; J_n) \geqslant \int_{J_n} H_1'(x, y)\, dy$ holds at every point x, except at most those of a set E_n of linear measure zero. Therefore, writing $E=\sum_n E_n$, we obtain the inequality $\mathrm{W}_1(F; x; J) \geqslant \int_J H_1'(x, y)\, dy$, whenever J has rational extremities and x lies outside the set E of linear measure zero. If we now regard the two sides of this inequality, for a given value of x outside the set E, as functions of the linear interval J, we obtain by derivation with respect to this interval (on account of Theorem 7.9, Chap. IV) for almost all y, the inequality

$$(6.4)\qquad |F_y'(x, y)| \geqslant H_1'(x, y).$$

Therefore, since the derivatives $H_1'(x, y)$ and $F_y'(x, y)$ are measurable (cf. Theorem 4.1), it follows from Fubini's theorem (in the form (8.6), Chap. III) that the set of the points (x, y) at which the relation (6.4) is not fulfilled, is of plane measure zero. By (6.3) we therefore have almost everywhere the first of the relations (6.2).

The proof of the second relation now follows by symmetry, and that of the third from the remark that if we write $G_1(I) = \mathrm{G}_1(F; I)$, $G_2(I) = \mathrm{G}_2(F; I)$ and $G(I) = \mathrm{G}(F; I)$, we have by Theorem 3.8,

$$H'(x, y) = G'(x, y) = \{[G_1'(x, y)]^2 + [G_2'(x, y)]^2 + 1\}^{\frac{1}{2}} =$$
$$= \{[H_1'(x, y)]^2 + [H_2'(x, y)]^2 + 1\}^{\frac{1}{2}} = \{[F_y'(x, y)]^2 + [F_x'(x, y)]^2 + 1\}^{\frac{1}{2}}$$

at almost every point (x, y) of the plane. This completes the proof.

(6.5) ***Theorem.*** *In order that the function of an interval $H(I) = \mathrm{H}(F; I)$, corresponding to a continuous function $F(x, y)$ of bounded variation on an interval $I_0 = [a_1, b_1; a_2, b_2]$, be absolutely continuous on this interval, it is necessary and sufficient that the function $F(x, y)$ itself be absolutely continuous; and when this is the case, we have*

$$(6.6)\qquad H(I_0) = \iint_{I_0} \{[F_x'(x, y)]^2 + [F_y'(x, y)]^2 + 1\}^{1/2}\, dx\, dy.$$

Proof. By Theorem 5.3, absolute continuity of the function $H(I)$ is equivalent to absolute continuity of the functions $H_1(I)$ and $H_2(I)$ together.

Therefore if the function H is absolutely continuous on I_0, we have, by Theorem 6.1, for any interval $I_\xi=[a_1, \xi; a_2, b_2]$, where $a_1 \leqslant \xi \leqslant b_1$, the relation

$$\int_{a_1}^{\xi} \mathrm{W}_1(F; x; a_2, b_2)\, dx = H_1(I_\xi) = \iint_{I_\xi} |F'_y(x, y)|\, dx\, dy = \int_{a_1}^{\xi} \Big[\int_{a_2}^{b_2} |F'_y(x, y)|\, dy\Big]\, dx,$$

and, taking the derivative with respect to ξ, we obtain for almost every value of x,

$$\mathrm{W}_1(F; x; a_2, b_2) = \int_{a_2}^{b_2} |F'_y(x, y)|\, dy. \tag{6.7}$$

Now, for any given value of x (for which $F(x, \eta)$ is of bounded variation in η) the difference $\mathrm{W}_1(F; x; a_2, \eta) - \int_{a_2}^{\eta} |F'_y(x, y)|\, dy$ is a non-negative and non-decreasing function of the variable η (cf. Theorem 7.4, Chap. IV). It therefore follows from (6.7) that we have for almost every value of x, and for any $\eta \in [a_2, b_2]$,

$$\mathrm{W}_1(F; x; a_2, \eta) = \int_{a_2}^{\eta} |F'_y(x, y)|\, dy,$$

i. e. that the function $\mathrm{W}_1(F; x; a_2, \eta)$, and consequently also $F(x, \eta)$, is absolutely continuous with respect to η on $[a_2, b_2]$ for almost every value of x. By the symmetry of the variables, we conclude also that the function $F(\xi, y)$ is at the same time absolutely continuous with respect to ξ on $[a_1, b_1]$ for almost every value of y. The function F, which is by hypothesis of bounded variation on I_0, is therefore absolutely continuous in the Tonelli sense on this interval.

Conversely, if the function F is absolutely continuous on I_0, we have by Theorems 7.8 and 7.9, Chap. IV, for every subinterval $I=[\alpha_1, \beta_1; \alpha_2, \beta_2]$ of I_0, the relations:

$$H_1(I) = \int_{\alpha_1}^{\beta_1} \mathrm{W}_1(F; x; \alpha_2, \beta_2)\, dx = \iint_I |F'_y(x, y)|\, dx\, dy,$$

$$H_2(I) = \int_{\alpha_2}^{\beta_2} \mathrm{W}_2(F; y; \alpha_1, \beta_1)\, dy = \iint_I |F'_x(x, y)|\, dx\, dy,$$

so that the two functions of an interval H_1 and H_2, and therefore also H, are absolutely continuous.

Finally, since the function H is absolutely continuous, the formula (6.6) is a direct consequence of the third of the relations (6.2), the latter being valid almost everywhere on account of Theorem 6.1.

Up to the present we have regarded the expression $\mathrm{H}(F; I)$ as a function of an interval I. If we treat this expression as a functional depending on the function F, we obtain the following theorem, whose geometrical interpretation will appear in § 8 when the theorem appears to be a generalization of Theorem 2.1.

(6.8) ***Theorem.*** *Given any sequence of continuous functions $\{F_n\}$ which converges to a continuous function F, we have for every interval I*

$$\liminf_n \mathrm{H}(F_n; I) \geqslant \mathrm{H}(F; I). \tag{6.9}$$

Proof. Denoting by $\mathfrak{Z}_p$ the subdivision of I into p^2 equal intervals, similar to I, we have by Theorem 5.3 for any pair of integers p and n, $\mathrm{H}(F_n; I) \geqslant \mathrm{G}(F_n; \mathfrak{Z}_p)$, and by Fatou's Lemma (Chap. I, Theorem 12.10), for every integer p, $\liminf_n \mathrm{G}(F_n; \mathfrak{Z}_p) \geqslant \mathrm{G}(F; \mathfrak{Z}_p)$. We therefore have $\liminf_n \mathrm{H}(F_n; I) \geqslant \mathrm{G}(F; \mathfrak{Z}_p)$, and this leads to (6.9) when $p \to \infty$.

§ 7. Radò's Theorem. Before passing to the proof of the result of Radò, according to which the area of any surface $z=F(x, y)$ on an interval I is equal to $\mathrm{H}(F; I)$, we shall prove the following

(7.1) ***Theorem.*** *If a continuous function $F(x, y)$ has on an interval $I_0=[a_1, b_1; a_2, b_2]$ continuous partial derivatives, there exists a sequence of polyhedra $\{z=P_n(x, y)\}$ inscribed in the surface $z=F(x, y)$, such that the sequence converges uniformly to this surface and such that*

$$\lim_n \mathrm{S}_0(P_n; I_0) = \iint_{I_0} \{[F'_x(x, y)]^2 + [F'_y(x, y)]^2 + 1\}^{\frac{1}{2}}\, dx\, dy = \mathrm{H}(F; I). \tag{7.2}$$

Proof. Let $\mathfrak{Z}_n = \{I_{n,1}, I_{n,2}, \ldots, I_{n,n^2}\}$ denote the subdivision of I_0 into n^2 equal intervals similar to I_0, and $(x_{n,i}, y_{n,i})$, where $i=1, 2, \ldots, n^2$, the lower left-hand vertex of $I_{n,i}$. Let us divide any interval $I_{n,i}$ into two right-angled triangles $T'_{n,i}$ and $T''_{n,i}$ by a diagonal, in such a way that the vertex $(x_{n,i}, y_{n,i})$ is that of the right angle of $T'_{n,i}$. Consider for any n the polyhedron $z=P_n(x, y)$ inscribed in the surface $z=F(x, y)$ and corresponding to the net formed on I_0 by the $2n^2$ triangles $T'_{n,i}$ and $T''_{n,i}$ where $i=1, 2, \ldots, n^2$.

For brevity let $h_n=(b_1-a_1)/n$ and $k_n=(b_2-a_2)/n$; and let μ_n denote the upper bound of the differences $|F'_x(x'', y'')-F'_x(x', y')|$ and $|F'_y(x'', y'')-F'_y(x', y')|$ for all points (x', y') and (x'', y'') of I_0 such that $|x''-x'|\leqslant h_n$ and $|y''-y'|\leqslant k_n$.

Now if $s'_{n,i}$ and $s''_{n,i}$ denote respectively the elementary areas of the faces of the polyhedron $z=P_n(x, y)$ which correspond to the triangles $T'_{n,i}$ and $T''_{n,i}$, we notice at once that the areas of the projections of the former of these faces on the planes xz and yz are respectively equal to

$$\tfrac{1}{2}h_n\cdot|F(x_{n,i}, y_{n,i}+k_n)-F(x_{n,i}, y_{n,i})|=\tfrac{1}{2}h_nk_n\cdot|F'_y(x_{n,i}, y'_{n,i})|$$

and

$$\tfrac{1}{2}k_n\cdot|F(x_{n,i}+h_n, y_{n,i})-F(x_{n,i}, y_{n,i})|=\tfrac{1}{2}h_nk_n\cdot|F'_x(x'_{n,i}, y_{n,i})|$$

where $x_{n,i}\leqslant x'_{n,i}\leqslant x_{n,i}+h_n$ and $y_{n,i}\leqslant y'_{n,i}\leqslant y_{n,i}+k_n$.

We therefore have $s'_{n,i}=\frac{1}{2}\{[F'_x(x'_{n,i},y_{n,i})]^2+[F'_y(x_{n,i},y'_{n,i})]^2+1\}^{1/2}\cdot|I_{n,i}|$, and so, by the inequality (5.1), p. 171,

$$\sum_{i=1}^{n^2} s'_{n,i}-\frac{1}{2}\sum_{i=1}^{n^2}\{[F'_x(x_{n,i}, y_{n,i})]^2+[F'_y(x_{n,i}, y_{n,i})]^2+1\}^{1/2}\cdot|I_{n,i}|\leqslant\frac{1}{2}\cdot\sqrt{2}\,\mu_n\cdot|I_0|.$$

Since the partial derivatives F'_x and F'_y are by hypothesis continuous, it follows by making $n\to\infty$ that

$$\lim_n \sum_{i=1}^{n^2} s'_{n,i}=\frac{1}{2}\int\int_{I_0}\{[F'_x(x, y)]^2+[F'_y(x, y)]^2+1\}^{1/2}\,dx\,dy,$$

and the same limit is clearly obtained for the sum of the $s''_{n,i}$. By addition, together with an appeal to Theorem 6.5, we now derive the formula (7.2) and this completes the proof.

In what follows we shall apply the method of mean value integrals. Given in the plane a summable function $F(x, y)$, the sequence of functions $F_n(x, y)=n^2\int_0^{1/n}\int_0^{1/n}F(x+u, y+v)\,du\,dv$ where $n=1, 2, \ldots,$ will be called *sequence of mean value integrals* of the function $F(x, y)$. It is clear that *if the function F is continuous*, (i) *the sequence of its mean value integrals $\{F_n(x,y)\}$ converges to $F(x, y)$ at every point (x, y) of the plane, and uniformly on any interval, and* (ii) *the partial derivatives $\partial F_n/\partial x$ and $\partial F_n/\partial y$ exist everywhere and are* *continuous*. In fact, at any point (x, y) a direct calculation gives

$$\partial F_n(x, y)/\partial x = n^2 \int_0^{1/n} [F(x+1/n, y+v) - F(x, y+v)]\,dv$$

and

$$\partial F_n(x, y)/\partial y = n^2 \int_0^{1/n} [F(x+u, y+1/n) - F(x+u, y)]\,du.$$

It was T. Radò [2] who first applied in the theory of area of surfaces the method of mean value integrals. The rôle of these mean values is due to the fact that in the case in which the given function F is continuous, the sequence of areas of the surfaces $z = F_n(x, y)$ on any interval tends to the area of the surface $z = F(x, y)$ (*vide*, below, Theorem 7.3).

In the definition given above, the functions F_n are defined at each point (x, y) as "mean values" of the function F over squares of which (x, y) is a vertex; it goes without saying that we could also make use of mean values taken over squares, or circles, having (x, y) as their centres. These mean values over circles are used for instance in potential theory (cf. F. Riesz [4] and G. C. Evans [1]).

(7.3) ***Radò's Theorem.*** *If $F(x, y)$ is a continuous function and $\{F_n(x, y)\}$ is the sequence of mean value integrals of $F(x, y)$, then*

(7.4) $$\mathrm{H}(F; I_0) = \mathrm{S}(F; I_0) = \lim_n \mathrm{S}(F_n; I_0)$$

for every interval I_0.

Proof. Let $\{z = P_n(x, y)\}$ be a sequence of polyhedra converging uniformly to the surface $z = F(x, y)$, such that

(7.5) $$\lim_n \mathrm{S}_0(P_n; I_0) = \mathrm{S}(F; I_0).$$

Since the functions $P_n(x, y)$ are absolutely continuous, it follows from Theorem 6.5 (cf. also § 2, p. 165) that $\mathrm{S}_0(P_n; I_0) = \mathrm{H}(P_n; I_0)$ for every n. Consequently, since the sequences of functions $\{F_n\}$ and $\{P_n\}$ converge uniformly to the function F, it follows by using successively Theorem 2.1, the formula (7.5) and Theorem 6.8, that

(7.6) $$\liminf_n \mathrm{S}(F_n; I_0) \geqslant \mathrm{S}(F; I_0) = \lim_n \mathrm{H}(P_n; I_0) \geqslant \mathrm{H}(F; I_0).$$

Now if the function F is not of bounded variation on I_0, it follows from Theorem 5.13 that $\mathrm{H}(F; I_0) = +\infty$ and consequently the formula (7.4) follows at once from (7.6). We may therefore assume that the function F is of bounded variation on I_0, and further (cf. § 4, p. 170) that F is continuous and of bounded variation on each interval of the plane.

Let us agree to denote, for any set E in the plane, by $E^{(u,v)}$ the parallel translation of E by the vector (u, v) (cf. Chap. III, § 11); similarly, for a family of sets $\mathfrak{E}$ in the plane, $\mathfrak{E}^{(u,v)}$ will denote the family of all the sets obtained from sets $(\mathfrak{E})$ by subjecting them to this translation. For any subinterval $I = [a_1, b_1; a_2, b_2]$ we then obtain

$$G_1(F_n; I) = \int_{a_1}^{b_1} |F_n(x, b_2) - F_n(x, a_2)| \, dx \leqslant$$

$$\leqslant n^2 \int_{a_1}^{b_1} \Big[\int_0^{1/n} \int_0^{1/n} |F(x+u, b_2+v) - F(x+u, a_2+v)| \, du \, dv \Big] dx =$$

$$= n^2 \int_0^{1/n} \int_0^{1/n} G_1(F; I^{(u,v)}) \, du \, dv,$$

and a similar formula for G_2. Hence by the inequality (5.2), p. 171,

$$G(F_n; I) = \{[G_1(F_n; I)]^2 + [G_2(F_n; I)]^2 + |I|^2\}^{1/2} \leqslant$$

$$\leqslant n^2 \int_0^{1/n} \int_0^{1/n} \{[G_1(F; I^{(u,v)})]^2 + [G_2(F; I^{(u,v)})]^2 + |I^{(u,v)}|^2\}^{1/2} \, du \, dv =$$

$$= n^2 \int_0^{1/n} \int_0^{1/n} G(F; I^{(u,v)}) \, du \, dv.$$

Denoting by $\mathfrak{I}_p$ the subdivision of I_0 into p^2 equal intervals similar to I_0, we obtain therefore, for every p,

$$G(F_n; \mathfrak{I}_p) \leqslant n^2 \int_0^{1/n} \int_0^{1/n} G(F; \mathfrak{I}_p^{(u,v)}) \, du \, dv;$$

and since by Lemma 3.4, $G(F; \mathfrak{I}_p^{(u,v)})$ tends to $H(F; I_0^{(u,v)})$ as $p \to \infty$, uniformly in u and v, we obtain in the limit

$$(7.7) \qquad H(F_n; I_0) \leqslant n^2 \int_0^{1/n} \int_0^{1/n} H(F; I_0^{(u,v)}) \, du \, dv.$$

Finally the areas of the figures $I_0^{(u,v)} \ominus I_0$ and $I_0 \ominus I_0^{(u,v)}$ tend to 0 with u and v and each of these figures is a sum of two intervals. Hence since the expression $H(F; I)$ is by Theorem 6.1 a continuous function of the interval I, we have $\lim_{u \to 0, \, v \to 0} H(F; I_0^{(u,v)}) = H(F; I_0)$. On the other hand, since the functions $F_n(x, y)$ have continuous partial derivatives, we have, by Theorem 7.1, $S(F_n; I_0) \leqslant H(F_n; I_0)$ for each n. Therefore making $n \to \infty$ in (7.7), we find $\limsup_n S(F_n; I_0) \leqslant$ $\leqslant H(F; I_0)$, which in conjunction with (7.6) gives the required relation (7.4).

§ 8. Tonelli's Theorem. The theorem of Radò just established, enables us to replace in all the theorems of this chapter the expression $H(F; I)$ by the surface area $S(F; I)$.

Thus for instance, Theorem 6.5 (formula (6.6)) expresses the fact that *the elementary area of a polyhedron coincides with its area according to the general definition of area of a surface.*

Theorem 6.8 contains a generalization of Theorem 2.1; it enables us to replace in its statement uniform convergence by ordinary convergence: we thus obtain a theorem similar to Lemma of Fatou (Chap. I, Theorem 12.10). It follows that the uniform convergence of the inscribed polygons, required in the definition of area, may be replaced by the ordinary convergence, so that the area of a continuous surface $z=F(x, y)$ is the lower limit of the areas of polyhedra tending to this surface. Further, by Theorem 7.1, *if a function $F(x, y)$ has continuous partial derivatives, there exists a sequence of polyhedra inscribed in the surface $z=F(x, y)$, tending uniformly to the latter and having areas which converge to the area of this surface.* (For further generalizations *vide* S. Kempisty [1]. Cf. also on this subject H. Rademacher [3], W. H. Young [5], M. Fréchet [2] and T. Radó [5].) Finally, we obtain the following theorem, which sums up the most essential considerations of this chapter:

(8.1) ***Tonelli's Theorem.*** a) *In order that a continuous surface $z=F(x,y)$ have a finite area on an interval I_0, it is necessary and sufficient that the function $F(x, y)$ be of bounded variation on I_0.*

b) *When this is the case, we have*

$$S(F; I_0) \geqslant \iint\limits_{I_0} \left[\left(\frac{\partial F}{\partial x}\right)^2 + \left(\frac{\partial F}{\partial y}\right)^2 + 1\right]^{1/2} dx\, dy;$$

the expression $S(I)=S(F; I)$ is then an additive continuous function of the interval $I \subset I_0$ and we have for almost every point $(x, y) \in I_0$

$$S'(x, y) = \left[\left(\frac{\partial F}{\partial x}\right)^2 + \left(\frac{\partial F}{\partial y}\right)^2 + 1\right]^{1/2}.$$

c) *In order that we should have*

$$S(F; I_0) = \iint\limits_{I_0} \left[\left(\frac{\partial F}{\partial x}\right)^2 + \left(\frac{\partial F}{\partial y}\right)^2 + 1\right]^{1/2} dx\, dy, \tag{8.2}$$

it is necessary and sufficient that the function $F(x, y)$ be absolutely continuous on I_0; and in order that this be the case it is necessary and sufficient that the area $S(F; I)$ be an absolutely continuous function of the interval $I \subset I_0$.

Proof. The assertion a) follows directly from Theorem 5.13; b) and c) follows from Theorems 6.1 and 6.5 on account of Theorem 7.4, Chap. IV.

With regard to Theorem 8.1 *vide* L. Tonelli [5; 6; 7]. The necessity of condition a) was established a little earlier by G. Lampariello [1].

According to Tonelli's theorem, the relation of equality (8.2) can hold for a continuous surface $z=F(x,y)$ only in the case in which the function F is absolutely continuous. Nevertheless, as proved by L. C. Young, this relation will remain valid for arbitrary continuous surfaces, as soon as we replace on the right-hand side the partial derivatives by ratios of finite differences and transpose the passage to the limit outside the integral sign. In fact:

(8.3) ***Theorem.*** *For any continuous surface $z=F(x,y)$ and any interval I_0 we have*

$$(8.4)\quad \mathrm{S}(F;I_0)=\lim_{\alpha,\beta\to0}\iint_{I_0}\left\{\left[\frac{F(x+\alpha,y)-F(x,y)}{\alpha}\right]^2+\left[\frac{F(x,y+\beta)-F(x,y)}{\beta}\right]^2+1\right\}^{1/2}dx\,dy;$$

and in order that the function F be of bounded variation on I_0, it is necessary and sufficient that

$$(8.5)\quad \limsup_{\alpha,\beta\to0}\frac{1}{|\alpha|+|\beta|}\iint_{I_0}|F(x+\alpha,y+\beta)-F(x,y)|\,dx\,dy<+\infty.$$

Proof. Let $\{F_n\}$ be the sequence of mean value integrals (cf. § 7, p. 178) of the function F. Denote, for brevity, by $R(x,y;\alpha,\beta)$ the expression under the integral sign on the right-hand side of (8.4), and by $R_n(x,y;\alpha,\beta)$, for each positive integer n, the expression obtained from $R(x,y;\alpha,\beta)$ by replacing F by F_n. Finally let us write for $n=1,2,\ldots$

$$R_n(x,y)=\lim_{\alpha,\beta\to0}R_n(x,y;\alpha,\beta)=\{[\partial F_n(x,y)/\partial x]^2+[\partial F_n(x,y)/\partial y]^2+1\}^{1/2}.$$

In order to establish the identity (8.4), it evidently suffices to show that

$$(8.6)\qquad \mathrm{S}(F;I_0)\leqslant\liminf_{\alpha,\beta\to0}\iint_{I_0}R(x,y;\alpha,\beta)\,dx\,dy$$

and

$$(8.7)\qquad \mathrm{S}(F;I_0)\geqslant\limsup_{\alpha,\beta\to0}\iint_{I_0}R(x,y;\alpha,\beta)\,dx\,dy.$$

For this purpose, let I be any interval in the interior of I_0. By means of the inequality (5.2), p. 171, we easily find that

$$(8.8) \qquad R_n(x, y; \alpha, \beta) \leqslant n^2 \int_0^{1/n}\int_0^{1/n} R(x+u, y+v; \alpha, \beta)\, du\, dv.$$

Now let n be a positive integer, sufficiently large in order that $(x, y) \in I$, $|u| < 1/n$ and $|v| < 1/n$ should imply $(x+u, y+v) \in I_0$. We then have $\int\int_I R(x+u, y+v; \alpha, \beta)\, dx\, dy \leqslant \int\int_{I_0} R(x, y; \alpha, \beta)\, dx\, dy$ and consequently, by (8.8), $\int\int_I R_n(x, y; \alpha, \beta)\, dx\, dy \leqslant \int\int_{I_0} R(x, y; \alpha, \beta)\, dx\, dy$. Making $\alpha \to 0$ and $\beta \to 0$, we obtain in the limit $\mathrm{S}(F_n; I) \leqslant \liminf_{\alpha, \beta \to 0} \int\int_{I_0} R(x, y; \alpha, \beta)\, dx\, dy$. This relation being thus established for each interval $I \subset I_0^\circ$, we may replace, on its left-hand side, I by I_0, and making still $n \to \infty$ we obtain the relation (8.6).

In order to prove the relation (8.7), let us first observe that the latter is obvious in the case in which $\mathrm{S}(F; I_0) = +\infty$. We may therefore assume that the function $F(x, y)$ is of bounded variation on I_0 and moreover (cf. § 4, p. 170) of bounded variation on every interval in the plane and periodic with respect to each variable. We can therefore determine an interval $J_0 = [a_1, b_1; a_2, b_2]$ containing I_0 in its interior, such that its sides $b_1 - a_1$ and $b_2 - a_2$ are the periods of $F(x, y)$ with respect to x and y respectively.

This being so, we find easily, on account of the inequality (5.1), p. 171, that, for any pair of positive integers n and k,

$$R_n(x, y; \alpha, \beta) \leqslant \frac{1}{k} \sum_{j=0}^{k-1} R_n(x + j\alpha/k,\ y + j\beta/k;\ \alpha/k, \beta/k).$$

By integrating the two sides of this inequality over J_0, and taking account of the periodicity of the function F, we obtain

$$\int\int_{J_0} R_n(x, y; \alpha, \beta)\, dx\, dy \leqslant \int\int_{J_0} R_n(x, y;\ \alpha/k, \beta/k)\, dx\, dy;$$

and hence, passing to the limit, making first $k \to \infty$, and then $n \to \infty$, we find by Radò's Theorem 7.3,

$$\iint\limits_{J_0} R(x,y;\alpha,\beta)\,dx\,dy \leqslant \lim_n \iint\limits_{J_0} R_n(x,y)\,dx\,dy = \lim_n \mathrm{S}(F_n;J_0) = \mathrm{S}(F;J_0),$$

and so

$$\limsup_{\alpha,\beta\to 0} \iint\limits_{J_0} R(x,y;\alpha,\beta)\,dx\,dy \leqslant \mathrm{S}(F;J_0). \tag{8.9}$$

Now, by the result already established in the inequality (8.6), we have $\liminf\limits_{\alpha,\beta\to 0} \iint\limits_{I} R(x,y;\alpha,\beta)\,dx\,dy \geqslant \mathrm{S}(F;I)$ for every interval I. It follows at once that (8.9) remains valid when we replace the interval J_0 by any subinterval of J_0, and in particular by the interval I_0. We thus obtain the relation (8.7).

Finally let us remark that on account of the relation (8.4), in order that the area of the surface $z=F(x,y)$ on I_0 be finite, it is necessary and sufficient that

$$\limsup_{\alpha\to 0} \frac{1}{|\alpha|} \iint\limits_{I_0} |F(x+\alpha,y)-F(x,y)|\,dx\,dy < +\infty$$

and

$$\limsup_{\beta\to 0} \frac{1}{|\beta|} \iint\limits_{I_0} |F(x,y+\beta)-F(x,y)|\,dx\,dy < +\infty.$$

Now this pair of relations is easily seen to be equivalent to the relation (8.5) which therefore expresses a condition necessary and sufficient in order that the function F should be of bounded variation on I_0. This completes the proof.

A statement analogous to Theorem 8.3 can be made for curves (cf. Chap. IV, § 8). *If C is a continuous curve defined by the equations $x=X(t)$, $y=Y(t)$, its length on any interval $I_0=[a,b]$ is given by the formula*

$$\mathrm{S}(C;I_0) = \lim_{h\to 0} \int_a^b \left\{\left[\frac{X(t+h)-X(t)}{h}\right]^2 + \left[\frac{Y(t+h)-Y(t)}{h}\right]^2\right\}^{1/2} dt. \tag{8.10}$$

In particular therefore, *in order that a continuous functions $G(t)$ be of bounded variation on an interval $[a,b]$, it is necessary and sufficient that*

$$\limsup_{h\to 0} \frac{1}{|h|} \int_a^b |G(t+h)-G(t)|\,dt < +\infty. \tag{8.11}$$

This assertion can be proved by the method of mean value integrals in a manner quite similar to that we made use of in the theory of areas of surfaces $z=F(x, y)$, but for curves this method can be very much simplified. Let us observe further that the relation (8.11) may be interpreted in a more general sense. In fact, given any summable function $G(t)$, the relation (8.11) is the necessary and sufficient condition in order that the function G be almost everywhere on $[a, b]$ equal to a function of bounded variation (*vide* G. H. Hardy and J. E. Littlewood [1]; cf. also A. Zygmund [I, p. 106]).

Finally the relation (8.10) holds for any rectifiable curve given by the equations $x=X(t)$, $y=Y(t)$, where the functions $X(t)$ and $Y(t)$ are not necessarily continuous, provided however that for each t the point $(X(t), Y(t))$ lies on the segment joining the points $(X(t-), Y(t-))$ and $(X(t+), Y(t+))$.

CHAPTER VI.

Major and minor functions.

§ 1. Introduction. Major and minor functions (defined in § 3 of this chapter) were first introduced by Ch. J. de la Vallée Poussin in his study of the properties of the Lebesgue integral and those of additive functions of a set. Entirely equivalent notions (of "Ober"- and "Unterfunktionen") were introduced independently by O. Perron [1], who based on them a new definition of integral, which does not require the theory of measure. Although, in its original form, this definition concerned only integration of bounded functions, its extension to unbounded functions was easy and led, as shown by O. Bauer [1], to a process of integration more general than that of Lebesgue. Moreover, as we shall see in § 6, the Perron integral may be regarded as a synthesis of two fundamental conceptions of integration: one corresponding to the idea of definite integral as limit of certain approximating sums, and the other to that of indefinite integral understood as a primitive function.

It is usual to associate these two conceptions of integration with the names of Leibniz and Newton. In accordance with this distinction (which is largely a matter of convention) we shall call a function of a real variable F *indefinite integral*, or *primitive*, *of Newton* for a function f, if F has everywhere its derivative finite and equal to f. The function f will then be termed *integrable in the sense of Newton*, and the increment of the function F on an interval I_0, will be called *definite integral of Newton* of f on I_0. As is seen immediately, this definition implies that any function which is integrable in the sense of Newton is everywhere finite. This restriction is essential (cf. the example of § 7, p. 206) for the unicity of integration in the sense of Newton, which then follows from classical theorems of Analysis, or, if we like, from Theorem 3.1, or from Theorem 7.1 of this chapter.

The theory of the integral was first developed on Newtonian lines. This is easily accounted for if we think how much simpler the inverse of the operation of derivation must have seemed than the notion of definite integral as defined by Leibniz. It was A. Cauchy [I, t. 4, p. 122] who returned to the idea of Leibniz in order to apply it to integration of continuous functions, for which the methods of Cauchy and Newton are actually completely equivalent. This equivalence disappears, however, as soon as we pass on, with Riemann, to integration of discontinuous functions. In fact, even in the domain of bounded functions to which the Riemann process applies, there exist on the one hand (as we see at once) functions which are integrable in the sense of Riemann but have no primitive, and on the other hand (as shown by V. Volterra [1]; cf. also H. Lebesgue [II, p. 100]) functions which have a primitive but are not integrable in the Riemann sense. Also the Lebesgue process of integration does not include the integral of Newton, not even when the functions to be integrated are everywhere finite.

Thus, the function $F(x) = x^2 \sin(\pi/x^2)$ for $x \neq 0$, completed by writing $F(0) = 0$, has in the whole interval $[0, 1]$ a finite derivative which vanishes for $x = 0$ and which is bounded on every interval $[\varepsilon, 1]$, where $0 < \varepsilon < 1$. On every interval $[\varepsilon, 1]$ the function $F(x)$ is therefore absolutely continuous. On the other hand, on the whole interval $[0,1]$ the function is not even of bounded variation. Hence $F'(x)$ is not summable on $[0,1]$, since its indefinite Lebesgue integral could then differ only by an additive constant from $F(x)$ on $[0,1]$, and this is impossible.

We have thus been led to the problem of determining a process of integration which includes both that of Lebesgue and that of Newton. As an application of the method of major and minor functions, we shall consider in this chapter (§§ 6 and 7) the solution of this problem constituted by the Perron integral. Another solution, the Denjoy integrals, will be treated in Chapter VIII.

The notions of major and minor functions, and their applications to Lebesgue integration, will be discussed here for arbitrary spaces $\boldsymbol{R}_m$. In defining the Perron integral, however, we shall limit ourselves to functions of one real variable. Although recently various authors have treated the extension of this integral to Euclidean spaces of any number of dimensions, the present state of the theory does not allow us to decide as to the importance of this generalization. On the contrary, in the domain of functions of a real variable, the method of major and minor functions as a means of generalizing the notion of integral has already repeatedly shown its fruitfulness. In the memoir of J. Marcinkiewicz and A. Zygmund [1], the reader will find new applications of this method in connection with certain fundamental problems of the theory of trigonometrical series (cf. also J. Ridder [11]).

§ 2. Derivation with respect to normal sequences of nets. Given a regular sequence $\mathfrak{N}=\{\mathfrak{N}_k\}$ of nets of intervals (*vide* Chap. III, § 2) in a space $\boldsymbol{R}_m$ and a function of an interval F in $\boldsymbol{R}_m$, we shall call *upper derivate* of F at a point x *with respect to the sequence of nets* $\mathfrak{N}$ the upper limit of the ratio $F(Q)/|Q|$ as $\delta(Q)\to 0$, where Q denotes any interval containing x and belonging to one of the nets of the sequence $\mathfrak{N}$. By symmetry we define similarly the *lower derivate* of F at x *with respect to the sequence of nets* $\mathfrak{N}$. We shall denote these two derivates by $(\mathfrak{N})\,\overline{F}(x)$ and $(\mathfrak{N})\,\underline{F}(x)$. When they are equal at a point x, their common value will be denoted by $(\mathfrak{N})\,F'(x)$ and called *derivative* of F at x *with respect to the sequence of nets* $\mathfrak{N}$.

These definitions are similar to those given in § 15, Chap. IV, in connection with derivation of additive functions of a set $(\mathfrak{B})$ in a metrical space. It should be observed, however, that additive functions of a set $(\mathfrak{B})$ correspond to additive functions of an interval of bounded variation, whereas in the present § we treat derivation of additive functions of an interval without supposing them *a priori* of bounded variation. For this reason it will be necessary to impose certain restrictions on the nets considered in this §, and to distinguish a class of nets which we shall call, for brevity, normal nets. The latter are, in point of fact, the nets occurring most frequently in applications (cf., for instance, Chap. III, p. 58).

A system of intervals will be called a *normal net* in the space $\boldsymbol{R}_m$, when it consists of the closed intervals $[a_k^{(1)}, a_{k+1}^{(1)}; a_k^{(2)}, a_{k+1}^{(2)}; \ldots; a_k^{(m)}, a_{k+1}^{(m)}]$ for $k=0, \pm 1, \pm 2, \ldots$, which are determined by systems of numbers $a_k^{(i)}$ subject to the conditions $a_k^{(i)} < a_{k+1}^{(i)}$ for $i=1, 2, \ldots, m$ and $k=\ldots, -1, 0, +1, \ldots$, and $\lim\limits_{k\to\pm\infty} a_k^{(i)} = \pm\infty$. A regular sequence of normal nets will be termed *normal sequence.*

(2.1) ***Theorem.*** *Let* $\mathfrak{N}=\{\mathfrak{N}_k\}$ *be a normal sequence of nets,* $g(x)$ *a function which is summable in the space* $\boldsymbol{R}_m$ *and* F *a continuous additive function of an interval such that* (i) $(\mathfrak{N})\underline{F}(x) > -\infty$ *at every point* x, *except at most those of an enumerable set, and* (ii) $F'(x) \geqslant g(x)$ *at almost all the points* x *at which the function* F *is derivable in the ordinary sense.*

Then for every interval I, *we have*

$$F(I) \geqslant \int_I g(x)\,dx; \tag{2.2}$$

i. e. F *is a function of bounded variation, whose function of singularities is monotone non-negative.*

Proof. Consider the points in every neighbourhood of which there exist intervals I for which the inequality (2.2) is false, and let P denote the set of these points. The set P is evidently closed, and we see easily that the relation (2.2) must hold for every interval I such that $I^\circ \subset CP$. For if this were not the case, we could determine first an interval $I \subset CP$ such that $F(I) < \int_I g(x)\,dx$, and then, by the method of successive subdivisions, a descending sequence $\{I_n\}$ of subintervals of I such that $\delta(I_n) \to 0$ as $n \to \infty$ and that $F(I_n) < \int_{I_n} g(x)\,dx$ for $n=1, 2, \ldots$. Therefore, denoting by a the common point of the intervals I_n, we should have $a \in P$, which is clearly impossible.

It follows that in order to establish the validity of the inequality (2.2) for all intervals I, we need only prove that $P=0$. Suppose therefore, if possible, that $P \neq 0$. Let us denote, for any pair of positive integers k and h, by $N_{k,h}$ the sum of all the intervals I of the net $\mathfrak{N}_k$ for which $F(I) > -h \cdot |I|$. Therefore by writing $N_h = \prod_{k=h}^{\infty} N_{k,h}$, we obtain a sequence $\{N_h\}$ of closed sets whose sum, according to condition (i), covers the whole space except for an at most enumerable set. Consequently, on account of Baire's Theorem (Chap. II, Theorem 9.2), the set P contains a portion which either consists of a single point, or else is contained in a set N_h. The former case is excluded since it is evident from the continuity and additivity of the function F that the set P contains no isolated points. Therefore there exists a positive integer h_0 and an open sphere S such that $0 \neq P \cdot S \subset N_{h_0}$. Let us write $H(I) = F(I) + h_0 \cdot |I| + \int_I |g(x)|\,dx$ where I is any interval. We shall have $H(I) \geqslant 0$ for any interval I such that $I^\circ \subset CP$, as well as for any interval I belonging to a net $\mathfrak{N}_k$ of index $k \geqslant h_0$ and having points of the set N_{h_0} in its interior. Therefore $H(I) \geqslant 0$ for any interval $I \subset S$ belonging to a net $\mathfrak{N}_k$ of index $k \geqslant h_0$, and consequently, by additivity and continuity of H, we have $H(I) \geqslant 0$, i.e. $F(I) \geqslant -h_0 \cdot |I| - \int_I |g(x)|\,dx$, for any interval $I \subset S$ whatsoever. It follows at once that the function F is of bounded variation in S and that the function of singularities of F (cf. Chap. IV, p. 120) is monotone non-negative in S.

Hence, by condition (ii), $F(I) \geqslant \int_I F'(x)\,dx \geqslant \int_I g(x)\,dx$ for every interval $I \subset S$. But since $P \cdot S \neq 0$ we thus arrive at a contradiction and this completes the proof.

As an immediate corollary of Theorem 2.1, we have

(2.3) ***Theorem.*** *If $\mathfrak{N}$ is a normal sequence of nets in the space $\boldsymbol{R}_m$ and if F is a continuous additive function of an interval such that:* (i) $-\infty < (\mathfrak{N})\underline{F}(x) \leqslant (\mathfrak{N})\overline{F}(x) < +\infty$ *for each point x except at most the points of an enumerable set,* (ii) *the (ordinary) derivative $F'(x)$ is summable on each portion of the set of the points at which this derivative exists; then the function F is almost everywhere derivable and is the indefinite integral of its derivative.*

For Theorems 2.1 and 2.3 cf. J. Ridder [2]. Let us remark that in the case where the function F is of bounded variation, these theorems are included in Theorem 15.7, Chap. IV, which concerns derivation of additive functions of a set in an abstract metrical space.

It follows easily from Theorem 15.12, Chap. IV, that $F'(x) = (\mathfrak{N})F'(x)$ almost everywhere for any regular sequence of nets of intervals $\mathfrak{N}$ and for any additive function of an interval F which is continuous and of bounded variation. This remark enables us to replace condition (ii) of Theorem 2.1 by the following: (ii-*bis*) $F'(x) = (\mathfrak{N})F'(x) \geqslant g(x)$ *at almost all the points x at which the two derivatives $F'(x)$ and $(\mathfrak{N})F'(x)$ exist, are finite and equal.* Similarly we may modify condition (ii) of Theorem 2.3.

As it follows from an example due to A. J. Ward [7], the inequality $(\mathfrak{N})\underline{F}(x) > -\infty$ in condition (i) of Theorem 2.1 cannot be replaced by $(\mathfrak{N})\overline{F}(x) > -\infty$.

§ 3. Major and minor functions. Before introducing the fundamental definitions of the theory of the Perron integral, we shall prove

(3.1) ***Théorem.*** *If an additive function of an interval F (not necessarily continuous) has a non-negative lower derivate at each point x of an interval I_0, then $F(I_0) \geqslant 0$.*

Proof. Let ε be any positive number and write $G(I) = F(I) + \varepsilon \cdot |I|$ for every interval I. Then $\underline{G}(x) \geqslant \varepsilon > 0$ at each point $x \in I_0$. Suppose that $G(I_0) \leqslant 0$. By the method of successive subdivisions, we could then determine a descending sequence $\{I_n\}$ of intervals similar to I_0, such that $G(I_n) \leqslant 0$ for $n = 0, 1, 2, \ldots$ and that $\delta(I_n) \to 0$ as $n \to \infty$. Therefore, denoting by x_0 the common point of the intervals I_n, we should have $\underline{G}(x_0) \leqslant 0$ which is impossible. Hence $G(I_0) > 0$, and this gives $F(I_0) > -\varepsilon \cdot |I_0|$ for each $\varepsilon > 0$, and finally $F(I_0) \geqslant 0$.

An additive function of an interval F is termed *major* [*minor*] *function* of a function of a point f on a figure R_0 if, at every point x of this figure, $-\infty \neq \underline{F}_s(x) \geqslant f(x)$ $[+\infty \neq \overline{F}_s(x) \leqslant f(x)]$. It follows at once from Theorem 3.1 that if the functions of an interval U and V are respectively a major and a minor function of a function f on a figure R_0, their difference $U-V$ is monotone non-negative on R_0.

(3.2) ***Theorem.*** *If f is a summable function, then, for each $\varepsilon>0$, the function f has an absolutely continuous major function U and an absolutely continuous minor function V such that, for each interval I,*

(3.3) $$0 \leqslant U(I) - \int_I f(x)\,dx \leqslant \varepsilon \quad \textit{and} \quad 0 \leqslant \int_I f(x)\,dx - V(I) \leqslant \varepsilon.$$

Proof. On account of the theorem of Vitali-Carathéodory (Chap. III, Theorem 7.6) we can associate with the function f two summable functions, one a lower semi-continuous function g and the other an upper semi-continuous function h, such that (i) $-\infty \neq g(x) \geqslant f(x) \geqslant h(x) \neq +\infty$ at every point x and that (ii) $\int_I [g(x)-f(x)]\,dx < \varepsilon$ and $\int_I [f(x)-h(x)]\,dx < \varepsilon$ for every interval I.

Therefore, if we denote by U and V the indefinite integrals of the functions g and h respectively, we find by Theorem 2.2, Chap. IV, that $\underline{U}_s(x) \geqslant g(x) \geqslant h(x) \geqslant \overline{V}_s(x)$, and so, on account of (i), that $-\infty \neq \underline{U}_s(x) \geqslant f(x)$ and $+\infty \neq \overline{V}_s(x) \leqslant f(x)$ at each point x. Finally, (ii) then implies the relations (3.3) and this completes the proof.

Theorem 3.2 can easily be inverted. Thus: *in order that a function of a point f be summable, it is necessary and sufficient that for each $\varepsilon>0$ there exist two absolutely continuous functions of an interval U and V, the one a major and the other a minor function of f, which fulfil the condition $U(I)-V(I)<\varepsilon$ for every interval I.* (These absolutely continuous functions may clearly be replaced by functions of bounded variation, and if the function f is supposed measurable, then, of course, for its summability there suffices the existence of two functions of bounded variation, one of which is a major and the other a minor function of f.)

*** § 4. Derivation with respect to binary sequences of nets.** The theorems of § 2 concerned derivation of additive functions with respect to any normal sequence of nets of intervals. For certain purposes however, more special sequences of nets are required. We shall say that a normal sequence $\{\mathfrak{N}_k\}_{k=1,2,\dots}$ of nets in the space $\boldsymbol{R}_m$ is *binary*, if the net $\mathfrak{N}_{k+1}$ (where $k=1, 2, \dots$) is obtained by subdividing each interval N of the net $\mathfrak{N}_k$ into 2^m equal intervals similar to N.

An application of this notion may be found in the following theorem which is proved similarly to Lemma 11.8 of Chap. IV: *If* $\mathfrak{N}$ *is a binary sequence of nets, any additive function of an interval* F *is derivable with respect to* $\mathfrak{N}$ *at almost all the points at which either* $(\mathfrak{N})\underline{F}(x) > -\infty$ *or* $(\mathfrak{N})\overline{F}(x) < +\infty$.

Another application, of particular interest, is due to A. S. Besicovitch [3] who, by using derivation with respect to a binary sequence of nets, established a theorem on complex functions (*vide* below § 5). The substance of Besicovitch's result is contained in Theorem 4.4 below. We must first, however, give some subsidiary definitions.

For definiteness, just as in § 11, Chap. IV, we shall fix in the space $\boldsymbol{R}_m$ a binary sequence of nets $\mathfrak{Q} = \{\mathfrak{Q}_k\}$, where $\mathfrak{Q}_k$ denotes, for $k = 1, 2, \ldots$, the net formed by the cubes

$$[p_1/2^k, (p_1+1)/2^k; \; p_2/2^k, (p_2+1)/2^k; \; \ldots; \; p_m/2^k, (p_m+1)/2^k]$$

where $p_1, p_2, \ldots, p_m$ are arbitrary integers; it goes without saying that in Theorem 4.4 this sequence may be replaced by any binary sequence whatsoever.

Given a non-negative number α, we shall say that a function of an interval F fulfils the *condition* (l_α^+) [*condition* (l_α^-)] at a point x, if $\liminf_{\delta(I)\to 0} F(I)/[\delta(I)]^\alpha \geqslant 0$ [$\limsup_{\delta(I)\to 0} F(I)/[\delta(I)]^\alpha \leqslant 0$], where I is any interval containing x. If a function f fulfils the condition (l_α^+) [(l_α^-)] at every point of a figure R, we shall say simply that f fulfils this condition on R. Finally, we shall say that a function fulfils the *condition* (l_α) at a point, or on a figure, if it fulfils simultaneously the conditions (l_α^+) and (l_α^-).

We recall further the notation $\Lambda_\alpha(E)$ for the α-dimensional measure of a set E (cf. Chap. II, p. 53).

(4.1) **Lemma.** *Given a set* E *in the space* $\boldsymbol{R}_m$, *together with a positive integer* k_0 *and a non-negative number* $\alpha < m$, *there exists for each* $\varepsilon > 0$ *a sequence* $\{Q_n\}$ *of intervals belonging to the nets* $\mathfrak{Q}_k$ *for* $k \geqslant k_0$, *which fulfils the following conditions*:

(i) $$\sum_n [\delta(Q_n)]^\alpha \leqslant (4m)^m \cdot [\Lambda_\alpha(E) + \varepsilon];$$

(ii) *to each point* x *of* E *there corresponds a positive integer* $k \geqslant k_0$ *such that all the intervals of the net* $\mathfrak{Q}_k$ *which contain the point* x *belong to the sequence* $\{Q_n\}$.

Proof. Let us cover E by a sequence $\{E_i\}_{i=1,2,\ldots}$ of sets such that $0 < \delta(E_i) < 1/2^{k_0+1}$ for $i = 1, 2, \ldots$ and such that

(4.2) $$\sum_i [\delta(E_i)]^\alpha \leqslant \Lambda_\alpha(E) + \varepsilon.$$

Let us denote by k_i, for each $i=1,2,\ldots$, a positive integer such that

(4.3) $$1/2^{k_i} > \delta(E_i) \geqslant 1/2^{k_i+1}$$

We easily see that $k_i > k_0$ for every i, and that each net $\mathfrak{Q}_{k_i}$, for $i=1,2,\ldots$, can contain at most 2^m intervals having points in common with E_i. Let $\{Q_n\}_{n=1,2,\ldots}$ be the sequence of all the intervals belonging to the nets $\mathfrak{Q}_{k_1}, \mathfrak{Q}_{k_2}, \ldots, \mathfrak{Q}_{k_i}, \ldots$ and having points in common with the sets $E_1, E_2, \ldots, E_i, \ldots$ respectively. The sequence $\{Q_n\}$ clearly fulfils the condition (ii). Moreover, we find on account of (4.3),

$$\sum_n [\delta(Q_n)]^\alpha \leqslant 2^m \cdot \sum_i m^\alpha \cdot 2^{-\alpha k_i} \leqslant 2^m\, m^\alpha\, 2^\alpha \cdot \sum_i 2^{-\alpha(k_i+1)} \leqslant (4m)^m \cdot \sum_i [\delta(E_i)]^\alpha,$$

and this by (4.2) gives at once the condition (i).

(4.4) ***Theorem.*** *Suppose that F is a continuous additive function of an interval in the space $\boldsymbol{R}_m$ and fulfils the condition* (1_α) *where* $0 \leqslant \alpha < m$, *and that g is a summable function. Suppose further that* (i) $(\mathfrak{Q})\underline{F}(x) > -\infty$ *at every point x except at most those of a set E expressible as the sum of an enumerable infinity of sets of finite measure* (Λ_α), *and that* (ii) $(\mathfrak{Q})\underline{F}(x) \geqslant g(x)$ *at almost all points x; then*

(4.5) $$F(I_0) \geqslant \int_{I_0} g(x)\,dx$$

for every interval I_0.

Proof. Since the function F is continuous, it will suffice to prove (4.5) in the case in which the interval I_0 belongs to one of the nets $\mathfrak{Q}_k$, to the net $\mathfrak{Q}_{k_0}$, say. Further by changing, if necessary, the values of g on a set of measure zero, we can assume that the inequality $(\mathfrak{Q})\underline{F}(x) \geqslant g(x)$ holds at every point x.

Let ε be a positive number and let V be a minor function of g (cf. § 3, particularly Theorem 3.2) such that

(4.6) $$V(I_0) > \int_{I_0} g(x)\,dx - \varepsilon.$$

Let us write $G(I) = F(I) - V(I) + \varepsilon \cdot |I|$, where I denotes any interval. We shall have $(\mathfrak{Q})\underline{G}(x) \geqslant (\mathfrak{Q})\underline{F}(x) - \overline{V}(x) + \varepsilon \geqslant \varepsilon > 0$ at every point x except at most at the points of E. Finally, since $\overline{V}_s(x) < +\infty$ at every point x, the function V fulfils the condition (1_α^-) and the function G therefore fulfils the condition (1_α^+).

Let us now represent the set E as the sum of a sequence $\{E_i\}_{i=1,2,\dots}$ of sets of finite measure (Λ_α), and denote, for each pair of positive integers i and n, by $R_{i,n}$ the set of the points x such that the inequality $G(I) > -\varepsilon\cdot[\delta(I)]^\alpha/2^i\,[\Lambda_\alpha(E_i)+1]$ holds whenever I is an interval containing x and belonging to one of the nets $\mathfrak{Q}_k$ for $k \geqslant n$. The sets $R_{i,n}$ are evidently measurable $(\mathfrak{B})$ (they are actually sets $(\mathfrak{G}_\delta)$). Moreover, since the function G fulfils the condition (l_α^+), the sum $\sum_n R_{i,n}$ must, for each integer i, cover the whole space $\boldsymbol{R}_m$. Hence, writing $E_{i,n} = E_i\cdot(R_{i,n} - R_{i,n-1})$ for $n > 1$, and $E_{i,1} = E_i\cdot R_{i,1}$, we find that

$$(4.7)\qquad \Lambda_\alpha(E_i) = \sum_n \Lambda_\alpha(E_{i,n}) \quad \textit{for} \quad i=1,2,\dots.$$

This being so, it follows from Lemma 4.1 that for each pair of positive integers i and n, we can determine a sequence $\{Q_{i,n}^{(j)}\}_{j=1,2,\dots}$ of cubes which belong to the nets $\mathfrak{Q}_k$ for $k \geqslant n$, and fulfil the following conditions:

$$(4.8)\qquad \sum_j [\delta(Q_{i,n}^{(j)})]^\alpha \leqslant (4m)^m\cdot[\Lambda_\alpha(E_{i,n}) + 1/2^n];$$

(4.9) *to each point* $x \in E_{i,n}$ *there corresponds an integer* $k \geqslant k_0$ *such that each cube of the net* $\mathfrak{Q}_k$, *containing* x, *belongs to the sequence* $\{Q_{i,n}^{(j)}\}_{j=1,2,\dots}$;

(4.10) *each cube* $Q_{i,n}^{(j)}$ *has points in common with the set* $E_{i,n}$ *and therefore fulfils the inequality* $G(Q_{i,n}^{(j)}) > -\varepsilon\cdot[\delta(Q_{i,n}^{(j)})]^\alpha/2^i\cdot[\Lambda_\alpha(E_i)+1]$.

For brevity, let us agree to say that an interval has the property (A), when it is representable as the sum of a finite number of non-overlapping intervals I each of which either fulfils the inequality $G(I) > 0$, or else coincides with one of the cubes $Q_{i,n}^{(j)}$. We remark that on account of (4.10), (4.8) and (4.7), the inequality

$$G(R) \geqslant -\varepsilon\cdot\sum_{i,n,j}[\delta(Q_{i,n}^{(j)})]^\alpha/2^i[\Lambda_\alpha(E_i)+1] \geqslant$$
$$\geqslant -(4m)^m\,\varepsilon\cdot\sum_{i,n}[\Lambda_\alpha(E_{i,n}) + 1/2^n]/2^i[\Lambda_\alpha(E_i)+1] = -(4m)^m\cdot\varepsilon$$

is valid whenever R is a figure consisting of any finite number of non-overlapping cubes $Q_{i,n}^{(j)}$, and therefore that the inequality $G(I) \geqslant -(4m)^m\cdot\varepsilon$ must hold for every interval I having the property (A).

We shall now show that the interval I_0 itself has the property (A), so that $G(I_0) \geqslant -(4m)^m \varepsilon$. Let us suppose the contrary. We could then, starting with I_0, construct a decreasing sequence $\{I_p\}$ of cubes belonging to the nets $\mathfrak{Q}_k$ and none of which has the property (A). Let x_0 be the common point of these cubes. Then either $x_0 \in E$, and consequently, by (4.9), the sequence contains cubes $Q_{i,n}^{(j)}$; or $x_0 \in CE$, so that $(\mathfrak{Q})\underline{G}(x_0) > 0$, and therefore $G(I_p) > 0$ for each sufficiently large p. Thus in both cases, the sequence $\{I_p\}$ would contain intervals with the property (A) and we arrive at a contradiction. It follows that $G(I_0) \geqslant -(4m)^m \varepsilon$, and therefore, by (4.6), that

$$F(I_0) = G(I_0) + V(I_0) - \varepsilon \cdot |I_0| \geqslant \int_{I_0} g(x)\,dx - [1 + (4m)^m + |I_0|]\varepsilon;$$

since ε is an arbitrary positive number, this gives the relation (4.5).

*** § 5. Applications to functions of a complex variable.** We now interpret the points of the plane $\boldsymbol{R}_2$ as complex numbers and, as usual, we call *complex function of a complex variable* every function of the form $u + iv$ where u and v are real functions in the whole plane, or in an open set. The functions u and v are termed *real part* and *imaginary part* of the function f. A complex function is said to be *continuous* (at a point, or in an open set), if its real and imaginary parts are both continuous.

Given a complex function f, continuous in an open set G, and having the real and imaginary parts u and v respectively, we shall write for every interval $I = [a_1, b_1; a_2, b_2]$ contained in G:

(5.1)
$$\mathrm{J}_1(f; I) = -\int_{a_1}^{b_1} [u(x, b_2) - u(x, a_2)]\,dx - \int_{a_2}^{b_2} [v(b_1, y) - v(a_1, y)]\,dy,$$
$$\mathrm{J}_2(f; I) = \int_{a_2}^{b_2} [u(b_1, y) - u(a_1, y)]\,dy - \int_{a_1}^{b_1} [v(x, b_2) - v(x, a_2)]\,dx,$$

and

$$\mathrm{J}(f; I) = \mathrm{J}_1(f; I) + i\mathrm{J}_2(f; I).$$

The expression $\mathrm{J}(f; I)$, which will also be denoted by $\int_{(I)} f\,dz$, will be called curvilinear integral of the function f along the boundary of the interval I. The function f will be termed *holomorphic* in an open set G, if $\mathrm{J}(f; I) = 0$ for every interval $I \subset G$. (The equivalence of this definition of the term „holomorphic" — used here in place of terms such as "regular", "analytic", etc. — with the more familiar definitions of the theory of complex functions, follows from the well-known theorem of Morera [1].) We verify at once that this relation holds when $f(z)=az+b$ where a and b are any complex constants.

If f is a complex function, continuous in an open set G, the expressions $J_1(f; I)$ and $J_2(f; I)$ are continuous additive functions of the interval I in G. Moreover

$$|J_1(f; I)| \leqslant |J(f; I)| \quad \textit{and} \quad |J_2(f; I)| \leqslant |J(f; I)|$$

for each interval I in G. On account of Theorem 2.3, we therefore obtain at once the following theorem due to J. Wolff [1] (cf. also H. Looman [2] and J. Ridder [1; 2]):

(5.2) ***Theorem.*** *A complex function f, continuous in an open set G, is holomorphic in G if at almost all points z of G,*

$$\liminf_{\delta(Q)\to 0} \frac{1}{|Q|} \left| \int_{(Q)} f(z)\, dz \right| = 0,$$

and if at all points z of G, except at most those of an enumerable set,

$$\limsup_{\delta(Q)\to 0} \frac{1}{|Q|} \left| \int_{(Q)} f(z)\, dz \right| < +\infty,$$

where Q denotes any square containing z.

A complex function is called *derivable* at a point z_0, if the ratio $[f(z)-f(z_0)]/(z-z_0)$ tends to a finite limit when z tends to z_0 in any manner. This limit is called *derivative* of f at z_0 and is denoted by $f'(z_0)$.

Let f be any complex function, defined in the neighbourhood of a point z_0. If we have $\limsup_{h\to 0} |[f(z_0+h)-f(z_0)]/h| < +\infty$, we can write $f(z)=f(z_0)+M(z)\cdot(z-z_0)$, where $M(z)$ is a function of z which is bounded in the neighbourhood of z_0; and we then easily find that the ratio $|J(f; Q)|/|Q|$, and *a fortiori* the ratios $|J_1(f; Q)|/|Q|$ and $|J_2(f; Q)|/|Q|$, must remain bounded when Q denotes any sufficiently small square containing z_0. If, further, the function f is derivable at z_0, we have $f(z)=f(z_0)+f'(z_0)\cdot(z-z_0)+\varepsilon(z)\cdot(z-z_0)$, where $|\varepsilon(z)|\to 0$ as $z\to z_0$, and the ratios in question tend to zero as $\delta(Q)\to 0$. Finally, let us observe that if the function f is continuous, the expressions $J_1(f; I)$ and $J_2(f; I)$, considered as functions of the interval I, both fulfil the condition (l_1) of § 4. Therefore, if we apply Theorem 4.4, we obtain the following theorem due to A. S. Besicovitch [3] (cf. also S. Saks and A. Zygmund [2]):

(5.3) ***Theorem.*** *A complex function f, continuous in an open set G, is holomorphic in G if it is derivable at almost all the points of G and if further* $\limsup_{h\to 0} |[f(z+h)-f(z)]/h| < +\infty$ *at each point z of G except at most those of a set which is the sum of a sequence of sets of finite length.*

The theorem of Besicovitch may be regarded as a generalization of the classical theorem of E. Goursat [1]: *A complex function f, continuous in an open set G, is holomorphic in G if it is everywhere derivable in G.* T. Pompeiù [1] showed that it is enough to suppose f derivable almost everywhere, provided that we restrict the expression $\limsup_{h\to 0} |[f(z+h)-f(z)]/h|$ to be bounded in G. Finally, H. Looman [3] (cf. also J. Ridder [2]) replaced the condition that the expression $\limsup_{h\to 0} [f(z+h)-f(z)]/h|$ is bounded by the condition that this expression is finite at each point of G. Theorem 5.3 evidently includes all these generalizations.

The theorems of Morera and of Goursat, and their generalizations furnished by Theorems 5.2 and 5.3, contain criteria for holomorphism which are based on the notion of curvilinear integral and of derivation in the complex domain. The classical theorem of Cauchy is an instance of a criterion of a different kind, expressible in terms of real variable conditions on the real and imaginary parts of a complex function; we have in fact, according to this theorem: in order that a continuous function of a complex variable $f(z) = u(x, y) + iv(x, y)$ be holomorphie in an open set G, it is necessary and sufficient that the partial derivatives u'_x, u'_y, v'_x, v'_y should all exist in G and be continuous, and that they everywhere fulfil the Cauchy-Riemann equations $u'_x = v'_y$, and $u'_y = -v'_x$.

A series of researches begun by P. Montel [1] has been devoted to the reduction of these conditions, particularly that of the continuity of the partial derivatives. The problem was finally solved by H. Looman [2] and D. Menchoff (*vide* the first ed. of this book, p. 243, and D. Menchoff [I]) who succeeded in removing completely the condition in question without replacing it by any other. It is remarkable that a classical problem of such an elementary aspect should only have been solved by a quite essential use of methods of the theory of real functions.

(5.4) ***Lemma.*** *Let w be a real function of one variable, derivable almost everywhere in an interval $[a, b]$; let F be a closed non-empty subset of this interval, and let N be a finite constant such that*

$$|w(x_2)-w(x_1)|\leqslant N\cdot|x_2-x_1|$$

whenever $x_1 \in F$ and $x_2 \in [a, b]$. Then

$$\left|w(b)-w(a)-\int_F w'(x)\,dx\right|\leqslant N\cdot(b-a-|F|). \tag{5.5}$$

Proof. Let us denote by F_1 the set obtained by adding the points a and b to the set F. The function $\widetilde{w}$, equal to w on F_1 and linear on the intervals contiguous to F_1, is evidently absolutely continuous on $[a, b]$ (and even fulfils the Lipschitz condition). Hence

$$w(b)-w(a)=\widetilde{w}(b)-\widetilde{w}(a)=\int_a^b \widetilde{w}'(x)\,dx. \tag{5.6}$$

Now $\widetilde{w}'(x)=w'(x)$ at almost all the points x of F and $|\widetilde{w}'(x)|\leqslant N$ at each point x outside F. The relation (5.5) therefore follows at once from (5.6).

(5.7) ***Lemma.*** *Let $w(x, y)$ be a real function whose partial derivatives with respect to the two variables x and y exist at every point of a square Q, except at most at the points of an enumerable set; and let F be a closed non-empty subset of Q, and N a finite constant such that*

$$|w(x_2, y_1)-w(x_1, y_1)|\leqslant N\cdot|x_2-x_1| \text{ and } |w(x_1, y_2)-w(x_1, y_1)|\leqslant N\cdot|y_2-y_1|$$

whenever $(x_1, y_1) \in F$, $(x_2, y_1) \in Q$, and $(x_1, y_2) \in Q$.

Then if $[a_1, b_1; a_2, b_2]$ denotes the smallest interval (which may be degenerate) containing F, we have

$$\begin{aligned}&\left|\int_{a_1}^{b_1}[w(x, b_2)-w(x, a_2)]\,dx-\iint_F w'_y(x, y)\,dx\,dy\right|\leqslant 5N\cdot|Q-F|\\ &\left|\int_{a_2}^{b_2}[w(b_1, y)-w(a_1, y)]\,dy-\iint_F w'_x(x, y)\,dx\,dy\right|\leqslant 5N\cdot|Q-F|.\end{aligned} \tag{5.8}$$

Proof. Let us choose arbitrarily two points (x', a_2) and (x'', b_2) belonging to the set F and situated on the two sides of the interval $[a_1, b_1; a_2, b_2]$ parallel to the x-axis. For any point ξ of $[a_1, b_1]$ we have $|w(\xi, b_2)-w(\xi, a_2)|\leqslant|w(\xi, b_2)-w(x'', b_2)|+|w(x'', b_2)-w(x', b_2)|+$ $+|w(x', b_2)-w(x', a_2)|+|w(x', a_2)-w(\xi, a_2)|$; and hence, denoting by l

the length of the side of the square Q, we obtain

$$(5.9)\qquad \begin{aligned}&|w(\xi, b_2)-w(\xi, a_2)|\leqslant\\ &\leqslant N\cdot[|x''-\xi|+|x'-x''|+|a_2-b_2|+|\xi-x'|]\leqslant 4Nl.\end{aligned}$$

We now denote for any point ξ of $[a_1, b_1]$, by F_ξ the set of all the points y of $[a_2, b_2]$ such that $(\xi, y)\in F$. Let A be the set of the points ξ of the interval $[a_1, b_1]$ for each of which $F_\xi \neq 0$, and let B denote the set of the remaining points of $[a_1, b_1]$. On account of Lemma 5.4 we have

$$\left|w(\xi, b_2)-w(\xi, a_2)-\int_{F_\xi} w_y(\xi, y)\,dy\right|\leqslant N\cdot(b_2-a_2-|F_\xi|)$$

whenever $\xi\in A$, and if we integrate the two sides of this inequality with respect to ξ on the set A, we find

$$(5.10)\qquad \begin{aligned}&\left|\int_A [w(\xi, b_2)-w(\xi, a_2)]\,d\xi-\int\int_F w'_y(\xi, y)\,dy\,d\xi\right|\leqslant\\ &\leqslant N\cdot[(b_1-a_1)(b_2-a_2)-|F|]\leqslant N\cdot|Q-F|.\end{aligned}$$

On the other hand if we integrate (5.9) with respect to ξ on the set B, we obtain $\left|\int_B [w(\xi, b_2)-w(\xi, a_2)]\,d\xi\right|\leqslant 4Nl\cdot|B|\leqslant 4N\cdot|Q-F|$, and by adding this to (5.10) we obtain the first of the inequalities (5.8). The second inequality follows by symmetry.

(5.11) ***Theorem of Looman-Menchoff.*** *If the functions $u(x, y)$ and $v(x, y)$, continuous in an open set G, are derivable with respect to x and with respect to y at each point of G except at most at the points of an enumerable set, and if $u'_x(x, y)=v'_y(x, y)$ and $u'_y(x, y)=-v'_x(x, y)$ at almost all the points (x, y) of G, then the complex function $f=u+iv$ is holomorphic in G.*

Proof. Let us denote by F the set of the points (x, y) of G such that the function f is not holomorphic in any neighbourhood of (x, y). The set F is evidently closed in G and the function f is holomorphic in $G-F$. It thus has to be proved that F is empty.

Suppose therefore, if possible, that $F\neq 0$ and let F_n denote, for each positive integer n, the set of the points (x, y) of G such that, whenever $|h|\leqslant 1/n$, none of the four differences $u(x+h, y)-u(x, y)$ $u(x, y+h)-u(x, y)$, $v(x+h, y)-v(x, y)$, $v(x, y+h)-v(x, y)$ exceeds $|nh|$ in absolute value. By continuity of the functions u and v, each of the sets F_n is closed in G. On the other hand, the sets F_n cover the whole set G, except at most an enumerable set consisting of the points at which the functions u and v are not both derivable with respect to x and with respect to y simultaneously. Therefore, on account of Baire's Theorem (Chap. II, Theorem 9.1), the set $F \subset G$ contains a portion which either reduces to a single point, or else is contained entirely in one of the F_n. The former possibility is ruled out, since, as we easily see on account of the continuity of f, the set F cannot contain any isolated points. There must therefore exist a positive integer N and an open sphere S such that $0 \neq F \cdot S \subset F_N$.

Let Q be any square contained in S. such that $\delta(Q) \leqslant 1/N$ and $Q \cdot F \neq 0$. We denote by $I = [a_1, b_1; a_2, b_2]$ the smallest interval containing $Q \cdot F$. By applying the evaluations of Lemma 5.7 to the integrals on the left-hand sides of the formulae (5.1) and by taking into account the relations $u'_x(x, y) = v'_y(x, y)$ and $u'_y(x, y) = -v'_x(x, y)$ which are, by hypothesis, fulfilled almost everywhere, we find $|\mathrm{J}_1(f; I)| \leqslant 10N \cdot |Q - F|$ and $|\mathrm{J}_2(f; I)| \leqslant 10N \cdot |Q - F|$, and therefore $|\mathrm{J}(f; I)| \leqslant 20N \cdot |Q - F|$. This last inequality may also be written $|\mathrm{J}(f; Q)| \leqslant 20N \cdot |Q - F|$, since the figure $Q \ominus I$ contains no points of F in its interior, and since therefore $\mathrm{J}(f; R) = 0$ for each interval R contained in $Q \ominus I$.

Now let $z_0 = (x_0, y_0)$ be any point of S, and let Q be any square containing z_0. By what has just been shown, if $z_0 \in F$ we have $|\mathrm{J}(f; Q)|/|Q| \leqslant 20N \cdot |Q - F|/|Q|$ as soon as $\delta(Q) \leqslant 1/N$; the ratio $\mathrm{J}(f; Q)/|Q|$ therefore remains bounded as $\delta(Q) \to 0$ and tends to zero whenever z_0 is a point of density of F. Further $|\mathrm{J}(f; Q)|/|Q| \to 0$ as $\delta(Q) \to 0$, whenever $z_0 \in S - F$, since $\mathrm{J}(f; Q) = 0$ for every square Q which does not contain points of F. Therefore by Theorem 2.3, the function f must be holomorphic in S. This is, however, excluded since $S \cdot F \neq 0$. We thus arrive at a contradiction and this completes the proof.

Theorem 5.11 was stated (even in a more general form) by P. Montel [2] as early as 1913, but without proof. The proof supplied by H. Looman [2] in 1923 was found to contain a serious gap which was only finally filled in by D. Menchoff (cf. D. Menchoff [I] and the first edition of this book, p. 243).

By making use of general theorems on derivates (*vide*, below, Chap. IX) it is possible to weaken slightly the hypotheses of the theorem. Thus instead of assuming partial derivability of the function u and v, it is sufficient to suppose that at each point of G (except at most those of an enumerable set) these functions have with respect to each variable, x and y, their partial Dini derivates finite. This condition implies (cf. Chap. VII, § 10, p. 236, or Chap. IX, § 4) partial derivability of the functions u and v with respect to each variable at almost all points of G (this generalization of the theorem of Looman-Menchoff does not require any alteration of the proof; for other and much deeper generalizations, *vide* the memoirs of D. Menchoff [1; 2]).

The extension of Theorem 5.11 which we have indicated, includes in particular the theorem of Looman mentioned above, p. 197, but not however the theorem of Besicovitch (5.3). It would be interesting to establish a theorem which would include both the theorem of Besicovitch and that of Looman-Menchoff.

§ 6. The Perron integral. For functions of one real variable, as announced in § 1, the method of major and minor functions leads to an important generalization of the Lebesgue integral.

A function of a real variable, f, is termed *integrable in the sense of Perron*, or *$\mathcal{P}$-integrable*, on a figure R_0 in $\boldsymbol{R}_1$, if 1° f has both major and minor functions on R_0, and if 2° the lower bound of the numbers $U(R_0)$, where U is any major function of f on R_0, and the upper bound of the numbers $V(R_0)$, where V is any minor function of f, are equal. The common value of the two bounds is then called *definite Perron integral*, or *definite $\mathcal{P}$-integral*, of f on R_0, and denoted by $(\mathcal{P})\int\limits_{R_0} f(x)\,dx$. It is evident that *for $\mathcal{P}$-integrability of a function f on a figure R_0 it is necessary and sufficient that for each $\varepsilon>0$ there should exist a major function U and a minor function V of f on R_0 such that $U(R_0)-V(R_0)<\varepsilon$.*

Since (cf. § 3, p. 190) the function $U-V$ is monotone non-decreasing for every major function U and every minor function V of f, it follows that *every function which is $\mathcal{P}$-integrable on a figure R_0, is so also on every figure $R\subset R_0$.* The function of an interval $P(I)=(\mathcal{P})\int\limits_I f(x)\,dx$, thus defined for every interval $I\subset R_0$, is called *indefinite Perron integral*, or *indefinite $\mathcal{P}$-integral*, of f on R_0. As we see at once, $P(I)$ is an additive function of the interval I. Moreover, given any positive number ε, there exist always a major function U and a minor function V of f, such that $0\leqslant U(I)-P(I)\leqslant\varepsilon$ and $0\leqslant P(I)-V(I)\leqslant\varepsilon$ for every interval $I\subset R_0$; and since $\underline{U}(x)>-\infty$ and $\overline{V}(x)<+\infty$ at each point x of R_0, it follows at once that the function P is continuous. Just as in the case of the Lebesgue integral, a function of a real variable is termed *indefinite $\mathcal{P}$-integral* [*major function, minor function*] of a function f, if this is the case for the function of an interval determined by it (cf. Chap. III, § 13).

As we see at once from Theorem 3.2, *every function which is integrable in the sense of Lebesgue on a figure R_0, is so in the sense of Perron, and its definite Lebesgue and Perron integrals over R_0 are equal.* On the other hand, if F is the primitive of Newton (cf. § 1) of a function f, the function F is at the same time a major and a minor function of f, and therefore is the indefinite $\mathcal{P}$-integral of f. It follows that *Perron's process of integration includes both that of Lebesgue and that of Newton.*

We shall establish some fundamental properties of the Perron integral.

(6.1) **Theorem.** *Every $\mathcal{P}$-integrable function is measurable, and is almost everywhere finite and equal to the derivative of its indefinite integral.*

Proof. Let f be a function of a real variable, $\mathcal{P}$-integrable on an interval I_0, and let P be its indefinite $\mathcal{P}$-integral on I_0. It has to be proved that the function P has at almost all points x, a finite derivative equal to $f(x)$.

For this purpose, let ε be any positive number and U a major function of f such that

$$U(I_0)-P(I_0)<\varepsilon^2. \tag{6.2}$$

Let us write $H=U-P$. The function H, as monotone non-decreasing, is almost everywhere derivable, and if we denote by E the set of the points x of I_0 at which $H'(x)\geqslant\varepsilon$, we find, by (6.2) and Theorem 7.4, Chap. IV, that $|E|<\varepsilon$.

Now at each point $x\in I_0$ where the function H is derivable, $\underline{U}(x)=H'(x)+\underline{P}(x)$; hence $\underline{P}(x)>-\infty$ and $\underline{P}(x)\geqslant\underline{U}(x)-\varepsilon\geqslant f(x)-\varepsilon$ at almost all the points x of I_0-E. Therefore, since $|E|\leqslant\varepsilon$, ε being an arbitrary positive number, it follows that $-\infty\neq\underline{P}(x)\geqslant f(x)$ at almost all the points x of I_0. By symmetry this gives also $+\infty\neq\overline{P}(x)\leqslant f(x)$, and finally $\infty\neq P'(x)=f(x)$ almost everywhere in I_0.

(6.3) **Theorem.** *If two functions f and g are almost everywhere equal on a figure R_0 and one of them is $\mathcal{P}$-integrable on R_0, so is the other and the definite $\mathcal{P}$-integrals of f and g over R_0 are equal.*

Proof. Suppose that the function f is $\mathcal{P}$-integrable and denote by A the value of its definite integral over R_0. Let ε be any positive number and let U and V be two functions of an interval, which are respectively a major and a minor function of f on R_0 and which fulfil the inequalities

(6.4) $U(R_0) \geqslant A \geqslant V(R_0)$ *and* $U(R_0) - V(R_0) \leqslant \varepsilon/3$.

Let us denote by E the set of the points x at which $f(x) \neq g(x)$. The function equal to $+\infty$ at all the points of E and to 0 everywhere else is therefore almost everywhere zero, and by Theorem 3.2 has a major function G such that $0 \leqslant G(R_0) \leqslant \varepsilon/3$. We have $\underline{G}(x) = +\infty$ at each point $x \in E$ and writing $U_1 = U + G$, $V_1 = V - G$, we see that the functions of an interval U_1 and V_1 thus defined are respectively a major and a minor function of the function g on R_0. Moreover by (6.4), $U_1(R_0) \geqslant A \geqslant V_1(R_0)$ and $U_1(R_0) - V_1(R_0) \leqslant \varepsilon$. Therefore the function g is $\mathscr{P}$-integrable on R_0 and $A = (\mathscr{P}) \int_{R_0} g(x)\, dx$, which completes the proof.

(6.5) ***Theorem.*** *Every function f which is $\mathscr{P}$-integrable and almost everywhere non-negative on a figure R_0, is summable on this figure.*

Proof. We may assume, by Theorem 6.3, that the function f is everywhere non-negative on R_0. Therefore if U is any major function of f, we have $\underline{U}(x) \geqslant f(x) \geqslant 0$ at every point $x \in R_0$, and consequently, by Theorem 3.1, the function U is monotone non-decreasing. Its derivative $U'(x)$ is therefore summable on R_0, and, since $U'(x) \geqslant f(x) \geqslant 0$ almost everywhere, the function f is also summable on R_0.

Theorem 6.5 shows that, although Perron integration is more general than Lebesgue integration, the two processes are completely equivalent in the case of integration of functions of constant sign.

§ 7. Derivates of functions of a real variable.

Certain of the theorems of §§ 2 and 3 can be given a more complete statement when we deal with functions of one real variable. We shall begin with the following proposition which is due to Zygmund:

(7.1) ***Theorem.*** *If $F(x)$ is a finite function of a real variable such that* (i) $\limsup_{h\to 0+} F(x-h) \leqslant F(x) \leqslant \limsup_{h\to 0+} F(x+h)$ *at every point x, and* (ii) *the set of the values assumed by $F(x)$ at the points x where $\overline{F}^+(x) \leqslant 0$ contains no non-degenerate interval, then the function F is monotone non-decreasing.*

Proof. Suppose, if possible, that there exist two points a and b such that $a < b$ and that $F(b) < F(a)$. Then, denoting by E the set of the points x at which $\overline{F}^+(x) \leqslant 0$, we can determine a value y_0 not belonging to the set $F[E]$ and such that $F(b) < y_0 < F(a)$. Let

x_0 be the upper bound of the points x of $[a, b]$, for which $F(x) \geqslant y_0$. We shall obviously have $a < x_0 < b$, $F(x_0) = y_0$, and $F(x) \leqslant y_0$ for each point x of the interval $[x_0, b]$. Therefore $\overline{F}^+(x_0) \leqslant 0$, although x_0 does not belong to E. This is in contradiction with the definition of the set E.

Let us mention the following consequence of Theorem 7.1:

Dini's Theorem. *Given on an interval $I = [a, b]$ a continuous function $F(x)$, the upper and lower bounds of each of its four Dini derivates are respectively equal to the upper and lower bounds of the ratio $\dfrac{F(x_2) - F(x_1)}{x_2 - x_1}$, where x_1 and x_2 are any points of I.*

Let, for instance, m be the lower bound of the derivate $\overline{F}^+(x)$ on the interval I, and suppose first that $m > -\infty$. Then, if m' denotes any finite number less than m, the function $F(x) - m' \cdot x$ has everywhere on $[a, b]$ its upper right-hand derivate positive; and so by Theorem 7.1, $F(x_2) - F(x_1) \geqslant m' \cdot (x_2 - x_1)$, and therefore also $[F(x_2) - F(x_1)]/(x_2 - x_1) \geqslant m$, for every pair of points x_1 and x_2 of I such that $x_1 < x_2$. Since the inequality just obtained is trivial in the case $m = -\infty$, the theorem follows.

An immediate consequence is the following theorem:

If any one of the four Dini derivates of a continuous function is continuous at a point, so are the three others, and all four derivates in question are equal, so that the function considered is derivable at this point.

These two propositions were proved by U. Dini [I] in 1878.

(7.2) ***Theorem.*** *If H is a finite function of one variable such that* (i) $\limsup_{h \to 0+} H(x-h) \leqslant H(x) \leqslant \limsup_{h \to 0+} H(x+h)$ *at every point x, and* (ii) $\overline{H}^+(x) \geqslant 0$ *at every point x except at most at those of an enumerable set, then the function H is monotone non-decreasing.*

Proof. Let ε be a positive number and write $F(x) = H(x) + \varepsilon x$. We have $\overline{F}^+(x) \geqslant \varepsilon > 0$ at each point x except at most at those of a finite or enumerable set E. The set $F[E]$ being, with E, at most enumerable, it follows from Theorem 7.1 that the function $F(x) = H(x) + \varepsilon x$ is non-decreasing for each $\varepsilon > 0$; and by making $\varepsilon \to 0$ we obtain the assertion of the theorem.

(7.3) ***Theorem.*** *Suppose that F is a continuous function and g a $\mathfrak{P}$-integrable function of a real variable, and that, further, we have* (i) $\overline{F}^+(x) \geqslant g(x)$ *at almost all points x and* (ii) $\overline{F}^+(x) > -\infty$ *at every point x, except at most at those of an enumerable set; then*

$$F(b) - F(a) \geqslant (\mathfrak{P}) \int_a^b g(x)\, dx \tag{7.4}$$

for every pair of points a and b such that $a < b$.

If, in addition, (i_1) $\overline{F}^+(x) \geqslant g(x) \geqslant \underline{F}^+(x)$ *at almost all points* x *and* (ii_1) $\overline{F}^+(x) > -\infty$ *and* $\underline{F}^+(x) < +\infty$ *at every point* x *except at most at those of an enumerable set, then the function* F *is an indefinite* $\mathcal{P}$*-integral of* g.

Proof. We may obviously assume that $\overline{F}^+(x) \geqslant g(x)$ at every point x. Therefore, denoting by V any minor function of g, and writing $H=F-V$, we shall have $\overline{H}^+(x) \geqslant \overline{F}^+(x) - \overline{V}^+(x) \geqslant 0$ at every point x, except at most at those of a finite or enumerable set where $\overline{F}^+(x) = -\infty$. Further, since the function F is continuous, the inequality $\overline{V}(x) < +\infty$, which holds at every point x, implies that the function H satisfies the condition (i) of Theorem 7.2. Consequently, by Theorem 7.2, $H(b)-H(a) \geqslant 0$, i.e. $F(b)-F(a) \geqslant V(b)-V(a)$, and since V is any minor function of g, we obtain the inequality (7.4).

The second part of the assertion is an immediate consequence of the first part.

As we easily see, the condition of continuity of the function F in the first part of Theorem 7.3 may be replaced by the condition (i) of Theorem 7.1.

Theorem 7.3 constitutes, on account of Theorem 7.4, Chap. IV, a generalization of the following theorem of Lebesgue [I, p. 122; 2; 3; 4; II, p. 183]: *in order that one of the derivates of a continuous function, supposed finite, be summable, it is necessary and sufficient that this function be of bounded variation; its absolute variation is the integral of the absolute value of the derivate in question.* Let us add that in the case in which the function F is assumed to be of bounded variation, Theorem 7.3 is included in Theorem 9.6 of Chap. IV.

The condition (ii) of the first part of Theorem 7.3, as well as the condition (ii_1) of the second, is quite essential for the validity of the theorem. It is possible, in fact, to give an example of a continuous function whose derivative exists everywhere and is summable, without the function being the indefinite integral of its derivative, and this because the latter assumes infinite values. To see this, we shall first show that given any closed set E of measure zero in an interval $J_0=[a,b]$, there exists a function G, absolutely continuous and increasing in J_0, which has a derivative everywhere in J_0 and fulfils the conditions

(7.5) $\qquad G'(x)=+\infty \quad$ *for* $\quad x \in E \qquad$ *and* $\qquad G'(x) \neq +\infty \quad$ *for* $\quad x \in J_0 - E$.

Let us suppose for simplicity that E contains the end-points a and b of J_0 and let us denote by $\{[a_n, b_n]\}$ the sequence of the intervals contiguous to E. Let $\{h_n\}$ be a sequence of positive numbers such that

(7.6) $\qquad \lim\limits_n h_n/(b_n-a_n)=+\infty \qquad$ and $\qquad$ (7.7) $\qquad \sum\limits_{n=1}^{\infty} h_n = 1$

(it suffices to write, for instance, $h_n=\sqrt{r_n}-\sqrt{r_{n+1}}$, where $r_n=\dfrac{1}{b-a}\sum\limits_{i=n}^{\infty}(b_i-a_i)$).

Let us write

(7.8) $$g(x)=\begin{cases} h_n/(x-a_n)^{1/2}(b_n-x)^{1/2}, & \textit{when} \quad a_n<x<b_n, \\ +\infty, & \textit{when} \quad x \in E. \end{cases}$$

Thus defined the function $g(x)$ is non-negative on J_0 and summable on J_0 since $\int_{a_n}^{b_n} g(x)\,dx=\pi h_n$, so that by (7.7) we have $\int_a^b g(x)\,dx=\pi$. Let G be the indefinite integral of g on J_0. In order to verify that the function G fulfils the conditions (7.5), we observe that the function $g(x)$ is continuous for every $x \in J_0-E$; on the other hand, if we denote by m_n the lower bound of $g(x)$ in $[a_n, b_n]$ we derive from (7.6) that $\lim\limits_n m_n = \lim\limits_n 2h_n/(b_n-a_n)=+\infty$, from which it follows that $\lim\limits_{x\to x_0} g(x)=+\infty=g(x_0)$ for every $x_0 \in E$. Consequently $G'(x)=g(x)$ for every x, and therefore, by (7.8), the conditions (7.5) hold.

Now let (cf. Chap. III, (13.4)), $H(x)$ be a continuous non-decreasing singular function on J_0, which is constant on each interval contiguous to the set E, and such that $H(a)\neq H(b)$. Let us put $F=G+H$. As we verify easily from (7.5), we have $F'(x)=G'(x)=g(x)$ at every point x of J_0. The function F therefore has everywhere a derivative which is summable on J_0. But, since H is the function of singularities of the function F, the latter is certainly not absolutely continuous, let alone the indefinite integral of its derivative. (The functions G and F provide at the same time an example of two functions whose derivatives, finite or infinite, exist and are everywhere equal, without the difference $G-F$ being a constant; cf. H. Hahn [1] and S. Ruziewicz [1].)

In connection with these examples, it may be interesting to mention the following theorem (*vide* G. Goldowsky [1] and L. Tonelli [8]):

(7.9) ***Theorem.*** *If a continuous function F has a (finite or infinite) derivative at each point of $\boldsymbol{R}_1$ except perhaps at the points of an enumerable set, and if this derivative is almost everywhere non-negative, the function F is monotone non-decreasing.*

Proof. Let E be the set of the points x such that the function F is not monotone in any neighbourhood of x. The set E is evidently closed, and the function F is non-decreasing on every interval contained in CE. It therefore has to be proved that the set E is empty.

Suppose, if possible, that $E\neq 0$, and denote for every positive integer n by P_n the set of the points x for which the inequality $0<x'-x<1/n$ implies $F(x')-F(x)\leqslant -(x'-x)$ however we choose x'. Similarly let Q_n be the set of the points x for which the same inequality implies $F(x')-F(x)\geqslant -2(x'-x)$. We see easily that the sets P_n and Q_n are closed, and that they cover the whole straight line $\boldsymbol{R}_1$ except at most the finite or enumerable set of the points at which the function F is without a derivative. Consequently, by Baire's Theorem (Chap. II, Theorem 9.2) the set E must contain a portion which either 1° reduces to a single point, or else 2° is contained in one of the sets P_n, or finally 3° is contained in one of the sets Q_n. The first case is obviously impossible, since the set E has no isolated points. Let us therefore consider case 2°, and suppose that there exists a positive integer n_0 and an open interval I such that $0\neq E\cdot I\subset P_{n_0}$. We may clearly suppose that $\delta(I)<1/n_0$. Since by hypothesis, $F'(x)\geqslant 0$ almost everywhere, the set P_{n_0} is certainly non-dense. Let $[a,b]$ denote any interval contiguous to $E\cdot I$. The function F is then non-decreasing on $[a,b]$ and this contradicts the fact that, since a and b belong to P_{n_0} and $b-a<1/n_0$, we have

$$F(b)-F(a)\leqslant -(b-a)<0.$$

There now remains only case 3°. In this case there exists an open interval I such that the set $E \cdot I$ is non-empty and is contained in one of the sets Q_n. But then $\overline{F}^+(x) \geqslant -2$ everywhere in I, and $F'(x) \geqslant 0$ almost everywhere, in I. Therefore, by Theorem 7.3, the function F is non-decreasing in I, and this again is impossible since the interval I contains points of E in its interior.

We thus arrive at a contradiction in each of the three cases, and this proves our assertion.

Let us mention a corollary of Theorem 7.9:

If F is a continuous function having a derivative at every point, except perhaps at those of an enumerable set, and if there exists a finite constant M such that $|F'(x)| \leqslant M$ at almost all points x, then the function F is the indefinite integral of its derivative.

***§ 8. The Perron-Stieltjes integral.** Among the various generalizations of the Stieltjes type for the Perron integral (*vide* for instance R. L. Jeffery [2; 3], J. Ridder [9] and A. J. Ward [3]), that due to Ward has the advantage of including the others and of defining the process of Stieltjes integration with respect to any finite function whatsoever. In this § we shall give the fundamental definitions and results of the theory of Ward. For a deeper analysis, in the case in which the function with respect to which we integrate is of generalized bounded variation in the restricted sense (*vide* below, Chap. VII) the reader should consult the memoir of Ward referred to.

As in the two preceding §§ we shall consider only functions defined in $\boldsymbol{R}_1$, i. e. functions of a linear interval or of a real variable. We shall, moreover, restrict ourselves to integration of finite functions. This restriction is essential for the methods which we shall employ.

Given two finite functions f and G, an additive function of an interval U will be termed *major function* of f *with respect to* G on an interval I_0, if to each point x there corresponds a number $\varepsilon > 0$ such that $U(I) \geqslant f(x) G(I)$ for every interval I containing x and of length less than ε. The definition of *minor function with respect to* G is symmetrical, and by following the method of § 6, p. 201, with the help of the notions of major and minor functions with respect to G, we define *Perron-Stieltjes integration*, or *$\mathscr{PS}$-integration* with respect to any finite function G whatever. The $\mathscr{PS}$-integral of a function f with respect to a function G on an interval $I_0 = [a, b]$ will be denoted by $(\mathscr{PS}) \int_{I_0} f(x)\, dG(x)$, or by $(\mathscr{PS}) \int_a^b f(x)\, dG(x)$.

If U and V are respectively a major and a minor function of the same function f with respect to the same function G, their difference $U-V$ is evidently monotone non-decreasing. The criterion for $\mathcal{PS}$-integrability of a function is entirely similar to that for $\mathcal{P}$-integrability given in § 6, p. 201, and it follows that every function which is $\mathcal{PS}$-integrable on an interval I_0, is so equally on each subinterval of I_0. We are thus led to the notion of *indefinite $\mathcal{PS}$-integral* with respect to any finite function G. This indefinite integral is an additive function of an interval, and is continuous at each point of continuity of the function G. Finally we observe that the $\mathcal{PS}$-integral possesses the distributive property which we may express as follows: *If each of the two finite functions f_1 and f_2 is $\mathcal{PS}$-integrable on an interval I_0 with respect to each of the two functions G_1 and G_2, then each linear combination of the functions f_1 and f_2 is $\mathcal{PS}$-integrable with respect to each linear combination of the functions G_1 and G_2, and we have*

$$(\mathcal{PS})\int_{I_0}(a_1f_1+a_2f_2)\,d(b_1G_1+b_2G_2)=\sum_{i,k=1,2}a_ib_k\cdot(\mathcal{PS})\int_{I_0}f_i\,dG_k$$

for all numbers a_1, a_2, b_1 and b_2.

If $G(x)=x$ for every point x (or, what amounts practically to the same, if $G(I)=|I|$ for each interval I) $\mathcal{PS}$-integration with respect to G coincides with $\mathcal{P}$-integration. In fact, if f is any finite function, each major [minor] function of f with respect to the function $G(x)=x$ in the sense of Ward, is at the same time a major [minor] function of f in the sense of the definition of § 3; the converse is not true in general, but we see at once that if U is a major function of f in the sense of § 3, the function $U(x)+\varepsilon x$ is for each $\varepsilon>0$ a major function of f with respect to $G(x)=x$. Thus the Perron-Stieltjes integral includes the ordinary Perron integral, at any rate as regards integration of finite functions. On the other hand, the Perron-Stieltjes integral includes also the Lebesgue-Stieltjes integral. We have in fact

(8.1) ***Theorem.*** *A finite function f integrable in the Lebesgue-Stieltjes sense on an interval $I_0=[a_0,b_0]$ with respect to a function of bounded variation G, is so also in the Perron-Stieltjes sense and we have*

$$(8.2)\quad (\mathcal{PS})\int_{a_0}^{b_0}f\,dG=\int_{a_0}^{b_0}f\,dG-\{f(a_0)[G(a_0)-G(a_0-)]+f(b_0)[G(b_0+)-G(b_0)]\}.$$

Proof. Let us denote for brevity, by A the right-hand side of the relation (8.2). We may evidently assume that the function f is non-negative and it is enough to consider only the following two cases:

1° G is a continuous non-decreasing function. The proof is then just as in Theorem 3.2. Let ε be any positive number. Since the function f is finite, there exists by the theorem of Vitali-Carathéodory (Chap. III, § 7) a lower semi-continuous function g, integrable (G) in the Lebesgue-Stieltjes sense, such that $g(x) > f(x)$ at each point x and such that $\int_{I_0} [g(x) - f(x)]\, dG(x) < \varepsilon$. Denoting by U the indefinite integral (G) of the function g, and taking account of the lower semi-continuity of g, we see easily that U is a major function of f with respect to G on I_0. Moreover, the function G being continuous by hypothesis, the number A is equal to the integral $\int_{a_0}^{b_0} f\, dG$ and we find $0 \leqslant U(I_0) - A < \varepsilon$. By symmetry we determine also a minor function V of f with respect to G on I_0 in such a manner that $0 \leqslant A - V(I_0) < \varepsilon$, and this establishes $\mathcal{PS}$-integrability of f on I_0 and at the same time the validity of the formula (8.2).

2° G is a non-decreasing saltus-function. Let us denote by $\{x_n\}_{n=1,2,\ldots}$ the sequence of the points of discontinuity of G which are in the interior of the interval I_0; and let ε be any positive number and $\{k_n\}_{n=1,2,\ldots}$ a sequence of positive numbers such that

$$(8.3) \qquad \sum_n k_n \cdot [G(x_n+) - G(x_n-)] < \varepsilon \quad \textit{and} \quad \lim_n k_n = +\infty.$$

Let us define a function h in $\boldsymbol{R}_1$, by writing: $h(x) = f(x)$ for all the points x of I_0 which are distinct from the points x_n; $h(x_n) = f(x_n) + k_n$ for $n = 1, 2, \ldots$; and $h(x) = f(a_0)$ for $x < a_0$, and $h(x) = f(b_0)$ for $x > b_0$. Finally let us write, for each interval $I = [a, b]$,

$$U(I) = \int_a^b h(x)\, dG(x) - \{h(a)[G(a) - G(a-)] + h(b)[G(b+) - G(b)]\}.$$

The function of an interval U thus defined is evidently additive, and as we easily verify, is a major function of f with respect to G on I_0. Moreover, it follows at once from (8.3) that $0 \leqslant U(I_0) - A \leqslant \varepsilon$. Similarly we determine a minor function V of f with respect to G so as to have $0 \leqslant A - V(I_0) \leqslant \varepsilon$; hence $A = (\mathcal{PS}) \int_{I_0} f\, dG$, and this completes the proof.

Formula (8.2) brings out the fact that the definite Perron-Stieltjes and Lebesgue-Stieltjes integrals are not always equal, even for a function f integrable in both senses. This is due to the fact that the indefinite integral of Lebesgue-Stieltjes is not in general an additive function of an interval. We could, of course, modify the definition of this integral so as to ensure its additivity as a function of an interval. The term in brackets { } would then disappear from the formula (8.2), but it would then be necessary to give up the additivity of the indefinite Lebesgue-Stieltjes integral considered as a function of a set (cf. Chap. VIII, § 2).

Let us mention further the following generalization of Theorem 6.1 on derivation of the indefinite Perron integral:

(8.4) ***Theorem.*** *If P is an indefinite $\mathcal{PS}$-integral of a finite function f with respect to a function G, then, at almost all points x, the ratio*

$$[P(I)-f(x)\,G(I)]/|I| \tag{8.5}$$

tends to 0 as $\delta(I)\to 0$, where I denotes any interval containing x.

Hence at almost all points x, $\overline{P}(x)=f(x)\,\overline{G}(x)$ and $\underline{P}(x)=f(x)\,\underline{G}(x)$ or else $\overline{P}(x)=f(x)\,\underline{G}(x)$ and $\underline{P}(x)=f(x)\,\overline{G}(x)$ according as $f(x)\geqslant 0$ or $f(x)\leqslant 0$; in particular $P'(x)=0$ at almost all points x where $f(x)=0$.

Proof. The proof is quite similar to that of Theorem 6.1. Let I_0 be an interval, ε a positive number, and U a major function of f with respect to G on I_0 such that $U(I_0)-P(I_0)<\varepsilon^2$. We write $H=U-P$. The function H is monotone non-decreasing, and we have $H'(x)<\varepsilon$ at every point $x\in I_0$ except at most those of a set E of measure less than ε. Now, since $U(I)-f(x)\,G(I)\geqslant 0$ for every point x and for every sufficiently small interval I containing x, the lower limit of the ratio (8.5), as $\delta(I)\to 0$, exceeds $-\varepsilon$ at each point x except at most at those of E. Therefore, ε being any positive number, this limit is non-negative for almost all points x. Combining this with the symmetrical result for the upper limit of the same ratio, we complete the proof.

Another generalization of Theorem 6.1, also due to Ward, uses the following definition of relative derivation, which is slightly different from that given in Chap. IV, § 2 (cf. A. J. Ward [3] and A. Roussel [1]).

Given two finite functions of a real variable F and G, we shall say that a number a is the *Roussel derivative* of the function F with respect to G at a point x_0, if when I denotes any interval containing x_0, we have (i) $F(I)-a\cdot G(I)\to 0$ and (ii) $|F(I)-a\cdot G(I)|/\mathrm{O}(G;I)\to 0$, as $\delta(I)\to 0$ (the ratio in (ii) is to be interpreted to mean 0 whenever its numerator and denominator vanish together; $\mathrm{O}(G;I)$ denotes, in accordance with Chap. III, p. 60, the oscillation of G on I).

When the oscillation of the function G at x_0 is finite, the condition (ii) evidently implies (i); however, when $o(G; x_0) = +\infty$, the condition (i) plays an essential part, whereas (ii) is then satisfied independently of F and of a.

It is also to be observed that when $o(G; x_0) < +\infty$, and when F is a function which has the relative derivative $F'_G(x_0)$ (cf. Chap. IV, § 2, p. 109), the latter is also the Roussel derivative of F with respect to G. Finally, in the case of derivation with respect to monotone functions, the two methods are completely equivalent. In particular therefore, when $G(x) = x$, Roussel derivation with respect to G it equivalent to ordinary derivation.

The proof of the theorem on Roussel derivability of the indefinite $\mathcal{PS}$-integral is much the same as that of Theorems 6.1 and 8.4; it depends, however, on the following lemma which may be regarded as a generalization of a result of W. Sierpiński [4].

(8.6) ***Lemma.*** *Let G be a finite function of a real variable, E a bounded set in $\boldsymbol{R}_1$, and $\mathfrak{J}$ a system of intervals such that each point of E is a (right- or left-hand) end-point of an interval ($\mathfrak{J}$) of arbitrarily small length.*

Then, given any number $\mu < |G[E]|$, we can select from $\mathfrak{J}$ a finite system $\{I_k\}$ of non-overlapping intervals such that

$$\sum_k |G[I_k]| \geqslant \frac{1}{2}\mu.$$

Proof. Suppose, for simplicity, that the set E lies in the open interval $(0,1)$. For each positive integer n, let A_n and B_n denote respectively the sets of the points of E each of which is respectively a left- or right-hand end-point of an interval ($\mathfrak{J}$) contained in $(0,1)$ and of length exceeding $1/n$. We evidently have $E = \lim\limits_n (A_n + B_n)$ and there therefore exists a positive integer n_0 such that $|G[A_{n_0} + B_{n_0}]| > \mu$. Suppose, for definiteness, that $|G[A_{n_0}]| > \frac{1}{2}\mu$.

Now, it is easily seen that, if $|G[A_{n_0}]| = +\infty$, there exists a point x_0 such that $|G[A_{n_0} \cdot J]| = +\infty$ for any interval J containing x_0 in its interior. Hence, from the family of intervals ($\mathfrak{J}$) whose left-hand end-points belong to A_{n_0} and whose lengths exceed $1/n_0$, we can obviously select an interval I so as to have $|G[I]| \geqslant |G[A_{n_0} \cdot I]| > \frac{1}{2}\mu$.

Suppose now that $|G[A_{n_0}]| < +\infty$. Then, by induction, we can extract from $\mathfrak{J}$ a finite sequence of intervals $\{I_k = (a_k, b_k)\}_{k=1,2,\dots,p}$ in such a manner that, writing for symmetry $b_0 = 0$ and $a_{p+1} = 1$, we have: (i) $b_k - a_k > 1/n_0$ for $k = 1, 2, \dots, p$, (ii) $b_{k-1} < a_k$ and $|G[A_{n_0} \cdot (b_{k-1}, a_k)]| \leqslant (|G[A_{n_0}]| - \frac{1}{2}\mu)/n_0$ for $k = 1, 2, \dots, p$, and (iii) the interval (b_p, a_{p+1}) $(b_p, 1)$ contains no points of A_{n_0}. Since, on account of (i), we certainly have $p < n_0$, it follows from (ii) and (iii) that $\sum_k |G[I_k]| \geqslant |G[A_{n_0}]| - p\cdot(|G[A_{n_0}]| - \frac{1}{2}\mu)/n_0 \geqslant \frac{1}{2}\mu$, i. e. that the system of intervals $\{I_k\}$ fulfils the required conditions.

(8.7) ***Theorem.*** *Every finite function f which is $\mathcal{PS}$-integrable with respect to a function G on an interval I_0, is the Roussel derivative with respect to G of its indefinite $\mathcal{PS}$-integral at each point x of I_0 except at most those of a set E such that $|G[E]| = 0$.*

Proof. Let ε be any positive number and U a major function of f with respect to G such that $U(I_0) - P(I_0) < \varepsilon^2$, where P denotes the indefinite $\mathcal{PS}$-integral of f. Let us write $H = U - P$, and denote by E_ε the set of the points x of I_0 for which there exist intervals I of arbitrarily small lengths, such that $x \in I$ and that $H(I) \geqslant \varepsilon\cdot|G[I]|$. It follows that each point of E_ε is an end-point of intervals I, as small as we please, which fulfil the inequality $H(I) \geqslant \frac{1}{2}\varepsilon\cdot|G[I]|$. Therefore, denoting by μ any number less than $|G[E_\varepsilon]|$ and applying Lemma 8.6, we can determine in I_0 a finite system of non-overlapping intervals $\{I_k\}$ such that $H(I_k) \geqslant \frac{1}{2}\varepsilon\cdot|G[I_k]|$ for $k = 1, 2, \dots, p$ and that $\sum_k |G[I_k]| \geqslant \frac{1}{2}\mu$. Consequently, since H is non-decreasing, $\varepsilon^2 > H(I_0) \geqslant \varepsilon\mu/4$; and therefore $\mu < 4\varepsilon$, and hence $|G[E_\varepsilon]| \leqslant 4\varepsilon$.

Now let x be any point of I_0. We have for every sufficiently small interval I containing x,

$$P(I) - f(x)\,G(I) = U(I) - f(x)\,G(I) - H(I) \geqslant -H(I) > -\varepsilon^2;$$

and, unless x belongs to the set E_ε, we also have

$$P(I) - f(x)\,G(I) \geqslant -H(I) \geqslant -\varepsilon\cdot|G[I]| \geqslant -\varepsilon\cdot \mathrm{O}(G; I).$$

Combining this with the similar upper evaluations of $P(I) - f(x)\,G(I)$ obtained by symmetry, we see, since ε is an arbitrary positive number, that f is the Roussel derivative of the function P with respect to G, at every point x of I_0 except at most those of a set E such that $|G[E]| = 0$.

CHAPTER VII.

Functions of generalized bounded variation.

§ 1. Introduction. The definition adopted in Chap. I (§ 10) as starting point of our exposition of the Lebesgue integral, connects the latter with the conception of definite integral due to Leibniz, Cauchy and Riemann (cf. Chap. I, § 1 and Chap. VI, § 1). On account of the results of § 7, Chap. IV, we may, however, also regard the Lebesgue integral as a special modification of that of Newton (cf. Chap. VI, § 1) and define it as follows:

(L) *A function of a real variable f is integrable if there exists a function F such that* (i) $F'(x)=f(x)$ *at almost all points x and* (ii) *F is absolutely continuous.*

The function F (then uniquely determined apart from an additive constant) is the indefinite integral of the function f.

A definition of integral is usually called descriptive when it is based on differential properties of the indefinite integral and therefore connected with the Newtonian notion of primitive; this is the case of the definition (L) of the Lebesgue integral. In the note of F. Riesz [9] the reader will find an elementary and elegant account of the fundamental properties of the Lebesgue integral based on a descriptive definition differing slightly from the one given above (an account based directly on the definition (L) is given in the first edition of this book).

By contrast to the descriptive definitions, we call constructive the definitions of integral which are based on the conception of definite integral of Leibniz-Cauchy, i. e. on approximation by the usual finite sums. Thus for instance, the classical definition given by H. Lebesgue [1] in his Thesis may be regarded as constructive (the reader will find a very suggestive explanation of this definition in the note by H. Lebesgue [8]); cf. also the definitions of Lebesgue integral given in the following memoirs: W. H. Young [3], T. H. Hildebrandt [1], F. Riesz [1] and A. Denjoy [7; 8].

As is readily seen, the definition (L) constitutes a modification of that of the integral of Newton, in two directions: firstly, a generalization which enables us to disregard sets of measure zero in the fundamental relation $F'(x)=f(x)$; and secondly, an essential restriction, which excludes all but the absolutely continuous functions from the domain of continuous primitive functions considered. Some such restriction is, in fact, indispensable, unless we give up the principle of unicity for the integral: to see this it is enough to consider, for instance, singular functions which are continuous and not constant, and whose derivatives vanish almost everywhere (cf. Chap. III, § 13, p. 101).

But although the condition (ii) cannot be wholly removed from the definition (L), it is possible to replace it by much weaker conditions, and the corresponding generalizations of the notion of absolute continuity give rise to extensions of the Lebesgue integral, known as the integrals $\mathfrak{D}_*$ and $\mathfrak{D}$ of Denjoy.

We shall treat in this Chapter two generalizations of absolutely continuous functions: the functions which are generalized absolutely continuous in the restricted sense or ACG$_*$, and those which are generalized absolutely continuous in the wide sense or ACG. If, in the definition (L), we replace the condition (ii) by the conditions that the function F is ACG$_*$ or ACG respectively, we obtain the descriptive definitions of the integrals $\mathfrak{D}_*$ and $\mathfrak{D}$. It must be added however that the second of these definitions requires a simultaneous generalization of the notion of derivative, to which is assigned the name of approximate derivative (or asymptotic derivative) and which corresponds to approximate continuity (*vide* Chap. IV, § 10). A function which is ACG (unlike those which are absolutely continuous or which are ACG$_*$) may in fact fail, at each point of a set of positive measure, to be derivable in the ordinary sense, and yet be almost everywhere derivable in the approximate sense. Therefore, in order to obtain the definition of the integral $\mathfrak{D}$ from the definition (L), it is necessary not only to modify the condition (ii) as explained above, but also to replace in the condition (i) the ordinary by the approximate derivative.

The integrals $\mathfrak{D}_*$ and $\mathfrak{D}$ will be studied in the next chapter; the preliminary discussion of their definitions just given, is intended to emphasize the important part played by the generalizations of the notion of absolute continuity, which are treated in this chapter. The results of which an account is given in the following §§ are essentially due to Denjoy, Lusin and Khintchine. The first definition of the integral $\mathfrak{D}_*$ was given in notes dating from 1912 by A. Denjoy [2; 3] who employed the constructive method based on a transfinite process (*vide* Chap. VIII, § 5). These notes at once attracted the attention of N. Lusin [2] who originated the descriptive theory of this integral. Finally, A. Khintchine [1; 2] and

A. Denjoy [4] defined, independently and almost at the same time, the process of integration $\mathfrak{D}$ as a generalization of the integral $\mathfrak{D}_*$. A systematic account of these researches may be found in the memoir of A. Denjoy [6].

As shown by W. H. Young [6] the generalization of the Denjoy integrals can be carried still further if we give up, partially at least, the continuity of the indefinite integral. For subsequent researches in this direction, *vide* J. C. Burkill [5; 6; 7], J. Ridder [6;7], M. D. Kennedy and S. Pollard [1], S. Verblunsky [1], and J. Marcinkiewicz and A. Zygmund [1].

Except in a few general definitions in § 3, we shall consider in this chapter only functions of a real variable. As therefore we shall be employing in $\boldsymbol{R}_1$ notions established in the preceding chapters for arbitrary spaces $\boldsymbol{R}_m$, it will be convenient to add a few complementary definitions.

We shall say that a point a is a *right-hand point of accumulation* for a linear set E, if each interval $[a, a+h]$, where $h>0$, contains an infinity of points of E. A point of E which is not a right-hand point of accumulation for the set E is termed *isolated on the right* of this set. The definitions of *left-hand points of accumulation* and of points *isolated on the left* are obtained by symmetry.

Similarly, for each linear set E, in addition to the densities defined in § 10, Chap. IV, we define at each point x four unilateral densities: two *outer right-hand, upper* and *lower*, and two *outer left-hand, upper* and *lower, densities* of E. We shall understand by these four numbers the values of four corresponding Dini derivates of the measure-function (cf. Chap. IV, § 6) of E at the point x. If at a point x, two of these densities on the same side (right or left) are equal to 1, the point x is termed *unilateral (right- or left-hand) point of outer density* for the set E. The term "outer" is omitted from these expressions if the set E is measurable.

Finally, we shall extend the notation of linear interval and denote, for each point a of $\boldsymbol{R}_1$, by $(-\infty, a)$, $(-\infty, a]$, $(a, +\infty)$ and $[a, +\infty)$ the half-lines $x<a$, $x\leqslant a$, $x>a$ and $x\geqslant a$ respectively.

***§ 2. A theorem of Lusin.** While discussing the significance of the condition (ii) in the definition (L) of an integral, we remarked that a continuous function which is almost everywhere derivable is by no means determined (apart from the additive constant) when we are given its derivative almost everywhere. It is, however, of greater interest that, for a function f, the property of being almost everywhere the derivative of a continuous function, itself represents no restriction at all, except, of course, in so far as it implies that the function f is measurable and almost everywhere finite (this last assertion follows, for instance, from the corollaries to Theorem 10.1, p. 236). We shall prove this result, which is due to N. Lusin [I; 4] (cf. also E. W. Hobson [II, p. 284]), by means of two lemmas.

(2.1) ***Lemma.*** *If g is a function summable on an interval $[a,b]$, there exists, for each $\varepsilon>0$, a continuous function G such that* (i) $G'(x)=g(x)$ *almost everywhere on* $[a, b]$, (ii) $G(a)=G(b)=0$, *and* (iii) $|G(x)|\leqslant\varepsilon$ *at every point x of $[a,b]$.*

Proof. Let $H(x)$ be the indefinite integral of $g(x)$. We insert in $[a,b]$ a finite sequence of points $a=a_0<a_1<...<a_n=b$ such that the oscillation of H is less than ε on each of the intervals $[a_i, a_{i+1}]$ where $i=0, 1, ..., n-1$. Let F (cf. (13.4), Chap. III, p. 101) be a function which is continuous and singular on $[a,b]$, monotone on each interval $[a_i, a_{i+1}]$ and coincides with the function H at the end-points of these intervals. Writing $G=H-F$, we shall have (i) $G'(x)=H'(x)-F'(x)=H'(x)=g(x)$ at almost all the points x of $[a,b]$, (ii) $G(a)=G(b)=0$, and finally (iii) $|G(x)|=|H(x)-F(x)|\leqslant\varepsilon$ on each interval $[a_i, a_{i+1}]$, and therefore on the whole interval $[a, b]$.

(2.2) ***Lemma.*** *If g is a function which is summable on an interval $J=[a,b]$ and if P is a closed set in J, there exists for each $\varepsilon>0$ a continuous function G such that* (i) $G'(x)=g(x)$ *at almost all the points x of $J-P$,* (ii) $G(x)=0$ *and* $G'(x)=0$ *at all the points x of P and* (iii) $|G(x+h)|\leqslant\varepsilon\cdot|h|$ *for every x of P and every h.*

Proof. Let us represent the open set $J^{\circ}-P$ as the sum of a sequence $\{I_k=(a_k, b_k)\}_{k=1,2,...}$ of non-overlapping open intervals, and insert in each interval I_k an increasing sequence of points $\{a_k^{(i)}\}_{i=...,-1,0,1,...}$ infinite in both directions and tending to a_k or b_k according as $i\to-\infty$ or $i\to+\infty$. Let us further denote, for each $k=1, 2, ...,$ and $i=0, \pm1, \pm2,...$, by $\varepsilon_k^{(i)}$ the smaller of the numbers $\varepsilon\cdot(a_k^{(i)}-a_k)/(k+|i|)$ and $\varepsilon\cdot(b_k-a_k^{(i+1)})/(k+|i|)$. Lemma 2.1 enables us to determine in each open interval I_k a continuous function G_k such that $G_k'(x)=g(x)$ almost everywhere on I_k, $G(a_k^{(i)})=0$ for $i=0, \pm1, \pm2, ...,$ and $|G_k(x)|\leqslant\varepsilon_k^{(i)}$ when $a_k^{(i)}\leqslant x\leqslant a_k^{(i+1)}$. If we now write $G(x)=G_k(x)$ for $x\in I_k$ and $k=1, 2, ...,$ and $G(x)=0$ elsewhere on $\boldsymbol{R}_1$, we see at once that the function G is continuous and fulfils the required conditions (i), (ii) and (iii).

(2.3) ***Lusin's Theorem.*** *If f is a function which is measurable and almost everywhere finite on an interval $J=[a,b]$, there always exists a continuous function F such that $F'(x)=f(x)$ almost everywhere on J.*

Proof. We shall define by induction a sequence of continuous functions $\{G_n\}_{n=0,1,...}$, each of these functions being almost everywhere derivable, and a sequence of closed sets $\{P_n\}_{n=0,1,...}$ in J, such that, writing $Q_n=\sum_{k=0}^{n} P_k$ and $F_n=\sum_{k=0}^{n} G_k$, the following conditions will be satisfied for $n=1,2,...$.

(a) $F_n'(x)=f(x)$ *for* $x \in Q_n$,

(b) $G_n(x)=0$ *for* $x \in Q_{n-1}$,

(c) $|G_n(x+h)|\leqslant|h|/2^n$ *for every* $x \in Q_{n-1}$ *and every* h,

(d) $|J-Q_n|\leqslant 1/n$.

For this purpose, we choose $G_0(x)=0$ identically and $P_0=0$, and we suppose that for $n=0,1,...,r$ the closed sets P_n and the continuous functions G_n, almost everywhere derivable, have been defined so as to satisfy the conditions (a), (b), (c) and (d) for each $n\leqslant r$. Since the function f is measurable and almost everywhere finite, and since the function F_r is almost everywhere derivable, we can determine a measurable subset E_r of $J-Q_r$ such that

$$(2.4) \qquad |J-Q_r-E_r|<1/(r+1),$$

and such that the derivative $F_r'(x)$ exists at each point x of the set E_r and is bounded, together with the function $f(x)$, on this set. Hence by Lemma 2.2, we can determine a continuous function G_{r+1}, almost everywhere derivable, in such a manner that (i) $G_{r+1}'(x)=$ $=f(x)-F_r'(x)$ at almost all points of $E_r \subset J-Q_r$, (ii) $G_{r+1}(x)=G_{r+1}'(x)=0$ at all points of Q_r, and (iii) $|G_{r+1}(x+h)|\leqslant|h|/2^{r+1}$ for every $x \in Q_r$ and every h.

Now it follows from the first of these conditions and from (2.4), that there exists a closed set $P_{r+1}\subset E_r$ such that:

$$(2.5)\quad |J-Q_r-P_{r+1}|<1/(r+1), \qquad (2.6)\quad G_{r+1}'(x)=f(x)-F_r'(x) \textit{ for } x \in P_{r+1},$$

and we easily verify, on account of (2.6), (ii), (iii) and (2.5), that the conditions (a), (b), (c) and (d), still remain valid for $n=r+1$.

Let us now write:

$$(2.7)\quad F(x)=\lim_k F_k(x)=\sum_k G_k(x), \qquad (2.8)\quad Q=\lim_k Q_k=\sum_k P_k.$$

In view of the condition (c), the series occurring in (2.7) converges uniformly, and the function F is therefore continuous. Let x_0 be any point of Q. Then for every sufficiently large integer n we have $x_0 \epsilon Q_n$, and since

$$\frac{F(x_0+h)-F(x_0)}{h}=\frac{F_n(x_0+h)-F_n(x_0)}{h}+\sum_{k=n+1}^{\infty}\frac{G_k(x_0+h)-G_k(x_0)}{h},$$

we find, on account of the conditions (a), (b) and (c), that

$$\limsup_{h\to 0}\left|\frac{F(x_0+h)-F(x_0)}{h}-f(x_0)\right|\leqslant 1/2^n,$$

and so, that $F'(x_0)=f(x_0)$. Now it follows from the condition (d) that $|J-Q|=0$; we therefore have $F'(x)=f(x)$ at almost all the points x of J, and this completes the proof.

Theorem 2.3 remains valid for any space R_m:

If f is a measurable function which is almost everywhere finite in a space R_m, there exists an additive continuous function of an interval F such that $F'(x)=f(x)$ almost everywhere in R_m.

The proof is almost the same as that of Theorem 2.3. We may also, in the foregoing statement, replace the ordinary derivative $F'(x)$ by the strong derivative (*vide* Chap. IV, § 2, p. 106), but the proof is then more elaborate.

It may be remarked further that Lusin's theorem in the form (2.3), is obvious if the function f is summable; for f is then almost everywhere the derivative of its indefinite integral. But this is no longer so when we wish to determine a function F with a strong derivative almost everywhere equal to f (cf. Chap. IV, p. 132). Nevertheless, it can be shown that *given in a space R_m any summable function of a point f, there always exists an additive continuous function of an interval, of bounded variation, F, such that $F'_s(x)=f(x)$ almost everywhere in R_m.*

Lusin's method is applicable in several other arguments. It has been used, for instance, by J. Marcinkiewicz [1], to derive the theorem:

There exists a continuous function of a real variable F which has the following property: with each measurable function f, almost everywhere finite, there can be associated a sequence of positive numbers $\{h_n\}$ tending to 0 such that

$$\lim_n [F(x+h_n)-F(x)]/h_n=f(x)$$

at almost all the points x.

§ 3. Approximate limits and derivatives. Given any function F defined in the neighbourhood of a point x_0 of a space R_m, we shall call *approximate upper limit* of F at x_0 the lower bound of all the numbers y ($+\infty$ included) for which the set $\underset{x}{E}[F(x)>y]$ has x_0 as a point of dispersion (cf. Chap. IV, § 10). Similarly, the *approximate lower limit* of the function F at the point x_0 is the upper bound of the numbers y for which the set $\underset{x}{\mathrm{E}}[F(x)<y]$ has x_0 as a point of dispersion. These two approximate limits of F at x_0 are called also *extreme* approximate limits and denoted by $\limsup_{x\to x_0} \mathrm{ap}\, F(x)$ and $\liminf_{x\to x_0} \mathrm{ap}\, F(x)$ respectively. When they are equal, their common value is termed *approximate limit* of F at x_0 and denoted by $\lim_{x\to x_0} \mathrm{ap}\, F(x)$.

It is easily seen that if E is a measurable set for which x_0 is a point of density, then, in the preceding definitions of extreme approximate limits, the sets $\underset{x}{\mathrm{E}}[F(x)>y]$ and $\underset{x}{\mathrm{E}}[F(x)<y]$ may be replaced by the sets $\underset{x}{\mathrm{E}}[F(x)>y;\, x\in E]$ and $\underset{x}{\mathrm{E}}[F(x)<y;\, x\in E]$ respectively. Hence

(3.1) ***Theorem.*** *If two functions coincide on a measurable set E, their approximate extreme limits coincide at almost all points of E, and in fact at every point of density of E.*

We see further that *if x_0 is a point of density for a measurable set E and if the limit of $F(x)$ exists as x tends to x_0 on E, then this limit is at the same time the approximate limit of F at the point x_0.* Therefore, if a function F is approximately continuous (cf. Chap. IV, p. 131) at a point x_0, we must have $F(x_0)=\lim_{x\to x_0} \mathrm{ap}\, F(x)$.

If x_0 is a point of density for a measurable set E and if, further, the function F is measurable on E, it is easily seen that the approximate upper limit of F at x_0 is the lower bound of the numbers y for which the set $\underset{x}{\mathrm{E}}[F(x)\leqslant y;\, x\in E]$ has x_0 as a point of density. It follows, by the definition of approximate lower limit, that *with the same hypotheses on the set E and on the function F, in order that $l=\lim_{x\to x_0} \mathrm{ap}\, F(x)$, it is necessary and sufficient that for each $\varepsilon>0$ the set $\underset{x}{\mathrm{E}}[l-\varepsilon\leqslant F(x)\leqslant l+\varepsilon;\, x\in E]$ should have the point x_0 as a point of density.*

Let us remark finally that the following inequalities hold between approximate and ordinary extreme limits:

(3.2) $$\liminf_{x\to x_0} F(x)\leqslant \liminf_{x\to x_0} \mathrm{ap}\, F(x)\leqslant \limsup_{x\to x_0} \mathrm{ap}\, F(x)\leqslant \limsup_{x\to x_0} F(x);$$

and hence the approximate limit exists and is equal to the ordinary limit, wherever the latter exists.

In order to understand better the meaning of the definitions of approximate limits, it may be remarked that the definitions of the ordinary limits are expressible in a very similar form. Thus the upper limit of $F(x)$ at x_0 may be defined as the lower bound of all the numbers y for which x_0 is not a point of accumulation for the set $\underset{x}{\mathrm{E}}[F(x)>y]$. The inequality (3.2) then becomes obvious.

For functions of a real variable, in addition to the approximate limits defined above, and which in this case we call *bilateral*, we introduce also four *unilateral* approximate limits. The *approximate upper right-hand limit* of a function F at a point x_0 is the lower bound of the numbers y for which the set $\underset{x}{\mathrm{E}}[F(x)>y;\, x>x_0]$ has x_0 as a point of dispersion. This limit is written $\limsup_{x\to x_0+} \mathrm{ap}\, F(x)$. The three other approximate extreme unilateral limits are defined and denoted similarly.

These generalizations of the notion of limit lead very naturally to parallel generalizations of derivates. Thus, given a finite function of a real variable F, we define at each point x_0 the *approximate right-hand upper derivate* $\overline{F}^{+}_{\mathrm{ap}}(x_0)$ and *lower derivate* $\underline{F}^{+}_{\mathrm{ap}}(x_0)$, the *approximate left-hand upper derivate* $\overline{F}^{-}_{\mathrm{ap}}(x_0)$ and *lower derivate* $\underline{F}^{-}_{\mathrm{ap}}(x_0)$, and the *approximate bilateral upper derivate* $\overline{F}_{\mathrm{ap}}(x_0)$ and *lower derivate* $\underline{F}_{\mathrm{ap}}(x_0)$, as the corresponding approximate extreme limits of the ratio $[F(x)-F(x_0)]/(x-x_0)$ as $x\to x_0$. When all these derivates are equal (or, what comes to the same, when $\overline{F}_{\mathrm{ap}}(x_0)=\underline{F}_{\mathrm{ap}}(x_0)$), their common value is called *approximate derivative* of F at x_0 and is denoted by $F'_{\mathrm{ap}}(x_0)$; if further, this derivative is finite, the function F is said to be *approximately derivable* at x_0.

For some further generalizations, such as "preponderant derivates" ("nombres dérivés prépondérants"), and for a deeper study of the properties of approximate derivates, the reader should consult A. Denjoy [6] and A. Khintchine [5].

The properties of bilateral approximate limits, discussed above, can be taken over, with the obvious formal modifications, so as to apply to unilateral approximate limits. In particular, Theorem 3.1 may be completed as follows:

(3.3) ***Theorem.*** *If two functions of a real variable coincide on a measurable set E, their approximate extreme limits and their approximate derivates coincide respectively at almost all points of E, and in fact at every point of density of E.*

Also, if a function F is measurable on a set E, we have $F'_{\mathrm{ap}}(x)=F'_E(x)$ at almost all the points x of E at which the function F has a derivative with respect to the set E.

§ 4. Functions VB and VBG. We shall denote by $\mathrm{V}(F; E)$, and call *weak variation* of a finite function $F(x)$ on a set E, the upper bound of the numbers $\sum_i |F(b_i) - F(a_i)|$ where $\{[a_i, b_i]\}$ is any sequence of non-overlapping intervals whose end-points belong to E. If $\mathrm{V}(F; E) < +\infty$, the function F is said to be *of bounded variation in the wide sense* on the set E, or, simply, *of bounded variation* on E, or VB on E.

In the special case in which the set E is a closed interval, we clearly have $\mathrm{V}(F; E) = \mathrm{W}(F; E)$, i. e. the weak variation of the function F on E then coincides with its absolute variation in the sense of Chap. III, § 13.

The definition of functions of bounded variation in the wide sense on a set thus constitutes a generalization (for functions of a real variable) of that of functions of bounded variation on an interval. If E is a linear figure formed of disconnected intervals we only get the inequality $\mathrm{V}(F; E) \geqslant \mathrm{W}(F; E)$, but it is easy to see that even then the relation $\mathrm{W}(F; E) < +\infty$ always implies $\mathrm{V}(F; E) < +\infty$.

Plainly, *every function which is* VB *on a set E is bounded on E and is* VB *on each subset of E.* Again, *any function F which is continuous on a set E and* VB *on a set $A \subset E$ everywhere dense in E* (cf. Chap. II, § 2) *is* VB *on the whole set E* (for then $\mathrm{V}(F; E) = \mathrm{V}(F; A)$). Finally, if F and G are two functions which are bounded on a set E and M denotes the upper bound of the absolute values of these functions on E, we have $\mathrm{V}(aF + bG; E) \leqslant |a| \cdot \mathrm{V}(F; E) + |b| \cdot \mathrm{V}(G; E)$ for each pair of constants a and b, and $\mathrm{V}(F \cdot G; E) \leqslant M \cdot [\mathrm{V}(F; E) + \mathrm{V}(G; E)]$ (cf. Chap. III, p. 97). Hence *every linear combination, with constant coefficients, of two functions which are* VB *on a set, and the product of the two functions, are themselves* VB *on this set.*

A function $F(x)$ is said to be *of generalized bounded variation in the wide sense* on a set E, or simply, *of generalized bounded variation* on E, or again, for short, VBG on E, if E is the sum of a finite or enumerable sequence of sets on each of which $F(x)$ is VB. From what has just been proved for functions which are VB we see at once that *every linear combination of two functions which are* VBG *on a set, and the product of the two functions, are themselves* VBG *on this set.*

(4.1) ***Lemma.*** *In order that a function F be bounded and non-decreasing [of bounded variation] on a set E, it is necessary and sufficient that F coincide on E with a function which is bounded and non-decreasing [of bounded variation] on the whole straight line R_1.*

Proof. Let us denote for each x, by $E_{(x)}$ the set of the points of E which belong to the interval $(-\infty, x]$. We shall consider two cases separately.

1° The function F is bounded and non-decreasing on E. For each x, let $G(x)$ denote the upper bound of the function F on the set $E_{(x)}$, or else the lower bound of the function F on E, according as $E_{(x)} \neq 0$ or $E_{(x)} = 0$. The function G thus defined is evidently bounded and non-decreasing on the whole straight line $\boldsymbol{R}_1$ and coincides with the function F on E.

2° The function F is VB on E. For each point x, let $V(x) = \mathrm{V}(F; E_{(x)})$ if $E_{(x)} \neq 0$, and $V(x) = 0$ if $E_{(x)} = 0$. We see at once that the function $V(x)$ is monotone and bounded on the whole straight line $\boldsymbol{R}_1$ and that $V(x) - F(x)$ is non-decreasing and bounded on E. Hence, by what has just been proved in 1°, there exists a function $G(x)$ which is bounded and non-decreasing on $\boldsymbol{R}_1$ and which coincides on E with $V(x) - F(x)$. We have therefore $F(x) = V(x) - G(x)$ for every $x \in E$, and since the function $V(x) - G(x)$, as difference of two bounded monotone functions, is clearly of bounded variation on $\boldsymbol{R}_1$, this completes the proof.

(4.2) ***Theorem.*** *Let F be a function which is measurable on a set E and which is* VB *on a set $E_1 \subset E$. Then* (i) *F is approximately derivable at almost all points of E_1 and* (ii) *there exists a measurable set E_2 such that $E_1 \subset E_2 \subset E$ and that F is* VB *on E_2.*

Proof. By Lemma 4.1, there exists a function G which coincides with F on the set E_1 and which is of bounded variation on the whole straight line $\boldsymbol{R}_1$. Let E_2 be the set of the points x of E at which $F(x) = G(x)$. Then since F is, by hypothesis, measurable on E, the set E_2 must be measurable. Moreover, as $E_1 \subset E_2 \subset E$, the function F is, with G, of bounded variation on E_2, and by Lebesgue's Theorem 5.4, Chap. IV, and Theorem 3.3, the finite approximate derivative $F'_{\mathrm{ap}}(x) = G'(x)$ exists at almost all the points x of E_2.

Theorem 4.2 leads at once to the following theorem, which for the Denjoy integral takes the place of Lebesgue's Theorem on derivability of functions of bounded variation:

(4.3) ***Theorem of Denjoy-Khintchine.*** *A function which is measurable and* VBG *on a set is approximately derivable at almost all points of this set.*

Finally, if we make use of Theorem 9.1, Chap. IV, and Lemma 4.1, we may complete Theorem 4.2 as follows:

(4.4) ***Theorem.*** *A function F which is* VB *on a set E, is derivable with respect to the set E at almost all points of E. Moreover, if N denotes the set of the points at which the derivative $F'_E(x)$ (finite or infinite) does not exist, then the graph of the function F on N is of length zero and consequently the set of the values taken by F on N is of measure zero*; *in symbols* $\Lambda\{B(F; N)\} = |F[N]| = 0$.

For an extension of Theorem 4.3 to functions of two variables, *vide* V. G. Čelidze [1].

§ 5. Functions AC and ACG. A finite function F will be termed *absolutely continuous in the wide sense* on a set E, or *absolutely continuous* on E, or simply AC on E, if given any $\varepsilon > 0$ there exists an $\eta > 0$ such that for every sequence of non-overlapping intervals $\{[a_k, b_k]\}$ whose end-points belong to E, the inequality $\sum_k (b_k - a_k) < \eta$ implies $\sum_k |F(b_k) - F(a_k)| < \varepsilon$.

A function F will be termed *generalized absolutely continuous function in the wide sense* on a set E, or *generalized absolutely continuous function* on E, or finally ACG on E, if F is continuous on E and if E is the sum of a finite or enumerable sequence of sets E_n on each of which F is AC.

These definitions generalize that of functions absolutely continuous on a linear interval (cf. Chap. III, §§ 12, 13) and allow us to generalize certain fundamental properties of the latter. We see at once, by the arguments of the preceding §, that *every linear combination of two functions which are* AC [ACG] *on a bounded set, and the product of such functions, are themselves* AC [ACG] *on this set*. Further, *every function which is* AC *on a bounded set E is* VB *on E*. In fact, if F is such a function, there exists an $\eta_0 > 0$ such that $V(F; E \cdot I) \leqslant 1$ for each interval I of length $< \eta_0$. It follows that F is bounded on E. Let M be the upper bound of the absolute values of F on E, and let J be an interval containing E; then, J is the sum of a finite number of non-overlapping intervals $J_1, J_2, \ldots, J_p$ each of which is of length $< \eta_0$, and we find $V(F; E) \leqslant \sum_k V(F; E \cdot J_k) + 2pM < +\infty$.

It follows at once that any function which is ACG on a set E (bounded or unbounded) is VBG on E, and therefore, by the theorem of Denjoy-Khintchine given in the preceding §, *every function which is* ACG *on a measurable set is approximately derivable at almost all points of this set.*

Nevertheless we can construct an example of a function which is ACG on an interval and which is not derivable in the ordinary sense at the points of a set of positive measure.

For this purpose, let H denote a bounded, perfect, non-dense set of positive measure, with the bounds a and b. Let $I=[a,b]$ and let $\{I_n=[a_n,b_n]\}$ be the sequence of the intervals contiguous to H. We denote further by ϱ_n the length of the largest subinterval of $[a,b]$ which does not overlap the first n intervals $I_1, I_2, \dots, I_n$ of this sequence. Plainly

(5.1) $$\lim_n |I_n|=0 \quad \textit{and} \quad \lim_n \varrho_n=0.$$

Now let c_n denote for each $n=1,2,\dots$, the centre of the interval I_n, and let F be the function defined on the interval I by the following conditions: 1° $F(x)=0$ for $x \in H$; 2° $F(c_n)=|I_n|+\varrho_n$ for $n=1,2,\dots$; 3° the function F is linear in each of the intervals $[a_n,c_n]$ and $[c_n,b_n]$ where $n=1,2,\dots$. Thus defined, the function F is continuous on I by (5.1) and is AC on H and on each I_n; since $I=H+\sum_n I_n$, it follows that F is ACG on I.

We shall show that F is not derivable at any point $x \in H$. In fact, since F vanishes on H, we have

(5.2) $$\underline{F}(x)\leqslant 0\leqslant \overline{F}(x) \quad \textit{for every} \quad x\in H.$$

If therefore a point x_0 is a left-hand end-point of an I_n, there can be no derivative $F'(x_0)$ since it is clear that $\overline{F}(x_0)=F^+(x_0)>0$ and therefore, by (5.2), that $\overline{F}(x_0)\neq\underline{F}(x_0)$. Similarly, $\underline{F}(x_0)<0\leqslant\overline{F}(x_0)$ if x_0 is a right-hand end-point of an interval I_0.

If, on the other hand, $x_0 \in H$, $x_0\neq a_n$ and $x_0\neq b_n$ for $n=1,2,\dots$, denote by i_n the suffix of that interval of the system $I_1, I_2, \dots, I_n$ which is nearest to x_0. Then $\lim_n i_n=+\infty$ and $0<|c_{i_n}-x_0|<|I_{i_n}|+\varrho_n$, and so, by the definition of $F(x)$, we have $F(c_{i_n})-F(x_0)=|I_{i_n}|+\varrho_{i_n}\geqslant|I_{i_n}|+\varrho_n>|c_{i_n}-x_0|$. Since $\lim_n c_{i_n}=x_0$, it follows that either $\overline{F}(x_0)\geqslant 1$ or $\underline{F}(x_0)\leqslant -1$, which by (5.2), proves that F is not derivable at x_0.

Let us remark, in conclusion, that *a function F which is continuous on a set E and which is* AC *on a subset of E everywhere dense in E, is* AC *on the whole set E.*

§ 6. Lusin's condition (N). A finite function F is said to fulfil the *condition* (N) on a set E, if $|F[H]|=0$ for every set $H\subset E$ of measure zero (for the notation cf. Chap. III, p. 100). Clearly, *a function which fulfils the condition* (N) *on each of the sets of a finite or enumerable sequence, also fulfils this condition on the sum of these sets.*

The condition (N) was introduced by N. Lusin [I, p. 109], who was the first to recognize the importance of this condition in the theory of the integral. It is easy to see that in the domain of continuous functions the condition (N) is necessary and sufficient in order that the function should transform every measurable set into a measurable set (cf. H. Rademacher [1] and H. Hahn [I, p. 586]). Among the more recent researches devoted to the condition (N) and to other similar conditions (cf., below, Chap. IX) the reader should consult above all N. Bary [3].

(6.1) ***Theorem.*** *A function which is* ACG *on a set necessarily fulfils the condition* (N) *on this set.*

Proof. Since each set on which a function is ACG is the sum of a sequence of sets on which the function is AC, it will suffice to prove that $|F[H]|=0$ whenever H is a set of measure zero and F a function AC on H.

For this purpose, let ε be any positive number. We denote, for brevity, by $M(E)$ and $m(E)$ respectively the upper and lower bounds of F on E, when E is any subset of H, and we write $M(E)=m(E)=0$ in the case in which $E=0$. Since the function F is AC on H, there exists a number $\eta>0$ such that $\sum_k [M(H\cdot I_k)-m(H\cdot I_k)]<\varepsilon$ for every sequence of non-overlapping intervals $\{I_k\}$ which satisfies the condition $\sum_k |I_k|<\eta$. Now since the set H is of measure zero, we can determine a sequence of non-overlapping intervals $\{I_k\}$ which satisfies this last condition and which covers, at the same time, the whole set E. Therefore, since $|F[H\cdot I_k]|\leqslant M(H\cdot I_k)-m(H\cdot I_k)$ for each k, it follows that $|F[H]|\leqslant\varepsilon$. Hence, ε being arbitrary, $|F[H]|=0$.

It follows from Theorem 7.8 (1°), Chap. IV, that every function which is absolutely continuous on an interval and whose derivative is almost everywhere non-negative, is monotone non-decreasing. With the help of Theorem 6.1, this result can be extended to functions which are ACG and we have:

(6.2) ***Theorem.*** *Every function $F(x)$ which is* ACG *on an interval I and for which we have almost everywhere in this interval $F'_{\mathrm{ap}}(x)\geqslant 0$, or more generally, $\overline{F}^+(x)\geqslant 0$, is monotone non-decreasing.*

In particular therefore, if the approximate derivative of a function which is ACG *on an interval vanishes almost everywhere on this interval, then the function is a constant.*

Proof. Let ε be any positive number and let $G(x)=F(x)+\varepsilon x$. The function G is then ACG on the interval I (together with the function F), and moreover, we have $\overline{G}^+(x)=\overline{F}^+(x)+\varepsilon\geqslant\varepsilon>0$ at almost all the points x of I. Hence, denoting by H the set of the points x at which $\overline{G}^+(x)\leqslant 0$, we have $|H|=0$, and this implies, by Theorem 6.1, that $|G[H]|=0$. Thus the set $G[H]$ cannot contain any non-degenerate interval, and by Theorem 7.1, Chap. VI, the function $G(x)=F(x)+\varepsilon x$ is non-decreasing on I. It follows at once, by making $\varepsilon\to 0$, that the function F is itself non-decreasing.

If we analyze the preceding proof, we notice that the hypothesis of generalized absolute continuity of $F(x)$ has been used only to show that every function of the form $F(x)+\varepsilon x$, where $\varepsilon>0$, fulfils the condition (N). It is remarkable that the condition (N) need not remain satisfied when we add a linear function to a function fulfilling the condition, even when this last function is restricted to be continuous (*vide* S. Mazurkiewicz [1]). For this reason it is not enough to suppose in the preceding proof that the function $F(x)$ merely fulfils the condition (N).

Nevertheless, Theorem 6.2 itself does remain true for arbitrary functions which fulfil the condition (N). The theorems which will be proved in Chap. IX, § 7, include a more general result, namely that *every continuous function which fulfils the condition* (N) *and whose derivative is non-negative at almost all the points at which it exists, is monotone non-decreasing.*

We shall show (*vide*, below, Theorem 6.8) that for continuous functions of generalized bounded variation on closed sets, the converse of Theorem 6.1 is true, i. e. that in this case the condition (N) is equivalent to generalized absolute continuity. Similarly, for continuous functions of bounded variation the condition (N) is equivalent to absolute continuity in the ordinary sense.

We shall begin with a lemma which will also prove useful elsewhere.

(6.3) ***Lemma.*** *If, for a finite function F, the inequalities $\overline{F}^{+}(x)\leqslant M$ and $\underline{F}^{-}(x)\geqslant -M$, where M is a finite non-negative number, hold at each point x of a set D, then* $|F[D]|\leqslant M\cdot|D|$.

Proof. Let ε be any positive number. Let D_n denote for each positive integer n the set of the points x of D for which we have $F(t)-F(x)\leqslant(M+\varepsilon)\cdot|t-x|$ whenever $|t-x|\leqslant 1/n$. The sets D_n evidently constitute an ascending sequence and we see easily that $D=\lim\limits_n D_n$.

With each D_n we can associate a sequence of intervals $\{I_k^{(n)}\}_{k=1,2,\ldots}$ which covers D_n and fulfils the condition

$$\sum_k |I_k^{(n)}|\leqslant|D_n|+\varepsilon, \tag{6.4}$$

and in which, further, no $I_k^{(n)}$ has length greater than $1/n$. By definition of D_n, we therefore have, for every pair x_1, x_2 of points of $D_n\cdot I_k^{(n)}$, the inequality $|F(x_2)-F(x_1)|\leqslant(M+\varepsilon)\cdot|x_2-x_1|\leqslant(M+\varepsilon)\cdot|I_k^{(n)}|$, so that $|F[D_n\cdot I_k^{(n)}]|\leqslant(M+\varepsilon)\cdot|I_k^{(n)}|$. In view of the inequality (6.4) it therefore follows that, for every n,

$$|F[D_n]|\leqslant\sum_k|F[D_n\cdot I_k^{(n)}]|\leqslant(M+\varepsilon)\cdot\sum_k|I_k^{(n)}|\leqslant(M+\varepsilon)\cdot(|D_n|+\varepsilon);$$

and, by making first $n\to\infty$ and then $\varepsilon\to 0$, we derive $|F[D]|\leqslant M\cdot|D|$.

(6.5) ***Theorem.*** *If a function F is derivable at every point of a measurable set D, then*

(6.6)
$$|F[D]| \leqslant \int_D |F'(x)|\, dx.$$

Proof. We may clearly assume that the set D is bounded. Given any $\varepsilon>0$, let D_n denote, for each positive integer n, the set of the points $x \in D$, at which $(n-1)\varepsilon \leqslant |F'(x)| < n\cdot\varepsilon$. We then have, by the preceding lemma,

$$|F[D]| \leqslant \sum_{n=1}^{\infty} |F[D_n]| \leqslant \sum_{n=1}^{\infty} n\varepsilon\cdot|D_n| \leqslant \int_D |F'(x)|\,dx + \varepsilon\cdot|D|,$$

and hence, ε being arbitrary, the inequality (6.6).

The formula (6.6) remains true when we replace in it the derivative $F'(x)$ by any Dini derivate, provided however that we restrict the latter to be finite in D. The proof then becomes rather more elaborate and requires certain general theorems on derivates which will be established later (*vide* Chap. IX, § 4).

(6.7) ***Theorem.*** *In order that a function $F(x)$ which is continuous and* VB *on a bounded closed set E, be* AC *on E, it is necessary and sufficient that $F(x)$ fulfil the condition* (N) *on this set.*

Proof. In view of Theorem 6.1, it remains to be shown that the condition is sufficient.

Suppose then that F fulfils the condition (N) on E. Let a_0 and b_0 be the bounds of E, and let G denote the function which coincides with F at the points of E and is linear in the intervals contiguous to E. The function G is evidently continuous and of bounded variation, and fulfils the condition (N) on the whole interval $[a_0, b_0]$.

Given any subinterval $I=[a,b]$ of $[a_0,b_0]$, let us denote by D the set of the points of I, at which the function G is derivable, and write $H=I-D$. Plainly $|H|=0$, and therefore also $|G[H]|=0$.

On the other hand, since the interval with the end-points $G(a)$ and $G(b)$ is contained in $G[I]$, we have by Theorem 6.5

$$|G(b)-G(a)| \leqslant |G[D]| + |G[H]| = |G[D]| \leqslant \int_a^b |G'(x)|\, dx.$$

Since this inequality is valid for every subinterval $I=[a,b]$ of $[a_0,b_0]$ and since by Theorem 7.4, Chap. IV, the derivative $G'(x)$ is summable on $[a_0,b_0]$, it follows that the function G is AC on $[a_0,b_0]$, and therefore that F is AC on the set E, where F and G coincide.

It is easy to see that the same argument leads to a more general theorem: *in order that a continuous function F which is continuous on an interval I_0 be absolutely continuous on this interval, it is necessary and sufficient that F fulfil the condition* (N) *on I_0 and that its derivative exist almost everywhere on I_0 and be summable on I_0*. This theorem will again be generalized in Chap. IX, § 7.

(6.8) ***Theorem.*** *In order that a function F which is continuous and* VBG *on a closed set E be* ACG *on E, it is necessary and sufficient that F fulfil the condition* (N) *on this set.*

Proof. In view of Theorem 6.1, we need only prove the condition (N) sufficient. Now, since F is VBG on the set E, this set is expressible as the sum of a sequence of bounded sets $\{E_n\}$ such that the function F is VB on each E_n. By continuity of F on the closed set E, we may suppose (cf. § 4, p. 221) that each set E_n is closed. Since further F fulfils the condition (N) on E, it follows from Theorem 6.7 that the function F is AC on each E_n, and therefore ACG on E.

§ 7. Functions VB$_*$ and VBG$_*$. We shall denote by $\mathrm{V}_*(F;E)$ and term *strong variation* of a finite function F on a set E, the upper bound of the sums $\sum_k \mathrm{O}(F;I_k)$ where $\{I_k\}$ is any sequence of non-overlapping intervals whose end-points belong to E (in accordance with Chap. III, p. 60, $\mathrm{O}(F;I_k)$ denotes the oscillation of F on the interval I_k). If $\mathrm{V}_*(F,E)<+\infty$, the function F will be said to be *of bounded variation in the restricted sense* on the set E, or VB$_*$ on E.

Following the order of the definitions of § 1, we shall say further that a finite function is *of generalized bounded variation in the restricted sense*, or simply, is VBG$_*$ on a set E, if E is the sum of a finite or enumerable sequence of sets on each of which the function is VB$_*$.

In the special case in which the set E is a closed interval, we clearly have $\mathrm{V}_*(F;E)=\mathrm{V}(F;E)=\mathrm{W}(F;E)$. It is easy to see that we always have $\mathrm{V}(F;E)\leqslant\mathrm{V}_*(F;E)$; so that *every function which is* VB$_*$ *on a set, is* VB *on this set*, and consequently, *every function which is* VBG$_*$ *on a set, is* VBG *on this set*. We next observe (by using trivial inequalities for the VB$_*$ case, and thence passing on to the VBG$_*$ case) that *every linear combination, with constant coefficients, of two functions which are* VB$_*$ [VBG$_*$], *and also the product of two such functions, are themselves* VB$_*$ [VBG$_*$].

Let us observe that, for a function, the property of being VB, VBG, AC, or ACG, on a set E depends solely on the behaviour of the function on E; whereas the property of being VB_* or VBG_* on E depends on the behaviour of the function on the whole of an interval containing the set E. In other words, of two functions which coincide on a set E, one may be VB_* or VBG_* on E and the other not. The same remark applies to the property of being AC_* or ACG_* with which we shall be concerned in the next §.

We have remarked in § 4, p. 221, that a function which is continuous on a set E and which is VB on an everywhere dense subset of E, is necessarily VB on E. A similar result is true for functions which are VB_*, the assumption of continuity of the given function being now superfluous. We have in fact:

(7.1) ***Theorem.*** *Every finite function F which is VB_* on a bounded set E is equally so on the closure $\bar{E}$ of this set.*

Proof. Let a and b denote the bounds of E and therefore also of $\bar{E}$. Let $a=a_0<a_1<...<a_n=b$ be any finite sequence of points of $\bar{E}$; we write $I=[a,b]$ and $I_k=[a_{k-1}, a_k]$ for $k=1,2,...,n$. We shall say that an interval I_k is of the first class if it contains points of E, and otherwise of the second class. The intervals I_1 and I_n are clearly of the first class, and we see easily that, if an interval I_k is of the second class, then both the adjacent intervals I_{k-1} and I_{k+1} are certainly of the first class.

Let us denote by $1=i_0<i_1<...<i_r=n$ the suffixes of the intervals I_k of the first class and by $j_0<j_1<...<j_s$ those of the second. With each interval I_{i_h} of the first class we associate a point $b_h \in I_{i_h} \cdot E$ and we write $J_h=[b_{h-1}, b_h]$ for $h=1,2,...,r$. It is easy to see that

$$\sum_{h=0}^{r} O(F; I_{i_h}) \leqslant O(F; I_1) + O(F; I_n) + 2 \cdot \sum_{h=1}^{r} O(F; J_h)$$

and

$$\sum_{h=0}^{s} O(F; I_{j_h}) \leqslant \sum_{h=1}^{r} O(F; J_h).$$

Hence, $\sum_{k=1}^{n} O(F; I_k) \leqslant 3 \cdot \sum_{h=1}^{r} O(F; J_h) + 2 \cdot O(F; I) \leqslant 3 \cdot [V_*(F; E) + O(F; I)]$, and therefore $V_*(F; \bar{E}) \leqslant 3 \cdot [V_*(F; E) + O(F; I)] < +\infty$. This completes the proof.

(7.2) **Theorem.** *If a function F is* VBG_* *on a set E, then F is derivable at almost all points of this set; and further if N denotes the set of the points x of E at which the function has no derivative, finite or infinite, then* $|F[N]|=\Lambda\{\mathrm{B}(F;N)\}=0$.

Proof. We may clearly suppose that the set E is bounded and that the function F is VB_* on E. Moreover, by Theorem 7.1, we may suppose that the set E is closed.

Let therefore a and b denote the bounds of E on the left and on the right, and $\{I_n\}_{n=1,2,\dots}$ the sequence of the intervals contiguous to E. Writing m_n and M_n respectively for the lower and upper bounds of F on I_n, we define two functions $m(x)$ and $M(x)$ on $[a,b]$ making $m(x)=m_n$ and $M(x)=M_n$ for $x\in I_n^\circ$ where $n=1,2,\dots$, and $m(x)=M(x)=F(x)$ for $x\in E$. The two functions $m(x)$ and $M(x)$ thus defined are plainly of bounded variation on the whole interval $[a,b]$ and coincide with $F(x)$ on the set E. Therefore, denoting by N_0 the set of the points $x\in E$ at which either one at least of the (finite or infinite) derivatives $M'(x)$ and $m'(x)$ does not exist, or both exist without being equal, we find by Theorem 9.1, Chap. IV, that

$$|F[N_0]|=|\Lambda\{\mathrm{B}(F;N_0)\}|=0. \tag{7.3}$$

On the other hand, $m(x)=F(x)=M(x)$ at every point x of E, while $m(x)\leqslant F(x)\leqslant M(x)$ on the whole interval $[a,b]$. It follows that the derivative $F'(x)=m'(x)=M'(x)$ exists at each point x of E, except at most those of the set N_0 which is subject to the relation (7.3). Finally, since the functions $m(x)$ and $M(x)$ are derivable almost everywhere on the interval $[a,b]$, the function F must be derivable at almost all points of E, and this completes the proof.

Theorem 7.2 (for continuous functions and in a slightly less complete form) was first proved by Denjoy and by Lusin, independently. It plays in the theory of the Denjoy-Perron integral (*vide*, below, Chap. VIII) a part similar to that of Lebesgue's Theorem (Chap. IV, § 5) in the theory of the Lebesgue integral. A corresponding part is played in the theory of the Denjoy-Khintchine integral by Theorem 4.3. But the latter is stated in terms of approximate derivation (cf. the example of p. 224) whereas Theorem 7.2, which requires no modification of the notion of derivative, is, for functions of a real variable, a direct generalization of Lebesgue's Theorem.

§ 8. Functions AC_* and ACG_*. A finite function F is said to be *absolutely continuous in the restricted sense* on a bounded set E, or to be AC_* on E, if F is bounded on an interval containing E and if to each $\varepsilon>0$ there corresponds an $\eta>0$ such that, for every finite sequence of non-overlapping intervals $\{I_k\}$ whose end-points belong to E, the inequality $\sum_k|I_k|<\eta$ implies $\sum_k O(F;I_k)<\varepsilon$.

A function will be termed *generalized absolutely continuous* on a set E, or ACG_* on E, if the function is continuous on E and if the set E is expressible as the sum of a sequence of bounded sets on each of which the function is AC_*.

In the case in which the set E is an interval, the class of functions AC_* on E coincides with that of the functions which are absolutely continuous on E in the ordinary sense. Every function which is AC_* on an arbitrary set E is AC on E, and every function which is ACG_* on E is ACG on E. On the other hand, *any function which is* AC_* *on a bounded set is* VB_* *on this set*, and therefore, *any function which is* ACG_* *on a set is* VBG_* *on this set.* To see this, let F be AC_* on a bounded set E. We can then determine a positive number η_0 such that $V_*(F;E\cdot I)\leqslant 1$ for every interval I of length less than η_0. Let J be the smallest interval containing E, let M be the upper bound of $|F(x)|$ on J, and suppose J expressed as the sum of a finite number of non-overlapping intervals $J_1, J_2, \ldots, J_p$ each of length less than η_0. We shall then have

$$V_*(F;E)\leqslant\sum_{k=1}^{p}V_*(F;E\cdot J_k)+2Mp\leqslant(2M+1)\cdot p<+\infty,$$

and this shows that the function F is VB_* on E.

Thus a function which is AC_* on a bounded set E is both AC and VB_* on this set, and similarly a function which is ACG_* on E is both ACG and VBG_* on E. The converse also is true, provided that the set E is restricted to be closed (*vide*, below, Theorem 8.8). Instead of giving a special proof of this result, we shall establish some more general theorems about the relations between the notions

VB, AC, VB_*, AC_*, VBG, ACG, VBG_* and ACG_*.

(8.1) ***Lemma.*** *Let E denote a bounded closed set, $\{J_k\}$ the sequence of the intervals contiguous to E, and I_0 the smallest interval containing E. Then, for any function F which is finite on I_0, we have*

(8.2) $$O(F;I_0)\leqslant V(F;E)+2\cdot\sum_k O(F;J_k).$$

Proof. Let M, m and M_0, m_0 be the bounds (upper, lower) of F, on E and on I_0 respectively. Let M_0' be any finite number less than M_0, and x_0 a point of I_0 such that $M_0' \leqslant F(x_0)$. If we have $x_0 \in E$, this inequality implies $M_0' \leqslant M$, while if x_0 belongs to an interval, J_{k_0} say, of the sequence $\{J_k\}$, $M_0' \leqslant M + O(F; J_{k_0})$. Hence

(8.3) $$M_0 \leqslant M + \sum_k O(F; J_k),$$

and similarly

(8.4) $$m_0 \geqslant m - \sum_k O(F; J_k).$$

On subtracting (8.4) from (8.3), we obtain, since $M - m \leqslant V(F; E)$, the relation (8.2).

(8.5) ***Theorem.*** *In order that a function F which is* VB [AC] *on a bounded closed set E, be* VB$_*$ [AC$_*$] *on E, it is necessary and sufficient that the series of its oscillations on the intervals contiguous to E be convergent.*

Proof. The necessity of these conditions is obvious (cf. above p. 231); we have therefore only to prove them sufficient.

Let then $\{J_k\}$ denote the sequence of the intervals contiguous to E, and suppose that

(8.6) $$\sum_k O(F; J_k) < +\infty.$$

We shall consider the two cases separately:

1° The function F is VB on E, i. e. $V(F; E) < +\infty$. Then by Lemma 8.1, we have for every sequence $\{I_n\}$ of non-overlapping intervals whose end-points belong to E,

$$\sum_n O(F; I_n) \leqslant \sum_n V(F; E \cdot I_n) + 2 \cdot \sum_k O(F; J_k) \leqslant V(F; E) + 2 \cdot \sum_k O(F; J_k).$$

It follows by (8.6) that $V_*(F; E) < +\infty$, i. e. that the function F is VB$_*$ on E.

2° The function F is AC on E. Then, given any $\varepsilon > 0$, there exists a number $\eta > 0$ such that, for every sequence of non-overlapping intervals $\{I_n\}$ whose end-points belong to E, the inequality $\sum_n |I_n| < \eta$ implies $\sum_n V(F; E \cdot I_n) < \varepsilon/2$. Now by (8.6), there exists a positive integer k_0 such that

(8.7) $$\sum_{k=k_0+1}^{\infty} O(F; J_k) < \varepsilon/4.$$

Denote by η_0 the smallest of the k_0+1 numbers $\eta, |J_1|, |J_2|, \ldots, |J_{k_0}|$, and let $\{\tilde{I}_n\}$ be any sequence of non-overlapping intervals with end-points in E, the sum of whose lengths is less than η_0. None of these intervals $\tilde{I}_n$ can contain one of the first k_0 intervals of the sequence $\{J_n\}$, and it follows from (8.7) and from Lemma 8.1, that $\sum_n O(F; \tilde{I}_n) \leqslant \sum_n V(F; E \cdot \tilde{I}_n) + \varepsilon/2 \leqslant \varepsilon$. Therefore the function F is AC_* on E, and this completes the proof.

(8.8) ***Theorem.*** *In order that a function F be* AC_* [ACG_*] *on a bounded closed set E, it is necessary and sufficient that F be both* VB_* *and* AC [VBG_* *and* ACG] *on E.*

Proof. The necessity of these conditions is obvious, so that we have only to prove them sufficient.

Now, if the function F is both VB_* and AC on E, it follows at once from Theorem 8.5 that F is AC_* on E. If on the other hand, F is VBG_* and ACG on E, we can express the set E as the sum of a sequence of sets $\{E_n\}$ on each of which F is both VB_* and AC. Since F is ACG, and so continuous, on the set E, which is by hypothesis closed, F is AC on the closure $\bar{E}_n$ of each E_n. Similarly, by Theorem 7.1, F is VB_* on each $\bar{E}_n$. Therefore by what has just been proved, F is AC_* on each of the sets $\bar{E}_n$ and so, ACG_* on the set E.

Theorem 8.8 ceases to hold if we remove the restriction that the set E is closed. Let E be the set of irrational points, and $\{a_n\}_{n=1,2,\dots}$ the sequence of rational points, of the interval [0, 1]; and let $F(x) = 0$ for $x \in E$, and $F(a_n) = 1/2^n$ for $n = 1, 2, \dots$. The function F thus defined is evidently VB_* and AC on E. To show that F is not AC_*, nor even ACG_*, on E, suppose that the set E is the sum of a sequence of sets $\{E_n\}$ on each of which F is AC_*. By Baire's Theorem (Chap. II, Theorem 9.2), one at least of the sets E_n would be everywhere dense in a (non-degenerate) subinterval of [0, 1]. But this is plainly impossible, since every subinterval of [0, 1] contains, in its interior, points of discontinuity of the function F.

§ 9. Definitions of Denjoy-Lusin. The definitions which we have adopted in this chapter for the classes of functions VBG, ACG, VBG_* and ACG_* are based on the ideas of A. Khintchine [3]. Rather different definitions were given by N. Lusin [I] and A. Denjoy [6], which are equivalent to those of Khintchine when we restrict ourselves to continuous functions. We give them here, in the form of necessary and sufficient conditions, in the following theorem.

(9.1) ***Theorem.*** *In order that a function which is continuous on a closed set E, be* VBG [VBG_*, ACG, ACG_*] *on E, it is necessary and sufficient that every closed subset of E contain a portion on which the function is* VB [VB_*, AC, AC_*].

Proof. We shall deal only with the VBG case, the proof for the other three cases being quite similar.

1° The condition is necessary. Let F be a function which is continuous and VBG on E. We can then express the set E as the sum of a sequence of sets $\{E_n\}$ on each of which the function F is VB and, by continuity of F, the sets E_n may be supposed closed. Then by Baire's Theorem (Chap. II, § 9), every closed subset of E has a portion P contained wholly in one of the sets E_n. The function F, which is VB on each E_n, is thus certainly VB on P.

2° The condition is sufficient. Suppose that F is a continuous function on E and that every closed subset of E contains a portion on which F is VB. Let $\{I_n\}$ be the sequence of all the open intervals I with rational end-points such that F is VBG on $E \cdot I$. Let $Q = \sum_n E \cdot I_n$ and $H = E - Q$. Plainly F is VBG on Q and we need only prove that the set H is empty.

Suppose therefore that $H \neq 0$. Since H is clearly a closed set, there exists, by hypothesis, an open interval J such that $H \cdot J \neq 0$ and that the function F is VB on $H \cdot J$. We may evidently assume that the end-points of J are rational. Therefore, the function F, which is VBG on the set Q, is also VBG on the set $E \cdot J \subset H \cdot J + Q$. This requires J to belong to the sequence of intervals $\{I_n\}$ and we have a contradiction, since the set H, by definition, has no points in common with any of the intervals I_n.

Theorem 9.1 shows in particular that every continuous function which is VBG on an interval I is at the same time VB on some subinterval of I. It follows that for every continuous function which is VBG on an interval I, there exists an everywhere dense system of subintervals on each of which the function is almost everywhere derivable, although this function may, as shown in § 5, have no derivative at the points of a set of positive measure.

§ 10. Criteria for the classes of functions VBG_*, ACG_*, VBG and ACG. A series of theorems enabling us to distinguish certain types of functions of generalized bounded variation and certain types of generalized absolutely continuous functions, are due to A. Denjoy [6].

(10.1) ***Theorem.*** *If $F(x)$ is a function which fulfils at all points of a set, except at most those of an enumerable subset, one of the inequalities*

$$\overline{F}(x) < +\infty \quad \text{or} \quad \underline{F}(x) > -\infty, \tag{10.2}$$

then the function $F(x)$ is VBG_* *on this set.*

Proof. It is enough to show that the set E of the points at which we have, say, $\overline{F}(x)<+\infty$, is the sum of an enumerable infinity of sets on each of which F is VB$_*$.

For any positive integer n, let E_n denote the set of the points x of E such that for every t,

$$(10.3) \qquad 0<|t-x|\leqslant 1/n \quad \textit{implies} \quad [F(t)-F(x)]/(t-x)\leqslant n.$$

Further, for each integer i, let E_n^i denote the part of E_n situated in the interval $[i/n, (i+1)/n]$, and a_n^i, b_n^i the lower and upper bounds of those of the E_n^i which are not empty. We have clearly $E=\sum_{n=1}^{\infty} E_n=\sum_{n=1}^{\infty}\sum_{i=-\infty}^{+\infty} E_n^i$.

Let now $F_n(x)=F(x)-nx$. For every point $x\in E_n$ and for every point t which fulfils the first of the inequalities (10.3), we then have $[F_n(t)-F_n(x)]/(t-x)\leqslant 0$. In particular, given any pair of points x_1, x_2 (where $x_1\leqslant x_2$) of E_n^i, we obtain

$$(10.4) \qquad F_n(a_n^i)\geqslant F_n(x_1)\geqslant F_n(x_2)\geqslant F_n(b_n^i),$$

and for every t such that $x_1\leqslant t\leqslant x_2$ we find that $F_n(x_1)\geqslant F_n(t)\geqslant F_n(x_2)$. This last relation implies that, for every interval $I=[\alpha,\beta]$ whose end-points belong to the set E_n^i, we have $\mathrm{O}(F_n;I)=F_n(\alpha)-F_n(\beta)$, and therefore by (10.4), for every sequence $\{I_j=[\alpha_j,\beta_j]\}$ of such intervals (which do not overlap),

$$\sum_j \mathrm{O}(F_n;I_j)=\sum_j [F_n(\alpha_j)-F_n(\beta_j)]\leqslant F_n(a_n^i)-F_n(b_n^i).$$

The function $F_n(x)$, and therefore also the function $F(x)=F_n(x)+nx$, is thus VB$_*$ on every set E_n^i and this completes the proof.

(10.5) ***Theorem.*** *If $F(x)$ is a function which fulfils at all points of a set E, except, perhaps, at those of an enumerable set, one at least of the conditions*

$$(10.6) \qquad -\infty<\underline{F}^+(x)\leqslant\overline{F}^+(x)<+\infty \quad \textit{or} \quad -\infty<\underline{F}^-(x)\leqslant\overline{F}^-(x)<+\infty,$$

then the set E is the sum of an at most enumerable infinity of sets on each of which the function F is AC$_*$.

If, therefore, we are given further that $F(x)$ is continuous on E, then $F(x)$ is ACG$_*$ on E.

Proof. It is enough to show that if at every point x of a set A the two extreme right-hand derivates $\overline{F}^{+}(x)$ and $\underline{F}^{+}(x)$ are finite, then A is expressible as the sum of an at most enumerable infinity of sets on each of which the function F is AC_*.

Let A_n denote, for each positive integer n, the set of the points $x \in A$ such that, for every t,

$$(10.7) \qquad 0 \leqslant t-x \leqslant 1/n \quad \textit{implies} \quad |F(t)-F(x)| \leqslant n\cdot(t-x);$$

and, for each integer i, let A_n^i denote the common part of A_n and of the interval $[i/n, (i+1)/n]$. Plainly $A = \sum_{n=1}^{\infty} A_n = \sum_{n=1}^{\infty} \sum_{i=-\infty}^{+\infty} A_n^i$.

Now, if $I=[x_1, x_2]$ is any interval whose end-points belong to A_n^i, we have, for every $t \in I$, the inequality $0 \leqslant t-x_1 \leqslant 1/n$, and so, on account of (10.7), $|F(t)-F(x_1)| \leqslant n\cdot(t-x_1) \leqslant n\cdot|I|$. This gives us $O(F;I) \leqslant 2n\cdot|I|$; and therefore for any finite sequence $\{I_j\}$ of such intervals, $\sum_j O(F;I_j) \leqslant 2n\cdot\sum_j |I_j|$. It follows that the function F is AC_* on each of the sets A_n^i, and this completes the proof.

Theorem 10.5 shows, in particular, that every function which is continuous and everywhere derivable (even only unilaterally) is ACG_*. Nevertheless as we saw in Chap. VI, p. 187, such a function need not be absolutely continuous.

In view of Theorem 7.2, we may state also the following corollary of Theorems 10.1 and 10.5: *A function F which fulfils at each point of a set E one at least of the inequalities* (10.2) *or* (10.6), *is derivable at almost all points of E.* In particular therefore, *the set of the points at which a function has (on one side at least) its derivative infinite, is of measure zero.* These statements will be generalized in Chap. IX, §4.

Theorems 10.1 and 10.5 contain sufficient conditions in order that a function be VBG_* or ACG_*, but these conditions are clearly not necessary. Nevertheless, by employing the notion of derivates relative to a function (cf. Chap. IV, p. 108), it is easy to establish conditions similar to those of the preceding theorems, the conditions being this time both sufficient and necessary. Thus, as shown by A. J. Ward [3]:

In order that a finite function F be VBG_* on a set E, it is necessary and sufficient that there exist a bounded increasing function U such that the extreme derivates of F with respect to U are finite at each point of E except, perhaps, those of an enumerable set.

1° In order to establish the necessity of the condition, let us suppose first that the function F is VB_* on E. In view of Theorem 7.1 we may assume that the set E is bounded and closed. Let $[a,b]$ be the smallest interval containing E, and, for each point x of the interval $[a,b]$, let $V_1(x)$ and $V_2(x)$ denote the strong variations of F (cf. § 7) on the parts of E contained in the intervals $[a, x]$ and $[x, b]$ respectively. Finally for each x of $[a, b]$, let $V(x)=V_1(x)-V_2(x)+x$. The function V thus defined is increasing and finite on $[a, b]$, and can therefore be continued as a bounded increasing function on the whole straight line R_1. We see at once that throughout the set E, except at most at the points a and b, the derivates of the function F with respect to V are finite and indeed cannot exceed in absolute value the number 1.

Suppose now given any function F which is VBG_* on E. The set E is then expressible as the sum of a sequence $\{E_n\}$ of sets on each of which the function F is VB_*. Consequently, by what has just been proved, there exists for each n a bounded increasing function V_n with respect to which the function F possesses finite derivates at each point of the set E_n except at most at the bounds of this set. Therefore, denoting by M_n the upper bound of $|V_n(x)|$ and writing $U(x)=\sum_n V_n(x)/2^n M_n$, we see at once that the function U thus defined is increasing and bounded and that at each point of E, except perhaps those of an enumerable set, the function F possesses finite derivates with respect to U.

2° The condition is sufficient. Let F be a finite function having at each point of E, except perhaps at those of an enumerable subset, finite derivates with respect to a bounded increasing function U. For each positive integer n, let E_n denote the set of the points x of E for which the inequality $|t-x|\leqslant 1/n$ implies $|F(t)-F(x)|\leqslant n\cdot|U(t)-U(x)|$; and let each E_n be expressed as the sum of a sequence $\{E_n^i\}_{i=1,2,...}$ of sets of diameter less than $1/n$. We see easily (as in the proof of Theorem 10.1) that the function F is VB_* on each set E_n^i, and since the sets E_n^i plainly cover all but an enumerable subset of E, it follows at once that the function F is VBG_* on E. This completes the proof.

If we analyze the first part of the above argument, we see that if the function F is VBG_* on E and moreover bounded on an interval containing the set $\bar{E}$ in its interior, there exists an increasing bounded function U with respect to which the function F has its derivates finite at each point of E. Moreover, if the function F is continuous on an interval containing $\bar{E}$ in its interior, the function U may be defined in such a way as to be itself continuous (cf. the proof of Lemma 3.4, Chap. VIII). Finally, it can be shown that *in order that a function F be ACG_* on an open interval I, it is necessary and sufficient that there exist an increasing and absolutely continuous function with respect to which the function F has its derivates finite at every point of I.*

(10.8) Theorem. *If at every point x of a set E, except perhaps at the points of an enumerable subset, a function F fulfils any one of the inequalities*

(10.9) $\bar{F}^+(x)<+\infty,\quad \underline{F}^+(x)>-\infty,\quad \bar{F}^-(x)<+\infty,\quad \underline{F}^-(x)>-\infty,$

(10.10) $\bar{F}_{ap}(x)<+\infty,\ \underline{F}_{ap}(x)>-\infty,$

then F is VBG on E.

Proof. We need only consider the case of the first of the inequalities (10.9) and that of the first of the inequalities (10.10). It is therefore sufficient to show that each of the sets $A = \underset{x}{\mathrm{E}}[\overline{F}^{+}(x) < +\infty]$ and $B = \underset{x}{\mathrm{E}}[\overline{F}_{\mathrm{ap}}(x) < +\infty]$ is expressible as the sum of an enumerable infinity of sets on each of which F is of bounded variation.

Consider first the set A. Given any positive integer n, let A_n denote the set of all the points $x \epsilon A$ such that, for every t,

$$(10.11) \qquad 0 \leqslant t - x \leqslant 1/n \quad \textit{implies} \quad F(t) - F(x) \leqslant n \cdot (t - x),$$

and by A_n^i, for each integer i, the part of A_n contained in the interval $[i/n, (i+1)/n]$. Let $F_n(x) = F(x) - nx$.

For every pair x_1, x_2 of points of A_n^i, where $x_1 \leqslant x_2$, we have $0 \leqslant x_2 - x_1 \leqslant 1/n$, and so, by (10.11), $F(x_2) - F(x_1) \leqslant n \cdot (x_2 - x_1)$, i. e. $F_n(x_2) - F_n(x_1) \leqslant 0$. The function $F_n(x)$ is thus monotone non-increasing on each set A_n^i, and it follows that A_n^i is expressible as the sum of a sequence of sets $\{A_n^{i,j}\}_{j=1,2,\ldots}$ on each which $F_n(x)$ is monotone and bounded. The function $F(x) = F_n(x) + nx$ is then plainly of bounded variation on each of the sets $A_n^{i,j}$, and moreover we have $A = \sum_{n=1}^{\infty} A_n = \sum_{n=1}^{\infty} \sum_{i=-\infty}^{+\infty} \sum_{j=1}^{\infty} A_n^{i,j}$.

Consider now the set B. From the definitions of approximate upper limit and approximate upper derivate (cf. § 3, p. 220), it follows at once that to each point $x \epsilon B$ we can make correspond a positive integer n such that the set $\underset{\xi}{E}\left[\frac{F(\xi) - F(x)}{\xi - x} \geqslant n\right]$ has the point x as a point of dispersion. Therefore, denoting by B_n the set of the points $x \epsilon B$ such that the inequality $0 \leqslant h \leqslant 1/n$ implies both the inequalities

$$(10.12) \qquad |\underset{\xi}{\mathrm{E}}[F(\xi) - F(x) \geqslant n \cdot (\xi - x);\ x \leqslant \xi \leqslant x + h]| \leqslant h/3$$

and

$$(10.13) \qquad |\underset{\xi}{\mathrm{E}}[F(x) - F(\xi) \geqslant n \cdot (x - \xi);\ x - h \leqslant \xi \leqslant x]| \leqslant h/3,$$

we have $B = \sum_{n=1}^{\infty} B_n$. We denote further, for every integer i, by B_n^i the part of B_n contained in the interval $[i/n, (i+1)/n]$ and we write as before, $F_n(x) = F(x) - nx$.

The main part of the proof consists in showing that, for every i, the function $F_n(x)$ is monotone on B_n^i.

For this purpose, let x_1, x_2 be any pair of points of a B_n^i, and let $x_1 < x_2$. We plainly have $0 < x_2 - x_1 \leqslant 1/n$, so that by writing $x = x_1$ and $h = x_2 - x_1$ in (10.12), we obtain

$$|\underset{\xi}{\mathrm{E}}[F(\xi) - F(x_1) \geqslant n\cdot(\xi - x_1);\quad x_1 \leqslant \xi \leqslant x_2]| \leqslant (x_2 - x_1)/3.$$

Similarly, from (10.13) with $x = x_2$ and $h = x_2 - x_1$, we derive

$$|\underset{\xi}{\mathrm{E}}[F(x_2) - F(\xi) \geqslant n\cdot(x_2 - \xi);\quad x_1 \leqslant \xi \leqslant x_2]| \leqslant (x_2 - x_1)/3.$$

The two inequalities thus obtained show that the interval $[x_1, x_2]$ contains a point ξ_0 such that

$$F(\xi_0) - F(x_1) < n\cdot(\xi_0 - x_1) \qquad \textit{and} \qquad F(x_2) - F(\xi_0) < n\cdot(x_2 - \xi_0).$$

By adding these two inequalities term by term, we obtain $F(x_2) - F(x_1) < n\cdot(x_2 - x_1)$, and so finally $F_n(x_2) - F_n(x_1) < 0$.

We have thus shown that the function $F_n(x)$ is monotone decreasing on each B_n^i. It follows that B_n^i is expressible as the sum of a sequence of sets $\{B_n^{i,j}\}_{j=1,2,\dots}$ on each of which $F_n(x)$ is monotone and bounded, and on which the function $F(x) = F_n(x) + nx$ is therefore of bounded variation. Moreover, we have $B = \sum_{n=1}^{\infty} B_n = \sum_{n=1}^{\infty} \sum_{i=-\infty}^{+\infty} \sum_{j=1}^{\infty} B_n^{i,j}$. This completes the proof.

On account of Theorem 4.2, it follows immediately from Theorem 10.8 that *any measurable function which satisfies one of the inequalities* (10.9) or (10.10) *at each point of a set E, is approximately derivable at almost all points of E*. This proposition will be generalized and completed in Chap. IX (§§ 9 and 10).

(10.14) ***Theorem.*** *If two extreme approximate derivates on the same side are finite for a function $F(x)$ at every point of a set E, except at most in an enumerable subset, then the set E is the sum of a sequence of sets on each of which $F(x)$ is absolutely continuous.*

Consequently, if the function $F(x)$ is further given to be continuous on E, then $F(x)$ is ACG *on E.*

Proof. It is clearly enough to show, for instance, that the set $A = \underset{x}{\mathrm{E}}[-\infty < \underline{F}^+_{\mathrm{ap}}(x) \leqslant \overline{F}^+_{\mathrm{ap}}(x) < +\infty]$ is the sum of an at most enumerable infinity of sets on each of which F is AC.

Now we can make correspond, to each point $x \in A$, a positive integer n such that x is a point of dispersion for the set $\underset{\xi}{E}[|F(\xi)-F(x)|\geqslant n\cdot(\xi-x)]$ (cf. § 3, p. 220). Hence, denoting by A_n the set of the points $x \in A$ such that, for every h, the inequality $0 \leqslant h \leqslant 2/n$ implies

$$(10.15)\qquad \left|\underset{\xi}{E}[|F(\xi)-F(x)|\geqslant n\cdot(\xi-x);\ x\leqslant\xi\leqslant x+h]\right|\leqslant h/4,$$

we have $A=\sum_{n=1}^{\infty}A_n$; and, denoting as before by A_n^i (for each integer i) the part of A_n contained in the interval $[i/n, (i+1)/n]$, we obtain $A=\sum_{n=1}^{\infty}\sum_{i=-\infty}^{+\infty}A_n^i$.

Consider now any two points x_1 and x_2 of A_n^i, where $x_1<x_2$, and let $x_3=2x_2-x_1$.

We have, on the one hand, $0<x_3-x_1=2\cdot(x_3-x_2)\leqslant 2/n$, so that by writing $x=x_1$ and $h=x_3-x_1$ in (10.15), we obtain the inequality

$$\left|\underset{\xi}{E}[|F(\xi)-F(x_1)|\geqslant n\cdot(\xi-x_1);\ x_1\leqslant\xi\leqslant x_3]\right|\leqslant(x_3-x_1)/4=(x_3-x_2)/2,$$

and *a fortiori*

$$(10.16)\qquad \left|\underset{\xi}{E}[|F(\xi)-F(x_1)|\geqslant n\cdot(\xi-x_1);\ x_2\leqslant\xi\leqslant x_3]\right|\leqslant(x_3-x_2)/2.$$

On the other hand, we have $0\leqslant x_3-x_2=x_2-x_1\leqslant 1/n$, and so by (10.15) with $x=x_2$ and $h=x_3-x_2$, we find

$$(10.17)\qquad \left|\underset{\xi}{E}[|F(\xi)-F(x_2)|\geqslant n\cdot(\xi-x_2);\ x_2\leqslant\xi\leqslant x_3]\right|\leqslant(x_3-x_2)/4.$$

The inequalities (10.16) and (10.17) show that there exists a point ξ_0 in $[x_2, x_3]$ such that we have at the same time

$$|F(\xi_0)-F(x_1)|<n\cdot(\xi_0-x_1)\leqslant n\cdot(x_3-x_1)=2n\cdot(x_2-x_1),$$

$$|F(\xi_0)-F(x_2)|<n.(\xi_0-x_2)\leqslant n\cdot(x_3-x_1)=2n\cdot(x_2-x_1),$$

and this requires $|F(x_2)-F(x_1)|<4n\cdot|x_2-x_1|$. This last inequality is thus established for every pair of points x_1, x_2 of any one of the sets A_n^i, and it follows at once that F is AC on each of the sets A_n^i. This completes the proof.

Theorem 10.8 shows in particular that a continuous function which is everywhere approximately derivable, even unilaterally, is necessarily ACG.

In Chap. IX, § 9, we shall give two further criteria for a function to be ACG_* or ACG.

CHAPTER VIII.

Denjoy integrals.

§ 1. Descriptive definition of the Denjoy integrals. We shall base the study of the Denjoy integrals on their descriptive definition. The essential ideas have already been sketched in Chap. VII, § 1. We now complete them further as follows.

A function of a real variable f will be termed *$\mathfrak{D}$-integrable* on an interval $I=[a,b]$ if there exists a function F which is ACG on I and which has f for its approximate derivative almost everywhere. The function F is then called *indefinite $\mathfrak{D}$-integral* of f on I. Its increment $F(I)=F(b)-F(a)$ over the interval I is termed *definite $\mathfrak{D}$-integral of f* over I and is denoted by

$$(\mathfrak{D})\int_I f(x)\,dx \qquad \text{or} \qquad (\mathfrak{D})\int_a^b f(x)\,dx.$$

Similarly, a function f will be termed *$\mathfrak{D}_*$-integrable* on an interval $I=[a,b]$, if there exists a function F which is ACG_* on I and which has f for its ordinary derivative almost everywhere. The function F is then called *indefinite $\mathfrak{D}_*$-integral* of f on I; the difference $F(I)=F(b)-F(a)$ is termed *definite $\mathfrak{D}_*$-integral* of f over I and denoted by $(\mathfrak{D}_*)\int_I f(x)\,dx$ or by $(\mathfrak{D}_*)\int_a^b f(x)\,dx$.

For uniformity of notation, the Lebesgue integral will frequently be called *$\mathfrak{L}$-integral.*

The integrals $\mathfrak{D}$ and $\mathfrak{D}_*$ are often given the names of *Denjoy integrals in the wide sense*, and *in the restricted sense*, respectively. The first of these is also termed *Denjoy-Khintchine integral* (cf. Chap. VII, § 1), and the second, *Denjoy-Perron integral* (for the latter, as we shall see below in § 3, is equivalent to the Perron integral considered in Chap. VI).

It is immediate, by Theorem 6.2, Chap. VII, that when a function is $\mathfrak{D}$- or $\mathfrak{D}_*$-integrable on an interval, its definite Denjoy integrals are uniquely determined on this interval (its indefinite integrals being determined except for an additive constant). More generally, *if two functions are equal almost everywhere and the one is integrable in the Denjoy sense (wide or restricted) on an interval I_0, then so is the other and the two functions have the same definite integral over I_0.* Another immediate consequence of the preceding definitions is the distributive property for Denjoy integrals. Thus, *if two functions g and h are $\mathfrak{D}$- or $\mathfrak{D}_*$-integrable on an interval I, the same is true of any linear combination $ag+bh$ of these functions, and we have*

$$(\mathfrak{D})\int_I [a\cdot g(x)+b\cdot h(x)]\, dx = a\cdot(\mathfrak{D})\int_I g(x)\,dx + b\cdot(\mathfrak{D})\int_I h(x)\,dx.$$

It follows from Theorem 10.14, Chap. VII, that *a continuous function which is approximately derivable at all points except, perhaps, at those of an enumerable set, is necessarily an indefinite $\mathfrak{D}$-integral of its approximate derivative.* Similarly, by Theorem 10.5. Chap. VII, *a continuous function which is derivable (in the ordinary sense) at all but an enumerable set of points, is an indefinite $\mathfrak{D}_*$-integral of its derivative.* The process of integration $\mathfrak{D}_*$ therefore includes that of Newton (cf. Chap. VI, § 1). The fundamental relations between the Denjoy and Lebesgue processes are given in the following

(1.1) ***Theorem.*** 1° *A function f which is $\mathfrak{D}_*$-integrable on an interval I is necessarily also $\mathfrak{D}$-integrable on I and we have $(\mathfrak{D})\int_I f\,dx = (\mathfrak{D}_*)\int_I f\,dx$.*

2° *A function f which is $\mathfrak{L}$-integrable on an interval I is necessarily $\mathfrak{D}_*$-integrable on I and we have $(\mathfrak{D}_*)\int_I f\,dx = \int_I f\,dx$.*

3° *A function which is $\mathfrak{D}$-integrable and almost everywhere non-negative on an interval I is necessarily $\mathfrak{L}$-integrable on I.*

Proof. 1° and 2° follow at once from the definitions of the Denjoy integrals and from the descriptive definition of the Lebesgue integral (Chap. VII, § 1). As regards 3°, it is sufficient to recall the fact that, in view of Theorem 6.2, Chap. VII, a function which is ACG and whose approximate derivative is almost everywhere non-negative, is necessarily monotone non-decreasing, and therefore its derivative is summable.

Part 3⁰ of Theorem 1.1 shows that for functions of constant sign the Denjoy processes are equivalent to that of Lebesgue (cf. Theorem 6.5, Chap. VI, for the corresponding result concerning the Perron integral). Hence, we derive the following further extension of Lebesgue's theorem on term by term integration of monotone sequences of functions (Chap. I, Theorem 12.6).

(1.2) ***Theorem.*** *Given a non-decreasing sequence $\{f_n\}$ of functions which are $\mathfrak{D}$-integrable on an interval I and whose $\mathfrak{D}$-integrals over I constitute a sequence bounded above, the function $f(x) = \lim_n f_n(x)$ is itself, necessarily, $\mathfrak{D}$-integrable on I and we have*

$$(\mathfrak{D})\int_I f(x)\,dx = \lim_n\,(\mathfrak{D})\int_I f_n(x)\,dx.$$

Exactly the same is true with $\mathfrak{D}_*$ in place of $\mathfrak{D}$ in the hypothesis and conclusion.

Proof. This theorem reduces at once to the theorem of Lebesgue just referred to, for we need only consider in place of the functions f_n, the functions $f_n - f_1$, which are integrable in the Denjoy sense and non-negative, and which are therefore integrable in the Lebesgue sense on account of Theorem 1.1 (3^0).

We shall show later on (Chap. IX, § 11) that the extreme approximate derivates of any measurable function are themselves measurable functions. This includes the result that any function which is $\mathfrak{D}$-integrable is measurable. In the meantime we give an independent proof of this last assertion.

(1.3) ***Theorem.*** *A function which is $\mathfrak{D}$-integrable is necessarily measurable and almost everywhere finite.*

Proof. Let f be $\mathfrak{D}$-integrable on an interval I and let F be its indefinite integral. The function F is therefore ACG on I, so that I is the sum of a sequence $\{E_n\}$ of closed sets on each of which F is AC. By Lemma 4.1, Chap. VII, there exists for each n a function F_n of bounded variation on I, which coincides with F on E_n. We therefore have almost everywhere on E_n the relation $f(x) = F'_{\mathrm{ap}}(x) = F'_n(x)$; and since the derivative of a function of bounded variation is measurable and almost everywhere finite, it follows that f is measurable and almost everywhere finite on each E_n and consequently on the whole interval I.

Finally, let us mention as an immediate consequence of Theorem 9.1, Chap. VII,

(1.4) ***Theorem.*** *If a function f is $\mathfrak{D}$-integrable on an interval I_0, then every closed subset of I_0 contains a portion Q such that the function f is summable on $\bar{Q}$ and such that the series of the definite $\mathfrak{D}$-integrals of f over the intervals contiguous to $\bar{Q}$ is absolutely convergent.*

Similarly, if the function f is $\mathfrak{D}_*$-integrable on I_0, then every closed subset of I_0 contains a portion Q such that the function f is summable on $\bar{Q}$ and such that the series of the oscillations of the indefinite $\mathfrak{D}_*$-integrals of f over the intervals contiguous to $\bar{Q}$ is convergent.

§ 2. Integration by parts. We have already observed (Chap. VI, p. 210) that a slight modification of the definition of Lebesgue-Stieltjes integral leads to an indefinite integral which is an additive function of an interval. As this modification will be useful to us in the present §, we now formulate it explicitly.

Given a finite function g integrable in the Lebesgue-Stieltjes sense with respect to a function of bounded variation F on an interval $I=[a,b]$, we shall write

$$(\mathcal{S})\int_a^b g\,dF=\int_a^b g\,dF-\{g(a)\cdot[F(a)-F(a-)]+g(b)\cdot[F(b+)-F(b)]\}.$$

The number $(\mathcal{S})\int_a^b g\,dF$ will be called *definite $\mathcal{S}$-integral of g with respect to F* over I. As we see at once, this number (unlike the Lebesgue-Stieltjes integral) does not depend on the values taken by the function F outside the interval I, and for each point c of $[a,b]$ we have

$$(\mathcal{S})\int_a^c g\,dF+(\mathcal{S})\int_c^b g\,dF=(\mathcal{S})\int_a^b g\,dF.$$

(2.1) ***Theorem.*** *Let g be a bounded function integrable with respect to a monotone non-decreasing function F on an interval $[a,b]$. Then:*

(i) $(\mathcal{S})\int_a^b g\,dF=\mu\cdot[F(b)-F(a)]$, *where μ is a number between the bounds of the function g on $[a,b]$;*

(ii) *writing* $S(x)=(\mathcal{S})\int_a^x g\,dF$ *for* $a\leqslant x\leqslant b$, *we have* $S'(x)=g(x)\cdot F'(x)$ *at almost all points of continuity of the function g, and in fact at every point x where g is continuous and F derivable.*

Proof. Clearly (i) follows at once from the obvious inequality $m\cdot[F(b)-F(a)]\leqslant(\mathcal{S})\int_a^b g\,dF\leqslant M\cdot[F(b)-F(a)]$, where m and M are the lower and upper bounds of g on $[a,b]$. In order to establish (ii), consider a point x_0 at which g is continuous and F is derivable. We may suppose, by subtracting a constant from g if necessary, that $g(x_0)=0$. Denoting, for each interval J, by $\varepsilon(J)$ the upper bound of $|g(x)|$ on J, we have $|S(J)|/|J|\leqslant\varepsilon(J)\cdot F(J)/|J|$ and taking J to be an interval containing x_0 and of length tending to zero, we find $S'(x_0)=0=g(x_0)$. This completes the proof.

(2.2) ***Lemma.*** *Let F be a function of bounded variation on an interval $I_0=[a,b]$, G a continuous function on I_0, and H the function defined on I_0 by the formula*

$$H(x)=F(x)\,G(x)-(\mathcal{S})\int_a^x G(t)\,dF(t)\qquad \textit{for}\quad a\leqslant x\leqslant b. \tag{2.3}$$

Then, if the function G is ACG [ACG$_*$] *on I_0, so is the function H.*

Proof. We may clearly assume F to be monotone non-decreasing. Denoting by M_0 the upper bound of $|F(x)|$ on I_0, we shall begin by proving that for every interval $I\subset I_0$ we must have

$$|H(I)|\leqslant M_0\cdot|G(I)|+\mathrm{O}(G;I)\cdot F(I)\quad \textit{and}\quad \mathrm{O}(H;I)\leqslant 3M_0\cdot\mathrm{O}(G;I). \tag{2.4}$$

In fact, by Theorem 2.1 (i), we have, for every subinterval $J=[\alpha,\beta]$ of I,

$$\begin{aligned} H(\beta)-H(\alpha)&=[G(\beta)-G(\alpha)]\cdot F(\beta)+[F(\beta)-F(\alpha)]\cdot G(\alpha)-(\mathcal{S})\int_\alpha^\beta G(t)\,dF(t)\\ &=[G(\beta)-G(\alpha)]\cdot F(\beta)+[F(\beta)-F(\alpha)]\cdot[G(\alpha)-\mu], \end{aligned}$$

where μ is a number between the bounds of G on J. Consequently, $|H(J)|\leqslant M_0\cdot|G(J)|+\mathrm{O}(G;J)\cdot F(J)$, and the first of the relations (2.4) follows by choosing $J=I$. On the other hand, we derive $|H(J)|\leqslant 3M_0\cdot\mathrm{O}(G;I)$ for every interval $J\subset I$, and hence the second relation (2.4).

Hence, since the function G is continuous, the function H is continuous also. Further, if $\{I_k\}$ is any finite sequence of non-overlapping intervals and if ω denotes the largest of the numbers $\mathrm{O}(G;I_k)$, we obtain from the relations (2.4)

$$\sum_k|H(I_k)|\leqslant M_0\cdot\sum_k|G(I_k)|+\omega\cdot F(I_0)\quad \textit{and}\quad \sum_k\mathrm{O}(H;I_k)\leqslant 3M_0\cdot\sum_k\mathrm{O}(G;I_k).$$

The first of these inequalities implies that if the function G is AC on a set E, so is the function H, and consequently, that if the function G is ACG on the whole interval I_0, then the function H is also ACG on I_0. Similarly, the second of the above inequalities shows that if G is ACG_* on I_0 then so is F, and this completes the proof.

We can now complete Theorem 14.8, Chap. III, which concerned integration by parts for the Lebesgue integral, by establishing a similar theorem for the Denjoy integrals:

(2.5) **Theorem.** *If $F(x)$ is a function of bounded variation and $g(x)$ a function $\mathfrak{D}$- or $\mathfrak{D}_*$-integrable on an interval $I_0=[a,b]$, then the function $F(x)\,g(x)$ is integrable on I_0 in the same sense, and moreover denoting by G the indefinite integral of g, we have*

$$(\mathfrak{D})\int_a^b F(x)g(x)\,dx = G(b)F(b)-G(a)F(a)-(\mathfrak{S})\int_a^b G(x)\,dF(x).$$

Proof. We shall establish the theorem for the $\mathfrak{D}$-integral. The proof for the $\mathfrak{D}_*$-integral is quite similar.

By Lemma 2.2, the function H defined by the formula (2.3) is ACG on I_0. Moreover, by Theorem 2.1 (ii), if we form the approximate derivative of both sides of (2.3), we obtain almost everywhere the relation $H'_{ap}(x)=F(x)G'_{ap}(x)=F(x)g(x)$. It follows that the function $F(x)g(x)$ is $\mathfrak{D}$-integrable on the interval I_0 and that $(\mathfrak{D})\int_a^b F(x)\,g(x)\,dx=H(b)-H(a)$. This last relation is equivalent to the one to be proved.

The idea of the above proof, which is directly based on the *descriptive* definition of the Denjoy integrals, is due to Zygmund. For another proof, depending on the constructive definition of these integrals, cf. for instance E. W. Hobson [I, p. 711]. For an interesting generalization of the theorem on integration by parts to the $\mathfrak{PS}$-integral (cf. Chap. VI, § 8) *vide* A. J. Ward [3].

From Theorem 2.5, there follows easily the second mean value theorem for the Denjoy integral, which may be regarded as a generalization of Theorem 14.10, Chap. III.

(2.6) **Theorem.** *Given a non-decreasing function F on an interval $I_0=[a,b]$ and a function g which is $\mathfrak{D}$-integrable on I_0, there must exist a point ξ in I_0 such that*

$$(\mathfrak{D})\int_a^b g(x)F(x)\,dx = F(a)\cdot(\mathfrak{D})\int_a^\xi g(x)\,dx + F(b)\cdot(\mathfrak{D})\int_\xi^b g(x)\,dx.$$

Proof. Writing $G(x)=(\mathfrak{D})\int_a^x g(t)\,dt$, we have by Theorems 2.5 and 2.1 (i) the relation

$$(\mathfrak{D})\int_a^b g(x)\,F(x)\,dx = G(b)\,F(b) - (\mathfrak{S})\int_a^b G(x)\,dF(x) =$$

$$= G(b)F(b) - \mu\cdot[F(b)-F(a)] = \mu\cdot F(a) + [G(b)-\mu]\cdot F(b),$$

where μ is a number between the bounds of $G(x)$ on I. It follows that there exists a point ξ in I_0 such that $\mu=G(\xi)$, and the relation just obtained becomes

$$(\mathfrak{D})\int_a^b g(x)\,F(x)\,dx = F(a)\cdot G(\xi) + F(b)\cdot[G(b)-G(\xi)],$$

which, by definition of $G(x)$, reduces to the required formula.

§ 3. Theorem of Hake-Alexandroff-Looman. The relations between the Denjoy integrals and those of Lebesgue and of Newton having already been obtained in § 1, we now proceed to establish an important result of Hake, Alexandroff and Looman, which asserts the equivalence of integration in the restricted Denjoy sense with Perron integration.

At the same time we shall show that in the definition of Perron integral (Chap. VI, § 6) we need only take account of the continuous major and minor functions. In order to make this assertion quite precise, let us agree to say that a function f is *$\mathcal{P}_0$-integrable* on an interval I_0 if 1^0 the function has continuous major and minor functions on I_0 and 2^0 denoting by U any continuous major function and by V any continuous minor function of f on I_0, the lower bound of the numbers $U(I_0)$ is equal to the upper bound of the numbers $V(I_0)$. The function f is then plainly $\mathcal{P}$-integrable on I_0, the definite $\mathcal{P}$-integral of f on I_0 being equal to this common bound. We have to prove the converse, i. e. that every function which is $\mathcal{P}$-integrable is also $\mathcal{P}_0$-integrable.

(3.1) ***Lemma.*** *If a function f is $\mathcal{P}_0$-integrable on each interval interior to an interval $[a,b]$ and if the definite $\mathcal{P}$-integral over the interval $[a+\varepsilon, b-\eta]$ tends to a finite limit as $\varepsilon\to 0+$ and $\eta\to 0+$, then the function f is $\mathcal{P}_0$-integrable on the whole interval $[a,b]$.*

Proof. It is clearly sufficient (by halving the given interval) to consider the case of a function f which is $\mathscr{P}_0$-integrable on each interval of the form $[a, b-\varepsilon]$ where $0<\varepsilon<b-a$. Let $P(x)=(\mathscr{P})\int_a^x f\,dx$ for $a\leqslant x<b$ and $p=P(b-)$.

We choose any positive number σ. Writing for symmetry $a_0=a$, we consider any increasing sequence of points $\{a_k\}_{k=0,1,\dots}$ which converges to b. The function f being $\mathscr{P}_0$-integrable on each interval $[a_k, a_{k+1}]$, we easily define, on the half open interval $[a,b)$, a continuous function F such that F is a major function of f on each of the intervals $[a_k, a_{k+1}]$ and that $[F(x)-F(a_k)]-[P(x)-P(a_k)]<\sigma/2^k$ for $a_k\leqslant x\leqslant a_{k+1}$ and $k=0,1,\dots$. By the second of these conditions the oscillation of the function F on the interval $[a_k, b)$ tends to 0 as $k\to\infty$, and therefore F has a finite limit $F(b-)$ at the point b. Writing $F(x)=F(a)+(x-a)^{1/3}$ for $x<a$, and $F(x)=F(b-)$ for $x\geqslant b$, we extend the definition of F to make this function continuous on the whole straight line $\boldsymbol{R}_1$, and the following conditions are then satisfied:

(3.2) $-\infty\neq \underline{F}(x)\geqslant f(x)$ *for* $a\leqslant x<b$ and (3.3) $F(b)-F(a)\leqslant p+2\sigma$.

Now let c be an interior point of $[a,b]$ such that the oscillation of F on $[c,b]$ is less than σ. For each point x of $[c,b]$, let $O(x)$ denote the oscillation of F on $[x,b]$. The function $O(x)$ is continuous and non-increasing on the interval $[c,b]$, and we extend its definition on to the whole straight line $\boldsymbol{R}_1$ by making $O(x)=O(c)$ for $x<c$ and $O(x)=O(b)=0$ for $x>b$. We now write $G(x)=F(x)-O(x)$ and $U(x)=G(x)+\sigma\cdot(x-b)^{1/3}/(b-a)^{1/3}$. Since the function $\sigma\cdot(x-b)^{1/3}/(b-a)^{1/3}-O(x)$ is non-decreasing, it follows at once from (3.2) that $-\infty\neq\underline{U}(x)\geqslant f(x)$ for $a\leqslant x<b$. Moreover, since $G(b)-G(x)$ is non-negative for each point x of the interval $[c,b]$, and 0 for $x\geqslant b$, we find $\underline{G}(b)\geqslant 0$, and therefore $\underline{U}(b)=+\infty$. Hence U is a continuous major function of f on the interval $[a,b]$ and fulfils, by (3.3), the inequality $U(b)-U(a)\leqslant F(b)-F(a)+2\sigma\leqslant p+4\sigma$. Similarly we define a function V which is a continuous minor function of f on $[a,b]$ and fulfils the condition $V(b)-V(a)\geqslant p-4\sigma$. It follows that the function f is $\mathscr{P}_0$-integrable on $[a,b]$. This completes the proof.

(3.4) ***Lemma.*** *Let Q be a closed and bounded set, a, b its bounds, $\{I_k = [a_k, b_k]\}$ the sequence of intervals contiguous to Q, and f a function which is summable on Q and $\mathscr{P}_0$-integrable on each interval contiguous to Q.*

Then, if the series of the oscillations of the indefinite $\mathscr{P}$-integrals of the function f on the intervals I_k converges, the function f is $\mathscr{P}_0$-integrable on the whole interval $[a, b]$ and we have

$$(3.5)\qquad (\mathscr{P})\int_a^b f\,dx = \int_Q f\,dx + \sum_k (\mathscr{P})\int_{a_k}^{b_k} f\,dx.$$

Proof. Let ε be a positive number and let K be a positive integer such that

$$(3.6)\qquad \sum_{k=K+1}^{\infty} O_k < \varepsilon,$$

where O_k denotes the oscillation of the indefinite $\mathscr{P}$-integral of f on the interval I_k. Denote by f_1 the function which agrees with f on the set Q and on the intervals I_k for $k \leqslant K$, and which is 0 elsewhere. By Theorem 3.2, Chap. VI, and by the hypotheses of the lemma, the function f_1 has a continuous major function U_1 and a continuous minor function V_1 such that

$$(3.7)\qquad U_1(b) - U_1(a) - \varepsilon \leqslant \int_Q f\,dx + \sum_{k=1}^{K} (\mathscr{P})\int_{I_k} f\,dx \leqslant V_1(b) - V_1(a) + \varepsilon.$$

We shall now define a continuous major function for $f - f_1$.

Let F_k be, for each k, a continuous major function of f on the interval I_k such that $F_k(a_k) = 0$ and $O(F_k; I_k) \leqslant 2O_k$, and let $A_k(x)$ and $B_k(x)$ denote, for any point $x \in I_k$, the oscillations of the function F_k on the intervals $[a_k, x]$ and $[x, b_k]$ respectively. We write $G(x) = F_k(x) + A_k(x) - [B_k(x) - B_k(a_k)]$ when $x \in I_k^{\circ}$ and $k > K$, and $G(x) = 0$ elsewhere. Finally, for each x, we write

$$U_2(x) = G(x) + \sum_k^{(x)} G(b_k -),$$

where the summation $\sum\limits_k^{(x)}$ is extended over the indices k for which $b_k \leqslant x$. Since, for every k, we have $G(a_k +) = G(a_k) = 0$ and $O(G; I_k) \leqslant 3 \cdot O(F_k; I_k) \leqslant 6 \cdot O_k$, the function U_2 is continuous on the straight line $\boldsymbol{R}_1$, and since the function G vanishes identically on each interval I_k for $k \leqslant K$, we have by (3.6),

$$(3.8)\qquad U_2(b) - U_2(a) \leqslant 6 \cdot \sum_{k=K+1}^{\infty} O_k \leqslant 6\varepsilon.$$

Now, for each k, we have $G(x)\geqslant 0$ and $G(b_k-)-G(x)\geqslant 0$ for every point $x\in I_k$. Therefore the increment of the function U_2 is non-negative on each interval containing points of the set Q, and consequently $\underline{U}_2(x)\geqslant 0=f(x)-f_1(x)$ at each point x of this set. Again, since the function G vanishes on each interval I_k for $k\leqslant K$, we have $\underline{U}_2(x)=0=f(x)-f_1(x)$, whenever $x\in I_k^\circ$ for $k\leqslant K$. Finally, since the function $A_k(x)-B_k(x)$ is non-decreasing on each I_k, we see that $-\infty\neq\underline{U}_2(x)\geqslant\underline{F}_k(x)\geqslant f(x)=f(x)-f_1(x)$ at each point $x\in I_k^\circ$ for $k>K$. Thus U_2 is a continuous major function of $f-f_1$ on $[a,b]$. Similarly, we determine a continuous minor function V_2 of $f-f_1$, subject to the condition $V_2(b)-V_2(a)\geqslant -6\varepsilon$ which corresponds to (3.8). Therefore, writing $U=U_1+U_2$ and $V=V_1+V_2$, we obtain a continuous major function U and a continuous minor function V for f on $[a,b]$, and if we denote by p the right-hand side of (3.5), we obtain from (3.6) and (3.7), $U(b)-U(a)-8\varepsilon\leqslant p\leqslant V(b)-V(a)+8\varepsilon$. The function f is thus $\mathscr{P}_0$-integrable on the interval $[a,b]$ and its definite $\mathscr{P}$-integral over this interval is given by the formula (3.5).

(3.9) ***Theorem.*** *A function f which is $\mathscr{D}_*$-integrable on an interval I_0 is necessarily $\mathscr{P}_0$-integrable on I_0, and we have*

$$(\mathscr{D}_*)\int_{I_0} f\,dx=(\mathscr{P})\int_{I_0} f\,dx.$$

Proof. Let F be an indefinite $\mathscr{D}_*$-integral of f on I_0. We call an interval $I\subset I_0$ regular, if the function f is $\mathscr{P}_0$-integrable on I and if the function F is on I an indefinite $\mathscr{P}$-integral of f. Further, we call a point $x\in I_0$ regular, if each sufficiently small interval $I\subset I_0$ containing x is regular. Let P be the set of the non-regular points of I_0. We see at once that the set P is closed and that every subinterval of I_0 which contains no points of this set is regular. We have to prove that the set P is empty.

Suppose, if possible, that $P\neq 0$. By Lemma 3.1 we see easily that every interval contiguous to P is regular and that the set P therefore has no isolated points. On the other hand, by Theorem 9.1, Chap. VII, the set P contains a portion P_0 on which the function F is AC_*. Let J_0 be the smallest interval containing P_0. Since the set P has no isolated points, the same is true of any portion of P, and therefore $P\cdot J_0^\circ\neq 0$. It follows that in order to obtain a contradiction, which will justify our assertion, we need only prove that the interval J_0 is regular.

To show this, let J be any subinterval of J_0 and let Q be the set consisting of the points of the set $P \cdot J$ and of the end-points of J. We denote by $\{I_n\}$ the sequence of the intervals contiguous to Q and by G the function which coincides with F on Q and is linear on the intervals I_n. Plainly the function G is absolutely continuous on J. Therefore, since $G'(x)=F'(x)=f(x)$ at almost all points x of Q, and since $G(I_n)=F(I_n)$ for each n, we obtain

$$(3.10) \qquad F(J)=G(J)=\int_J G'(x)\,dx=\sum_n F(I_n)+\int_Q f(x)\,dx.$$

Now the function f is summable on Q and $\mathscr{P}_0$-integrable on each interval I_n and moreover, F is an indefinite $\mathscr{P}$-integral of f on each of these intervals. The series of the oscillations of F on the intervals I_n being convergent, it follows, by Lemma 3.4, that the function f is $\mathscr{P}_0$-integrable on J and that, on account of (3.10), $F(J)=(\mathscr{P})\int_J f\,dx$. Therefore, since J is any subinterval of J_0, the interval J_0 is regular and this completes the proof.

(3.11) ***Theorem.*** *A function which is $\mathscr{P}$-integrable on an interval I_0 is necessarily $\mathfrak{D}_*$-integrable on I_0.*

Proof. Let f be a function $\mathscr{P}$-integrable on an interval I_0 and let P be its indefinite $\mathscr{P}$-integral. We shall show that the function P is an indefinite $\mathfrak{D}_*$-integral of f. Since $P'(x)=f(x)$ almost everywhere (cf. Theorem 6.1, Chap. VI), it is enough to show that the function P is ACG_* on I_0, i. e. that any closed set $Q \subset I_0$ contains a portion on which the function P is AC_*.

Let H be any major function of f. Since $\underline{H}(x) > -\infty$ at each point x of I_0, the function H is by Theorem 10.1, Chap. VII, VBG_* on I_0, and hence I_0 is expressible as the sum of a sequence of closed sets (cf. Theorem 7.1, Chap. VII) on each of which the function H is VB_*. It follows, by Baire's Theorem (Theorem 9.2, Chap. II) that the set Q contains a portion Q_0 on which the function H is VB_*. Since the difference $P-H$ is a monotone function, the function P is actually VB_* on Q_0. We shall show that P is further AC_* on Q_0.

For this purpose, we denote by $J_0=[a,b]$ the smallest interval containing Q_0. Let ε be any positive number and U a major function of f on I_0 such that

$$(3.12) \qquad U(I_0)-P(I_0)<\varepsilon.$$

Let P_1 and U_1 denote the functions which coincide on $\bar{Q}_0$ with the functions P and U respectively, and which are linear on the intervals contiguous to $\bar{Q}_0$ and constant on the half-lines $(-\infty, a]$ and $[b, +\infty)$. The function P_1 is clearly of bounded variation. On the other hand, we see easily that $\underline{U}_1(x) > -\infty$ at every point, and that $\underline{U}_1(x) \geqslant P'_1(x)$ at almost all points, of the interval J_0. Therefore, writing $f_1(x) = P'_1(x)$ wherever the second of the above inequalities holds, and $f_1(x) = -\infty$ elsewhere, we see at once that the function $f_1(x)$ is summable on J_0 and has U_1 for a major function. It follows that $U_1(I) \geqslant \int_I f_1(x)\,dx$ for each interval $I \subset J_0$, and therefore that the function of singularities (cf. Chap. IV, p. 120) of U_1 is monotone non-decreasing on J_0. Let T_1 be the function of singularities of P_1. Since the function $P_1 - U_1$ is monotone non-increasing on J_0 and since, by (3.12), we have $0 \geqslant P_1(J_0) - U_1(J_0) = P(J_0) - U(J_0) \geqslant -\varepsilon$, it follows that $T_1(I) \geqslant -\varepsilon$ for each interval $I \subset J_0$; and ε being any positive number, this requires $T_1(I) \geqslant 0$ for every interval $I \subset J_0$. Similarly, by considering minor functions of f in place of major functions, we find $T_1(I) \leqslant 0$, and therefore, finally, $T_1(I) = 0$, for each interval $I \subset J_0$. The function P_1 is thus absolutely continuous on J_0. This requires the function P to be AC on the set Q_0 as well as VB_*, and therefore AC_* on this set on account of Theorem 8.8, Chap. VII. Thus every closed set $Q \subset I_0$ contains a portion Q_0 on which the function P is AC_*, and this completes the proof.

The first of the theorems proved in this §, which together establish the equivalence of the processes of $\mathcal{D}_*$-, $\mathcal{P}_0$- and $\mathcal{P}$-integration, was derived in 1921 by H. Hake [1] from the constructive definition of the integral $\mathcal{D}_*$ (*vide* below, § 5). The second theorem was obtained some years later by P. Alexandroff [1; 2] and H. Looman [4] independently. For an interesting extension of these results to Perron-Stieltjes integral, *vide* A. J. Ward [3].

It should, perhaps, be added that in their original definitions O. Perron [1] and O. Bauer [1] employed only continuous major and minor functions. The equivalence of the original Perron-Bauer definition with that of Chap. VI, § 6, has therefore been established here as a consequence of Theorems 3.9 et 3.11.

Let us remark further that in the definition of Perron integral, ordinary major and minor functions may be replaced by generalized continuous major and minor functions defined as follows. A function U is a *generalized continuous major function* of a function f on an interval I if 1° U is continuous and VBG_* on I, 2° the set of the values assumed by U at the points at which $U'(x) = -\infty$, is of measure zero, and 3° $\underline{U}(x) \geqslant f(x)$ at almost all points x. The definition of *generalized continuous minor functions* is obtained by symmetry.

We shall conclude this § with the following result, due to Marcinkiewicz:

(3.13) ***Theorem.*** *A measurable function f which has on I_0 at least one continuous major function and at least one continuous minor function, is necessarily $\mathscr{P}$-integrable on I_0.*

Proof. Let U and V be respectively a continuous major function and a continuous minor function of f on I_0. We shall call a point $x \in I_0$ regular if the function f is $\mathscr{P}$-integrable on each sufficiently small interval $I \subset I_0$ which contains x. Let Q be the set of the points x of I_0 which are not regular. The set Q is plainly closed and we see at once that the function f is $\mathscr{P}$-integrable on each subinterval of I_0 which contains no points of Q. Thus it has to be proved that $Q=0$.

Suppose, if possible, that $Q\neq 0$. For every interval I on which the function f is $\mathscr{P}$-integrable, we have $U(I)\geqslant(\mathscr{P})\int_I f(x)\,dx\geqslant V(I)$. Therefore, if $[a,b]$ is an interval contiguous to Q, the definite $\mathscr{P}$-integral of f on the interval $[a+\varepsilon, b-\eta]$ interior to $[a,b]$ tends to a finite limit as $\varepsilon\to 0$ and $\eta\to 0$. By Lemma 3.1, the function f is thus $\mathscr{P}$-integrable on each interval contiguous to Q. It follows, in particular, that Q can have no isolated points.

Now let Q_0 be a portion of Q on which the functions U and V are both VB_*. Such a portion exists by Theorem 9.1, Chap. VII, since the functions U and V are VBG_* on I_0 on account of Theorem 10.1, Chap. VII. Let J_0 be the smallest interval containing Q_0. Since $\underline{U}(x)\geqslant f(x)\geqslant \overline{V}(x)$ everywhere on I_0, the function f is summable on $\bar{Q}_0$ together with the two derivatives $\underline{U}(x)$ and $\overline{V}(x)$. On the other hand, denoting by $\{I_n\}$ the sequence of the intervals contiguous to $\bar{Q}_0$ and by O_n the oscillation on I_n of the indefinite $\mathscr{P}$-integral of f, we shall have $O_n\leqslant \mathrm{O}(U;I_n)+\mathrm{O}(V;I_n)$ for every n, and so $\sum_n O_n<+\infty$. It follows by Lemma 3.4, that the function f is $\mathscr{P}$-integrable on the whole interval J_0. But this is clearly impossible, for since the set Q has no isolated points, the interval J_0 contains in its interior some points of Q. We thus arrive at a contradiction which completes the proof.

Just as in the definition of the Perron integral, we may replace, in Theorem 3.13, ordinary major and minor functions by generalized continuous ones (cf. above, p. 252). Nevertheless, the conditions of Theorem 3.13 differ from those of the definition of Chap. VI, § 6, in that continuity is essential. In fact, if we write $f(x)=0$ for $x\leqslant 0$ and $f(x)=-1/x^2$ for $x>0$, $U(x)=0$ identically in $\boldsymbol{R}_1$ and $V(x)=0$ for $x\leqslant 0$ and $V(x)=1/x$ for $x>0$, we see at once that U and V are respectively a major and a minor function of f; and yet f is evidently not $\mathscr{P}_0$-integrable on $[0, 1]$.

§ 1. General notion of integral. We shall deal in this § with some notions of a more abstract kind which we shall employ, in the next §, as a basis for the constructive definition of the Denjoy integrals.

Let $\mathfrak{T}$ be a functional operation by which there corresponds to each interval $I=[a,b]$ a class of functions defined on I, and to each function f of this class a finite real number. This class of functions will be called *domain of the operation* $\mathfrak{T}$ *on the interval* I, and the number associated with f will be denoted by $\mathfrak{T}(f;I)$.

An operation $\mathfrak{T}$ will be termed an *integral*, if the following three conditions are fulfilled:

(i) If a function f belongs to the domain of the operation $\mathfrak{T}$ on an interval I_0, the function belongs also to the domain of $\mathfrak{T}$ on any interval $I\subset I_0$, and $\mathfrak{T}(f;I)$ is a continuous additive function of the interval $I\subset I_0$.

(ii) If a function f belongs to the domain of the operation $\mathfrak{T}$ on two abutting intervals I_1 and I_2, the function belongs also to the domain of $\mathfrak{T}$ on the interval I_1+I_2.

(iii) A function f which vanishes identically on an interval I belongs to the domain of $\mathfrak{T}$ on I, and we have $\mathfrak{T}(f;I)=0$.

If $\mathfrak{T}$ is an integral, any function f which belongs to the domain of $\mathfrak{T}$ on an interval I_0 will be termed $\mathfrak{T}$*-integrable* on I_0 and the number $\mathfrak{T}(f;I_0)$ will be called *definite* $\mathfrak{T}$*-integral* of f on I_0. The function of an interval $I\subset I_0$, $\mathfrak{T}(f;I)$, which is additive and continuous on account of (i), will then be called *indefinite* $\mathfrak{T}$*-integral* of f on I_0 and its oscillation on I_0 (i. e. the upper bound of the numbers $|\mathfrak{T}(f;I)|$, where I denotes any subinterval of I_0) will be denoted by $\mathrm{O}(\mathfrak{T};f;I_0)$.

Two integrals $\mathfrak{T}_1$ and $\mathfrak{T}_2$ will be termed *compatible*, if $\mathfrak{T}_1(f;I)=\mathfrak{T}_2(f;I)$ for every interval I and for every function f which is both $\mathfrak{T}_1$- and $\mathfrak{T}_2$-integrable on I.

We shall say that the integral $\mathfrak{T}_2$ *includes* the integral $\mathfrak{T}_1$, if the two integrals are compatible and if every function which is $\mathfrak{T}_1$-integrable is also $\mathfrak{T}_2$-integrable. When this is so we shall write $\mathfrak{T}_1\subset\mathfrak{T}_2$.

Given an integral $\mathfrak{T}$ and a function g which vanishes outside a bounded set E, it is evident that if g is $\mathfrak{T}$-integrable on an interval I_0 which contains E in its interior, then g is so also on any interval I which contains E, and we have $\mathfrak{T}(g;I)=\mathfrak{T}(g;I_0)$.

This fact justifies the following definition: we shall say that a function f is *$\mathfrak{T}$-integrable on a bounded set E*, if the function g which coincides with f on E and is 0 elsewhere, is $\mathfrak{T}$-integrable on each interval $I \supset E$. The number $\mathfrak{T}(g; I)$ is then independent of the choice of the interval $I \supset E$; we shall call this number *definite $\mathfrak{T}$-integral* of the function f *on the set E* and we shall denote it by $\mathfrak{T}(f; E)$.

Of the known processes of integration, all those which give rise to a continuous indefinite integral (for instance those of Lebesgue, Newton, Denjoy, etc.) are easily seen to be integrals according to the above definition. If, however, we wished to include also discontinuous integrals (e. g. that of W. H. Young, cf. Chap. VII, p. 215) we should have to modify some details of the definition.

Given a function f on an interval I_0 and given an integral $\mathfrak{T}$, we shall say that a point $a \in I_0$ is a *$\mathfrak{T}$-singular point* of f in I_0 if there exist arbitrarily small intervals $I \subset I_0$ containing a on each of which the function f is not $\mathfrak{T}$-integrable. Denoting by S the set of these points, we see at once that the set S is closed and that the function f is $\mathfrak{T}$-integrable on every subinterval of I_0 which contains no points of S.

With each integral $\mathfrak{T}$ we now associate three "generalized" integrals $\mathfrak{T}^{\mathrm{C}}$, $\mathfrak{T}^{\mathrm{H}}$ and $\mathfrak{T}^{\mathrm{H}_*}$, defined as follows.

Given any interval I_0, the domain of the operation $\mathfrak{T}^{\mathrm{C}}$ on I_0 is the class of all the functions f which fulfil the following two conditions:

(c^1) the set of the $\mathfrak{T}$-singular points of f in I_0 is finite (or empty);

(c^2) there exists a continuous additive function of an interval F on I_0 such that $F(I) = \mathfrak{T}(f; I)$ whenever I is a subinterval of I_0 which contains no $\mathfrak{T}$-singular point of f.

Since such a function F (if existent) is uniquely determined by the conditions (c^1) and (c^2), we can write $\mathfrak{T}^{\mathrm{C}}(f; I_0) = F(I_0)$.

The domain of the operation $\mathfrak{T}^{\mathrm{H}}$ on I_0 is defined as the class of the functions f which fulfil the following conditions:

(h^1) if S denotes the set of all $\mathfrak{T}$-singular points of f in I_0, the function f is $\mathfrak{T}$-integrable on the set S and on each of the intervals I_k contiguous to the set consisting of the points of S and of the end-points of I_0;

(h^2) $\sum_k |\mathfrak{T}(f; I_k)| < +\infty$ and, in the case in which the sequence $\{I_k\}$ is infinite, $\lim_k \mathrm{O}(\mathfrak{T}; f; I_k) = 0$.

For any such function f, we write by definition:

$$\mathfrak{T}^{\mathrm{H}}(f; I_0) = \sum_k \mathfrak{T}(f; I_k) + \mathfrak{T}(f; S).$$

Finally, we obtain the definition of the operation $\mathfrak{T}^{\mathrm{H}_*}$ by replacing in the definition of the operation $\mathfrak{T}^{\mathrm{H}}$ the condition (h^2) by the more restrictive condition:

$$(h^2_*) \qquad \sum_k \mathrm{O}(\mathfrak{T}; f; I_k) < +\infty.$$

We verify at once that the operations $\mathfrak{T}^{\mathrm{C}}$, $\mathfrak{T}^{\mathrm{H}}$ and $\mathfrak{T}^{\mathrm{H}_*}$ all fulfil the conditions (i), (ii) and (iii), p. 254. These operations are therefore **integrals** according to the definition, p. 254, and we evidently have $\mathfrak{T} \subset \mathfrak{T}^{\mathrm{C}}$ and $\mathfrak{T} \subset \mathfrak{T}^{\mathrm{H}_*} \subset \mathfrak{T}^{\mathrm{H}}$. For brevity, we shall write $\mathfrak{T}^{\mathrm{CH}}$ and $\mathfrak{T}^{\mathrm{CH}_*}$ in place of $(\mathfrak{T}^{\mathrm{C}})^{\mathrm{H}}$ and $(\mathfrak{T}^{\mathrm{C}})^{\mathrm{H}_*}$ respectively.

The integral $\mathfrak{T}^{\mathrm{C}}$ and the integrals $\mathfrak{T}^{\mathrm{H}}$ and $\mathfrak{T}^{\mathrm{H}_*}$ may be regarded respectively as the Cauchy and the Harnack generalizations of the integral $\mathfrak{T}$. They correspond, in fact, to the classical processes employed by Cauchy and Harnack to extend integration from bounded to unbounded functions of certain classes. The original process of Harnack actually corresponds to the operation $\mathfrak{T}^{\mathrm{H}_*}$ rather than to the operation $\mathfrak{T}^{\mathrm{H}}$. Cf. A. Harnack [1], E. W. Hobson [I, Chap. VIII] and A. Rosenthal [I, p. 1053].

If we were to add to the conditions (h^1) and (h^2) which characterize the generalized integral $\mathfrak{T}^{\mathrm{H}}$, the condition that $\lim_k \mathrm{O}(\mathfrak{T}; f; I_k)/\varrho(x, I_k) = 0$ for almost all $x \in S$, we should arrive at a generalized integral $\mathfrak{T}^{\mathrm{H}'}$ intermediate between $\mathfrak{T}^{\mathrm{H}}$ and $\mathfrak{T}^{\mathrm{H}_*}$. By applying the process $\mathfrak{T}^{\mathrm{H}'}$ in the constructive definitions of Denjoy integrals of the next §, we should then obtain an integral $\mathfrak{D}'$, intermediate between $\mathfrak{D}$ and $\mathfrak{D}_*$. Its descriptive definition is very simple: *a function f is $\mathfrak{D}'$-integrable if it is $\mathfrak{D}$-integrable and if its indefinite $\mathfrak{D}$-integral is almost everywhere derivable (in the ordinary sense).* This integral has been discussed by A. Khintchine [1]; cf. also J. C. Burkill [1].

***§ 5. Constructive definition of the Denjoy integrals.** With the notation of the preceding §, we see at once that for each integral $\mathfrak{T} \subset \mathfrak{D}$, we have also $\mathfrak{T}^{\mathrm{C}} \subset \mathfrak{D}$; similarly the relation $\mathfrak{T} \subset \mathfrak{D}_*$ implies $\mathfrak{T}^{\mathrm{C}} \subset \mathfrak{D}_*$. It is not quite so obvious that the relations $\mathfrak{T} \subset \mathfrak{D}$ and $\mathfrak{T} \subset \mathfrak{D}_*$ imply respectively $\mathfrak{T}^{\mathrm{H}} \subset \mathfrak{D}$ and $\mathfrak{T}^{\mathrm{H}_*} \subset \mathfrak{D}_*$. This last assertion is a consequence of the following theorem which is analogous to Lemma 3.4.

(5.1) ***Theorem.*** *Let Q be a bounded closed set with the bounds a and b, and let $\{I_k\}$ be the sequence of intervals contiguous to Q; and suppose that f is a function $\mathfrak{D}$-integrable on the set Q as well as on each of the intervals I_k, and that (in the case in which the sequence $\{I_k\}$ is infinite)*

$$\sum_k \left|(\mathfrak{D})\int_{I_k} f\,dx\right| < +\infty \qquad \text{and} \qquad \lim_k \mathrm{O}(\mathfrak{D}; f; I_k) = 0.$$

Then the function f is $\mathfrak{D}$-integrable on the whole interval $I=[a,b]$ and we have

$$(5.2)\qquad (\mathfrak{D})\int_I f\,dx = (\mathfrak{D})\int_Q f\,dx + \sum_k (\mathfrak{D})\int_{I_k} f\,dx.$$

If we suppose, further, that the function f is $\mathfrak{D}_*$-integrable on Q as well as on each of the intervals I_k and that $\sum_k \mathrm{O}(\mathfrak{D}_*; f; I_k) < +\infty$, then the function f is $\mathfrak{D}_*$-integrable on I.

Proof. We shall prove the theorem for the $\mathfrak{D}$-integral. The case of the $\mathfrak{D}_*$-integral is similar.

Let $I(x)$ denote the interval $[a,x]$ where we suppose $x \in [a,b]$, and let

$$(5.3)\qquad F(x) = \sum_k (\mathfrak{D}) \int_{I_k \cdot I(x)} f(t)\,dt.$$

We shall show that the function F, thus defined, is ACG on the interval I. For this purpose, it will suffice to show that F is AC on the set Q, the function being evidently continuous on I and ACG on each of the intervals I_k.

Let $g(x)$ be the function equal to 0 for $x \in Q$ and to $\frac{1}{|I_k|}\cdot(\mathfrak{D})\int_{I_k} f(t)\,dt$ for $x \in I_k^\circ$ where $k=1, 2, \ldots$. The function g is summable on I and if $G(x)=\int_a^x g(t)\,dt$, the function F clearly coincides with G on Q; F is thus AC on Q and therefore ACG on I.

This being so, we have $F'_{\mathrm{ap}}(x)=G'(x)=g(x)=0$ at almost all points x of Q, while it follows at once from (5.3) that $F'_{\mathrm{ap}}(x)=f(x)$ at almost all points x of $I-Q$. Hence, F being ACG on I, it follows that the function equal to f on $I-Q$ and to 0 on Q has F for an indefinite $\mathfrak{D}$-integral. On the other hand, the function equal to f on Q and to 0 elsewhere is, by hypothesis, $\mathfrak{D}$-integrable on I. It follows that the function f itself is $\mathfrak{D}$-integrable on I, and that $(\mathfrak{D})\int_I f(x)\,dx = F(b)-F(a)+(\mathfrak{D})\int_Q f\,dx$, which, on account of (5.3), is equivalent to (5.2). This completes the proof.

We now pass on to the constructive definition of the Denjoy integrals. We begin by introducing the following notation.

Let $\{\mathfrak{T}^\xi\}$ be a sequence of integrals, in general transfinite, such that $\mathfrak{T}^\xi \subset \mathfrak{T}^\eta$ whenever $\xi<\eta$. We then denote by $\sum\limits_{\xi<\alpha}\mathfrak{T}^\xi$ the operation $\mathfrak{T}$ whose domain on each interval I is the sum of the domains of the operations $\mathfrak{T}^\xi$ for $\xi<\alpha$, and which is defined for every function f of its domain by the relation $\mathfrak{T}(f;I)=\mathfrak{T}^{\xi_0}(f;I)$, where ξ_0 is the least of the indices $\xi<\alpha$ such that f is $\mathfrak{T}^\xi$-integrable on I. It then follows, of course, that $\mathfrak{T}(f;I)=\mathfrak{T}^\xi(f;I)$ for every $\xi\geqslant\xi_0$, since by hypothesis $\mathfrak{T}^\xi$ then includes $\mathfrak{T}^{\xi_0}$.

This being so, let $\{\mathfrak{L}^\xi\}$ and $\{\mathfrak{L}^\xi_*\}$ be two transfinite sequences defined, by an induction starting with the Lebesgue integral $\mathfrak{L}$, as follows:

$$\mathfrak{L}^0=\mathfrak{L}^0_*=\mathfrak{L},$$

$$\mathfrak{L}^\alpha=\Big(\sum_{\xi<\alpha}\mathfrak{L}^\xi\Big)^{\mathrm{CH}} \quad \textit{and} \quad \mathfrak{L}^\alpha_*=\Big(\sum_{\xi<\alpha}\mathfrak{L}^\xi_*\Big)^{\mathrm{CH}_*} \quad \textit{for} \quad \alpha>0.$$

Denoting by Ω the smallest ordinal number of the third class (cf. for instance, W. Sierpiński [I, p. 235]) we shall show that

$$\mathfrak{D}=\sum_{\xi<\Omega}\mathfrak{L}^\xi=\mathfrak{L}^\Omega \quad \textit{and} \quad \mathfrak{D}_*=\sum_{\xi<\Omega}\mathfrak{L}^\xi_*=\mathfrak{L}^\Omega_*.$$

We shall restrict ourselves to the case of the $\mathfrak{D}$-integral (that of the $\mathfrak{D}_*$-integral being quite similar).

Since $\mathfrak{L}\subset\mathfrak{D}$, we find at once by induction (cf. above, p. 256) that for every ξ, $\mathfrak{L}^\xi\subset\mathfrak{D}$, and so, obviously, $\sum\limits_{\xi<\Omega}\mathfrak{L}^\xi\subset\mathfrak{D}$. In order to change this last relation into one of identity, it is enough to show that every function f which is $\mathfrak{D}$-integrable on an interval $I_0=[a,b]$, is $\mathfrak{L}^\xi$-integrable on I_0 for some index $\xi<\Omega$.

Let S^ξ denote the set of the $\mathfrak{L}^\xi$-singular points of f in I_0. The sequence $\{S^\xi\}$, as a descending sequence of closed sets, is stationary, i.e. there exists an index $\nu<\Omega$ such that $S^\nu=S^{\nu+1}$. (For if not, there would exist for every $\xi<\Omega$ a point $x_\xi\in S^\xi-S^{\xi+1}$, and therefore also an interval I_ξ with rational end-points, containing the point x_ξ of S^ξ but without points in common with the closed set $S^{\xi+1}$, nor therefore, with any of the sets $S^{\xi+2}, S^{\xi+3},\ldots$. We should thus obtain a transfinite sequence of type Ω of distinct intervals with rational end-points, and this is impossible.) We shall prove that $S^\nu=0$.

Suppose, if possible, that $S^\nu \neq 0$. We see at once that the function f is $\mathfrak{L}^\nu$-integrable on each interval $I \subset I_0$ which contains no points of S^ν. It follows that the function f is $(\mathfrak{L}^\nu)^{\mathrm{C}}$-integrable, and *a fortiori* $\mathfrak{L}^{\nu+1}$-integrable, on each interval contiguous to S^ν. Since $S^\nu = S^{\nu+1}$, it follows, in particular, that the set S^ν contains no isolated points.

The function f being, by hypothesis, $\mathfrak{D}$-integrable on I_0, the set S^ν (cf. Theorem 1.4) must contain a portion Q such that the function f is summable on $\bar{Q}$ and such that the series of the definite $\mathfrak{D}$-integrals of f over the intervals contiguous to $\bar{Q}$ converges absolutely. Since $\mathfrak{L} \subset (\mathfrak{L}^\nu)^{\mathrm{C}} \subset \mathfrak{D}$, it follows at once that the function f is $(\mathfrak{L}^\nu)^{\mathrm{CH}}$-integrable, i.e. $\mathfrak{L}^{\nu+1}$-integrable, on some interval J_0 containing Q. But this is clearly impossible, since, in view of the fact that the set S^ν has no isolated points, the interval J_0 certainly contains points of the set $S^\nu = S^{\nu+1}$ in its interior.

We thus have $S^\nu = 0$, which establishes the $\mathfrak{L}^\nu$-integrability of f on I_0 and completes the proof.

Various definitions, constructive and descriptive, of Denjoy integrals will be found in the papers mentioned in Chap. VI, p. 207, and Chap. VII, pp. 214-215, as well as in the following treatises and memoirs: N. Lusin [I; 4], T. H. Hildebrandt [1], P. Nalli [I], E. Kamke [I], A. Kolmogoroff [2], H. Lebesgue [7; II, Chap. X], A. Rosenthal [1] and P. Romanowski [1].

For further extensions to functions of two or more variables, see also H. Looman [1] and M. Krzyżański [1].

CHAPTER IX.

Derivates of functions of one or two real variables.

§ 1. Some elementary theorems. The first part of this chapter (§§ 1—10) is devoted to studying the various relations between the derivates of a function of a real variable. With the help of the notion of extreme differentials introduced by Haslam-Jones, certain of these relations will subsequently be extended, in the second part of the chapter (§§ 11—14), to functions of two variables.

Accordingly, the term "function" will be restricted in the first part of this chapter to mean function of one real variable.

Before proceeding to the theorems directly connected with the Lebesgue theory, we shall establish in this § some elementary results.

We first observe that *a linear set E contains at most a finite number, or an enumerable infinity, of points which are isolated on one side at least.* To fix the ideas, let A be the set of the points of E which are isolated points of E on the right. For each integer n, let A_n denote the set of the points x of A such that the interval $[x, x+1/n]$ contains no point of E other than x. Then it is plain that, for each integer k, the interval $[k/n, (k+1)/n]$ can have at most one point in common with A_n. Hence each set A_n is at most enumerable, and the same is true of the set $A = \sum_n A_n$.

We say that a finite function F assumes at a point x_0 a *strict maximum* if there exists an open interval I containing x_0 such that $F(x) < F(x_0)$ for every point $x \in I$ other than x_0. By symmetry we define a *strict minimum*.

(1.1) ***Theorem.*** *Given a finite function of a real variable F, each of the following sets is at most enumerable:*

(i) *the set of the points at which the function F assumes a strict maximum or minimum;*

(ii) *the set of the points x at which*

$$\limsup_{t\to x} F(t) > \limsup_{t\to x+} F(t) \qquad or \qquad \liminf_{t\to x} F(t) < \liminf_{t\to x+} F(t);$$

(iii) *the set of the points x at which*

$$\overline{F}^+(x) < \underline{F}^-(x) \qquad or \qquad \overline{F}^-(x) < \underline{F}^+(x).$$

Proof. *re* (i). Consider the set A of the points at which, for instance, the function F assumes a strict maximum, and let A_n denote, for each positive integer n, the set of the points x such that $F(t) < F(x)$ holds for each point $t \neq x$ of the interval $(x-1/n,\ x+1/n)$. We see at once that each set A_n is isolated, and therefore at most enumerable. Since $A = \sum_n A_n$, it follows that the set A is at most enumerable.

re (ii). Let us consider, for definiteness, the set B of the points x at which $\limsup_{t\to x} F(t) > \limsup_{t\to x+} F(t)$. We denote, for each pair of integers p and q, by $B_{p,q}$ the set of the points x such that

$$\limsup_{t\to x} F(t) > p/q > \limsup_{t\to x+} F(t).$$

Clearly each point of a set $B_{p,q}$ is, for that set, an isolated point on the right. Each of the sets $B_{p,q}$ is thus at most enumerable, and, since $B = \sum_{p,q} B_{p,q}$, the same is true of the whole set B.

re (iii). Consider the set C of the points x at which $\overline{F}^+(x) < \underline{F}^-(x)$, and denote, for each pair of integers $q > 0$ and p, by $C_{p,q}$ the set of the points x at which $\overline{F}^+(x) < p/q < \underline{F}^-(x)$. Write $F_{p,q}(x) = F(x) - px/q$. We find $\overline{F}^+_{p,q}(x) < 0 < \underline{F}^-_{p,q}(x)$ at each point $x \in C_{p,q}$, and this shows that the function $F_{p,q}$ assumes a strict maximum at each point of $C_{p,q}$. By the result just established, each set $C_{p,q}$ is at most enumerable, and consequently, the same is true of the whole set C.

It is sometimes convenient (*vide*, below, § 5) to appeal to a slightly more general form of the last part of Theorem 1.1, which concerns relative derivates (cf. Chap. IV, p. 108) and which reads thus:

(1.2) ***Theorem.*** *If U and F are two finite functions of a real variable, the set of the points t at which the derivative $U'(t) > 0$ (finite or infinite) exists and at which $\overline{F}^+_U(t) < \underline{F}^-_U(t)$, is at most enumerable.*

This is proved in the same way as the corresponding part of Theorem 1.1. In fact, if we denote, for every pair of integers $q>0$ and p, by $C_{p,q}$ the set of the points x at which $\overline{F}_U^+(x)<p/q<\underline{F}_U^-(x)$, we see at once that the function $F(x)-(p/q)\cdot U(x)$ assumes at each point of $C_{p,q}$ a strict maximum. Therefore each set $C_{p,q}$ is at most enumerable.

For Theorem 1.1 and its various generalizations, *vide*: A. Denjoy [1, p. 147], B. Levi [1], A. Rosenthal [1], A. Schönflies [I, p. 158], W. Sierpiński [1; 2] and G. C. Young [1]. As regards the enumerability of the set of the points at which the function assumes a strict maximum or minimum, it is easily seen that this result remains valid for functions in any separable metrical space (cf. F. Hausdorff [I, p. 363]). Mention should be made also of the elegant generalizations of Theorem 1.1, obtained successively by H. Blumberg [1], M. Schmeiser [1] and V. Jarník [3].

§ 2. Contingent of a set. We have mentioned earlier (in Chapter IV, p. 133), that certain theorems on derivates of functions may be stated as propositions concerning metrical properties of sets in Euclidean spaces. In connection with these results, we shall state in this § some definitions which begin with some well-known notions of Analytical Geometry.

By the *direction* of a half-line l in a space $\boldsymbol{R}_m$ (where $m\geqslant 2$) we shall mean the system of the m direction cosines of l. The half-line issuing from a point a and having the direction θ will be denoted by $a\theta$. The half-line issuing from a point a and containing a point $b\neq a$ will be denoted by $\overrightarrow{ab}$.

If we interpret the system of the m direction cosines of a half-line as a point in $\boldsymbol{R}_m$ (situated on the surface of a unit sphere), we may regard the set of all directions in a Euclidean space as a complete, separable, metrical space (cf. Chap. II, § 2). It is then clear what is to be understood by the terms: convergence and limit of a sequence of directions, everywhere dense set of directions, etc. We shall say further that a sequence of half-lines $\{l_n\}$ issuing from the same point a *converges* to a half-line l issuing from a, if the sequence of the directions of the half-lines l_n converges to the direction of l.

Given a set E in a space $\boldsymbol{R}_m$, a half-line l issuing from a point $a\in E$ will be called an *intermediate half-tangent* of E at a, if there exists a sequence $\{a_n\}$ of points of E distinct from a, converging to a and such that the sequence of half-lines $\{\overrightarrow{aa_n}\}$ converges to l. The set of all intermediate half-tangents of a set E at a point a is termed, following

G. Bouligand [I], the *contingent* of E at a and denoted by $\text{contg}_E a$ (by the contingent of E at an isolated point of E, we shall understand the empty set). A straight line passing through a which is formed of two intermediate half-tangents of E at a is called *intermediate tangent* of E at a. Similarly a hyperplane h passing through the point a is called *intermediate tangent hyperplane* of E at a, if each half-line issuing from a and situated in h is an intermediate half-tangent of E at a. In $\boldsymbol{R}_2$ the notions of intermediate tangent hyperplane and intermediate tangent are plainly equivalent.

Given in the space $\boldsymbol{R}_m$ a hyperplane h, $a_1x_1+a_2x_2+\ldots+a_mx_m=b$, (cf. Chapter III, § 2) the two *half-spaces* (*half-planes* if $m=2$) $a_1x_1+a_2x_2+\ldots+a_mx_m\geqslant b$ and $a_1x_1+a_2x_2+\ldots+a_mx_m\leqslant b$, into which h divides $\boldsymbol{R}_m$, will be termed *sides* of the hyperplane h. In the case in which h is an intermediate tangent hyperplane of a set E at a point a and in which, further, the contingent $\text{contg}_E a$ is wholly situated on one side of h, the side opposite to the latter is called *empty side* of h and the hyperplane h is termed *extreme tangent hyperplane* of E at a. The two sides of h may, of course, both be empty at the same time, and this occurs if the contingent of E at a coincides with the set of all half-lines issuing from a which lie in the hyperplane h itself. The hyperplane h is then termed *unique tangent hyperplane*, or simply, *tangent hyperplane*, of E at a.

For simplicity of wording, we shall restrict ourselves in the sequel to the case of sets situated either in the plane $\boldsymbol{R}_2$ or in the space $\boldsymbol{R}_3$. Needless to say, the extension to any space $\boldsymbol{R}_m$ presents no essential difficulty (an elegant statement, which sums up the results of §§ 3 and 13 of this chapter and which is valid for an arbitrary space $\boldsymbol{R}_m$, will be found in the note of F. Roger [2]).

As usual, the hyperplanes in $\boldsymbol{R}_2$ and $\boldsymbol{R}_3$ are termed *straight lines* and *planes* respectively. Moreover, in the case of plane sets we shall speak of *tangent* (intermediate, extreme, unique) in place of tangent straight line (intermediate, extreme, unique).

We shall discuss the case of the plane (§ 3) and that of the space (§ 13) separately, although the proofs of the fundamental theorems 3.6 and 13.7 which correspond to these two cases, are wholly analogous. The proof of the former is, however, more elementary, whereas the latter requires some subsidiary considerations connected with the notion of total differential (cf. below § 12).

§ 3. Fundamental theorems on the contingents of plane sets. For brevity, we shall say that the contingent of a plane set E at a point a is the *whole plane*, if it includes all half-lines issuing from this point. Similarly the contingent of E at a point a will be said to be a *half-plane*, if E has at this point an extreme tangent l and if $\mathrm{contg}_E a$ consists of all the half-lines issuing from a and situated on one side of l.

We shall see in this § that, given any plane set E, at each point a of E except at most in a subset of zero length, either 1° the contingent of E is the whole plane, or 2° it is a half-plane, or finally 3° the set E has a unique tangent. This result (together with the more precise result contained in Theorem 3.6) was first stated by A. Kolmogoroff and J. Verčenko [1;2]. It was rediscovered independently, and generalized to sets situated in any space $\boldsymbol{R}_m$, by F. Roger [2]. The proofs, together with some interesting applications of the theorem of Kolmogoroff and Verčenko, will be found in the notes of U. S. Haslam-Jones [2;3]. (For the first part of Theorem 3.6 cf. also A. S. Besicovitch [4].)

A finite function of a real variable F, defined on a linear set E, is said to fulfil the *Lipschitz condition* on E, if there exists a finite number N such that $|F(x_2)-F(x_1)|\leqslant N\cdot|x_2-x_1|$ whenever x_1 and x_2 are points of E. As we verify at once, we then have $\Lambda\{\mathrm{B}(F;E)\}\leqslant (N+1)\cdot|E|$ (for the notation, cf. Chap. II, § 8, and Chap. III, § 10). Thus, *if a function F fulfils the Lipschitz condition on a set E of finite [zero] outer measure, its graph* $\mathrm{B}(F;E)$ *on E is of finite [zero] length.*

It is also easy to see that any function which fulfils the Lipschitz condition on a linear set E, can be continued outside E so as to fulfil the Lipschitz condition on the whole straight line $\boldsymbol{R}_1$ and so as to be linear on each interval contiguous to $\bar{E}$.

(3.1) ***Lemma.*** *Let R be a plane set, θ a fixed direction and P the set of the points a of R at which* $\mathrm{contg}_R\, a$ *contains no half-line of direction θ. Then* (i) *the set P is the sum of a sequence of sets of finite length, and* (ii) *at each point a of P, except at most at those of a subset of length zero, the set R has an extreme tangent such that the side of the tangent containing the half-line $a\theta$ is its empty side.*

In the particular case in which θ is the direction of the positive semi-axis of y, the set P is expressible as the sum of an enumerable infinity of sets each of which is the graph of a function on a set on which the function fulfils the Lipschitz condition.

Proof. By changing, if necessary, the coordinate system, we may suppose in both parts of the theorem that θ is the direction of the positive semi-axis of y. Let us denote, for every positive integer n, by P_n the set of the points (x, y) of P such that the inequalities $|x'-x|\leqslant 1/n$ and $|y'-y|\leqslant 1/n$ imply $y'-y\leqslant n\cdot|x'-x|$ for every point (x', y') of R. Since there is no point a of P at which the contingent of R contains the half-line with the direction of the positive semi-axis of y, it is clear that $P=\sum\limits_n P_n$. Let us now express each P_n as the sum of a sequence $\{P_{n,k}\}_{k=1,2,\ldots}$ of sets with diameters less than $1/n$. We shall then have $|y_2-y_1|\leqslant n\cdot|x_2-x_1|$ for every pair of points, (x_1, y_1) and (x_2, y_2), belonging to the same set $P_{n,k}$. Let $Q_{n,k}$ be the orthogonal projection of $P_{n,k}$ on the axis of x. We easily see that each point of $Q_{n,k}$ is the projection of a single point of $P_{n,k}$. Consequently, the set $P_{n,k}$ may be considered as the graph of a function $F_{n,k}$ on $Q_{n,k}$. Moreover we have $|F_{n,k}(x_2)-F_{n,k}(x_1)|\leqslant n\cdot|x_2-x_1|$ for each pair of points x_1 and x_2 of $Q_{n,k}$, i. e. the function $F_{n,k}$ fulfils the Lipschitz condition on $Q_{n,k}$ and therefore (cf. above p. 264) each set $P_{n,k}=\mathrm{B}(F_{n,k}; Q_{n,k})$ is of finite length. Thus, since $P=\sum\limits_{n,k} P_{n,k}$, we obtain the required expression of the set P as the sum of an at most enumerable infinity of sets of finite length, which are at the same time graphs of functions fulfilling the Lipschitz condition on sets situated on the x-axis.

It remains to examine the existence of an extreme tangent to the set R at the points of P. For this purpose, let us keep fixed for the moment a pair of positive integers n and k, and let $\widetilde{Q}_{n,k}$ be the set of the points of $Q_{n,k}$ which are points of outer density for $Q_{n,k}$ and at which the function $F_{n,k}$ is derivable with respect to the set $Q_{n,k}$. Since the set $Q_{n,k}-\widetilde{Q}_{n,k}$ is of measure zero (cf. Theorem 4.4, Chap. VII) and since the function $F_{n,k}$ fulfils the Lipschitz condition on $Q_{n,k}$, it follows that $\Lambda[\mathrm{B}(F_{n,k}; Q_{n,k}-\widetilde{Q}_{n,k})]=0$.

We need, therefore, only prove that R has an extreme tangent at each point of the set $\mathrm{B}(F_{n,k}; \widetilde{Q}_{n,k})$ and that, further, the side of this tangent which contains a half-line in the direction of the positive semi-axis of y is its empty side.

Let (ξ_0, η_0) be any point of $\mathrm{B}(F_{n,k}; \widetilde{Q}_{n,k})$, and A_0 the derivative of $F_{n,k}$ at ξ_0 with respect to the set $Q_{n,k}$. Let ε be a positive number less than 1. Since ξ_0 is a point of outer density for the set $Q_{n,k}$, we can associate with each point (ξ, η), sufficiently close to (ξ_0, η_0), a point $\xi' \epsilon Q_{n,k}$ such that

(3.2) $|\xi'-\xi_0| \leqslant |\xi-\xi_0|$ and (3.3) $|\xi'-\xi| \leqslant \varepsilon \cdot |\xi-\xi_0|$

(for otherwise, the outer lower density of $Q_{n,k}$ at ξ_0 would not exceed $1-\varepsilon$).

Remembering now that $\eta_0 = F_{n,k}(\xi_0)$, let us write for brevity

$$D_{n,k}(\xi') = F_{n,k}(\xi') - \eta_0 - A_0 \cdot (\xi' - \xi_0).$$

We shall have

(3.4) $\eta - \eta_0 - A_0 \cdot (\xi - \xi_0) = D_{n,k}(\xi') + [\eta - F_{n,k}(\xi')] + A_0 \cdot (\xi' - \xi).$

Now suppose that the point (ξ, η) belongs to R and that $|\xi-\xi_0| \leqslant 1/2n^2$ and $|\eta-\eta_0| \leqslant 1/2n^2$. By (3.3), we have $|\xi'-\xi| \leqslant 1/n$, and, by (3.2), $|F_{n,k}(\xi')-\eta_0| \leqslant n \cdot |\xi'-\xi_0| \leqslant n \cdot |\xi-\xi_0| \leqslant 1/2n$, so that $|F_{n,k}(\xi')-\eta| \leqslant 1/n$. Since the point $(\xi', F_{n,k}(\xi'))$ belongs to $P_{n,k} \subset P_n$, it follows from the definition of the set P_n that $\eta - F_{n,k}(\xi') \leqslant n \cdot |\xi - \xi'|$, and using (3.3) again, we derive from (3.4) that

(3.5)
$$\eta - \eta_0 - A_0 \cdot (\xi - \xi_0) \leqslant |D_{n,k}(\xi')| + (n + |A_0|) \cdot |\xi' - \xi| \leqslant$$
$$\leqslant |D_{n,k}(\xi')| + \varepsilon \cdot (n + |A_0|) \cdot |\xi - \xi_0|.$$

Now as ξ, and therefore ξ', tends to ξ_0, the ratio $D_{n,k}(\xi')/(\xi'-\xi_0)$ tends to zero; the same is therefore true, on account of (3.3), of the ratio $D_{n,k}(\xi')/(\xi-\xi_0)$. Consequently, since ε is an arbitrary positive number less than 1, it follows from (3.5) that the upper limit of the ratio $[\eta - \eta_0 - A_0 \cdot (\xi - \xi_0)]/|\xi - \xi_0|$, as the point $(\xi, \eta) \epsilon R$ tends to (ξ_0, η_0), is non-positive. Further, since the line $y - \eta_0 = A_0 \cdot (x - \xi_0)$ is plainly an intermediate tangent of the set $B(F_{n,k}; Q_{n,k}) \subset R$ at the point (ξ_0, η_0), we see that this line is an extreme tangent of the set R at this point and that the half-plane $y - \eta_0 \geqslant A_0 \cdot (x - \xi_0)$, which contains the half-line issuing from (ξ_0, η_0) in the direction of the positive semi-axis of y, is an empty side of this tangent.

This completes the proof.

(3.6) ***Theorem.*** *Given a plane set R, let P be a subset of R at no point of which the contingent of R is the whole plane. Then* (i) *the set P is the sum of an enumerable infinity of sets of finite length and* (ii) *at every point of P, except at those of a set of length zero, either the set R has a unique tangent or else the contingent of R is a half-plane.*

Proof. Let $\{\theta_n\}$ be an everywhere dense sequence of directions in the plane and, for each positive integer n, let P_n denote the set of the points of P at which the contingent of R does not contain the half-line of direction θ_n. We clearly have $P=\sum_n P_n$, and by the preceding lemma each set P_n, and therefore the whole set P, is the sum of a sequence of sets of finite length. Further, the same lemma shows that the set R has an extreme tangent at every point of P, except at most in a set of length zero.

Now let Q be the set of the points of P at which 1° there exists an extreme tangent which is not a unique tangent and 2° the contingent of R is not a half-plane. For each positive integer n, let Q_n denote the set of the points b of Q such that the half-line $b\theta_n$ is situated on the non-empty side of the extreme tangent of R at b, but does not belong to $\text{contg}_R\, b$. Plainly $Q=\sum_n Q_n$. Now, by the preceding lemma, for every point $b \in Q_n$, except at most those of a set of length zero, the half-line $b\theta_n$ is situated on the empty side of the extreme tangent at b. It follows that all the sets Q_n, and therefore also the whole set Q, are of length zero. Hence, at every point of P, except perhaps those of a subset of length zero, either there is a unique tangent or the contingent at this point is a half-plane.

(3.7) ***Theorem.*** *Given a plane set R, let P be a subset of R at every point of which the set R has an extreme tangent parallel to a fixed straight line D. Then the orthogonal projection of P on the line at right angles to D is of linear measure zero.*

Proof. We may clearly assume that the line D coincides with the axis of x. Let S and T denote, respectively, the sets of the points (ξ, η) of P for which the half-planes $y \geqslant \eta$ and $y \leqslant \eta$ are respectively the empty sides of the extreme tangents. Consider the former of these sets. By Lemma 3.1, the set S is the sum of a sequence of the sets $\mathrm{B}(F_n; Q_n)$, where the Q_n are sets on the x-axis and the F_n functions fulfilling the Lipschitz condition on these sets, respectively. We may suppose (cf. p. 264) that each function F_n is defined, and fulfils the Lipschitz condition, on the whole x-axis and is linear on the intervals contiguous to the set $\bar{Q}_n$.

This being so, we easily see that, for every n, the relation $\underline{F}_n^-(x) \geqslant 0 \geqslant \overline{F}_n^+(x)$ holds at each point x of Q_n which is not an isolated point on any side for Q_n, i. e. (cf. § 1, p. 260) at all the points of Q_n, except at most those of an enumerable set. Thus by Lemma 6.0, Chap. VII, we have $|F_n[Q_n]|=0$ for every positive integer n, and since the projection of S on the y-axis coincides with the sum of the sets $F_n[Q_n]$, this projection is itself of measure zero. By symmetry, the same is true of the projection of the set T on the y-axis, and this completes the proof.

As an immediate corollary, we derive from Theorem 3.6 the following proposition:

(3.8) *Given a plane set R, let P be a subset of R at each point a of which there exists a straight line through a which contains no half-line of* $\mathrm{contg}_R\, a$. *Then the set R has a unique tangent at all the points of P except at most those of a subset of length zero.*

This result can be easily extended to the space (cf. F. Roger [2]) as follows:

(3.9) *Given a set R in the space $\boldsymbol{R}_3$, let P be a subset of R at each point a of which there exists a plane through a which contains no half-line of* $\mathrm{contg}_R\, a$. *Then* (i) *the set P is the sum of an enumerable infinity of sets of finite length and* (ii) *the set R has a unique tangent at all the points of P except at most those of a subset of length zero.*

Proof. Let $\{\theta_n\}$ be an everywhere dense sequence of directions in the space $\boldsymbol{R}_3$. For each positive integer h, let $P_{n,h}$ denote the set of the points a of P such that $|\cos(\overrightarrow{ab}, \theta_n)|>1/h$ for every point b of R distant less than $1/h$ from a. We express each set $P_{n,h}$ as the sum of a sequence $\{P_{n,h,k}\}_{k=1,2,\ldots}$ of sets of diameter less than $1/h$. We then have

$$P=\sum_{n,h} P_{n,h}=\sum_{n,h,k} P_{n,h,k}. \tag{3.10}$$

Keeping, for the moment, the indices n, h, k fixed, we choose a new system of rectangular coordinates, taking for the positive semi-axis of z the half-line of direction θ_n. Let α, β and γ be, respectively, the three positive semi-axes of the new coordinate-system. For any set, or any point, Q, we denote by $Q^{(\alpha)}$, $Q^{(\beta)}$ and $Q^{(\gamma)}$ the orthogonal projections of Q on the planes $\beta\gamma$, $\gamma\alpha$ and $\alpha\beta$, normal to the axes α, β and γ respectively.

We have $|\cos(\overrightarrow{ab}, \gamma)|>1/h$ whenever $a\in P_{n,h,k}$, $b\in R$ and $0<\varrho(a,b)<1/h$. It follows at once that there is no point $P^{(\alpha)}_{n,h,k}$ at which the contingent of the plane set $R^{(\alpha)}$ contains a half-line at right-angles to the semi-axis γ. Hence, by (3.8), the set $P^{(\alpha)}_{n,h,k}$ is the sum of an at most enumerable infinity of sets of finite length, and the set $R^{(\alpha)}$ has a unique tangent at all the points of $P^{(\alpha)}_{n,h,k}$ except at most those of a set $M_{n,h,k}$ of length zero. Similarly, the set $R^{(\beta)}$ has a unique tangent at all the points of $P^{(\beta)}_{n,h,k}$ except at most those of a set $N_{n,h,k}$ of length zero. It follows that the set R has a unique tangent at each point a of $P_{n,h,k}$, except perhaps when $a^{(\alpha)}\in M_{n,h,k}$ or when $a^{(\beta)}\in N_{n,h,k}$. Now we easily see that the two ratios $\varrho(a,b)/\varrho(a^{(\alpha)},b^{(\alpha)})$ and $\varrho(a,b)/\varrho(a^{(\beta)},b^{(\beta)})$ remain bounded (by h) when a and b belong to the set $P_{n,h,k}$. It follows that the set of the exceptional points of $P_{n,h,k}$ at which the set R has no unique tangent is, with the sets $M_{n,h,k}$ and $N_{n,h,k}$, of length zero. For the same reason, since the set $P^{(\alpha)}_{n,h,k}$ is the sum of an at most enumerable infinity of sets of finite length, so is also the set $P_{n,h,k}$. This completes the proof, on account of the relation (3.10).

§ 4. Denjoy's theorems. We shall apply the results of the preceding § to establish certain important relations, valid almost everywhere, which connect the Dini derivates of any function whatsoever, and which are known by the name of *the Denjoy relations*. For simplicity of wording, we agree to call *opposite derivates* of a function F at a point x_0 the Dini derivates $\overline{F}^+(x_0)$ and $\underline{F}^-(x_0)$, or else $\underline{F}^+(x_0)$ and $\overline{F}^-(x_0)$.

We shall begin with some preliminary remarks.

Let F be a finite function defined in a neighbourhood J of a point x_0 and let B denote the graph of F on J. It is clear that if the function F is derivable at the point x_0, the set B has at $(x_0,F(x_0))$ a unique tangent not parallel to the axis of y. Similarly, if two opposite derivates of F are finite and equal at x_0, the set B has at $(x_0,F(x_0))$ an extreme tangent $y-F(x_0)=k\cdot(x-x_0)$, whose angular coefficient k is equal to the common value of these derivates. Conversely, if at the point $(x_0,F(x_0))$ the set B has the extreme tangent $y-F(x_0)=k\cdot(x-x_0)$ where $k\neq\infty$, then 1° $\overline{F}^+(x_0)=\underline{F}^-(x_0)=k$ in the case in which the half-plane $y-y_0\geqslant k\cdot(x-x_0)$ is an empty side of this tangent and $\limsup_{x\to x_0} F(x)\leqslant F(x_0)$, and 2° $\underline{F}^+(x_0)=\overline{F}^-(x_0)=k$ in the case in which the half-plane $y-y_0\leqslant k\cdot(x-x_0)$ is an empty side and $\liminf_{x\to x_0} F(x)\geqslant F(x_0)$.

In the enunciations of the theorems which follow, we shall frequently be concerned with exceptional sets E, connected with a function F and subject to the condition $\Lambda\{\mathrm{B}(F;E)\}=0$. This condition evidently implies both $|E|=0$ and $|F[E]|=0$, since the sets E and $F[E]$ are merely the orthogonal projections of the set $\mathrm{B}(F;E)$ on the x- and y-axes, respectively.

(4.1) ***Theorem.*** *If at each point of a set E one of the extreme unilateral derivates of a function F is finite, this derivate is equal to its opposite derivate at every point of E except perhaps at the points of a set E_1 of measure zero such that $\Lambda\{\mathrm{B}(F;E_1)\}=0$.*

Proof. We may clearly suppose that the same derivate, $\overline{F}^+(x)$ say, is the one which is finite throughout E. We thus have $\limsup_{x\to x_0+} F(x)\leqslant F(x_0)$ at every point $x_0\in E$ and, on account of Theorem 1.1 (ii), we may even suppose that $\limsup_{x\to x_0} F(x)\leqslant F(x_0)$ at every point x_0 of E. Now, when $x_0\in E$, the contingent of $\mathrm{B}(F;E)$ at the point $(x_0,F(x_0))$ contains no half-line situated in the half-plane $x\geqslant x_0$ and having angular coefficient exceeding $\overline{F}^+(x_0)$. Therefore, by Theorem 3.6, the set $\mathrm{B}(F;E)$ has an extreme tangent at each of its points $(x_0, F(x_0))$, except for those of a subset B_1 of length zero, and this tangent has the half-plane $y-y_0 \geqslant \overline{F}^+(x_0)\cdot(x-x_0)$ for its empty side. Hence, denoting by E_1 the orthogonal projection of B_1 on the x-axis, we see, from the remarks made at the beginning of this §, that at every point x of the set $E-E_1$ the derivates $\overline{F}^+(x)$ and $\underline{F}^-(x)$ are equal. This completes the proof since $\Lambda\{\mathrm{B}(F;E_1)\}=\Lambda(B_1)=0$.

(4.2) ***Theorem.*** *If at each point of a set E a finite function F has either two finite Dini derivates on the same side, or else a finite extreme bilateral derivate ($\overline{F}(x)$ or $\underline{F}(x)$), then the function F is almost everywhere derivable in E; moreover, denoting by E_0 the set of the points x of E at which the function F is not derivable, we have $\Lambda\{\mathrm{B}(F;E_0)\}=0$.*

Proof. It will suffice to consider separately the following two cases:

1° The function F has two Dini derivates on the same side finite at each point of E. We then have, by Theorem 4.1,

$$\overline{F}^+(x)=\underline{F}^-(x) \quad \textit{and} \quad \underline{F}^+(x)=\overline{F}^-(x) \tag{4.3}$$

at each point x of E, except perhaps those of a set E_0 such that $\Lambda\{\mathrm{B}(F;E_0)\}=0$. But the relations (4.3) imply the equality of all four Dini derivates at the point x, and since two of them are finite, by hypothesis, at each point x of E, the function F is derivable throughout $E-E_0$.

2° The function F has an extreme bilateral derivate finite at each point of E. By applying twice over Theorem 4.1, and making use of the obvious relations $\overline{F}^+(x)\geqslant\underline{F}^+(x)$ and $\overline{F}^-(x)\geqslant\underline{F}^-(x)$, we see that the four Dini derivates are finite and equal at each point of E, except perhaps at those of a set on which the graph of F is of zero length. This completes the proof.

Theorem 4.2 (in a slightly less complete form, it is true) has already been mentioned in Chap. VII, p. 236, as a corollary of Theorems 10.1 and 10.5, Chap. VII. We have also stated that (as a consequence of these same theorems) the set of the points at which a function has a unique derivative (even a unilateral derivative) infinite, is necessarily of measure zero. We can now extend this result by taking the modulus, as follows:

(4.4) ***Theorem.*** *For any finite function F, the set of the points x at which $\lim\limits_{h\to 0+}|F(x+h)-F(x)|/h=+\infty$, is of measure zero.*

Proof. Denoting the set of the points in question by A, we see at once that the graph of the function F has at every point of the set $\mathrm{B}(F;A)$, except perhaps at those of a set of length zero, an extreme tangent parallel to the y-axis. Thus, by Theorem 3.7, the set A, which is the projection of the set $\mathrm{B}(F;A)$ on the x-axis, is of measure zero and this completes the proof.

It results, in particular, from Theorems 4.1, 4.2 and 4.4 that *the Dini derivates of any finite function F satisfy one of the following four relations at almost every point x*: 1° $\overline{F}^+(x)=\overline{F}^-(x)=+\infty$, $\underline{F}^+(x)=\underline{F}^-(x)=-\infty$; 2° $\overline{F}^+(x)=\underline{F}^-(x)\neq\infty$, $\underline{F}^+(x)=-\infty$, $\overline{F}^-(x)=+\infty$, 3° $\underline{F}^+(x)=\overline{F}^-(x)\neq\infty$; $\overline{F}^+(x)=+\infty$, $\underline{F}^-(x)=-\infty$; 4° $\overline{F}^+(x)=\underline{F}^+(x)=\overline{F}^-(x)=\underline{F}^-(x)\neq\infty$. For direct proofs of this theorem, which was established first by Denjoy for continuous functions and then generalized to arbitrary functions, *vide*: A. Denjoy [1], G. C. Young [2], F. Riesz [7], J. Ridder [4], J. C. Burkill and U. S. Haslam-Jones [1], and H. Blumberg [2] (cf. also A. N. Singh [1]). A further discussion of the Denjoy relations will be found in the notes of V. Jarník [1] (for functions of one variable) and of A. S. Besicovitch [6] and A. J. Ward [4] (for functions of two variables). For Theorem 4.4 see S. Saks and A. Zygmund [1] (cf. also S. Banach [1]).

A part of the Denjoy relations has recently been generalized to differential coefficients of higher orders; see the important memoirs of A. Denjoy [9], J. Marcinkiewicz and A. Zygmund [1], and J. Marcinkiewicz [2].

We may now supplement Lemma 6.3, Chap. VII, by the following result:

(4.5) ***Theorem.*** *Let M be a finite number and F a finite function such that $|\overline{F}^+(x)|\leqslant M$ at every point x of a set E. Then $|F[E]|\leqslant M\cdot|E|$.*

Proof. Let E_1 denote the set of the points x of E at which $\underline{F}^-(x)\neq\overline{F}^+(x)$. By Theorem 4.1, we have $\Lambda\{\mathrm{B}(F;E_1)\}=0$ and therefore, $|F[E_1]|=0$. On the other hand, since $|\underline{F}^-(x)|=|\overline{F}^+(x)|\leqslant M$ at each point $x\in E-E_1$, it follows from Lemma 6.3, Chap. VII, that $|F[E-E_1]|\leqslant M\cdot|E|$, and this completes the proof.

An immediate consequence is the following criterion for a function to fulfil Lusin's condition (N) (Chap. VII, § 6):

(4.6) ***Theorem.*** *If a finite function F has at each point x of a set E a finite Dini derivate, the function necessarily fulfils the condition (N) on E.*

Proof. It is enough to show that if at each point x of a set H of measure zero the function F has one of its Dini derivates, $\overline{F}^+$ say, finite, then $|F[H]|=0$. For this purpose, let H_n be the set of the points $x\in H$ at which $|\overline{F}^+(x)|\leqslant n$. We have, by Theorem 4.5, $|F[H_n]|\leqslant n\cdot|H_n|=0$ for each positive integer n, and hence $|F[H]|=0$.

It is easy to see that the hypotheses of Theorem 4.5 imply that $\Lambda\{B(F;E)\} \leqslant (M+1)\cdot|E|$. This remark enables us to complete Theorem 6.5 of Chap. VII, as follows: *If the derivate $\overline{F}^+$ of a finite function F is finite at every point of a measurable set E, except at those of an enumerable subset, then the function F, together with its derivate $\overline{F}^+$, is measurable on E and we have*

$$|F[E]| \leqslant \int_E |\overline{F}^+(x)|\,dx \quad \textit{and} \quad \Lambda\{B(F;E)\} = \int_E \{1+[\overline{F}^+(x)]^2\}^{1/2}\,dx.$$

We may note also the following consequence of Theorem 4.5: *If one of the four Dini derivates of a function F vanishes at every point of a set E, then $|F[E]|=0$.*

For functions $F(x)$ which are continuous, or more generally *continuous in the Darboux sense* (i.e. assume in each interval $[a, b]$ all the values between $F(a)$ and $F(b)$), we deduce at once the following result:

(4.7) ***Theorem.*** *If F is a finite function, continuous in the Darboux sense on an interval I, and if at each point of this interval, except those of an enumerable set, one at least of the four Dini derivates is equal to zero, then the function F is constant on I.*

* § 5. Relative derivates.

The Denjoy relations can be extended in various ways to relative derivates of a function with respect to another function. Let us remark that, in accordance with the definition given in Chap. IV, p. 108, the extreme derivates of any function with respect to a finite function U are determined at each point which belongs to no interval of constancy of the function U; consequently, the set of values taken by the function U at the points at which the extreme derivates with respect to U remain indeterminate is at most enumerable.

In the sequel it will be useful to employ the notation adopted in Chap. IV, § 8. Let us recall in particular, that if C is a curve given by the equations $x=X(t)$, $y=Y(t)$, its graph on a linear set E (i.e. the set of the points $(X(t), Y(t))$ for $t \in E$) is denoted by $B(C;E)$.

(5.1) ***Lemma.*** *If C is a curve given by the equations $x=U(t)$, $y=F(t)$, the set E of the points t at which $\overline{F}_U(t) < +\infty$, may be expressed as the sum of a sequence of sets $\{E_n\}$ such that*

(∇) *for every n and for every open interval I of length less than $1/n$, the set $B(C;I)$ has a unique tangent at every point of $B(C;I\cdot E_n)$ except those of a set of length zero.*

Proof. Let us denote, for each positive integer n, by E_n the set of the points t such that, provided that the differences $F(t')-F(t)$ and $U(t')-U(t)$ do not vanish simultaneously, the inequality $|t'-t| \leqslant 1/n$ implies $[F(t')-F(t)]/[U(t')-U(t)] \leqslant n$. We see at once that, for any open interval I of length less than $1/n$, the contingent of $B(C;I)$ at a point of $B(C;I\cdot E_n)$ cannot contain half-lines of angular coefficient greater than n, and can be, therefore, neither a whole plane, nor a half-plane (cf. § 3, p. 264). The property (∇) of the sequence $\{E_n\}$ thus appears as a direct consequence of Theorem 3.6.

(5.2) ***Theorem.*** *If U and F are continuous functions and we have $\overline{F}_U(t) < +\infty$ at every point t of a set E, then there is a finite derivative $F'_U(t)$ at each point t of E, except at the points of a set H such that $|U[H]| = 0$.*

Proof. Let C denote the curve given by the equations $x = U(t)$, $y = F(t)$. On account of Lemma 5.1, the set E is expressible as the sum of a sequence of sets $\{E_n\}$ which fulfil the condition (∇) of this lemma. Keeping fixed, for the moment, a positive integer n, let us consider an open interval I of length less than $1/n$. Let $B_n(I)$ denote the set of the points of $B(C;I\cdot E_n)$ at which the graph of the curve C on I either has no unique tangent, or else has a unique tangent parallel to the y-axis. Further, let $\widetilde{B}_n(I)$ be the projection of the set $B_n(I)$ on the x-axis. On account of the condition (∇) and Theorem 3.7, we have $|\widetilde{B}_n(I)| = 0$ Now since U and F are continuous, it is clear that the derivative $F_U(t)$ exists and is finite at each point $t \in I\cdot E_n$, provided that $U(t)$ does not belong to the set $\widetilde{B}_n(I)$. Hence, I being any open interval of length less than $1/n$, this derivative exists and is finite at each point $t \in E_n$, except at most at the points of a set H_n such that $|U[H_n]| = 0$. This completes the proof, since $E = \sum_n E_n$.

(5.3) ***Theorem.*** *If U is a continuous function and F any finite function for which $\overline{F}_U(t) = 0$ at each point t of a set E, then $|F[E]| = 0$.*

Proof. Let C denote, as in the proof of the preceding theorem, the curve $x = U(t)$, $y = F(t)$, and let E be expressed as the sum of a sequence of sets $\{E_n\}$ subject to the condition (∇) of Lemma 5.1. Keeping fixed, for a moment, a positive integer n, let us consider any open interval I of length less than $1/n$. At each point of $B(C;I\cdot E_n)$, except those of a set of length zero, the set $B(C;I)$ then has a unique tangent, and since the function U is continuous and $\overline{F}_U(t) = 0$ at each point $t \in E$, this tangent is parallel to the x-axis. It follows, by Theorem 3.7, that the set $F[I\cdot E_n]$, which coincides with the projection of the set $B(C;I\cdot E_n)$ on the y-axis, is of measure zero. Since I is any interval of length less than $1/n$, it follows that $|F[E_n]| = 0$ for each positive integer n, and finally that $|F[E]| = 0$.

The hypothesis of continuity of the function U is essential for the validity of Theorems 5.2 and 5.3 (the hypothesis of continuity of the function F, which is not required in Theorem 5.3, may, however, be removed also from Theorem 5.2). Let $F(t)=-t$ identically, and let $U(t)=t$ for irrational values and $U(t)=t+1$ for rational values of t. Denoting by E the set of irrational points of the interval $(0,1)$, we shall have at each point t of this set

$$\overline{F}_U(t)=\overline{F}_U^+(t)=\overline{F}_U^-(t)=0 \qquad \text{and} \qquad \underline{F}_U(t)=\underline{F}_U^+(t)=\underline{F}_U^-(t)=-1.$$

Nevertheless $|U[E]|=|F[E]|=1$. On the other hand, the hypothesis of continuity of the function U may be removed from Theorem 5.3, if we replace the condition $\overline{F}_U(t)=0$ by the more restrictive condition $F'_U(t)=0$. To see this, we shall first establish an elementary lemma.

(5.4) ***Lemma.*** *If U is a finite function on a set E, there exists a set $T\subset E$ such that the set $U[T]$ is at most enumerable and such that each point $\tau\,\epsilon\,E-T$ is the limit of a sequence of points $\{t_i\}$ of E which fulfils the conditions* (i) $t_i>\tau$ *and* $U(t_i)\neq U(\tau)$ *for each* $i=1,2,\dots$ *and* (ii) $\lim_i U(t_i)=U(\tau)$.

Proof. Let T be the set of the points $\tau\,\epsilon\,E$ none of which is the limit of a sequence $\{t_i\}$ of points of E subject to the conditions (i) and (ii) of the lemma. Let us denote, for each positive integer k, by T_k the set of the points τ of T for which there is no point $t\,\epsilon\,E$ such that both $0<t-\tau<1/k$ and $0<|U(t)-U(\tau)|<1/k$. We have $T=\sum_k T_k$. Plainly the function U cannot, on any portion of T_k of diameter less than $1/k$, assume two distinct values differing by less than $1/k$. It follows that each set $U[T_k]$ is at most enumerable, and the same is therefore true of the whole set $U[T]$.

(5.5) ***Theorem.*** *If U and F are any finite functions and $F'_U(t)=0$ or, more generally $\overline{F}_U^+(t)=\underline{F}_U^+(t)=0$, at each point t of a set E, then* $|F[E]|=0$.

Proof. Let C be the curve $x=U(t)$, $y=F(t)$, and let E_n denote, for each positive integer n, the set of the points t of E such that the inequality $0\leqslant t'-t\leqslant 1/n$ implies $|F(t')-F(t)|\leqslant|U(t')-U(t)|$ whatever be the point t'. We can express each set E_n as the sum of a sequence $\{E_{n,k}\}_{k=1,2,\dots}$ of sets of diameter less than $1/n$.

Let us keep n and k fixed for the moment. It is clear that the contingent of the set $\mathrm{B}(C;E_{n,k})$ cannot, at any point of this set, contain a half-line whose angular coefficient exceeds the number 1. Consequently, denoting by $B_{n,k}$ the set of the points of $\mathrm{B}(C;E_{n,k})$ at which the set $\mathrm{B}(C;E_{n,k})$ has no unique tangent, we see from Theorem 3.6 that $\Lambda(B_{n,k})=0$.

Now the set $E_{n,k}$ contains, by Lemma 5.4, a subset $T_{n,k}$ such that $U[T_{n,k}]$ is at most enumerable and that each point $\tau \epsilon E_{n,k}-T_{n,k}$ is the limit of a sequence $\{t_i\}$ of points of $E_{n,k}$ which fulfils the conditions (i) and (ii) of this lemma. Hence, the relations $\overline{F}_U^+(t)=\underline{F}_U^+(t)=0$ being satisfied, by hypothesis, at each point $t \epsilon E_{n,k}$, the set $\mathrm{B}(C;E_{n,k})$ has a unique tangent parallel to the x-axis at each point of the set $\mathrm{B}(C;E_{n,k}-T_{n,k})-B_{n,k}$. Since $\Lambda(B_{n,k})=0$, it thus follows from Theorem 3.7 that the set $F[E_{n,k}-T_{n,k}]$, which coincides with the projection of the set $\mathrm{B}(C;E_{n,k}-T_{n,k})$ on the y-axis, is of measure zero. The same is therefore true of the set $F[E_{n,k}]$, for the set $F[T_{n,k}]$ is, with $U[T_{n,k}]$, at most enumerable. It follows at once that $|F[E]|=0$, since $E=\sum_{n,k} E_{n,k}$.

We may mention an application of Theorems 5.3 and 5.5, which is connected with the following theorem of H. Lebesgue [II, p. 299]: *If the derivative of a continuous function F, with respect to a function U of bounded variation, is identically zero, then the function F is a constant.* J. Petrovski [1] and R. Caccioppoli [1] extended this theorem, in the case when the function U is continuous, by removing the hypothesis of bounded variation for U. At the same time, Petrovski remarked that it was sufficient for the validity of the theorem to suppose that the relation $F'_U(t)=0$ holds everywhere except in an enumerable set.

It is easy to see that this result is contained in each of the separate theorems 5.3 and 5.5. These theorems actually enable us to state the result of Petrovski and Caccioppoli in two slightly more general forms. Thus:

1° *Suppose that U and F are continuous functions and that at each point t, except at most those of an enumerable set, one at least of the four relations $\overline{F}_U(t)=0$, $\underline{F}_U(t)=0$, $\overline{F}_U^+(t)=\underline{F}_U^+(t)=0$ or $\overline{F}_U^-(t)=\underline{F}_U^-(t)=0$ is fulfilled. Then the function F is a constant.*

2° *Suppose that U is any finite function and F a continuous function, and let one of the relations $\overline{F}_U^+(t)=\underline{F}_U^+(t)=0$ or $\overline{F}_U^-(t)=\underline{F}_U^-(t)=0$ hold at each point t except at most those of an enumerable set. Then the function F is a constant.*

We observe further that, in both the statements 1° and 2°, we may replace the hypothesis of continuity of F by the hypothesis that F is continuous in the Darboux sense (cf. § 4, p. 272); moreover the condition that the exceptional set be at most enumerable may be replaced by the condition that the set of values assumed by the function F at the points of this set be of measure zero.

The Denjoy relations have a more complete extension to relative derivates when the function U of Theorem 5.2 is subjected to certain restrictions. Thus:

(5.6) ***Theorem.*** *Let U and F be finite functions, and suppose that, at each point t of a set E, the derivative $U'(t)$ (finite or infinite) exists and that $\overline{F}_U^+(t)<+\infty$. Then $\underline{F}_U^-(t)=\overline{F}_U^+(t)\neq\infty$ at each point t of E except at most the points of a set H such that $|U[H]|=0$.*

Proof. We may clearly restrict ourselves to the case in which the derivative $U'(t)$ is non-negative throughout E, and even, by Theorem 4.5, to the case in which (1°) $U'(\tau)>0$ at each point τ of E. We then have $\limsup_{t\to\tau-} U(t)\leqslant U(\tau)\leqslant\liminf_{t\to\tau+} U(t)$ at each point $\tau\epsilon E$, and consequently, on account of Theorem 1.1 (ii), we may suppose that (2°) the function U is continuous at each point of E. This implies that we then have also $\limsup_{t\to\tau+} F(t)\leqslant F(\tau)$ at each point τ of E, and hence, appealing again to Theorem 1.1 (ii), we may suppose further that (3°) $\limsup_{t\to\tau} F(t)\leqslant F(\tau)$ at each point $\tau\epsilon E$. Finally by Theorem 1.2, we may suppose (4°) $\underline{F}_U^-(\tau)\leqslant\overline{F}_U^+(\tau)$ at each point $\tau\epsilon E$.

Let now C be the curve defined by the equations $x=U(t)$, $y=F(t)$. We denote, for each positive integer n, by E_n the set of the points $t\epsilon E$ such that, for every point t', (i) the inequality $0<t'-t<1/n$ implies the two inequalities $U(t')>U(t)$ and $F(t')-F(t)<n\cdot[U(t')-U(t)]$, and (ii) the inequality $0<t-t'<1/n$ implies $U(t)>U(t')$.

Since, by hypothesis, $\overline{F}_U^+(t)<+\infty$ and since, by (1°), $U'(t)>0$ at each point t of E, we see that $E=\sum_n E_n$.

Keeping a positive integer n fixed for the moment, let I be any open interval of length less than $1/n$. Whenever (ξ,η) is a point of $\mathrm{B}(C;I\cdot E_n)$, the contingent of the set $\mathrm{B}(C;I)$ at (ξ,η) clearly contains no half-line which is situated in the half-plane $x\geqslant\xi$ and which has an angular coefficient exceeding n. Let $D(I)$ denote the set of the points of the set $\mathrm{B}(C;I)$ at which this set has an extreme tangent, non-parallel to the y-axis, with an empty side containing the half-line in the direction of the positive semi-axis of y. Further, let $B_n(I)$ be the set of the points of $\mathrm{B}(C;I\cdot E_n)$ which do not belong to $D(I)$, and let $\widetilde{B}_n(I)$ be the projection of $B_n(I)$ on the x-axis. By Theorems 3.6 and 3.7, the set $\widetilde{B}_n(I)$ is of measure zero.

This being so, let t_0 be any point of the set $I\cdot E_n$ such that $U(t_0)$ does not belong to the set $\widetilde{B}_n(I)$. Let us denote by k_0 the angular coefficient of the extreme tangent to the set $\mathrm{B}(C;I)$ at the point $(U(t_0),F(t_0))$. It follows easily from the hypotheses (1°), (2°) and (3°) that $\underline{F}_U^-(t_0)\geqslant k_0\geqslant\overline{F}_U^+(t_0)$, and this, in view of (4°), leads to the relation $\underline{F}_U^-(t_0)=\overline{F}_U^+(t_0)\neq\infty$.

Thus, since I is any open interval of length less than $1/n$, we find that the last relation holds at each point t_0 of E_n other than those belonging to a set H_n such that $|U[H_n]|=0$. This completes the proof, since we have seen that $E=\sum_n E_n$.

In view of Theorem 7.2, Chap. VII, we derive from Theorem 5.6 the following theorem which has been established in a different way by A. J. Ward [3]:

(5.7) *Suppose that the function U is* VBG$_*$ *and let F be any finite function. Let E be a set at each point t of which we have either $\overline{F}_U^+(t)<+\infty$ or $\underline{F}_U^-(t)>-\infty$. Then the derivates $\underline{F}_U^-$ and $\overline{F}_U^+$ are finite and equal at all points of E except at most those of a set H such that $|U[H]|=0$.*

It will result from the considerations of § 6 (see, in particular, Theorem 6.2) that Theorem 5.7 remains valid for all continuous functions U which fulfil the condition (T_1). Nevertheless, its conclusion ceases to hold if we allow U to be any function which is VBG or even ACG. To see this, let G be a non-negative continuous function which is ACG on the interval [0, 1] and for which $G(t)=0$ and $\underline{G}^-(t)<-1$ at any point t of a perfect set E of positive measure (for the construction of such a function cf. Chap. VII, § 5, p. 224). Let us choose $U(t)=t+G(t)$ and $F(t)=t$. We shall then have at every point t of E, $U(t)=t$, $\underline{U}^+(t)\geqslant 1$ and $\underline{U}^-(t)<0<\overline{U}^-(t)$, so that $0\leqslant\underline{F}_U^+(t)\leqslant\overline{F}_U^+(t)\leqslant 1$, while $\underline{F}_U^-(t)=-\infty$ and $\overline{F}_U^-(t)=+\infty$. Nevertheless $|U[E]|=|E|>0$. (This example is due to Ward.)

* **§ 6. The Banach conditions (T_1) and (T_2).** A finite function of a real variable F is said to fulfil the *condition* (T_1) on an interval I if almost every one of its values is assumed at most a finite number of times on I. A finite function F is said to fulfil the *condition* (T_2) on an interval I if almost every one of its values is assumed at most an enumerable infinity of times on I.

These two conditions were formulated by S. Banach [6]. We shall begin by studying the condition (T_1) and we shall establish a differential property which is equivalent to this condition in the case when F is continuous (*vide* below Theorem 6.2). Another equivalent condition, due to Nina Bary, will be established in § 8 (Theorem 8.3).

(6.1) ***Lemma.*** *Suppose that F is a continuous function and that E is a set at no point of which the function F has a derivative (finite or infinite). Suppose further that each point x of E is an isolated point of the set $\underset{t}{\mathrm{E}}[F(t)=F(x)]$. Then $\Lambda\{\mathrm{B}(F;E)\}=0$, and consequently $|E|=|F[E]|=0$.*

Proof. For each $x \in E$ there exists a neighbourhood I such that, when $t \in I$, the difference $F(t)-F(x)$ remains of constant sign as long as t remains on the same side of x; this difference then changes sign as t passes from one side of x to the other, except in the case in which the function F assumes a strict maximum or minimum at x. Therefore, if we denote by E_0 the set of the points at which the function assumes a strict maximum or minimum, we see at once that the four Dini derivates of F have the same sign at any point x of $E-E_0$. In other words, since, by hypothesis, the function F has no finite or infinite derivative at any point of E, we shall have at each point x of $E-E_0$ either $+\infty>\underline{F}(x)\geqslant 0$ or else $-\infty<\overline{F}(x)\leqslant 0$. Hence, by Theorem 4.2, $A\{B(F;E-E_0)\}=0$, and, since the set E_0 is at most enumerable (cf. Theorem 1.1), it follows that $A\{B(F;E)\}=0$.

(6.2) **Theorem.** *In order that a function F which is continuous on an interval I, fulfil the condition* (T_1) *on this interval, it is necessary and sufficient that the set of the values assumed by F at the points at which the function has no derivative (finite or infinite) be of measure zero.*

Proof. Denoting by Y the set of the values assumed an infinity of times by the function F on I, and denoting by E the set of the points of I at which F has no derivative, we have to prove that the relations $|Y|=0$ and $|F[E]|=0$ are equivalent.

1° $|Y|=0$ implies $|F[E]|=0$. Let X be the set of the points $x \in I$ such that $F(x) \in Y$. Then $F[X]=Y$, whence $|F[X]|=0$.

On the other hand, for each $x_0 \in E-X$, the set of the points x such that $F(x)=F(x_0)$, is finite, and consequently an isolated set. It follows from Lemma 6.1 that $|F[E-X]|=0$, and hence finally that $|F[E]|\leqslant|F[X]|+|F[E-X]|=0$.

2° $|F[E]|=0$ implies $|Y|=0$. Let H denote the set of the points x at which $F'(x)=0$. By Theorem 4.5, we have $|F[H]|=0$.

Now let y_0 be any point of $Y-F[E]$, and let E_0 denote the set of the points x at which $F(x)=y_0$. The set E_0 being infinite and closed, let x_0 be a point of accumulation of E_0. Since the function F has a derivative at each point of E_0, we find that $F'(x_0)=0$; thus $x_0 \in H$ and therefore $y_0 \in F[H]$. It follows that $Y-F[E]\subset F[H]$, and hence that $|Y-F[E]|=0$. Thus $|F[E]|=0$ implies $|Y|=0$ and the proof is complete.

(6.3) ***Theorem.*** *1° A continuous function which is* VBG_* *(in particular, one of bounded variation) on an interval I, necessarily fulfils the condition* (T_1) *on I.*

2° A continuous function which is VBG *on an interval I necessarily fulfils the condition* (T_2) *on I.*

Proof. On account of Theorem 7.2, Chap. VII, the first part of the theorem is an immediate corollary of Theorem 6.2. To establish 2°, let us suppose that F is continuous and VBG on an interval I. The interval I is then expressible as the sum of a sequence $\{E_n\}$ of closed sets on each of which the function F is VB. We may clearly suppose that each E_n contains the end-points of the interval I. Let us denote, for each positive integer n, by F_n, the function which is equal to F on E_n and which is linear on the intervals contiguous to E_n. The functions F_n are plainly of bounded variation on I, and therefore, by 1°, they fulfil the condition (T_1). It follows at once that the function F fulfils the condition (T_2) on I.

In the part of Theorem 6.3 (1°) that applies to functions which are VBG_*, the continuity hypothesis for the function F is not a superfluous one (thus, the function $F(x)=\sin(1/x)$ for $x\neq 0$ and $F(0)=0$ is VBG_* and does not fulfil the condition (T_1) on $[0, 1]$). This hypothesis may however be replaced by a weaker one, which consists in supposing that the function F has no points of discontinuity other than of the first kind (i. e. that, at each point x, both the unilateral limits $F(x+)$ and $F(x-)$ exist). In particular, functions of bounded variation, whether continuous or not, all fulfil the condition (T_1) (and from this it follows easily that the continuity hypothesis may be removed altogether from the second part (2°) of the theorem).

For functions of bounded variation, the condition (T_1) may also be deduced from the following general property of plane sets, established by W. Gross [1] (cf. J. Gillis [1]): *If E is a plane set and E_n denotes the set of the values of η such that the line $y=\eta$ contains at least n distinct points of the set E, then* $\Lambda(E)\geqslant n\cdot|E_n|$.

In connection with part 2° of Theorem 6.3, it may be noted further that functions which are VBG, or even ACG, need not fulfil the condition (T_1). An example is furnished by the function U considered in § 5, p. 277. The latter is also, as will follow from results to be established in § 7 (cf. in particular, Theorem 7.4), an example of a continuous function which is ACG, and consequently fulfils the condition (N), without fulfilling the condition (S) of Banach.

For continuous functions of bounded variation, the condition (T_1) is also a consequence of the following theorem of S. Banach [5] (cf. also N. Bary [3, p. 631]), which contains at the same time an important criterion for a continuous function to be of bounded variation:

(6.4) ***Theorem.*** *Let F be a continuous function on an interval $I_0=[a,b]$ and let $s(y)$ denote for each y the number (finite or infinite) of the points of I_0 at which F assumes the value y. Then the function $s(y)$ is measurable ($\mathfrak{B}$) and we have*

$$\int_{-\infty}^{+\infty} s(y)\,dy = \mathrm{W}(F;I_0). \tag{6.5}$$

Proof. For each positive integer n, let us put $I_1^{(n)}=[a,a+(b-a)/2^n]$ and $I_k^{(n)}=(a+(k-1)(b-a)/2^n, a+k(b-a)/2^n]$, when $k=2,3,...,2^n$. This defines a subdivision $\mathfrak{J}^{(n)}$ of the interval I_0 into 2^n subintervals, of which the first is closed and the others are half-open on the left. For $k=1,2,...,2^n$, let $s_k^{(n)}$ denote the characteristic function of the set $F[I_k^{(n)}]$, and let $s^{(n)}(y)=\sum_{k=1}^{2^n} s_k^{(n)}(y)$.

We see at once that the functions $s^{(n)}(y)$ constitute a non-decreasing sequence which converges at each point y to $s(y)$. Hence, the functions $s^{(n)}(y)$ being clearly measurable ($\mathfrak{B}$), so is also the function $s(y)$.

On the other hand, $\int_{-\infty}^{+\infty} s_k^{(n)}(y)dy=|F[I_k^{(n)}]|=\mathrm{O}(F;I_k^{(n)})$. Therefore, denoting by $W^{(n)}$ the sum of the oscillations of the function F on the intervals of the subdivision $\mathfrak{J}^{(n)}$, we obtain $\int_{-\infty}^{+\infty} s^{(n)}(y)=W^{(n)}$, and the relation (6.5) follows by making $n\to\infty$.

(6.6) ***Theorem.*** *If $F(x)$ is a continuous function which fulfils the condition (T_2) on an interval I_0, the set D of the points at which the derivative $F'(x)$ (finite or infinite) exists, is non-enumerably infinite.*

Moreover, if we write

$$P=\underset{x}{\mathrm{E}}[x\in D; F'(x)\geqslant 0] \quad \textit{and} \quad N=\underset{x}{\mathrm{E}}[x\in D; F'(x)\leqslant 0],$$

then, for each interval $I=[a,b]\subset I_0$, we have

$$-|F[N]|\leqslant F(b)-F(a)\leqslant |F[P]|. \tag{6.7}$$

Proof. We may, plainly, suppose that

$$F(a)\leqslant F(b), \tag{6.8}$$

since the other case may be discussed by changing the sign of the function F.

Let Y be the set of those values of F on I which are assumed by the function F at most an enumerable number of times on I. Denoting, for each y, by E_y the set of the points $x\in I$ such that

$F(x)=y$, we shall show that with each point $y \in Y$ we can associate a point $x_y \in E_y$, in such a manner that (i) $\bar{F}(x_y) \geqslant 0$ and (ii) x_y is an isolated point of the set E_y.

For this purpose, we remark first that if the set E_y reduces to a single point, the latter may be chosen for our x_y. For, in that case, the condition (ii) is clearly fulfilled, while the condition (i) holds on account of the hypothesis (6.8).

Let us therefore consider the other case, in which the set E_y contains more than one point. Then, since the function F is continuous by hypothesis and $y \in Y$, the set E_y is closed, and at most enumerable. This set, therefore, contains a pair of isolated points α, β between which it has no further points. (This is obvious, if the set E_y is finite. If E_y is infinite, its derived set (cf. Chap. II, p. 40) is itself closed, non-empty, and at most enumerable; the latter, therefore, contains an isolated point x_0. Thus near x_0 there are only isolated points of E_y. It will, therefore, suffice to choose, among the latter, any two consecutive points as our points α and β.) Consequently, at one at least of the points α and β, the upper derivate of $F(x)$ is non-negative. We choose this point as our x_y. We then see at once that the conditions (i) and (ii) are fulfilled.

This being established, let X denote the set of all the points x_y which are thus associated with the points $y \in Y$. It follows from the conditions (i) and (ii) and from Lemma 6.1, that $|F[X-P]|=|F[X-D]|=0$, and so, by definition of the set X, that $|Y|=|F[X]|=|F[X \cdot P]| \leqslant |F[P]|$. Since the condition ($T_2$) implies that $|F[I]|=|Y|$, we obtain, in view of (6.8), the inequality $-|F[N]| \leqslant 0 \leqslant F(b)-F(a) \leqslant |F[I]| \leqslant |F[P]|$, i.e. the inequality (6.7).

Finally, since this relation holds for every subinterval $[a,b]$ of I_0, we see that, unless the function F is a constant, one at least of the sets $F[N]$ and $F[P]$ is of positive measure. The set $D=N+P$ is thus non-enumerably infinite, and this completes the proof.

(6.9) ***Theorem.*** *Let F be a continuous function which fulfils the condition (T_2) and let g be a finite summable function. Suppose further that $F'(x) \leqslant g(x)$ at each point x at which the derivative $F'(x)$ exists, except perhaps those of an enumerable set or, more generally, those of a set E such that $|F[E]|=0$. Then the function F is of bounded variation and, for each interval $[a,b]$, we have*

$$F(b)-F(a) \leqslant \int_a^b F'(x)\,dx. \tag{6.10}$$

Proof. Let P be the set of the points x of $[a,b]$ at which the derivative $F'(x)$ exists and is non-negative. Then, since at each point $x \in P-E$ we have $0 \leqslant F'(x) \leqslant g(x) < +\infty$, it follows from Theorem 6.5, Chap. VII, that $|F[P-E]| \leqslant \int_P F'(x)\,dx \leqslant \int_a^b |g(x)|\,dx$. On the other hand, by hypothesis, $|F[E]|=0$. Hence, on account of Theorem 6.6, $F(b)-F(a) \leqslant \int_a^b |g(x)|\,dx$ for each interval $[a,b]$, and, in consequence, F is a function of bounded variation whose function of singularities is monotone non-increasing. The inequality (6.10) follows at once.

In view of Theorem 6.3 (2^0), we may apply Theorem 6.9, in particular, to continuous functions F which are VBG. We also observe that Theorem 6.9, when F is of bounded variation, may be deduced from de la Vallée Poussin's Decomposition Theorem (Chap. IV, § 9).

Theorem 6.9 may be generalized further, by replacing the condition that the function g is summable, by the condition that the latter is $\mathfrak{D}_*$-integrable (the function F then shows itself to be VBG$_*$). We thus obtain a proposition similar to Theorem 7.3, Chap. VI. The proof of Theorem 6.9 in this generalized form is, however, more complicated.

***§ 7. Three theorems of Banach.** We have repeatedly emphasized the importance of Lusin's condition (N) in the theory of the Denjoy integrals. We shall show in this §, that every continuous function which fulfils the condition (N), also fulfils the condition (T_2). This result due to S. Banach [6] (cf. also N. Bary [3, p. 195]) renders Theorems 6.6 and 6.9 applicable to functions which fulfil the condition (N).

We shall also study another condition, introduced by S. Banach [6] and termed condition (S). We say that a finite function F fulfils the *condition* (S) on an interval I_0, if to each number $\varepsilon>0$ there corresponds an $\eta>0$ such that, for each measurable set $E \subset I_0$, the inequality $|E|<\eta$ implies $|F[E]|<\varepsilon$. (This condition is essentially more restrictive than the condition (N); cf. the remarks, p. 279, also G. Fichtenholz [4].)

(7.1) ***Lemma.*** *Given a function F which is continuous on an interval I, every closed set $E \subset I$ contains a measurable set A on which the function F assumes each value $y \in F[E]$ exactly once.*

Proof. With each $y \in F[E]$ we associate the lower bound x_y of the set of the points x of E at which $F(x)=y$, and we denote by A the set of all the points x_y which correspond in this way to the values $y \in F[E]$. Since the set E is closed, we plainly have $A \subset E$ and F assumes on A each of the values $y \in F[E]$ exactly once.

In order to establish the measurability of A, let us denote, for each positive integer n, by E_n, the set of the points $x \in E$ such that E contains at least one point t which is subject to the conditions $F(t)=F(x)$ and $x-t \geqslant 1/n$. We have $A=E-\sum_n E_n$, where E is closed by hypothesis, and where each E_n is closed by continuity of F. The set A is thus measurable and this completes the proof.

(7.2) ***Lemma.*** *Let F be a continuous function which fulfils the condition* (N) *on an interval I. Then*

(i) *every measurable set $E \subset I$ contains, for each $\varepsilon > 0$, a measurable subset Q, such that $|F[E]-F[Q]| < \varepsilon$, and on which the function F assumes each of its values at most once;*

(ii) *every measurable set $E \subset I$ contains a measurable subset R, such that $|F[E]-F[R]|=0$, and on which the function F assumes each of its values at most an enumerable infinity of times.*

Proof. *re* (i). As a measurable set, E is the sum of a set H of measure zero and an ascending sequence of closed sets $\{E_n\}$. Since the function F fulfils the condition (N), we have $|F[H]|=0$, and hence, the sets $F[E_n]$ being measurable, there exists a positive integer n_0 such that $|F[E]-F[E_{n_0}]| < \varepsilon$. Now, by Lemma 7.1, there exists a closed set $Q \subset E_{n_0}$ such that each value $y \in F[E_{n_0}]$ is assumed exactly once by F on Q. This set Q plainly fulfils the conditions stated.

re (ii). In view of (i), there exists for each positive integer n a measurable set $Q_n \subset E$, such that $|F[E]-F[Q_n]| < 1/n$, and on which the function F assumes each of its values at most once. Therefore, writing $R=\sum_n Q_n$, we see immediately that $|F[E]-F[R]|=0$ and that on R the function F assumes each of its values at most an enumerable infinity of times. This completes the proof.

We shall establish in this § three theorems due to Banach on functions which fulfil the conditions (N) or (S). The first of these theorems, which concerns functions fulfilling the condition (N), is as follows:

(7.3) ***Theorem.*** *Any continuous function F which fulfils the condition* (N) *on an interval I, necessarily fulfils also the condition* (T_2) *on I.*

Proof. Let us denote, for each measurable set $E \subset I$, by $\mathfrak{R}_E$ the class of all measurable sets $R \subset E$ which are subject to the following two conditions: (i) $|F[E]-F[R]|=0$, and (ii) each value $y \in F[E]$ is assumed by the function F at most enumerably often on R. By Lemma 7.2, the class $\mathfrak{R}_E$ is non-empty, however we choose the measurable set $E \subset I$. We shall denote, for any such set E, by μ_E the upper bound of the measures of the sets ($\mathfrak{R}_E$).

Consider, in particular, a sequence $\{H_n\}$ of sets ($\mathfrak{R}_I$) such that $\lim\limits_n |H_n|=\mu_I$. Let $H=\sum\limits_n H_n$ and let U be a set ($\mathfrak{R}_{I-H}$). We verify at once that $|U|=0$, whence on account of the condition (N), $|F[U]|=0$. Therefore $|F[I-H]|=|F[U]|=0$, so that almost every value $y \in F[I]$ is assumed by F only on the set H, and therefore at most enumerably often.

The second of the theorems of Banach concerns functions which fulfil the condition (S).

(7.4) ***Theorem.*** *In order that a continuous function F be subject to the condition* (S) *on an interval I, it is necessary and sufficient that F be subject on I to both the conditions* (N) *and* (T_1).

Proof. 1° Suppose that the function F fulfils the condition (S) on I. Since this condition clearly implies the condition (N), we need only prove that F fulfils the condition (T_1).

Suppose then, if possible, that the set of the values assumed infinitely often on I by the function F, is of positive outer measure. Since this set is measurable by Theorem 6.4, it contains a closed subset Y of positive measure. Let X denote the set of all the points $x \in I$ such that $F(x) \in Y$. The set X, plainly, is also closed.

We shall now define by induction a sequence of measurable sets $\{X_i\}$ subject to the following conditions: (i) $X_i \cdot X_j=0$ whenever $i \neq j$, (ii) $|F[X_i]| \geqslant |Y|/2$ for $i=1,2,\ldots$, and (iii) the function F assumes each of its values at most once on each set X_i.

For this purpose, suppose defined the first k sets X_i for which the conditions (i), (ii) and (iii) are satisfied. Let $E_k=I-\sum\limits_{i=1}^{k} X_i$. Since, on $\sum\limits_{i=1}^{k} X_i$, the function F assumes each of its values at most a finite number of times, it follows that each value $y \in Y$ is necessarily assumed on the set E_k. By Lemma 7.2, this set therefore contains measurable subset X_{k+1} such that $|F[X_{k+1}]| \geqslant |F[E_k]|/2 \geqslant |Y|/2$ and that each value is assumed by F at most once on X_{k+1}. The sets $X_1, X_2, \ldots, X_{k+1}$ clearly fulfil the conditions (i), (ii) and (iii).

The sequence $\{X_i\}$ being thus defined, it follows from (i) that $\lim\limits_i |X_i| = 0$, and hence, remembering that the function F fulfils the condition (S), we have also $\lim\limits_i |F[X_i]| = 0$. But this clearly contradicts (ii), since $|Y| > 0$.

2^0 Suppose now that the function F fulfils the conditions (N) and (T_1), but not the condition (S). We could then determine a positive number σ and a sequence of sets $\{E_k\}$ in I so that for $k = 1, 2, \ldots$,

(7.5) $|E_k| < 1/2^k$, and (7.6) $|F[E_k]| > \sigma$.

Let us write $E = \limsup\limits_k E_k$ and $A = \limsup\limits_k F[E_k]$. We easily see that, if $y \in A$, then either $y \in F[E]$, or else the value y is assumed by F on I infinitely often (in fact there exists an increasing sequence of positive integers $\{k_i\}$ and a sequence of points $\{x_i\}$, every two of which are distinct, such that $x_i \in E_{k_i}$ and $F(x_i) = y$ for $i = 1, 2, \ldots$).

Now, on account of (7.5), we have $|E| = 0$, and therefore also $|F[E]| = 0$. On the other hand, by (7.6), $|A| \geqslant \sigma > 0$. Thus $|A - F[E]| \geqslant \sigma$, and since, as we have just seen, each value $y \in A - F[E]$ is assumed by F infinitely often on I, this contradicts the hypothesis that the function F fulfils the condition (T_1).

We shall establish next a "differentiability theorem" for the functions which fulfil the condition (N):

(7.7) ***Theorem.*** *In order that a continuous function F be absolutely continuous on an interval I_0, it is necessary and sufficient that the function F fulfil simultaneously the condition* (N) *and the condition*

$$\int_P F'(x)\,dx < +\infty, \tag{7.8}$$

where P denotes the set of the points at which the function F has a finite non-negative derivative.

Proof. Since the conditions of the theorem are obviously necessary (cf. Theorem 6.7, Chap. VII), let us suppose that the function F fulfils the condition (N) and the inequality (7.8). Let g be the function equal to $F'(x)$ for $x \in P$ and to 0 elsewhere. Then, if E denotes the set of the points x at which $F'(x) = +\infty$, we shall have $F'(x) \leqslant g(x)$ at every point x of $I_0 - E$ at which the derivative $F'(x)$ exists.

On the other hand, since $|E|=0$ (cf. Theorem 4.4, or Chap. VII, § 10, p. 236), we have $|F[E]|=0$, and, since the function F fulfils, by Theorem 7.3, the condition (T_2), it follows from Theorem 6.9 that F is of bounded variation on I_0. This completes the proof, since, by Theorem 6.7, Chap. VII, every continuous function of bounded variation, which fulfils the condition (N) is absolutely continuous.

Theorem 7.7 (in a slightly less general form) was first proved by N. Bary [2; 3, p. 199]. It shows in particular that *every continuous function $F(x)$, which is subject to the condition* (N) *and whose derivative is non-negative at almost every point where $F(x)$ is derivable, is monotone non-decreasing.* This proposition contains an essential generalization of Theorem 6.2, Chap. VII.

Theorem 7.7 may, moreover, be generalized still further. *If a continuous function $F(x)$ fulfils the condition* (N) *and if the function $g(x)$, equal to $F'(x)$ wherever $F(x)$ is derivable and to* 0 *elsewhere, has a major function* (in the Perron sense), *then the function $F(x)$ is* ACG_* *i. e. an indefinite $\mathcal{P}$-integral.*

For the part played by the conditions (N), (T_1) and (T_2) in the theory of Denjoy integrals, cf. also J. Ridder [8].

From Theorem 7.7 we obtain the third theorem of Banach:

(7.9) ***Theorem.*** *Any function which is continuous and subject to the condition* (N) *on an interval, is derivable at every point of a set of positive measure.*

* § 8. Superpositions of absolutely continuous functions.

Suppose given a bounded function G on an interval $[a,b]$, and a function H defined on the interval $[\alpha,\beta]$ where α and β denote respectively the lower and the upper bound of G on $[a,b]$. We call *superposition* of the functions G and H on $[a,b]$, the function $H(G(x))$. The function G is termed *inner function* and the function H *outer function* of this superposition.

If a function F is continuous and increasing on an interval $[a,b]$, the continuous increasing function G defined on the interval $[F(a),F(b)]$ so as to satisfy the identity $G(F(x))=x$ on $[a,b]$, will, as usual, be termed *inverse function* of F and denoted by F^{-1}.

It has long been known that the superposition of two absolutely continuous functions is not, in general, an absolutely continuous function. By means of the conditions discussed in the preceding §§, particularly the condition (S), Nina Bary and D. Menchoff succeeded in characterizing completely the class of functions expressible as superpositions of absolutely continuous functions. (Cf. also G. Fichtenholz [3].)

(8.1) ***Theorem.*** *Any function F which is continuous and subject to the condition* (T_1) *on an interval* $[a,b]$ *is expressible on this interval as a superposition of two continuous functions, of which the inner function is of bounded variation and the outer function is increasing and absolutely continuous.*

If, further, the function F fulfils the condition (N), *the inner function of this superposition is necessarily absolutely continuous also.*

Proof. Let α and β denote respectively the lower and upper bounds of F on $[a,b]$, and let $s_F(y)$ denote, for each y, the number (finite or infinite) of the points of the interval $[a,b]$ at which F assumes the value y. Since, by hypothesis, the function F is continuous and subject to the condition (T_1), we shall have $0<1/s_F(y)\leqslant 1$ for almost all the values y of the interval $[\alpha,\beta]$. Let us denote by U an indefinite integral of the function which is equal to $1/s_F(y)$ on $[\alpha,\beta]$ and to 1 elsewhere. We now write $G(x)=U[F(x)]$ for $x \in [a,b]$. We thus have $F(x)=U^{-1}[G(x)]$, and in order to establish the first part of the theorem, it is enough to show that (i) the function U^{-1} is absolutely continuous and (ii) the function G is of bounded variation.

Suppose, if possible, that the function U^{-1} (which is continuous and increasing together with U) is not absolutely continuous. Then (cf. Theorem 6.7, Chap. VII), there exists a set E of measure zero such that $|U^{-1}[E]|>0$. Writing $Q=U^{-1}[E]$, we thus have

$$(8.2)\qquad |Q|>0 \qquad \textit{and} \qquad |U[Q]|=0.$$

We may, plainly, suppose that the set E, and therefore the set Q, are sets ($\mathfrak{G}_\delta$). Thus (cf. Theorem 13.3, Chap. III)

$$|U[Q]|=\int_Q U'(y)\,dy,$$

which renders the relations (8.2) contradictory, since almost everywhere $U'(y)=1/s_F(y)>0$ for $y\in[\alpha,\beta]$ and $U'(y)=1$ outside the interval $[\alpha,\beta]$.

In order to establish (ii), we shall make use of the criterion of Theorem 6.4. Denote for each z by $s_G(z)$ the number of the points of the interval $[a,b]$ at which the function G assumes the value z. Since the function U is increasing, we clearly have $s_G(U(y))=s_F(y)$ for each y, and $s_G(z)=0$ for each z outside the interval $[U(\alpha), U(\beta)]$. Hence, remembering that the function U is absolutely continuous, we obtain (cf. Theorem 15.1, Chap. I)

$$\int_{-\infty}^{+\infty} s_G(z)\,dz = \int_{U(\alpha)}^{U(\beta)} s_G(z)\,dz = \int_{\alpha}^{\beta} s_G(U(y))\,dU(y) =$$

$$= \int_{\alpha}^{\beta} s_F(y)\,U'(y)\,dy = \int_{\alpha}^{\beta} dy = \beta - \alpha$$

which shows, by Theorem 6.4, that the function G is of bounded variation.

Finally, if the given function F fulfils the condition (N), so does the function $G(x) = U(F(x))$, and the latter, since it is of bounded variation, is absolutely continuous by Theorem 6.7, Chap. VII. This completes the proof.

(8.3) ***Theorem.*** 1^0 *In order that a continuous function F be expressible as a superposition of two continuous functions of which the inner function is of bounded variation and the outer function is absolutely continuous, it is necessary and sufficient that F fulfil the condition* (T_1).

2^0 *In order that a continuous function be representable as a superposition of two absolutely continuous functions, it is necessary and sufficient that the function fulfil both the conditions* (T_1) *and* (N), *or what amounts to the same, the condition* (S).

Proof. Since it follows at once from Theorem 8.1 that these conditions are sufficient, we need only prove them necessary.

Let therefore $F(x) = H(G(x))$ on an interval $[a, b]$, where G is a function of bounded variation and H an absolutely continuous function. Let α and β be respectively the lower and the upper bound of G on $[a, b]$. Let E_G and E_H denote the sets of the values which the functions G and H assume infinitely often on the intervals $[a, b]$ and $[\alpha, \beta]$, respectively. Since the functions G and H fulfil the condition (T_1), we have $|E_G| = |E_H| = 0$, and since the function H is, moreover, absolutely continuous, we have also $|H[E_G]| = 0$. Now we see at once that each value which is assumed infinitely often on $[a, b]$ by the function F, belongs either to E_H, or to $H[E_G]$. The set of these values is thus of measure zero, and the function F fulfils the condition (T_1).

If, further, the function G is absolutely continuous (as well as H), then the function F is a superposition of two functions which fulfil the condition (N), and, thei fore, itself fulfils this condition. This completes the proof.

Theorems 8.1 and 8.3 are due to Nina Bary [1; 3, pp. 208, 633] (cf. also S. Banach and S. Saks [1]). Part 2° of Theorem 8.3 was established a little earlier in a note of N. Bary and D. Menchoff [1] (cf. also N. Bary [3, p. 203]) in a form analogous to Theorem 6.2. Thus:

(8.4) ***Theorem.*** *In order that a function F which is continuous on an interval $[a,b]$ be on this interval a superposition of two absolutely continuous functions, it is necessary and sufficient that the set of the values assumed by the function F at the points of $[a,b]$ at which F is not derivable, be of measure zero.*

Proof. Let Q_F be the set of the points of $[a,b]$ at which F is not derivable. Suppose first that

1° $F(x)=H(G(x))$ on $[a,b]$, where H and G are absolutely continuous functions. Let Q_G and Q_H be respectively the sets of the points at which the functions G and H are not derivable. We have $|Q_G|=|Q_H|=0$ and, consequently, $|F[Q_G]|=|H[Q_H]|=0$. Now, we see at once that if the function F is not derivable at a point x, then either $x \in Q_G$, or $G(x) \in Q_H$. Therefore $F[Q_F] \subset F[Q_G]+H[Q_H]$, and hence, $|F[Q_F]|=0$.

Conversely, suppose that

2° $|F[Q_F]|=0$. By Theorem 6.2, the function then fulfils the condition (T_1). To show that F also fulfils the condition (N), consider any set of measure zero, E say, in $[a,b]$. Since the function F is derivable at each point of $E-Q_F$, we have, by Theorem 6.5, Chap. VII, $|F[E-Q_F]|=0$, and since, by hypothesis, $|F[Q_F]|=0$, we obtain $|F[E]|=0$. The function F thus fulfils both the conditions (T_1) and (N), and is, therefore, by Theorem 8.3 (2°), a superposition of two absolutely continuous functions.

It follows from Theorem 8.3 (2°) that *a superposition of any finite number of absolutely continuous functions is expressible as a superposition of two absolutely continuous functions.* For the superposition of any finite number of functions which fulfil the condition (S), itself fulfils this condition.

The results exposed in this § have been the starting point of the important researches of Nina Bary [3] on the representation of continuous functions by means of superpositions of absolutely continuous functions. Let us cite two of her fundamental theorems: 1° *Every continuous function is the sum of three superpositions of absolutely continuous functions, and there exist continuous functions which cannot be expressed as the sum of two such superpositions.* 2° *Every continuous function which fulfils the condition* (N)—*or, more generally, every continuous function which is derivable at every point of a set which has positive measure in each interval—is the sum of two superpositions of absolutely continuous functions, and there exist continuous functions which fulfil the condition* (N), *but are not expressible as one superposition of absolutely continuous functions* (the function $U(x)$ discussed above in § 6, p. 279, is an example of such a function).

For further researches, *vide* N. Bary [4] and J. Todd [1; 2].

§ 9. The condition (D). We shall now establish, for the extreme approximate derivates, a theorem, analogous to Theorem 4.6, but whose proof depends on a different idea. It is convenient to formulate it, from the beginning, in a slightly more general manner.

Given two positive numbers N and ε, we shall say that a function F fulfils at a point x_0 *the condition* $(D^+_{N,\varepsilon})$, if there exist positive numbers h, as small as we please, such that the difference between the outer measure of the set $\underset{x}{E}[F(x)-F(x_0)\geqslant N\cdot(x-x_0);\ 0\leqslant x-x_0\leqslant h]$ and that of the set $\underset{x}{E}[F(x)-F(x_0)\geqslant -N\cdot(x-x_0);\ 0\leqslant x-x_0\leqslant h]$ exceeds the number $h\varepsilon$ in absolute value. By symmetry, merely replacing $F(x)-F(x_0)$ and $x-x_0$ by $F(x_0)-F(x)$ and x_0-x respectively, we define the condition $(D^-_{N,\varepsilon})$.

If, for a point x_0, there exists a pair of finite positive numbers N and ε such that the function F fulfils at this point the condition $(D^+_{N,\varepsilon})$, or the condition $(D^-_{N,\varepsilon})$, we say that F fulfils at x_0 the *condition* (D).

For measurable functions the condition (D) may be formulated more simply: *a measurable function F fulfils at a point x_0, the condition* (D), *if there exists a finite positive number N such that x_0 is not a point of dispersion for the set of the points x at which* $|F(x)-F(x_0)\leqslant N\cdot|x-x_0|$.

(9.1) ***Theorem.*** *If any one of the four approximate extreme derivates of a function F is finite at a point x_0, then the function fulfils the condition* (D) *at this point.*

Proof. Suppose, to fix the ideas, that $|\overline{F}^+_{\rm ap}(x_0)|<+\infty$ and write $N=|\overline{F}^+_{\rm ap}(x_0)|+1$. Let E_1 and E_2 be the sets of the points x which are situated on the right of the point x_0 and which fulfil respectively the inequalities $F(x)-F(x_0)\geqslant N\cdot(x-x_0)$ and $F(x)-F(x_0)\geqslant -N\cdot(x-x_0)$. It follows at once from the definitions of approximate derivates (Chap. VII, § 3) that x_0 is a point of dispersion for the set E_1, while E_2 has at x_0 a positive upper outer density. Denoting the latter by δ, we see at once that the function F fulfils at x_0 the condition $(D^+_{N,\varepsilon})$ whatever be the positive number $\varepsilon<\delta$.

(9.2) ***Lemma.*** *Let N and ε be finite positive numbers and suppose that a finite function F fulfils the condition $(D^+_{N,\varepsilon})$ at each point of a set E. Then* $|F[E]|\leqslant(2N/\varepsilon)\cdot|E|$.

Proof. We shall first show that for every interval $I=[a,b]$,

$$|I|\geqslant(\varepsilon/2N)\cdot|F[E\cdot I]|. \tag{9.3}$$

For this purpose, we write, for every y,

$$H(y)=|\underset{x}{\mathrm{E}}[F(x)\geqslant y;\ x\in I]| \tag{9.4}$$

The function H thus defined is non-increasing and bounded on the whole straight line $(-\infty, +\infty)$; we have, in fact, for every y,

$$0\leqslant H(y)\leqslant|I|. \tag{9.5}$$

Given an arbitrary point y_0 of $F[E\cdot I]$, which is distinct from $F(b)$ and at which the function H is derivable, let us consider a point $x_0\in E\cdot I$ such that $F(x_0)=y_0$. Plainly $x_0\neq b$. Let us write, for brevity,

$$A(h,k)=\underset{x}{\mathrm{E}}[F(x)\geqslant y_0+k\cdot(x-x_0);\ 0\leqslant x-x_0\leqslant h]$$

and

$$B(h,k)=\underset{x}{\mathrm{E}}[F(x)\geqslant y_0+kh;\ 0\leqslant x-x_0\leqslant h].$$

For every subinterval $[x_0, x_0+h]$ of I, we then have the relation $B(h,N)\subset A(h,N)\subset A(h,-N)\subset B(h,-N)$, whence it follows easily, on account of (9.4), that

$$H(y_0-Nh)-H(y_0+Nh)\geqslant|B(h,-N)|-|B(h,N)|\geqslant|A(h,-N)|-|A(h,N)|.$$

Now, since F fulfils, by hypothesis, the condition $(\mathrm{D}^{+}_{N,\varepsilon})$ at x_0, there exist positive values h, as small as we please, such that

$$|A(h,-N)|-|A(h,N)|\geqslant h\varepsilon,$$

and therefore $H(y_0-Nh)-H(y_0+Nh)\geqslant h\varepsilon$. Hence, $H'(y_0)\leqslant-\varepsilon/2N$ for every point $y_0\neq F(b)$ of $F[E\cdot I]$ at which the function H is derivable. Therefore, denoting, for each positive integer n, by Q_n the part of the set $F[E\cdot I]$ contained in the interval $[-n, n]$, we find, on account of (9.5), $|I|\geqslant|H(n)-H(-n)|\geqslant\varepsilon\cdot|Q_n|/2N$, from which the inequality (9.3) follows by making $n\to\infty$.

This being established, let η be a positive number and $\{I_k\}$ a sequence of intervals such that

$$E\subset\sum_k I_k \qquad \textit{and} \qquad |E|+\eta\geqslant\sum_k|I_k|. \tag{9.6}$$

Since (9.3) holds for each interval I, it follows from (9.6) that $|E|+\eta\geqslant(\varepsilon/2N)\cdot\sum_k|F[E\cdot I_k]|\geqslant(\varepsilon/2N)\cdot|F[E]|$, whence, remembering that η is an arbitrary positive number, we see that $|F[E]|\leqslant(2N/\varepsilon)\cdot|E|$.

(9.7) **Theorem.** *If at each point of a set E, a finite function F fulfils the condition* (D) *(and so, in particular, if at each point of E the function F has one of its extreme approximate derivates finite), then the function F fulfils the condition* (N) *on E.*

Proof. Let H be any subset of E of measure zero, and let H_n denote, for each positive integer n, the set of the points x of H at which the function F fulfils the condition $(D^+_{n,1/n})$ or $(D^-_{n,1/n})$. We clearly have $H=\sum_n H_n$, and since, by Lemma 9.2, $|F[H_n]|\leqslant 4n^2\cdot|H_n|=0$, we obtain $|F[H]|=0$.

Theorem 9.7 enables us to complete Theorems 10.5 and 10.14 of Chap. VII, as follows:

(9.8) **Theorem.** 1^0 *Every finite function F which is continuous on a closed set E and which has at each point of E, except perhaps those of an enumerable subset, either two finite Dini derivates on the same side, or one finite extreme bilateral derivate, is* ACG_* *on E.*

2^0 *Every finite function F which is continuous on a closed set E and which has at each point of E, except perhaps those of an enumerable subset, either one finite Dini derivate, or one finite extreme approximate bilateral derivate, or finally two finite extreme approximate unilateral derivates on the same side, is* ACG *on E.*

Proof. By Theorems 10.1, 10.5, 10.8 and 10.14 of Chap. VII, the function F is VBG_* on E in case 1^0 and VBG on E in case 2^0. On the other hand, by Theorems 4.6 and 9.7, this function fulfils, in both cases, the condition (N) on E. Hence, by Theorems 6.8 and 8.8 of Chap. VII, the function is ACG_* on E in case 1^0, and ACG on E in case 2^0.

In the most important case in which the closed set E is an interval, Theorem 9.8 may further be stated in terms of Denjoy integrals. For this purpose, let us begin by noting the following proposition (cf. A. S. Besicovitch [2], and J. C. Burkill and U. S. Haslam-Jones [1]):

(9.9) **Theorem.** *If a finite function F is measurable on a set E and has at each point of this set one of its Dini derivates finite, then this derivate is, at almost all points of E, an approximate derivative of F.*

Proof. It follows from Theorem 10.8, Chap. VII, that the function F is VBG on E, and so, approximately derivable at almost all the points of E. Let us denote by E_1 the set of the points of E

at which one at least of the opposite Dini derivates $\overline{F}^+$ and $\underline{F}^-$ is finite. Plainly, $\underline{F}^-(x) \leqslant F'_{ap}(x) \leqslant \overline{F}^+(x)$ at each point x at which the approximate derivative $F'_{ap}(x)$ exists, and therefore by Theorem 4.1, $\underline{F}^-(x) = \overline{F}^+(x) = F'_{ap}(x)$ at almost all points x of E_1. Similarly, we show that $\underline{F}^+(x) = \overline{F}^-(x) = F'_{ap}(x)$ at almost all the points x of E at which one of the derivates $\underline{F}^+$ and $\overline{F}^-$ is finite. This completes the proof.

(9.10) ***Theorem.*** 1^0 *If f is a finite function which, at each point of an interval I_0, except those of an enumerable set, is equal to an extreme bilateral derivate of a continuous function F, then the function f is $\mathfrak{D}_*$-integrable on I_0 and the function F is an indefinite $\mathfrak{D}_*$-integral of f.*

2^0 *If f is a finite function which, at each point of an interval I_0, except those of an enumerable set, is equal either to a Dini derivate, or to an extreme approximate bilateral derivate of a continuous function F, then the function f is $\mathfrak{D}$-integrable on I_0 and the function F is an indefinite $\mathfrak{D}$-integral of f.*

Proof. In view of Theorem 9.8, the function F is ACG$_*$ in case 1^0, and ACG in case 2^0. Moreover, at almost all the points x of E, we have $F'(x) = f(x)$ in case 1^0, and by Theorem 9.9, $F'_{ap}(x) = f(x)$ in case 2^0. This proves the theorem.

Although Theorem 9.8 presents a formal analogy with Theorems 10.5 and 10.14 of Chap. VII, there is an essential difference between the result of this § and those of § 10, Chap. VII. We see, in the first place, that the criteria of Theorems 10.5 and 10.14 of Chap. VII concern functions which are given on quite arbitrary sets, whereas those of Theorem 9.8 are established only for closed sets. In the second place, if the derivates of a quite arbitrary function satisfy on a set E the conditions of Theorem 10.5, or of Theorem 10.14, of Chap. VII, then the set E can, by these theorems, be decomposed into a sequence of sets on which the function is absolutely continuous. On the contrary, Theorem 9.8 of this § does not enable us to draw any conclusion as to a similar decomposition of the set E (even when this set is an interval), unless the function considered is continuous.

Two examples will now be given to show that this feature of Theorem 9.8, which represents a restriction as compared with the results of § 10, Chap. VII, is essential for the validity of the theorem.

(i) Consider the function $F(x) = \sum_n [2^n x]/5^n$, where $[2^n x]$ denotes, as usual, the largest integer not exceeding $2^n x$. This function is increasing. Its lower right-hand derivate is finite everywhere, and even, as we easily see, vanishes identically. Nevertheless, there is no decomposition of the interval $J_0 = [0, 1]$ into a sequence of sets on which F is absolutely continuous, or even only uniformly continuous. In fact, no such decomposition can exist for a monotone function F whose points of discontinuity form a set everywhere dense in J_0.

For, if such a decomposition $\{E_1, E_2, ..., E_n, ...\}$ existed, one at least of the sets E_n would, by Baire's Theorem (Chap. II, § 9), be everywhere dense in an interval $I \subset J_0$. This is plainly impossible since the function F, monotone by hypothesis, is uniformly continuous on each set E_n and has points of discontinuity in the interior of I.

(ii) Let us now consider an example of a continuous function $F(x)$, increasing on the interval $J_0=[0,1]$, and which has its lower right-hand derivate zero at every point of a set E, without being ACG on E.

For this purpose, let us agree to call, for brevity, function attached to an interval $I=[a, b]$, any function $H(x)$, which is continuous and non-decreasing on I, and which fulfils the conditions:

(a) $H(x)$ is constant on each of the intervals I_k of a sequence $\{I_k\}$ of non-overlapping sub-intervals of I such that $|I|=\sum_k |I_k|$; the length of any sub-interval of I on which $H(x)$ is constant does not exceed $|I|/2$;

(b) $H(x)-H(a)\leqslant x-a$ and $H(b)-H(x)\leqslant b-x$ for every $x \in I$.

Such a function is easily obtained, by slightly modifying the construction of the function $f(x)$, considered in Chap. III, § 13, p. 101.

This being so, we shall define by induction a sequence $\{F_n(x)\}$ of functions attached to the interval J_0, beginning with an arbitrary function $F_1(x)$ attached to this interval. Given the function F_n attached to J_0, let $\{I_k^{(n)}=[a_k^{(n)}, b_k^{(n)}]\}$ be a sequence of the intervals of constancy of F_n in the interval J_0. (By an interval of constancy of a function in J_0 we mean here any interval $I \subset J_0$ such that the function is constant on I without being constant on any sub-interval of J_0 which contains I and is distinct from I.) For each $k=1,2,...$, we determine a function $H_k^{(n)}(x)$ attached to the interval $I_k^{(n)}$, and we write

$$F_{n+1}(x)=\begin{cases} \sum_i^{(x)}[H_i^{(n)}(b_i^{(n)})-H_i^{(n)}(a_i^{(n)})] & \text{for } x \in J_0-\sum_k I_k^{(n)} \\ H_k^{(n)}(x)-H_k^{(n)}(a_k^{(n)})+\sum_i^{(x)}[H_i^{(n)}(b_i^{(n)})-H_i^{(n)}(a_i^{(n)})] & \text{for } x \in I_k^{(n)},\ k=1,2,..., \end{cases}$$

the sum $\sum_i^{(x)}$ being extended over all the values i such that $b_i^{(n)} \leqslant x$.

The sequence $\{F_n(x)\}$ being thus defined, let

$$F(x)=\sum_n F_n(x)/2^n. \tag{9.11}$$

The function $F(x)$ is clearly continuous, increasing, and singular on J_0.

Consider the set $E=\prod_n \sum_k (I_k^{(n)})^\circ$, and let x_0 be any point of E. Then there exists a sequence $\{I_{k_n}^{(n)}\}_{n=1,2,...}$ of intervals each of which contains x_0 in its interior. Plainly, for each positive integer n, $F_j(b_{k_n}^{(n)})-F_j(x_0)=0$ if $j\leqslant n$, and $F_j(b_{k_n}^{(n)})-F_j(x_0)\leqslant b_{k_n}^{(n)}-x_0$ if $j>n$. Hence, by (9.11), $F(b_{k_n}^{(n)})-F(x_0)\leqslant(b_{k_n}^{(n)}-x_0)/2^n$ for each n, and therefore $\underline{F}^+(x_0)=0$.

Nevertheless, the function F is not ACG on E. To see this, suppose, if possible, that E is the sum of a sequence of sets E_n on each of which the function F is AC. Since the set J_0-E is the sum of a sequence of non-dense closed sets, one at least of the sets E_n is everywhere dense in a sub-interval I of J_0, and, since the function F is absolutely continuous on each E_n, this function would be so also on the whole interval I. This is clearly impossible, for the function F

§ 10. A theorem of Denjoy-Khintchine on approximate derivates. The considerations of the preceding § will now be completed by a theorem which establishes, for the extreme approximate derivates, relations similar to those which hold for Dini derivates (cf. § 4). This theorem was proved independently by A. Denjoy [6, p. 209] and by A. Khintchine [4; 5, p. 212] (cf. also J. C. Burkill and U. S. Haslam-Jones [1; 3]).

(10.1) ***Theorem.*** *If a finite function F is measurable on a set E and if, to each point x of E, there corresponds a measurable set $Q(x)$ such that* (i) *the lower unilateral density of $Q(x)$ at x is positive on at least one side of the point x and* (ii) $\overline{F}_{Q(x)}(x)<+\infty$ *or* $\underline{F}_{Q(x)}(x)>-\infty$, *then the function F is approximately derivable at almost all the points of E.*

Consequently, if a finite function F is measurable on a set E, then at almost every point of E either the function F is approximately derivable, or else $\overline{F}^{+}_{\mathrm{ap}}(x)=\overline{F}^{-}_{\mathrm{ap}}(x)=+\infty$ *and* $\underline{F}^{+}_{\mathrm{ap}}(x)=\underline{F}^{-}_{\mathrm{ap}}(x)=-\infty$.

Proof. In view of Lusin's Theorem (Chap. III, § 7), we may suppose that the set E is closed and that the function F is continuous on E. To fix the ideas, consider the set A of the points $x \in E$ such that (i_1) the lower right-hand density of $Q(x)$ at x is positive and (ii_1) $\overline{F}_{Q(x)}(x)<+\infty$. We shall show that the function F is approximately derivable at almost all the points of A. By symmetry, this assertion will remain valid for each of the other three subsets of E, defined by a similar specification of the conditions (i) and (ii) of the theorem.

Let us denote by P the set of the points of A at which the function F is not approximately derivable, and suppose, if possible, that $|P|>0$. For each positive integer n, let A_n be the set of the points x of E such that the inequality $0\leqslant h\leqslant 1/n$ implies

(10.2) $$|\underset{t}{\mathrm{E}}[F(t)-F(x)\leqslant n\cdot(t-x);\, t\in E;\, x\leqslant t\leqslant x+h]|\geqslant h/n.$$

The sets A_n are closed. To see this, let us keep an index n fixed for the moment, and let $\{x_i\}_{i=1,2,\dots}$ be a sequence of points of the set A_n converging to a point x_0. Let $h\leqslant 1/n$ be a non-negative number, and, for brevity, let $E_i=\underset{t}{\mathrm{E}}[F(t)-F(x_i)\leqslant n\cdot(t-x_i);\, t\in E;\, x_i\leqslant t\leqslant x_i+h]$ where $i=0,1,2,\dots$. We obtain $|E_i|\geqslant h/n$ for $i=1,2,\dots$, and since, by continuity of F on E, we have $E_0\supset\limsup_i E_i$, it follows (cf. Chap. I, Theorem 9.1) that $|E_0|\geqslant h/n$, which shows that $x_0\in A_n$, i.e. that A_n is a closed set.

Let us now denote, for every pair of positive integers n and k, by $A_{n,k}$ the set of the points x of A_n such that the inequality $0 \leqslant h \leqslant 1/k$ implies

(10.3) $$|\underset{t}{\mathrm{E}}[t \in A_n;\, x-h \leqslant t \leqslant x]| \geqslant (1-\tfrac{1}{2}n^{-1}) \cdot h.$$

We observe easily that the sets A_n, and therefore the sets $A_{n,k}$ also, cover the set A almost entirely. Hence, there exists a pair of positive integers n_0 and k_0 such that $|A_{n_0,k_0} \cdot P| > 0$. Let R denote a portion of the set $A_{n_0,k_0} \cdot P$ such that

(10.4) $|R| > 0$, (10.5) $\delta(R) < 1/n_0$ and (10.6) $\delta(R) < 1/k_0$.

Writing $G(x) = F(x) - (n_0+1) \cdot x$, we shall show that the function G is monotone non-increasing on R. Suppose therefore, if possible, that there exist two points a and b in R, where $a<b$, such that

(10.7) $$G(a) < G(b).$$

Let $J=[a,b]$. Since the set A_{n_0} is closed and the function G continuous on A_{n_0}, the function G attains, at a point c of the set $A_{n_0} \cdot J$, the lower bound of its values on this set. In virtue of (10.7) we have $c<b$. Since $c \in A_{n_0}$, and since, by (10.5), $0 \leqslant b-c \leqslant 1/n_0$, we may put $n=n_0$, $x=c$ and $h=b-c$ in the relation (10.2). We thus obtain

(10.8) $$|\underset{t}{\mathrm{E}}[G(t)-G(c) \leqslant -(t-c);\, t \in E;\, c \leqslant t \leqslant b]| \geqslant (b-c)/n_0.$$

Again, since $b \in R \subset A_{n_0,k_0}$ and since, by (10.6), $0 \leqslant b-c \leqslant 1/k_0$, we may put $n=n_0$, $x=b$ and $h=b-c$ in (10.3). This gives

(10.9) $$|\underset{t}{\mathrm{E}}[t \in A_{n_0};\, c \leqslant t \leqslant b]| \geqslant (1-\tfrac{1}{2}n_0^{-1}) \cdot (b-c).$$

Now the sets which occur in the relations (10.8) and (10.9) are both measurable; it therefore follows from these relations that there exist, in the open interval (c,b), points $t \in A_{n_0}$ for which $G(t)-G(c) \leqslant -(t-c) < 0$. This is plainly impossible, since the function G attains its minimum on the set $A_{n_0} \cdot J$ at the point c.

The function G is thus monotone on the set R, and since it is, moreover, measurable (indeed continuous) on the closed set $E \supset R$, it follows that G is approximately derivable at almost all the points of R. On the other hand, however, since $R \subset P$ the function F is approximately derivable at no point of R, and, in view of (10.4), we arrive at a contradiction. This completes the proof.

By a slight modification of the proof, we may extend Theorem 10.1, in a certain way, to functions which need not be measurable. Let us agree to understand by *approximate derivability* of a finite function F at a point x_0, the existence of a set for which x_0 is a point of outer density and with respect to which the function F is derivable (if the function F is measurable, this notion of approximate derivability clearly agrees with the definition of Chap. VII, § 3). When approximate derivability is interpreted thus in the statement of Theorem 10.1, this theorem remains valid without the hypothesis that the function F be measurable on the set E (although the hypothesis concerning the measurability of the sets $Q(x)$ remains essential).

From Theorem 10.1, we may deduce the following proposition: *If, for a finite function F, we can make correspond to each point x of a set E, a measurable set $Q(x)$ whose lower right-hand density at x is positive, and with respect to which the function has an infinite derivative at x, then the set E is of measure zero.* This theorem is similar to Theorem 4.4, but only partially generalizes the latter. It is not actually possible to replace, in Theorem 4.4, the ordinary, by the approximate, limit, without also removing the modulus sign in the expression $|F(x+h)-F(x)|$. This rather unexpected fact was brought to light by V. Jarník [2], who showed that there exist continuous functions F for which the relation $\lim\text{ap}_{h\to 0+} |F(x+h)-F(x)|/h=+\infty$ holds at almost all points x.

Finally, let us note that Theorem 10.1 is frequently stated in the following form:

If a finite function F is measurable on a set E, then at almost every point x of E either (i) *the function F is approximately derivable, or else* (ii) *there exists a measurable set $R(x)$ whose right-hand and left-hand upper densities are both equal to 1 at x, and with respect to which the two upper unilateral derivates of F at x are $+\infty$ and the two lower derivates $-\infty$.*

It has been shown by A. Khintchine [4] (cf. also V. Jarník [2]) that *there exist continuous functions for which the case* (ii) *holds at almost every point x.*

§ 11. Approximate partial derivates of functions of two variables. The §§ which follow will be devoted to generalizations of the results of § 4 for functions of two real variables (their extension to any number of variables presents, as already said, no fresh difficulty). In this § we shall establish some subsidiary results.

Given a plane set Q and a number η, we shall understand by the *outer linear measure* of Q *on the line* $y=\eta$, the measure of the linear set $\underset{t}{\mathrm{E}}[(t,\eta)\in Q]$. Similarly, we define the *outer linear measure* of Q *on a line* $x=\xi$, where ξ is any number. It follows from Fubini's Theorem in the form (8.6), Chap. III, that if Q is a measurable set whose linear measure on almost all the lines $y=\eta$ (i. e. on the lines $y=\eta$ for almost all values of η) is zero, then the set Q is of plane measure zero.

A point (x_0, y_0) will be termed *point of linear density* of a plane set Q *in the direction of the x-axis*, if x_0 is a point of density of the linear set $\underset{t}{\mathrm{E}}[(t,y_0)\in Q]$. We define similarly the *points of linear density of Q in the direction of the y-axis.*

(11.1) ***Theorem.*** *Almost all points of any measurable plane set Q are points of linear density for it both in the direction of the x-axis and in that of the y-axis.*

Proof. We may clearly assume that the set Q is closed. Consider, to fix the ideas, the set D of the points of Q which are points of density of Q in the direction of the x-axis. Since the set $Q-D$ is of linear measure zero on each line $y=\eta$, the proof of the relation $|Q-D|=0$ reduces to showing that the set D is measurable.

In order to do this, we write, for each point (x,y) and each pair of numbers a and b,

$$E(x,y;a,b)=\underset{t}{\mathrm{E}}[(t,y)\in Q;\ a\leqslant t\leqslant b],$$

and we denote, for each pair of positive integers n and k, by $Q_{n,k}$ the set of the points (x,y) of Q such that the inequalities $a<x<b$ and $b-a\leqslant 1/k$ imply $|E(x,y;a,b)|\geqslant(1-n^{-1})\cdot(b-a)$. Plainly $D=\prod_n\sum_k Q_{n,k}$.

We now remark that all the sets $Q_{n,k}$ are closed. To see this, we keep the indices n and k fixed for the moment, and consider an arbitrary sequence $\{(x_i,y_i)\}_{i=1,2,\dots}$ of points of $Q_{n,k}$ which converges to a point (x_0,y_0). Let a and b denote real numbers such that $a<x_0<b$ and $b-a\leqslant 1/k$. For every sufficiently large index i, we then have $a<x_i<b$, and so $|E(x_i,y_i;a,b)|\geqslant(1-n^{-1})\cdot(b-a)$. Now it is easy to see that $\limsup_i E(x_i,y_i;a,b)\subset E(x_0,y_0;a,b)$; it therefore follows from Theorem 9.1, Chap. I, that $|E(x_0,y_0;a,b)|\geqslant(1-n^{-1})\cdot(b-a)$, and so, that $(x_0,y_0)\in Q_{n,k}$.

Since the sets $Q_{n,k}$ are closed, D is a set $(\mathfrak{F}_{\sigma\delta})$ and this completes the proof.

If F is a finite function of two variables, the extreme approximate partial derivates of $F(x,y)$ with respect to x will be denoted by $\overline{F}^{+}_{\mathrm{ap}_x}$, $\underline{F}^{+}_{\mathrm{ap}_x}$, $\overline{F}^{-}_{\mathrm{ap}_x}$ and $\underline{F}^{-}_{\mathrm{ap}_x}$. If these derivates are equal at a point (x,y), their common value, i. e. the approximate partial derivative of F with respect to x, will be denoted by $F'_{\mathrm{ap}_x}(x,y)$. Analogous symbols will be used with respect to y. For the partial Dini derivates, we shall retain the notation of Chap. V, namely $\overline{F}^{+}_{x}$, $\underline{F}^{+}_{x}$, etc.

(11.2) **Theorem.** *If a finite function of two variables F is measurable on a set Q, its extreme approximate partial derivates are themselves measurable on Q.*

Proof. In view of Lusin's Theorem (Chap. III, § 7), we may suppose that the set Q is closed and that the function F is continuous on Q. Consider, to fix the ideas, the derivate $\overline{F}^{+}_{\mathrm{ap}_x}$. Let a be any finite number and let P be the set of the points (x,y) of Q at which $\overline{F}^{+}_{\mathrm{ap}_x}(x,y) \leqslant a$. We have to prove that the set P is measurable.

For this purpose, let D denote the set of the points of the set Q which are its points of linear density in the direction of the x-axis. Further, for every point (x,y) and every positive integer n, let $E_n(x,y)$ denote the set of the points t such that

$$t \geqslant x, \quad (t,y) \in Q \quad \textit{and} \quad F(t,y) - F(x,y) \leqslant (a+n^{-1}) \cdot (t-x).$$

We easily observe (cf. Chap. VII, § 3) that, in order that $\overline{F}^{+}_{\mathrm{ap}_x}(x_0,y_0) \leqslant a$ at a point $(x_0,y_0) \in D$, it is necessary and sufficient that the point (x_0,y_0) be a point of right-hand density for every set $E_n(x_0,y_0)$, where $n=1,2,\ldots$ Hence, denoting for every system of three positive integers n,k and p, by $Q_{n,k,p}$ the set of the points (x,y) of Q such that the inequality $0 \leqslant h \leqslant 1/p$ implies $|E_n(x,y) \cdot [x, x+h]| \geqslant (1-k^{-1}) \cdot h$, we have

$$P \cdot D = \prod_n \prod_k \sum_p Q_{n,k,p}. \tag{11.3}$$

Now the set Q is closed and the function F is continuous on Q, and by means of Theorem 9.1, Chap. I (cf. the proofs of Theorems 10.1 and 11.1) we easily prove that all the sets $Q_{n,k,p}$ are closed. Hence, by (11.3), the set $P \cdot D$ is measurable, and since, by Theorem 11.1, $|Q-D|=0$, we see that the set P is measurable also. This completes the proof.

It follows, in particular, from Theorem 11.2 that *the extreme approximate derivates of any finite measurable function of one real variable are themselves measurable functions.* We thus obtain a result analogous to Theorem 4.3, Chap. IV, which concerned the measurability of Dini derivates (cf. also Theorem 4.1, Chap. V, and the remark p. 171).

§ 12. Total and approximate differentials. A finite function of two real variables F is termed *totally differentiable*, or simply *differentiable*, at a point (x_0, y_0) if there exist two finite numbers A and B such that the ratio

$$(12.1)\quad [F(x,y)-F(x_0,y_0)-A\cdot(x-x_0)-B\cdot(y-y_0)]\,/\,[|x-x_0|+|y-y_0|]$$

tends to zero as $(x,y)\to(x_0,y_0)$. The pair of numbers $\{A,B\}$ is then termed *total differential* of the function F at the point (x_0,y_0) and we see at once that A and B are the partial derivatives of F at (x_0,y_0) with respect to x and to y respectively.

If, for a finite function of two variables F and for a point (x_0,y_0), there exist two finite numbers A and B such that the ratio (12.1) tends approximately to 0 as $(x,y)\to(x_0,y_0)$, the function F is termed *approximately differentiable* at (x_0,y_0) and the pair of numbers $\{A,B\}$ is called *approximate differential* of F at (x_0,y_0). The numbers A and B will be called *coefficients* of this differential.

We see at once that no function can have at a given point more than one differential, whether total or approximate.

The existence of a total differential of a function $F(x,y)$ at a point may be interpreted as the existence of a plane, tangent at this point to the surface $z=F(x,y)$ and non-perpendicular to the xy-plane. In this way the notion of total differentiability of functions of two variables corresponds exactly to the similar notion of derivability of functions of one variable. Nevertheless, whereas every function of bounded variation of one variable is almost everywhere derivable, a function of bounded variation (in the Tonelli sense), and even an absolutely continuous function, of two variables may be nowhere totally differentiable (cf. W. Stepanoff [3, p. 515]).

The coefficients of an approximate differential of a function at a point are not, in general, approximate partial derivatives of this function. Nevertheless they coincide with the latter almost everywhere, as results from the following theorem:

(12.2) ***Theorem.*** *In order that a finite function of two variables F, which is measurable on a set Q, be approximately differentiable at almost all the points of this set, it is necessary and sufficient that F be, almost everywhere in Q, approximately derivable with respect to each variable.*

When this is the case, the approximate partial derivates $F'_{\mathrm{ap}_x}(x,y)$ and $F'_{\mathrm{ap}_y}(x,y)$ are, at almost all the points (x,y) of Q, the coefficients of the approximate differential of F.

Proof. 1° Suppose that the function F is approximately differentiable at almost all the points of Q. We denote, for each positive integer n, by R_n the set of the points (ξ,η) of Q such that, for every square J containing (ξ,η), we have

$$(12.3)\qquad \Big|\underset{(x,y)}{\mathrm{E}}[|F(x,y)-F(\xi,\eta)|\leqslant n\cdot\delta(J);\,(x,y)\in J]\Big|\geqslant 3\cdot|J|/4$$

whenever $\delta(J)\leqslant 2/n$. Writing $R=\sum_n R_n$, we clearly have $|Q-R|=0$.

Let us now denote, for a general plane set E and any number η, by $E^{[\eta]}$ the linear set of the points ξ such that $(\xi,\eta)\in E$. Keeping fixed, for the moment, a positive integer n_0 and a real number η_0, we consider any two points ξ_1 and ξ_2 of $R_{n_0}^{[\eta_0]}$ for which $0\leqslant\xi_2-\xi_1\leqslant 1/n_0$, and we denote by J_0 the square $[\xi_1,\xi_2;\,\eta_0,\eta_0+\xi_2-\xi_1]$. We then have $\delta(J_0)\leqslant 2/n_0$, and so, putting $n=n_0$, $J=J_0$, $\eta=\eta_0$ in (12.3). and choosing $\xi=\xi_1$ and $\xi=\xi_2$ successively, we see at once that the square J_0 contains points (x,y) for which we have at the same time

$$|F(\xi_1,\eta_0)-F(x,y)|\leqslant n_0\cdot\delta(J_0)\leqslant 2n_0\cdot(\xi_2-\xi_1)$$

and

$$|F(\xi_2,\eta_0)-F(x,y)|\leqslant n_0\cdot\delta(J_0)\leqslant 2n_0\cdot(\xi_2-\xi_1).$$

Hence $|F(\xi_2,\eta_0)-F(\xi_1,\eta_0)|\leqslant 4n_0\cdot|\xi_2-\xi_1|$, which shows that, for any fixed η, $F(x,\eta)$, as a function of x, is AC on each set $R_n^{[\eta]}$, and so VBG on the whole set $R^{[\eta]}$ (cf. Chap. VII, § 5). Now R is (with Q) a plane measurable set, so that the linear set $R^{[\eta]}$ is measurable for almost every η. Hence (cf. Theorem 4.3, Chap. VII), for almost all η, the function $F(x,\eta)$ is approximately derivable with respect to x at almost all the points of $R^{[\eta]}$. Since further, by Theorem 11.2, the set of the points of R at which the function F is approximately derivable with respect to one variable, is measurable, it follows at once that the function F is approximately derivable with respect to x at almost all the points of R, and so, at the same time, at almost all the points of Q. Similarly, we establish the corresponding result concerning approximate derivability of F with respect to y.

2° Suppose that the function F is approximately derivable, at almost all the points of Q, with respect to x and with respect to y. We shall show that the function F then has, at almost all the points of Q, an approximate differential with coefficients $F'_{\mathrm{ap}_x}(x,y)$ and $F'_{\mathrm{ap}_y}(x,y)$. On account of Theorem 11.2 and of Lusin's Theorem (Chap. III, § 7), we may suppose that

(a) the set Q is bounded and closed, (b) the function F is approximately derivable with respect to each variable at all the points of Q, and (c) the function F, and both its approximate partial derivatives, are continuous on Q.

This being so, we write, for each point (ξ,η) of Q and each point (x,y) of the plane,

$$(12.4)\quad D(\xi,\eta;x,y)=|F(x,y)-F(\xi,\eta)-(x-\xi)\cdot F'_{\mathrm{ap}_x}(\xi,\eta)-(y-\eta)\cdot F'_{\mathrm{ap}_y}(\xi,\eta)|,$$
$$D_1(\xi,\eta;x)=|F(x,\eta)-F(\xi,\eta)-(x-\xi)\cdot F'_{\mathrm{ap}_x}(\xi,\eta)|,$$
$$D_2(\xi,\eta;y)=|F(\xi,y)-F(\xi,\eta)-(y-\eta)\cdot F'_{\mathrm{ap}_y}(\xi,\eta)|.$$

Let ε and τ be any positive numbers. We shall begin by defining a positive number σ and a closed subset A of Q such that $|Q-A|<\varepsilon$ and such that, for any point (ξ,η),

$$\text{(i)}\quad \begin{gathered}|\underset{x}{\mathrm{E}}[D_1(\xi,\eta;x)\leqslant\tau\cdot|x-\xi|;\ (x,\eta)\in Q;\ a\leqslant x\leqslant b]|\geqslant(1-\varepsilon)\cdot(b-a)\\ \textit{whenever}\quad (\xi,\eta)\in A,\quad a\leqslant\xi\leqslant b\quad \textit{and}\quad b-a<\sigma.\end{gathered}$$

For this purpose, let us denote, for each positive integer n, by A_n the set of the points (ξ,η) of Q such that the inequality in the first line of (i) is fulfilled whenever $a<\xi<b$ and $b-a<1/n$. Since the set Q is closed and since the function F and its derivatives F'_{ap_x} and F'_{ap_y} are continuous on Q, it is easily seen that all the sets A_n are closed. On the other hand, the sets A_n form an ascending sequence and we immediately see that the set $Q-\lim\limits_n A_n$ is of measure zero on each line $y=\eta$. Hence, this set being measurable, we have $|Q-\lim\limits_n A_n|=0$. Consequently $|Q-A_{n_0}|<\varepsilon$ for a sufficiently large index n_0, and writing $\sigma=1/n_0$ and $A=A_{n_0}$ we find that the inequality $|Q-A|<\varepsilon$ and the condition (i) are both satisfied.

In exactly the same way, but replacing the set Q by A and interchanging the rôle of the coordinates x and y, we determine now a positive number $\sigma_1<\sigma$ and a closed subset B of A such that $|A-B|<\varepsilon$ and that for any point (ξ,η)

$$\text{(ii)}\quad \begin{gathered}|\underset{y}{\mathrm{E}}[D_2(\xi,\eta;y)\leqslant\tau\cdot|y-\eta|;\ (\xi,y)\in A;\ a\leqslant y\leqslant b]|\geqslant(1-\varepsilon)\cdot(b-a)\\ \textit{whenever}\quad (\xi,\eta)\in B,\quad a\leqslant\eta\leqslant b\quad \textit{and}\quad b-a<\sigma_1.\end{gathered}$$

Finally, let $\sigma_2<\sigma_1$ be a positive number such that

$$|F'_{\mathrm{ap}_x}(x_2,y_2)-F'_{\mathrm{ap}_x}(x_1,y_1)|<\tau$$

for any pair of points (x_1,y_1) and (x_2,y_2) of Q subject to the conditions $|x_2-x_1|<\sigma_2$ and $|y_2-y_1|<\sigma_2$.

This being so, let (ξ_0, η_0) be any point of B. Let $J=[\alpha_1, \beta_1; \alpha_2, \beta_2]$ denote any interval such that $(\xi_0, \eta_0) \epsilon J$ and $\delta(J)<\sigma_2<\sigma_1<\sigma$. We write:

$$E_2 = \underset{y}{\mathrm{E}}[D_2(\xi_0, \eta_0; y) \leqslant \tau \cdot |y - \eta_0|; (\xi_0, y) \epsilon A; \alpha_2 \leqslant y \leqslant \beta_2],$$

and, for each y,

$$E_1(y) = \underset{x}{\mathrm{E}}[D_1(\xi_0, y; x) \leqslant \tau \cdot |x - \xi_0|; (x, y) \epsilon Q; \alpha_1 \leqslant x \leqslant \beta_1].$$

Then any point (x,y) such that $y \epsilon E_2$ and $x \epsilon E_1(y)$ belongs to the set $Q \cdot J$ and, for such a point, we have

$$D(\xi_0, \eta_0; x, y) \leqslant D_1(\xi_0, y; x) + D_2(\xi_0, \eta_0; y) + |x - \xi_0| \cdot |F'_{\mathrm{ap}_x}(\xi_0, y) - F'_{\mathrm{ap}_x}(\xi_0, y_0)| \leqslant$$
$$\leqslant 2\tau \cdot [|x - \xi_0| + |y - \eta_0|].$$

On the other hand, it follows at once from (ii) and (i) respectively, that $|E_2| \geqslant (1-\varepsilon) \cdot (\beta_2 - \alpha_2)$, and $|E_1(y)| \geqslant (1-\varepsilon) \cdot (\beta_1 - \alpha_1)$ whenever $y \epsilon E_2$. Hence, $D(\xi_0, \eta_0; x, y)$ being a measurable (indeed continuous) function of the point (x,y) on $Q \cdot J$, it follows that the set of the points $(x,y) \epsilon Q \cdot J$ such that $D(\xi_0, \eta_0; x, y) \leqslant 2\tau \cdot [|x-\xi_0| + |y - \eta_0|]$ is of measure at least equal to $(1-\varepsilon)^2 (\beta_1 - \alpha_1)(\beta_2 - \alpha_2) = (1-\varepsilon)^2 \cdot |J|$. The point (ξ_0, η_0) here denotes any point of the set B, and J any interval, containing (ξ_0, η_0), whose diameter is sufficiently small. Therefore, since $|Q - B| \leqslant |Q - A| + |A - B| \leqslant 2\varepsilon$, where ε is at our disposal, we see that, for every positive number τ, almost every point (ξ, η) of Q is a point of density for the set of the points (x, y) of Q which fulfil the inequality $D(\xi, \eta; x, y)/[|x-\xi| + |y-\eta|] \leqslant 2\tau$; and in view of (12.4), this completes the proof.

We notice a similarity between the preceding proof and that of the "Density Theorem" (Chap. IV, § 10). Actually the result just established constitutes a direct generalization of the Density Theorem. To see this, we need only interpret, in the statement of Theorem 12.2, the function F as the characteristic function of the set Q (cf. the first edition of this book, p. 231).

The notion of approximate differential, together with Theorem 12.2, are due to W. Stepanoff [3]. There is, however, a slight difference between the definition adopted here and that of Stepanoff, so that, in its original form, as proved by Stepanoff, Theorem 12.2 generalizes Theorem 6.1, Chap. IV, rather than the Density Theorem of § 10, Chap. IV.

We conclude this § by mentioning the following theorem, which, in view of Theorems 9.9 and 11.2, is an immediate consequence of Theorem 12.2:

(12.5) ***Theorem.*** *Suppose that a finite function of two variables F which is measurable on a set Q, has at each point of Q at least one finite Dini derivate with respect to x and at least one finite Dini derivate with respect to y.*

Then the function F is approximately differentiable at almost every point of Q.

§ 13. Fundamental theorems on the contingent of a set in space. Following F. Roger [2], we shall now extend to sets in the space $\boldsymbol{R}_3$, the results obtained in § 3. The proofs will be largely a repetition of those of § 3 with the obvious verbal changes. We shall therefore present them in a slightly more condensed form.

Generalizing the definitions of § 3, p. 264, to functions of two variables, we shall say that a function $F(x,y)$ fulfils the *Lipschitz condition* on a plane set E, if there exists a finite constant N such that $|F(x_2, y_2) - F(x_1, y_1)| \leqslant N \cdot [|x_2 - x_1| + |y_2 - y_1|]$ for every two points (x_1, y_1) and (x_2, y_2) of E. We verify at once that the graph of the function F on E is then of finite area whenever $|E| < +\infty$, and of area zero whenever, in particular, $|E| = 0$ (cf. Chap. II, § 8; more precisely, we have, for every set E, $\Lambda_2\{\mathrm{B}(F;E)\} \leqslant 4 \cdot (1+N^2) \cdot |E|$).

In the sequel we shall make use of the following notation for limits relative to a set. If E is a set (in any space) and t_0 is a point of accumulation for E, the lower and upper limits of a function $F(t)$ as t tends to t_0 on E will be written $\liminf_{E, t\to t_0} F(t)$ and $\limsup_{E, t\to t_0} F(t)$ respectively. Their common value, when they are equal, will be written $\lim_{E, t\to t_0} F(t)$.

(13.1) ***Lemma.*** *Let R be a set in the space $\boldsymbol{R}_3$, θ a fixed direction in this space and P the set of the points a of R at which* $\mathrm{contg}_R\, a$ *contains no half-line of direction θ. Then* (i) *the set P is the sum of a sequence of sets of finite area and* (ii) *at each point a of P, except at most at those of a subset of area zero, the set R has an extreme tangent plane, for which the side containing the half-line $a\theta$ is its empty side.*

In the particular case in which θ is the direction of the positive semi-axis of z, the set P is expressible as the sum of an enumerable infinity of sets each of which is the graph of a function on a plane set on which the function fulfils the Lipschitz condition.

Proof. We may clearly suppose (in the first part of the theorem also) that θ is the direction of the positive semi-axis of z. We denote, for every positive integer n, by P_n the set of the points (x,y,z) of P such that the inequalities $|x'-x|\leqslant 1/n$, $|y'-y|\leqslant 1/n$ and $|z'-z|\leqslant 1/n$ imply $z'-z\leqslant n\cdot[|x'-x|+|y'-y|]$ for every point (x',y',z') of R. We express, further, each P_n as the sum of a sequence $\{P_{n,k}\}_{k=1,2,...}$ of sets with diameters less than $1/n$. For every pair of points (x_1,y_1,z_1) and (x_2,y_2,z_2) of the same set $P_{n,k}$, we thus have $|z_2-z_1|\leqslant n\cdot[|x_2-x_1|+|y_2-y_1|]$, and if we denote by $Q_{n,k}$ the orthogonal projection of $P_{n,k}$ on the xy-plane, we easily see that the set $P_{n,k}$ may be regarded as the graph of a function $F_{n,k}$ on $Q_{n,k}$. Plainly $|F_{n,k}(x_2,y_2)-F_{n,k}(x_1,y_1)|\leqslant n\cdot[|x_2-x_1|+|y_2-y_1|]$ for every two points (x_1,y_1) and (x_2,y_2) of $Q_{n,k}$. Thus $F_{n,k}$ fulfils the Lipschitz condition on $Q_{n,k}$ and hence (cf. p. 304) $\Lambda_2(P_{n,k})=\Lambda_2\{\mathrm{B}(F_{n,k};Q_{n,k})\}<+\infty$. Thus $P=\sum_{n,k}P_{n,k}$ is the required expression of the set P.

It remains to discuss the existence of an extreme tangent plane to R at the points of P. For a fixed pair of positive integers n and k, the function $F_{n,k}$, which fulfils the Lipschitz condition on the set $Q_{n,k}$, can be continued at once, by continuity, on to the closure $\bar{Q}_{n,k}$ of this set, and then on to the whole plane by writing $F_{n,k}(x,y)=0$ outside $\bar{Q}_{n,k}$. On account of Theorem 12.2, the function $F_{n,k}$ is approximately differentiable at almost all the points of $\bar{Q}_{n,k}$. Hence, denoting by $\tilde{Q}_{n,k}$ the subset of $Q_{n,k}$ consisting of the points of density of $Q_{n,k}$ at which $F_{n,k}$ is approximately differentiable, we see that $|Q_{n,k}-\tilde{Q}_{n,k}|=0$ and hence, that $\Lambda_2\{\mathrm{B}(F_{n,k};Q_{n,k}-\tilde{Q}_{n,k})\}=0$. We need, therefore, only show that R has an extreme tangent plane at each point of $\mathrm{B}(F_{n,k};\tilde{Q}_{n,k})$, and that, further, the half-line with the direction of the positive semi-axis of z is contained in the empty side of this plane.

Let (ξ_0,η_0,ζ_0) be any point of $\mathrm{B}(F_{n,k};\tilde{Q}_{n,k})$ and let $\{A_0,B_0\}$ be the approximate differential of $F_{n,k}$ at the point (ξ_0,η_0). Let $\varepsilon<1$ be any positive number, and let E_ε be the set of the points $(x,y)\,\epsilon\,Q_{n,k}$ such that

$$|F_{n,k}(x,y)-F_{n,k}(\xi_0,\eta_0)-A_0\cdot(x-\xi_0)-B_0\cdot(y-\eta_0)|\leqslant\varepsilon\cdot[|x-\xi_0|+|y-\eta_0|].$$

Since the function $F_{n,k}$ is measurable, (ξ_0,η_0) is (cf. Chap. VII, § 3) a point of outer density for the set E_ε. Hence we can make correspond to each point (ξ,η,ζ), sufficiently near to (ξ_0,η_0,ζ_0), a point $(\xi',\eta')\,\epsilon\,E_\varepsilon$ such that:

(13.2) $\quad |\xi'-\xi_0|\leqslant|\xi-\xi_0| \quad$ *and* $\quad |\eta'-\eta_0|\leqslant|\eta-\eta_0|,$

(13.3) $\quad |\xi'-\xi|\leqslant\varepsilon\cdot|\xi-\xi_0| \quad$ *and* $\quad |\eta'-\eta|\leqslant\varepsilon\cdot|\eta-\eta_0|.$

Remembering that $\zeta_0=F_{n,k}(\xi_0,\eta_0)$, we now write for brevity $D_{n,k}(\xi',\eta')=F_{n,k}(\xi',\eta')-\zeta_0-A_0\cdot(\xi'-\xi_0)-B_0\cdot(\eta'-\eta_0)$. We thus have

(13.4)
$$\begin{aligned}&\zeta-\zeta_0-A_0\cdot(\xi-\xi_0)-B_0\cdot(\eta-\eta_0)=\\&=D_{n,k}(\xi',\eta')+[\zeta-F_{n,k}(\xi',\eta')]+[A_0\cdot(\xi'-\xi)+B_0\cdot(\eta'-\eta)].\end{aligned}$$

This being so, let (ξ,η,ζ) be a point of R such that each of the differences $|\xi-\xi_0|$, $|\eta-\eta_0|$ and $|\zeta-\zeta_0|$ is less than, or equal to, $1/4n^2$. Then by (13.3), we have $|\xi'-\xi|\leqslant 1/n$ and $|\eta'-\eta|\leqslant 1/n$, while, by (13.2), $|F_{n,k}(\xi',\eta')-\zeta_0|\leqslant n\cdot[|\xi'-\xi_0|+|\eta'-\eta_0|]\leqslant 1/2n$, and so $|F_{n,k}(\xi',\eta')-\zeta|\leqslant 1/n$. Since the point $(\xi',\eta',F_{n,k}(\xi',\eta'))$ belongs to $\mathrm{B}(F;E_\varepsilon)\subset P_n$, it follows that $\zeta-F_{n,k}(\xi',\eta')\leqslant n\cdot[|\xi-\xi'|+|\eta-\eta'|]$, and, again making use of (13.3), we deduce from (13.4) that

(13.5)
$$\begin{aligned}&\zeta-\zeta_0-A_0\cdot(\xi-\xi_0)-B_0\cdot(\eta-\eta_0)\leqslant\\&\leqslant|D_{n,k}(\xi',\eta')|+(n+|A_0|)\cdot|\xi'-\xi|+(n+|B_0|)\cdot|\eta'-\eta|\leqslant\\&\leqslant|D_{n,k}(\xi',\eta')|+\varepsilon\cdot(|A_0|+|B_0|+n)\cdot[|\xi-\xi_0|+|\eta-\eta_0|].\end{aligned}$$

We now observe that, since $(\xi',\eta')\in E_\varepsilon$, (13.2) implies

$$|D_{n,k}(\xi',\eta')|/[|\xi-\xi_0|+|\eta-\eta_0|]\leqslant|D_{n,k}(\xi',\eta')|/[|\xi'-\xi_0|+|\eta'-\eta_0|]\leqslant\varepsilon.$$

Hence, ε being an arbitrary positive number, we derive from (13.5)

(13.6)
$$\limsup_{(\xi,\eta,\zeta)\to(\xi_0,\eta_0,\zeta_0)}{}_R\;[\zeta-\zeta_0-A_0\cdot(\xi-\xi_0)-B_0\cdot(\eta-\eta_0)]/[|\xi-\xi_0|+|\eta-\eta_0|]\leqslant 0.$$

Moreover, since $\{A_0,B_0\}$ is the approximate differential of the function $F_{n,k}$ at (ξ_0,η_0) and since the point (ξ_0,η_0) is a point of outer density for the set $Q_{n,k}$, the plane $z-\zeta_0-A_0\cdot(x-\xi_0)-B_0\cdot(y-\eta_0)=0$ is certainly an intermediate tangent plane (cf. § 2, p. 263) of R at the point (ξ_0,η_0,ζ_0). It is therefore, by (13.6), an extreme tangent plane at this point, with an empty side consisting of the half-space $z-\zeta_0\geqslant A_0\cdot(x-\xi_0)+B_0\cdot(y-\eta_0)$. This completes the proof.

We shall employ in space a terminology similar to that of the plane (cf. § 3, p. 264) and agree to say that the contingent of a set $E\subset\boldsymbol{R}_3$ at a point a of E is the *whole space* if it includes all the half-lines issuing from the point a; and again, that the contingent of E at a point a of E is a *half-space*, if E has an extreme tangent plane at a and if $\mathrm{contg}_E\, a$ consists of all the half-lines issuing from a which are situated on one side of this plane. We make use of these terms to state the analogue of Theorem 3.6:

(13.7) ***Theorem.*** *Given a set R in $\boldsymbol{R}_3$, let P be a subset of R at no point of which the contingent of R is the whole space. Then* (i) *the set P is the sum of an enumerable infinity of sets of finite area and* (ii) *at every point of P, except at those of a set of area zero, either the set R has a unique tangent plane, or else the contingent of R is a half-space.*

The proof of this statement, which follows directly from Lemma 13.1, is quite similar to that of Theorem 3.6. We need only replace, in the proof of the latter, the terms length, tangent and half-plane by area, tangent plane and half-space, respectively.

It only remains to extend to space, Theorem 3.7. This extension, in the form (13.11) in which we shall establish it, is essentially little more than an immediate, and almost trivial, consequence of Theorem 3.7. Its proof requires however some subsidiary considerations of the measurability of certain sets.

(13.8) ***Lemma.*** *If Q is a set ($\mathfrak{F}_{\sigma\delta}$) in $\boldsymbol{R}_3$, its orthogonal projection on the xy-plane is a measurable set.*

Proof. Let us denote generally, for every set E situated in $\boldsymbol{R}_3$, by $\Gamma(E)$ its projection on the xy-plane. In order to establish the measurability of the set $\Gamma(Q)$, it will suffice to show that for each $\varepsilon>0$ there exists a closed set $P\subset\Gamma(Q)$ such that $|P|\geqslant|\Gamma(Q)|-\varepsilon$.

We express Q as the product of a sequence $\{Q_n\}_{n=1,2,\ldots}$ of sets ($\mathfrak{F}_\sigma$). It may clearly be assumed that the set Q is bounded and that, moreover, all the sets Q_n are situated in a fixed closed sphere S_0.

We shall define in $\boldsymbol{R}_3$, by induction, a sequence $\{F_n\}_{n=0,1,\ldots,}$ of closed sets subject to the following conditions for $n=1,2,\ldots$: (i) $F_n\subset F_{n-1}$, (ii) $F_n\subset Q_n$ and (iii) $|\Gamma(F_n\cdot Q)|\geqslant|\Gamma(F_{n-1}\cdot Q)|-\varepsilon/2^n$.

For this purpose, we choose $F_0=S_0$ and we suppose that the next $r-1$ sets F_n have been defined. We have $Q\subset Q_r$, and so $F_{r-1}\cdot Q_r\cdot Q=F_{r-1}\cdot Q$, and since $F_{r-1}\cdot Q_r$ is, with Q_r, a set ($\mathfrak{F}_\sigma$), there exists a closed set $F_r\subset F_{r-1}\cdot Q_r$ such that $|\Gamma(F_r\cdot Q)|\geqslant|\Gamma(F_{r-1}\cdot Q)|-\varepsilon/2^r$. This closed set F_r clearly fulfils (i), (ii) and (iii) for $n=r$.

Now let $F=\prod_n F_n=\lim_n F_n$. It follows from (ii) that $F\subset Q$, and therefore that $\Gamma(F)\subset\Gamma(Q)$. Further, $\Gamma(F)$ is a closed set, for, since $\{F_n\}$ is a descending sequence of closed and bounded sets, we easily see that $\Gamma(F)=\lim_n\Gamma(F_n)$. Finally this last relation coupled with (iii) shows that $|\Gamma(F)|\geqslant\lim_n|\Gamma(F_n\cdot Q)|\geqslant|\Gamma(F_0\cdot Q)|-\varepsilon=|\Gamma(Q)|-\varepsilon$, which completes the proof.

It would be easy to prove that the projection of a set $(\mathfrak{F}_{\sigma\delta})$ is the nucleus of a determining system formed of closed sets and thus to deduce Lemma 13.8 from Theorem 5.5, Chap. II. We have preferred, however, to give a direct elementary proof, based on a method due to N. Lusin [3]. The same argument shows that any continuous image of a set $(\mathfrak{F}_{\sigma\delta})$ is measurable.

It has been proved more generally (*vide*, for instance, W. Sierpiński [II, p. 149], or F. Hausdorff [II, p. 212]) that any continuous image of an analytic set (in particular, of a set measurable $(\mathfrak{B})$) situated in $\boldsymbol{R}_3$ is an analytic and, therefore, measurable set.

(13.9) ***Lemma.*** *Given a set R in $\boldsymbol{R}_3$, let Q be the set of the points (ξ, η, ζ) of R which fulfil the condition:*

(Δ) *the part of the contingent of R at the point (ξ, η, ζ), which is situated in the plane $x=\xi$, is wholly contained in one or other of the two half-spaces $y \geqslant \eta$ and $y \leqslant \eta$.*

Then the orthogonal projection of the set Q on the xy-plane is of plane measure zero.

Proof. We may clearly suppose that the set R is closed (for the contingent of any set R coincides, at all points of R, with that of the closure of R).

Let us denote generally, for any set E in $\boldsymbol{R}_3$ and any number ξ, by $E^{[\xi]}$ the set $\underset{(y,z)}{\mathrm{E}}[(\xi, y, z) \in E]$. It follows from Theorem 3.6 that, for every ξ, the plane set $R^{[\xi]}$ has an extreme tangent, parallel to the z-axis at every point of $Q^{[\xi]}$ except those of a set of length zero. Hence, by Theorem 3.7, the projection of Q on the xy-plane is of linear measure zero on each line $x=\xi$ of this plane, and, in order to prove that this projection is of plane measure zero, we need only show that the latter is measurable.

Let us denote, for each pair of positive integers k and n, by $A_{k,n}$ the set of the points (ξ, η, ζ) of R such that the inequalities

(13.10) $\quad |x-\xi|+|y-\eta|+|z-\zeta|<1/n \quad$ *and* $\quad |x-\xi|<[|y-\eta|+|z-\zeta|]/n$

imply, for any point $(x, y, z) \in R$, the inequality $y-\eta \leqslant [|x-\xi|+|z-\zeta|]/k$. Similarly, we shall denote by $B_{k,n}$ the set of the points (ξ, η, ζ) of R for which the inequalities (13.10) imply, for every point (x, y, z) of R, the inequality $y-\eta \geqslant -[|x-\xi|+|z-\zeta|]/k$. Writing

$$A=\prod_k \sum_n A_{k,n} \qquad \textit{and} \qquad B=\prod_k \sum_n B_{k,n},$$

we find that $Q=A+B$. On the other hand, since the set R is, by hypothesis, closed, we observe at once that each set $A_{k,n}$, and likewise each set $B_{k,n}$, is closed. The sets A and B, and so the set Q also, are thus sets $(\mathfrak{F}_{\sigma\delta})$, and in view of Lemma 13.8, the projection of Q on the xy-plane is a measurable set.

(13.11) ***Theorem.*** *Given a set R in $\mathbf{R}_3$, let P be a subset of R at every point of which the set R has an extreme tangent plane parallel to a fixed straight line D. Then the orthogonal projection of P on the plane perpendicular to D is of plane measure zero.*

Proof. We may clearly suppose that the straight line D is the z-axis. Let us denote by P_1 the set of the points of P at which the extreme tangent plane, parallel, by hypothesis, to the z-axis is not, however, parallel to the yz-plane. Similarly, P_2 will denote the set of the points of P at which the extreme tangent plane is not parallel to the xz-plane. We then have $P=P_1+P_2$.

Now we observe at once that each point (ξ,η,ζ) of P_1 fulfils the condition (Δ) of Lemma 13.9. It therefore follows from this lemma, that the projection of P_1 on the xy-plane is of plane measure zero.

By symmetry, the same is true of the projection of the set P_2. The proof is thus complete.

§ 14. Extreme differentials. Let F be a finite function of two real variables. A pair of finite numbers $\{A,B\}$ will be called *upper differential* of F at a point (x_0,y_0) if, when we write $z_0=F(x_0,y_0)$, (i) the plane $z-z_0=A\cdot(x-x_0)+B\cdot(y-y_0)$ is an intermediate tangent plane of the graph of the function F at the point (x_0,y_0,z_0) and

$$\text{(ii)} \qquad \limsup_{(x,y)\to(x_0,y_0)} \frac{F(x,y)-F(x_0,y_0)-A\cdot(x-x_0)-B\cdot(y-y_0)}{|x-x_0|+|y-y_0|}=0.$$

These conditions may clearly be replaced by the following: (i_1) the plane $z-z_0=A\cdot(x-x_0)+B\cdot(y-y_0)$ is an extreme tangent plane of the graph of F at (x_0,y_0,z_0) with the empty side $z-z_0\geqslant A\cdot(x-x_0)+B\cdot(y-y_0)$, and ($\mathrm{ii}_1$) $\limsup_{(x,y)\to(x_0,y_0)} F(x,y)\leqslant F(x_0,y_0)$.

The definition of *lower differential* is similar, and the two differentials, upper and lower, will be called *extreme differentials.*

If a function F has a total differential (cf. § 12, p. 300) at a point, this differential is both an upper and a lower differential of F at the point considered. Conversely, if a function F has at a point (x_0,y_0) both an upper and a lower differential, these are identical and then reduce to a total differential of F at (x_0,y_0).

For a finite function of one real variable F, the existence of an upper differential at a point x_0 is to be interpreted to mean that $\overline{F}^+(x_0)=\underline{F}^-(x_0)\neq\infty$ (in which case the number $\overline{F}^+(x_0)=\underline{F}^-(x_0)$ may be regarded as the upper differential of F at x_0). There is a similar interpretation for the lower differential of functions of one variable. This interpretation brings to light the relationship between the theorems of this § and those of § 4.

We propose to give an account of researches concerning the existence almost everywhere of total, approximate, or extreme differentials. These researches were begun by H. Rademacher [3], who established the first general sufficient condition in order that a continuous function be almost everywhere differentiable. W. Stepanoff [1; 3] later removed from Rademacher's reasoning certain superfluous hypotheses, and obtained a more complete result, valid for any measurable function: *In order that a function F which is measurable on a set E, should be differentiable almost everywhere in E, it is necessary and sufficient that the relation* $\limsup_{(x,y)\to(\xi,\eta)} |F(x,y)-F(\xi,\eta)|/[|x-\xi|+|y-\eta|]<+\infty$ *should hold at almost all the points* (ξ,η) *of E.* (Certain details of Stepanoff's proof, particularly those concerning measurability of the Dini partial derivates, have been subjected to criticism (cf. J. C. Burkill and U. S. Haslam-Jones [1].) U. S. Haslam-Jones [1] extended further the result of Stepanoff, and by introducing the notion of extreme differentials (which he called upper and lower derivate planes), obtained theorems analogous to those of Denjoy for functions of one variable. The researches of Haslam-Jones have been continued and completed by A. J. Ward [1; 4] who, in particular, removed the hypothesis of measurability in certain of Haslam-Jones's theorems.

We shall derive the results of Haslam-Jones from the theorems of the preceding § (cf. F. Roger [3]; direct proofs will be found in the memoirs of Haslam-Jones and Ward referred to, and in the first edition of this book).

In what follows, we shall make use of some subsidiary conventions of notation. If F is a function of two real variables and t denotes a point (x,y) of the plane $\boldsymbol{R}_2$, we shall frequently write $F(t)$ for $F(x,y)$. If $t_1=(x_1,y_1)$ and $t_2=(x_2,y_2)$ are two points of the plane, $|t_2-t_1|$ will denote the number $|x_2-x_1|+|y_2-y_1|$.

Given in the plane two distinct half-lines issuing from a point t_0, each of the two closed regions into which these half-lines divide the plane will be called *angle*. The point t_0 will be termed *vertex* of each of these angles.

We shall begin by proving a theorem somewhat analogous to Theorem 1.1 (ii).

(14.1) ***Theorem.*** *Let F be a finite function in the plane* $\boldsymbol{R}_2$ *and let E be a plane set, each point* τ *of which is the vertex of an angle* $A(\tau)$ *such that* $\limsup_{t\to\tau} {}_{A(\tau)} F(t)<\limsup_{t\to\tau} F(t)$. *Then the set E is of plane measure zero.*

Proof. Let us denote, for each pair of integers p and q, by $E_{p,q}$ the set of the points τ of E at which $\limsup_{t\to\tau} {}_{A(\tau)} F(t)<p/q<\limsup_{t\to\tau} F(t)$. For fixed p and q, we observe that no point $\tau\in E_{p,q}$ is a point of accumulation for the part of the set $E_{p,q}$ contained in the interior of the corresponding angle $A(\tau)$. Hence, no point of the set $E_{p,q}$ can be a point of outer density for this set. Each of the sets $E_{p,q}$ is thus of plane measure zero, and the same is therefore true of the whole set E.

As we easily see, in virtue of Theorem 3.6, each set $E_{p,q}$, and consequently the whole set E, is the sum of a sequence of sets of finite length (this of course, implies that E is of plane measure zero). Cf. A. Kolmogoroff and J. Verčenko [1].

(14.2) ***Theorem.*** *Let F be a finite function in the plane. Then*

(i) *if P is a plane set each point τ of which is the vertex of an angle $A(\tau)$ such that*

(14.3) $$\lim_{t \to \tau} {}_{A(\tau)} |F(t)-F(\tau)| / |t-\tau| = +\infty,$$

the set P is necessarily of plane measure zero;

(ii) *if Q is a plane set each point τ of which is the vertex of an angle $A_0(\tau)$ such that*

(14.4) $$\limsup_{t \to \tau} {}_{A_0(\tau)} [F(t)-F(\tau)] / |t-\tau| < +\infty,$$

the function F necessarily has an upper differential at almost all the points of Q;

(iii) *if R is a plane set each point τ of which is the vertex of two angles $A_1(\tau)$ and $A_2(\tau)$ such that*

$$\limsup_{t \to \tau} {}_{A_1(\tau)} [F(t)-F(\tau)] / |t-\tau| < +\infty$$

and

$$\liminf_{t \to \tau} {}_{A_2(\tau)} [F(t)-F(\tau)] / |t-\tau| > -\infty,$$

the function F is totally differentiable at almost all the points of R.

Proof. *re* (i). By Theorem 13.7 the set $\mathrm{B}(F;P)$ has, at each of its points except those of a subset of area zero, an extreme tangent plane. The latter is seen to be necessarily parallel to the z-axis. Hence, by Theorem. 13.11, the set P, as the projection of $\mathrm{B}(F;P)$ on the xy-plane, is of plane measure zero.

re (ii). It clearly follows from (14.4) that, at each point τ of Q, we have $\limsup_{t \to \tau} {}_{A_0(\tau)} F(t) \leqslant F(\tau)$. Hence, by Theorem 14.1, we have $\limsup_{t \to \tau} F(t) \leqslant F(\tau)$ at all the points τ of Q, except at most those of a set Q_0 of measure zero.

Let us now denote by B the graph of the function F (on the whole plane). Let B_1 be the set of the points of $\mathrm{B}(F;Q)$ at which the set B has no extreme tangent plane, and B_2 the set of the points of $\mathrm{B}(F;Q)$ at which such a tangent plane exists, but is parallel to the z-axis. Finally, let Q_1 and Q_2 be the projections of the sets B_1 and B_2 respectively, on the xy-plane. On account of Theorem 13.7, we easily verify that $\Lambda_2(B_1)=0$, and so, that $|Q_1|=0$. Similarly, it follows at once from Theorem 13.11 that $|Q_2|=0$. Now, if (ξ,η) is any point of $Q-(Q_1+Q_2)$, the set B has at $(\xi,\eta,F(\xi,\eta))$ an extreme tangent plane of the form $z-\zeta=M(\xi,\eta)\cdot(x-\xi)+N(\xi,\eta)\cdot(y-\eta)$, where $M(\xi,\eta)$ and $N(\xi,\eta)$ are finite numbers. We observe further without difficulty that the half-space

$$z-\zeta\geqslant M(\xi,\eta)\cdot(x-\xi)+N(\xi,\eta)\cdot(y-\eta)$$

is an empty side of this plane. Hence (cf. p. 309), at each point (ξ,η) of the set $Q-(Q_0+Q_1+Q_2)$, the pair of numbers $\{M(\xi,\eta),N(\xi,\eta)\}$ is an upper differential of the function F. This completes the proof, since $|Q_0+Q_1+Q_2|=0$.

Finally, (iii) is an immediate consequence of (ii).

In the case in which the function F is measurable, we can complete part (i) of Theorem 14.2 (which itself generalizes Theorem 4.4). Thus, *if F is any measurable function of two variables, the set of the points (x,y) at which* $\lim_{h\to0+}|F(x+h,y)-F(x,y)|/h=+\infty$, *is of plane measure zero.*

This proposition plainly follows from Theorem 4.4, except for measurability considerations, essential to the proof, which seem to require general theorems on the measurability of the projections of sets $(\mathfrak{B})$ (cf. p. 308).

We conclude with the following theorem (cf. A. J. Ward [1] and the first edition of this book, p. 234) which, in view of Theorem 14.2 (i), (ii), may be regarded as an extension of Theorem 9.9 to the functions of two variables:

(14.5) ***Theorem.*** *If F is a finite function of two variables, which is measurable on a set E and which has an extreme differential at each point of a set $Q\subset E$, then this differential is, at the same time, an approximate differential of F at almost all the points of Q.*

Proof. On account of Lusin's theorem (Chap. III, § 7) we may clearly suppose that the set E is closed and that the function F is continuous on E. Let us suppose further, for definiteness, that the function F has an upper differential at each point of Q, and let us denote, for each positive integer n, by Q_n the set of the points t of Q such that, for every point t', $|t'-t|<1/n$ implies the inequality $F(t')-F(t)<n\cdot|t'-t|$. Finally, let each set Q_n be expressed as the sum of a sequence $\{Q_{n,k}\}_{k=1,2,...}$ of sets with diameters less than $1/n$. We shall have $Q=\sum_{n,k} Q_{n,k}$.

We see at once that the function F fulfils the Lipschitz condition on each set $Q_{n,k}$, and therefore also on each set $\bar{Q}_{n,k}$. Hence, by Theorem 12.2, the function F has the approximate differential $\{F'_{\text{ap}_x}(x,y), F'_{\text{ap}_y}(x,y)\}$ at almost every point (x,y) of each set $\bar{Q}_{n,k}$, and therefore at almost every point (x,y) of the set Q.

Let us, on the other hand, denote, for each point (x,y) of Q, by $\{A(x,y), B(x,y)\}$ the upper differential of F at this point. It follows at once from the definition of upper differential, p. 309, that $\underline{F}_x^-(x,y) \geqslant A(x,y) \geqslant \overline{F}_x^+(x,y)$, and similarly $\underline{F}_y^-(x,y) \geqslant B(x,y) \geqslant \overline{F}_y^+(x,y)$, at each point (x,y) of Q. Hence, at each point (x,y) of Q at which the approximate partial derivates $F'_{\text{ap}_x}(x,y)$ and $F'_{\text{ap}_y}(x,y)$ exist, we have $A(x,y) = F'_{\text{ap}_x}(x,y)$ and $B(x,y) = F'_{\text{ap}_y}(x,y)$. The upper differential $\{A(x,y), B(x,y)\}$ of the function F thus coincides at almost all points (x,y) of Q with the approximate differential of F.

NOTE I.

On Haar's measure

by

Stefan Banach.

§ 1. This Note is devoted to the theory of measure due to Alfred Haar [1]. Haar's beautiful and important theory deals with measure in those locally compact separable spaces for which the notion of congruent sets is defined. His measure fulfils the usual conditions of ordinary Lebesgue measure: congruent sets are of equal measure and all Borel sets (more generally, all analytic sets) are measurable. The theory has important applications in that of continuous groups.

To complete the definitions of Chap. II, § 2, we shall say that a set situated in a metrical space is *compact*, if every infinite subset of the set in question has at least one point of accumulation. A metrical space is termed *locally compact* if each point of this space has a neighbourhood which is compact.

§ 2. In what follows we shall denote by E a fixed metrical space, separable and locally compact, and we shall suppose that, for the sets situated in E, the notion of *congruence* $\cong$ is defined so as to fulfil the following conditions:

i_1. $A \cong B$ *implies* $B \cong A$; $A \cong B$ *and* $B \cong C$ *imply* $A \cong C$;

i_2. *If* A *is a compact open set and* $A \cong B$, *then the set* B *is itself open and compact;*

i_3. *If* $A \cong B$ *and* $\{A_n\}$ *is a (finite or infinite) sequence of open compact sets such that* $A \subset \sum_n A_n$, *then there exists a sequence of sets* $\{B_n\}$ *such that* $B \subset \sum_n B_n$ *and such that* $A_n \cong B_n$ *for* $n = 1, 2, \ldots$;

i_4. *Whatever be the compact open set* A, *the class of the sets congruent to* A *covers the whole space* E;

i_5. *If* $\{S_n\}$ *is a sequence of compact concentric spheres with radii tending to* 0, *and* $\{G_n\}$ *is a sequence of sets such that* $G_n \cong S_n$, *then the relations* $a = \lim_n a_n$ *and* $b = \lim_n b_n$, *where* $a_n \in G_n$ *and* $b_n \in G_n$, *imply* $a = b$.

§ 3. Given two compact open sets A and B, the class of the sets congruent to A covers, by i_4, the set $\bar{B}$. It therefore follows from the theorem of Borel-Lebesgue that there exists a finite system of sets congruent to A which covers $\bar{B}$. Let $\mathrm{h}(B,A)$ denote the least number of sets which constitute such a system.

It is easy to show by means of i_1—i_5 that, for any three compact open sets A, B and C, the following propositions are valid:

ii_1. $C \subset B$ *implies* $\mathrm{h}(C,A) \leqslant \mathrm{h}(B,A)$;
ii_2. $\mathrm{h}(B+C,A) \leqslant \mathrm{h}(B,A)+\mathrm{h}(C,A)$;
ii_3. $B \cong C$ *implies* $\mathrm{h}(B,A)=\mathrm{h}(C,A)$;
ii_4. $\mathrm{h}(B,A) \leqslant \mathrm{h}(B,C)\cdot \mathrm{h}(C,A)$;
ii_5. If $\varrho(A,B)>0$ *and if* $\{S_n\}$ *is a sequence of compact concentric spheres with radii tending to* 0, *then there exists a positive integer* N *such that, for every* $n>N$,

(3.1) $$\mathrm{h}(A+B,S_n)=\mathrm{h}(A,S_n)+\mathrm{h}(B,S_n).$$

All these propositions are obvious, except perhaps ii_5. To prove the latter, let us suppose, if possible, that there exists an increasing sequence of positive integers $\{n_i\}$ such that (3.1) does not hold for any of the values $n=n_i$. There would then exist a sequence of sets $\{G_i\}$ such that $G_i \cong S_{n_i}$ while $A\cdot G_i \neq 0$ and $B\cdot G_i \neq 0$. Consider now arbitrary points $a_i \epsilon A\cdot G_i$ and $b_i \epsilon B\cdot G_i$. Since the sets A and B are compact, the sequences $\{a_i\}$ and $\{b_i\}$ contain respectively convergent subsequences $\{a_{i_j}\}$ and $\{b_{i_j}\}$. Let $a=\lim\limits_j a_{i_j}$ and $b=\lim\limits_j b_{i_j}$. By i_5 we must have $a=b$, and this is impossible since, by hypothesis, $\varrho(A,B)=0$.

We shall now suppose given a fixed compact open set G and a sequence $\{S_n\}$ of concentric spheres, with radii tending to 0, which are situated in G and therefore clearly compact. For every compact open set A, we write

$$l_n(A)=\frac{\mathrm{h}(A,S_n)}{\mathrm{h}(G,S_n)}.$$

We then have, by ii_4,

$$\mathrm{h}(A,S_n)\leqslant \mathrm{h}(A,G)\cdot \mathrm{h}(G,S_n) \quad \text{and} \quad \mathrm{h}(G,S_n)\leqslant \mathrm{h}(G,A)\cdot \mathrm{h}(A,S_n),$$

and hence for each $n=1,2,\ldots,$ $1/\mathrm{h}(G,A)\leqslant l_n(A)\leqslant \mathrm{h}(A,G)$.

Thus, $\{l_n(\mathrm{A})\}$ *is a bounded sequence whose terms exceed a fixed positive number.*

§ 4. We now make use of the following theorem (cf. S. Banach [I, p. 34] and S. Mazur [1]), in which $\{\xi_n\}$ and $\{\eta_n\}$ denote arbitrary bounded sequences of real numbers, a and b denote real numbers, and the symbols lim, lim sup and lim inf have their usual meaning:

To every bounded sequence $\{\xi_n\}$ *we can make correspond a number* $\underset{n}{Lim}\,\xi_n$, *termed generalized limit, in such a manner as to fulfil the following conditions*:

1) $\underset{n}{Lim}\,(a\xi_n+b\eta_n)=a\cdot\underset{n}{Lim}\,\xi_n+b\cdot\underset{n}{Lim}\,\eta_n$,

2) $\liminf_n \xi_n \leqslant \underset{n}{Lim}\,\xi_n \leqslant \limsup_n \xi_n$,

3) $\underset{n}{Lim}\,\xi_{n+1}=\underset{n}{Lim}\,\xi_n$.

The last condition implies that *the generalized limit remains unaltered, when we remove from a sequence a finite number of its terms.*

Let us now write, for every compact open set A,

$$l(A)=\underset{n}{Lim}\,l_n(A). \tag{4.1}$$

We then have, for any compact open sets A and B:

iii$_1$. $0<l(A)<+\infty$;

iii$_2$. $A\subset B$ *implies* $l(A)\leqslant l(B)$;

iii$_3$. $A\cong B$ *implies* $l(A)=l(B)$;

iii$_4$. $l(A+B)\leqslant l(A)+l(B)$;

iii$_5$. $\varrho(A,B)>0$ *implies* $l(A+B)=l(A)+l(B)$.

§ 5. This being so, we denote, for an arbitrary set $X\subset \boldsymbol{E}$, by $\Gamma(X)$ the lower bound of all the numbers $\sum_n l(A_n)$ where $\{A_n\}$ is any sequence of compact open sets such that $X\subset\sum_n A_n$. We shall show that the function of a set Γ, thus defined, fulfils the following conditions:

1° *We have always* $0\leqslant\Gamma(X)$ *and there exist sets* X *for which we have* $0<\Gamma(X)<+\infty$; *this is, in particular, the case of all compact open sets* X;

2° $X_1\subset X_2$ *implies* $\Gamma(X_1)\leqslant\Gamma(X_2)$;

3° $X\subset\sum_n X_n$ *implies* $\Gamma(X)\leqslant\sum_n\Gamma(X_n)$;

4° $\varrho(X_1,X_2)>0$ *implies* $\Gamma(X_1+X_2)=\Gamma(X_1)+\Gamma(X_2)$;

5° $X_1\cong X_2$ *implies* $\Gamma(X_1)=\Gamma(X_2)$.

Proof. 1^0. Let X be a compact open set. We have, by definition, $\Gamma(X) \leqslant l(X) < +\infty$.

On the other hand, there clearly exists for each $\varepsilon > 0$ a (finite or infinite) sequence of compact open sets $\{A_n\}$ such that $X \subset \sum_n A_n$ and $\Gamma(X) + \varepsilon \geqslant \sum_n l(A_n)$. Let S be any sphere contained in X. Since the set $\bar{S}$ is closed and compact, this set, and *a fortiori* the set S, is already covered by a finite subsequence $\{A_{n_i}\}$ of $\{A_n\}$. In view of iii_2 and iii_4, we thus have

$$l(S) \leqslant l(\sum_i A_{n_i}) \leqslant \sum_i l(A_{n_i}) \leqslant \sum_n l(A_n) \leqslant \Gamma(X) + \varepsilon.$$

Hence, ε being arbitrary, it follows that $l(S) \leqslant \Gamma(X)$, and finally, by iii_1, that $0 < \Gamma(X)$.

2^0 and 3^0 are obvious.

4^0. $\varrho(X_1, X_2) > 0$ implies that there exist two open sets G_1 and G_2 such that $X_1 \subset G_1$, $X_2 \subset G_2$ and $\varrho(G_1, G_2) > 0$. On the other hand, there exists for each $\varepsilon > 0$ a sequence of compact open sets $\{A_n\}$ such that

$$(5.1) \qquad X_1 + X_2 \subset \sum_n A_n \quad \textit{and} \quad \Gamma(X_1 + X_2) + \varepsilon \geqslant \sum_n l(A_n).$$

Write $A_n^{(1)} = A_n \cdot G_1$ and $A_n^{(2)} = A_n \cdot G_2$. Since the sets $A_n^{(1)}$ and $A_n^{(2)}$ are open and compact, and since their distance, like that of G_1 and G_2, is positive, we have, on account of iii_5 and iii_2,

$$(5.2) \qquad l(A_n^{(1)}) + l(A_n^{(2)}) = l(A_n^{(1)} + A_n^{(2)}) \leqslant l(A_n).$$

But, since on the other hand $X_1 \subset \sum_n A_n^{(1)}$ and $X_2 \subset \sum_n A_n^{(2)}$, we have the inequalities $\Gamma(X_1) \leqslant \sum_n l(A_n^{(1)})$ and $\Gamma(X_2) \leqslant \sum_n l(A_n^{(2)})$, so that, by (5.2), $\Gamma(X_1) + \Gamma(X_2) \leqslant \sum_n l(A_n)$. Hence by (5.1), ε being arbitrary, we obtain $\Gamma(X_1) + \Gamma(X_2) \leqslant \Gamma(X_1 + X_2)$, and finally by 3^0, $\Gamma(X_1) + \Gamma(X_2) = \Gamma(X_1 + X_2)$.

5^0 follows at once from i_3 and iii_3.

§ 6. It follows from the properties 1^0—4^0 of the function Γ that the latter is an outer measure in the sense of Carathéodory (cf. Chap. III, § 4) and therefore determines in $\boldsymbol{E}$ a class of sets measurable $(\mathfrak{L}_\Gamma)$, that we shall call, simply, *measurable sets*. We see at once that for each set X in $\boldsymbol{E}$ the number $\Gamma(X)$ is the lower bound of the measures (Γ) of the open sets containing X. It follows, in particular, that Γ is a regular outer measure (cf. Chap. II, § 6).

Finally, since the space $\boldsymbol{E}$ can be covered by a sequence of measurable sets of finite measure (e. g. by a sequence of compact spheres), we easily establish, for the measure Γ, conditions of measurability ($\mathfrak{L}_\Gamma$) similar to those of Theorem 6.6, Chap. III. In particular, we shall have:

(6.1) *In order that a set E be measurable, it is necessary and sufficient that there exist a set ($\mathfrak{G}_\delta$) containing E and differing from it by at most a set of measure zero.*

§ 7. We conclude this note by giving two examples of spaces $\boldsymbol{E}$ with the notion of congruence subject to the conditions of § 2.

Example 1. Let $\boldsymbol{E}$ be a metrical space which is separable and locally compact, and suppose that, among the one to one transformations, continuous both ways, by which the whole space $\boldsymbol{E}$ is transformed into the whole space $\boldsymbol{E}$, there exists a class $\mathfrak{M}$ of transformations subject to the conditions:

1) $T \in \mathfrak{M}$ *implies* $T^{-1} \in \mathfrak{M}$;

2) *If* $T_1 \in \mathfrak{M}$ *and* $T_2 \in \mathfrak{M}$, *then* $T_1 T_2 \in \mathfrak{M}$;

3) *For every pair a, b of points of E, there exists a transformation $T \in \mathfrak{M}$ such that $T(a) = b$;*

4) *If $\{a_n\}$ and $\{b_n\}$ are two convergent sequences of points of $\boldsymbol{E}$ such that* $\lim_n a_n = \lim_n b_n$, *and if $\{T_n\}$ is a sequence of transformations belonging to $\mathfrak{M}$ such that the sequences $\{T_n(a_n)\}$ and $\{T_n(b_n)\}$ are convergent also, then we have* $\lim_n T_n(a_n) = \lim_n T_n(b_n)$.

Two sets $A \subset \boldsymbol{E}$ and $B \subset \boldsymbol{E}$ will be termed *congruent*, if there exists a transformation $T \in \mathfrak{M}$ such that $T(A) = B$ (where $T(A)$ denotes the set into which A is transformed, i. e. the set of all the points $T(a)$ for which $a \in A$).

It is easy to verify that the conditions i_1—i_5 are fulfilled.

As special cases of such spaces $\boldsymbol{E}$ we may mention: Euclidean n-dimensional space with $\mathfrak{M}$ interpreted as the class of all translations and rotations; the 3-dimensional sphere with $\mathfrak{M}$ interpreted as the class of all rotations.

Let us observe that, in the space considered, the sets which are congruent to open sets are themselves open. On the other hand, on account of 5^0, p. 316, the sets congruent to sets of measure (Γ) zero are themselves of measure zero. It follows therefore from (6.1) that in the space $\boldsymbol{E}$ considered *the sets which are congruent to measurable sets, are themselves measurable.*

Example 2. Suppose that a metrical space $\boldsymbol{E}$, separable and locally compact, constitutes a group, i. e. that with each pair a, b of elements of $\boldsymbol{E}$ there is associated an element ab of $\boldsymbol{E}$, called *product*, in such a manner that the following conditions are fulfilled:

1) $(ab)c = a(bc)$ *(whatever be the elements a, b and c of $\boldsymbol{E}$)*;

2) *there exists in $\boldsymbol{E}$ a unit-element* 1 *such that we have* $1 \cdot a = a \cdot 1 = a$ *for every* $a \in E$;

3) *to each element $a \in \boldsymbol{E}$ there corresponds an inverse element $\overset{-1}{a} \in \boldsymbol{E}$ which fulfils the equation $a\overset{-1}{a} = 1$.*

Suppose further that $\boldsymbol{E}$ fulfils the conditions:

4) *if* $\lim\limits_n a_n = a$ *and* $\lim\limits_n b_n = b$, *then* $\lim\limits_n a_n b_n = ab$;

5) *if* $\lim\limits_n a_n = a$, *then* $\lim\limits_n \overset{-1}{a_n} = \overset{-1}{a}$.

Given any element $c \in \boldsymbol{E}$ and any set $B \subset \boldsymbol{E}$, we denote by cB the set of all the elements $a \in \boldsymbol{E}$ such that $a = cb$ where $b \in B$.

Given an element a of $\boldsymbol{E}$, we write, for every element $x \in \boldsymbol{E}$, $T_a(x) = ax$. Thus each element a of $\boldsymbol{E}$ determines a transformation T_a, clearly one to one and continuous both ways, of the space $\boldsymbol{E}$ into itself. Denoting the class of all these transformations by $\mathfrak{M}$, we see at once that the conditions 1)—4), p. 318, are fulfilled. In accordance with the definition of congruence employed in Example 1, two sets A and B in the space in question are congruent if there exists an element c such that $B = cA$.

NOTE II.

The Lebesgue integral in abstract spaces

by

Stefan Banach.

Introduction.

In this note we intend to establish some general theorems concerning the Lebesgue integral in abstract spaces. This subject has been discussed by several authors (for the references see this volume, pp. 4, 88, 116, 156 and 157). Our considerations differ from those of other writers in that they are not based on the notion of measure.

Let us fix a set of arbitrary elements $\boldsymbol{H}$ as an abstract space. We shall denote real functions (i. e. functions which admit real values) defined in $\boldsymbol{H}$ by $x(t)$, $y(t)$, $z(t)$,... where $t \epsilon \boldsymbol{H}$, or simply by $x, y, z, \ldots$. A set $\mathfrak{L}$ of real functions defined in $\boldsymbol{H}$ will be called *linear* if any linear combination, with constant coefficients, of two elements of $\mathfrak{L}$, also belongs to $\mathfrak{L}$.

Let $\mathfrak{L}$ be a linear set of functions defined in $\boldsymbol{H}$. A functional F defined in $\mathfrak{L}$ is termed *additive* if for any pair of elements x and y of $\mathfrak{L}$ and any real number a, we have $F(x+y)=F(x)+F(y)$ and $F(ax)=a \cdot F(x)$. The functional F is *non-negative* if $F(x) \geqslant 0$ for any non-negative function $x \epsilon \mathfrak{L}$.

We say that a functional F defined in $\mathfrak{L}$ is a *Lebesgue integral* (*$\mathfrak{L}$-integral*) in $\mathfrak{L}$ if the following conditions are satisfied:

A) The set $\mathfrak{L}$ is linear;

B) the functional F is additive and non-negative;

C) if 1° $\{z_n\} \subset \mathfrak{L}$ and $M \epsilon \mathfrak{L}$, 2° $|z_n(t)| \leqslant M(t)$ for $n=1,2,\ldots$ and $t \epsilon \boldsymbol{H}$, and 3° $\lim\limits_{n} z_n(t)=z(t)$ for $t \epsilon \boldsymbol{H}$, then $z \epsilon \boldsymbol{H}$ and $\lim\limits_{n} F(z_n)=F(z)$;

D) if $z \in \mathfrak{L}$, $F(z)=0$ and $|y(t)| \leqslant z(t)$ for $t \in \boldsymbol{H}$, then $y \in \mathfrak{L}$ and $F(y)=0$;

E) if 1° $\{z_n\} \subset \mathfrak{L}$, $z_n(t) \leqslant z_{n+1}(t)$ for $n=1,2,\ldots$, 2° $\lim\limits_n z_n(t)=z(t)$ for $t \in \boldsymbol{H}$, and 3° $\lim\limits_n F(z_n) < +\infty$, then $z \in \mathfrak{L}$ and $\lim\limits_n F(z_n)=F(z)$.

The Lebesgue integrals considered in this note will moreover satisfy the condition:

R) If $z \in \mathfrak{L}$, then $|z| \in \mathfrak{L}$.

In Part I, a condition is established under which an additive and non-negative functional defined in a linear set of functions $\mathfrak{C}$, may be extended to an $\mathcal{L}$-integral on a certain set $\mathfrak{L}$ containing $\mathfrak{C}$. The $\mathcal{L}$-integral and the set $\mathfrak{L}$ will be explicitly defined.

In Part II we admit that $\boldsymbol{H}$ is a metrical and compact space. We consider an $\mathcal{L}$-integral defined in sets containing all functions which are bounded and measurable in the Borel sense. It is shown that each $\mathcal{L}$-integral of this kind is determined by the values which it admits for continuous functions. Conversely, any additive and non-negative functional defined for all continuous functions may be extended as an $\mathcal{L}$-integral to the class of functions measurable ($\mathfrak{B}$). We thus obtain the most general $\mathcal{L}$-integral defined for all functions bounded and measurable ($\mathfrak{B}$).

In Part III we deal with an analogous problem supposing that $\boldsymbol{H}$ is the unit sphere of the Hilbert space. In particular, the integral of a continuous function is expressed by explicit formulae.

I. Abstract sets.

§ 1. We shall employ the following notations:

1. $x \geqslant y$ if $x(t) \geqslant y(t)$ for every $t \in \boldsymbol{H}$; in particular $x \geqslant 0$ means that $x(t) \geqslant 0$ for $t \in \boldsymbol{H}$;

2. $|x|=|x(t)|$ is the modulus of $x(t)$ in the ordinary sense;

3. $\max(x,y)=\frac{1}{2}(x+y+|x-y|)$, $\min(x,y)=\frac{1}{2}(x+y-|x-y|)$;

4. $\lim\limits_n x_n=x$ means that $\lim\limits_n x_n(t)=x(t)$ for $t \in \boldsymbol{H}$; the relations $\limsup\limits_n x_n=x$, $\liminf\limits_n x_n=x$ are defined similarly;

5. $\mathring{x}=\frac{1}{2}(x+|x|)$, $\underset{\circ}{x}=\frac{1}{2}(x-|x|)$ (cf. Chap. I, p. 13).

§ 2. For the rest of Part I of this note we shall fix a set $\mathfrak{E}$ of real functions defined in H, and a functional $f(x)$ defined for $x \in \mathfrak{E}$, subject to the following conditions:

(i_1) The set $\mathfrak{E}$ is linear;

(i_2) if $x \in \mathfrak{E}$, then $|x| \in \mathfrak{E}$;

(ii_1) the functional f is additive;

(ii_2) the functional f is non-negative;

(ii_3) if 1^0 $\{x_n\} \subset \mathfrak{E}$ and $M \in \mathfrak{E}$, 2^0 $|x_n| \leqslant M$ for $n=1,2,\ldots$, and 3^0 $\lim\limits_n x_n = 0$, then $\lim\limits_n f(x_n) = 0$.

It follows immediately from the conditions (i) that for any pair of elements x and y of $\mathfrak{E}$, $\max(x,y)$, $\min(x,y)$, $\mathring{x}$ and $\underset{\circ}{x}$ also belong to $\mathfrak{E}$. It follows further that the condition (ii_3) is equivalent to the following condition:

(ii'_3) If 1^0 $\{x_n\} \subset \mathfrak{E}$ and $m \in \mathfrak{E}$, 2^0 $x_n \geqslant m$ for $n=1,2,\ldots$, and 3^0 $\liminf\limits_n x_n \geqslant 0$, then $\liminf\limits_n f(x_n) \geqslant 0$.

§ 3. We shall establish the following

Theorem 1. *If the set $\mathfrak{E}$ and the functional f satisfy the conditions* (i) *and* (ii), *then there exists an $\mathcal{L}$-integral F, defined in a set $\mathfrak{L}$ containing $\mathfrak{E}$, such that $F(x) = f(x)$ whenever $x \in \mathfrak{E}$; moreover, this integral satisfies the condition* R).

The proof will result from several lemmas.

§ 4. We denote by $\mathfrak{L}^*$ the set of all functionals $z(t)$ defined in H for each of which there exist two sequences $\{x_n\} \subset \mathfrak{E}$, $\{y_n\} \subset \mathfrak{E}$ such that

$$\liminf_n x_n \geqslant z \geqslant \limsup_n y_n. \tag{1}$$

It is easily seen that the set $\mathfrak{L}^*$ is linear and that $\mathfrak{E} \subset \mathfrak{L}^*$.

Given a function $z \in \mathfrak{L}^*$, we shall term *upper $\mathcal{L}$-integral* of z the lower bound of all (finite or infinite) numbers g for each of which there exist a function $m \in \mathfrak{E}$ and a sequence of functions $\{x_n\}$ belonging to $\mathfrak{E}$ such that $x_n \geqslant m$ for $n=1,2,\ldots$, $\liminf\limits_n x_n \geqslant z$ and $g = \liminf\limits_n f(x_n)$.

The definition of the *lower $\mathcal{L}$-integral* is analogous to that of the upper $\mathcal{L}$-integral. The upper and lower $\mathcal{L}$-integrals of a function $z \in \mathfrak{L}^*$ will be denoted by $p(z)$ and $q(z)$ respectively. We obviously have $q(z) = -p(-z)$.

§ 5. The sequence $\{f(x_n)\}$ in the above definition of the upper $\mathfrak{L}$-integral, may obviously be supposed convergent (to a finite limit or $+\infty$). Further, if $\{x_n\}\subset\mathfrak{E}$, $m\in\mathfrak{E}$, $z\geqslant 0$, $x_n\geqslant m$ for $n=1,2,\ldots$ and $\liminf_n x_n\geqslant z$, then $\lim_n \mathring{x}_n=0$ and consequently, by the condition (ii$_3$), § 2, $\lim_n f(\mathring{x}_n)=0$. Hence, *if* $z\in\mathfrak{L}^*$, $z\geqslant 0$ *and* $p(z)<P<+\infty$, *there always exists a sequence of non-negative functions* $\{x_n\}$ *belonging to* $\mathfrak{E}$ *such that* $\liminf_n x_n\geqslant z$ *and* $f(x_n)<P$ *for* $n=1,2,\ldots$

Lemma 1. *For any function* $x\in\mathfrak{E}$ *we have* $p(x)=f(x)$.

Proof. Writing $x_n=x$ and $m=x$, we have

(1) $$\liminf_n x_n\geqslant x \quad \textit{and} \quad x_n\geqslant m \quad \textit{for} \quad n=1,2,\ldots,$$

whence $p(x)\leqslant f(x)$. On the other hand, if $x_1, x_2,\ldots$ and m are any functions which belong to $\mathfrak{E}$ and satisfy the relations (1), then $\liminf_n (x_n-x)\geqslant 0$ and $x_n-x\geqslant m-x$ for $n=1,2,\ldots$. It follows from (ii$_3'$), § 2, that $\liminf_n f(x_n-x)\geqslant 0$, i.e. $\liminf_n f(x_n)\geqslant f(x)$. Thus $p(x)\geqslant f(x)$, and finally $p(x)=f(x)$.

Lemma 2. *If* $z_1\in\mathfrak{L}^*$, $z_2\in\mathfrak{L}^*$ *and if, moreover,* $p(z_1)<+\infty$, $p(z_2)<+\infty$, *then* $p(z_1+z_2)\leqslant p(z_1)+p(z_2)$.

Proof. Let P_1 and P_2 be arbitrary numbers such that $p(z_1)<P_1$ and $p(z_2)<P_2$. There exist two sequences $\{x_n^{(1)}\}$, $\{x_n^{(2)}\}$ of functions belonging to $\mathfrak{E}$ and two functions $m_1\in\mathfrak{E}$ and $m_2\in\mathfrak{E}$ such that $\liminf_n x_n^{(j)}\geqslant z_j$ and $\lim_n f(x_n^{(j)})<P_j$ for $j=1,2$ and such that $x_n^{(j)}>m_j$ for $j=1,2$ and $n=1,2,\ldots$. Therefore, writing $x_n=x_n^{(1)}+x_n^{(2)}$ and $m=m_1+m_2$, we have $\liminf_n x_n\geqslant z_1+z_2$ and $x_n\geqslant m$ for $n=1,2,\ldots$. Consequently $p(z_1+z_2)\leqslant\lim_n f(x_n)=\lim_n f(x_n^{(1)})+\lim_n f(x_n^{(2)})<P_1+P_2$, whence $p(z_1+z_2)\leqslant p(z_1)+p(z_2)$.

Lemma 3. *For any function* $z\in\mathfrak{L}^*$, *we have* $p(z)\geqslant q(z)$.

Proof. Since $q(z)=-p(-z)$ (cf. § 4), the inequality $p(z)\geqslant q(z)$ is obvious if one of the numbers $p(z)$ or $p(-z)$ is $+\infty$; while, if $p(z)<+\infty$ and $p(-z)<+\infty$, it follows immediately from Lemma 2.

***Lemma* 4.** *If $z \in \mathfrak{L}^*$, $p(z) < +\infty$, then also $p(\mathring{z}) < +\infty$ and $p(z) = p(\mathring{z}) + p(\underset{\circ}{z})$.*

Proof. Given an arbitrary finite number $P > p(z)$, there exist a function $m \in \mathfrak{E}$ and a sequence $\{x_n\}$ of functions belonging to $\mathfrak{E}$ such that $x_n \geqslant m$ for $n = 1, 2, \ldots$, $\liminf_n x_n \geqslant z$ and $\lim_n f(x_n) < P$. Note that $\underset{\circ}{x}_n \geqslant \underset{\circ}{m}$, and consequently $f(\mathring{x}_n) \leqslant f(x_n) - f(\underset{\circ}{m})$, for $n = 1, 2, \ldots$, whence $p(\mathring{z}) \leqslant \liminf_n f(\mathring{x}_n) < +\infty$. Again

$$P > \lim_n f(x_n) \geqslant \liminf_n f(\mathring{x}_n) + \liminf_n f(\underset{\circ}{x}_n) \geqslant p(\mathring{z}) + p(\underset{\circ}{z}),$$

and therefore $p(z) \geqslant p(\mathring{z}) + p(\underset{\circ}{z})$; whence, in virtue of Lemma 2, $p(z) = p(\mathring{z}) + p(\underset{\circ}{z})$.

Finally, we mention two propositions which are directly obvious:

***Lemma* 5.** *If $z_1 \in \mathfrak{L}^*$, $z_2 \in \mathfrak{L}^*$ and $z_1 \leqslant z_2$, then $p(z_1) \leqslant p(z_2)$; in particular, if $z \in \mathfrak{L}^*$ and $z \geqslant 0$, then $p(z) \geqslant 0$.*

***Lemma* 6.** *If $z \in \mathfrak{L}^*$, then $p(\lambda z) = \lambda \cdot p(z)$ for any non-negative number λ.*

§ 6. We shall now denote by $\mathfrak{L}$ the set of all functions $z \in \mathfrak{L}^*$ for which $p(z) = q(z) \neq \infty$. The following proposition is an immediate consequence of Lemmas 2 and 6:

***Lemma* 7.** *If $z_1 \in \mathfrak{L}$ and $z_2 \in \mathfrak{L}$, then $(\lambda_1 z_1 + \lambda_2 z_2) \in \mathfrak{L}$ and $p(\lambda_1 z_1 + \lambda_2 z_2) = \lambda_1 p(z_1) + \lambda_2 p(z_2)$ for any pair of finite numbers λ_1 and λ_2.*

***Lemma* 8.** *If $z \in \mathfrak{L}$, then $|z| \in \mathfrak{L}$.*

Proof. Since $|z| = \mathring{z} - \underset{\circ}{z}$, it is enough to prove that $\mathring{z} \in \mathfrak{L}$ and $\underset{\circ}{z} \in \mathfrak{L}$. To this end, let us remark that, in virtue of Lemma 4, $p(\mathring{z}) < +\infty$, $p(\underset{\circ}{z}) > -\infty$ and $p(z) = p(\mathring{z}) + p(\underset{\circ}{z})$; by symmetry, $q(\underset{\circ}{z}) > -\infty$, $q(\mathring{z}) < +\infty$ and $q(z) = q(\mathring{z}) + q(\underset{\circ}{z})$. Since, by hypothesis, $p(z) = q(z)$, it follows that $[p(\mathring{z}) - q(\mathring{z})] + [p(\underset{\circ}{z}) - q(\underset{\circ}{z})] = 0$, and so by Lemma 3, $p(\mathring{z}) = q(\mathring{z}) \neq \infty$ and $p(\underset{\circ}{z}) = q(\underset{\circ}{z}) \neq \infty$.

***Lemma* 9.** *If z is the limit of a non-decreasing sequence $\{z_n\}$ of functions belonging to $\mathfrak{L}$ and $\lim_n p(z_n) < +\infty$, then $z \in \mathfrak{L}$ and $p(z) = \lim_n p(z_n)$.*

Proof. We can clearly assume (by subtracting, if necessary, the function z_1 from all functions of the sequence $\{z_n\}$) that $z_1 = 0$. Writing $w_n = z_{n+1} - z_n$ for $n = 1, 2, \ldots$, we shall now follow an argument similar to that of Theorem 12.3, Chap. I. First, we have $z \geqslant z_n$ and $p(z_n) = q(z_n)$ for every n, and so

(1) $$q(z) \geqslant \lim_n q(z_n) = \lim_n p(z_n).$$

To establish the opposite inequality, let ε be an arbitrary positive integer and let us associate (cf. the remark at the beginning of § 5) with each function w_n a sequence $\{x_n^{(k)}\}_{k=1,2,\dots}$ of non-negative functions belonging to $\mathfrak{E}$ such that

(2) $\liminf_k x_n^{(k)} \geqslant w_n$ and (3) $f(x_n^{(k)}) \leqslant p(w_n) + \varepsilon/2^n$.

Let us write $y_k = \sum_{n=1}^{k} x_n^{(k)}$. The functions y_k clearly belong to $\mathfrak{E}$ and, by (2), we have $\liminf_k y_k \geqslant \sum_k w_k = z$. On the other hand, in virtue of (3), we find $f(y_k) \leqslant \sum_{n=1}^{k} p(w_n) + \varepsilon \leqslant p(z_{k+1}) + \varepsilon \leqslant \lim_i p(z_i) + \varepsilon$ for $k = 1, 2, \dots$. Therefore, $p(z) \leqslant \liminf_k f(y_k) \leqslant \lim_k p(z_k) + \varepsilon$, and since ε is an arbitrary positive number, this combined with (1) gives $0 \leqslant p(z) = q(z) = \lim_k p(z_k) < +\infty$, which completes the proof.

Lemma 10. *If $M \in \mathfrak{L}$ and $\{z_n\}$ is a sequence of functions belonging to $\mathfrak{L}$ such that $|z_n| \leqslant M$ for $n = 1, 2, \dots$, then, putting $g = \liminf_n z_n$ and $h = \limsup_n z_n$, we have $g \in \mathfrak{L}$, $h \in \mathfrak{L}$, and*

$$p(g) \leqslant \liminf_n p(z_n) \leqslant \limsup_n p(z_n) \leqslant p(h).$$

Consequently, if the sequence $\{z_n\}$ is convergent and $z = \lim_n z_n$, then $p(z) = \lim_n p(z_n)$.

Proof. The lemma corresponds to Theorem 12.11, Chap. I, and its proof is analogous to that of the latter. Let us write, for each pair of integers i and $j \geqslant i$, $g_{ij} = \min(z_i, z_{i+1}, \dots, z_j)$. The sequence $\{g_{ij}\}_{j=i, i+1, \dots}$ is non-increasing, and consequently the sequence $\{M - g_{ij}\}_{j=i, i+1, \dots}$ is non-decreasing. Let $g_i = \lim_j g_{ij}$. Since the functions g_{ij} clearly belong to $\mathfrak{L}$, it follows from Lemma 9 that $M - g_i \in \mathfrak{L}$ and $p(M - g_i) = \lim_j p(M - g_{ij})$, i. e. $g_i \in \mathfrak{L}$ and $p(g_i) = \lim_j p(g_{ij})$. Hence, applying again Lemma 9 to the non-decreasing sequence $\{g_i\}$ which converges to g, we obtain $g \in \mathfrak{L}$ and

$$p(g) = \lim_i p(g_i) \leqslant \liminf_i p(z_i).$$

By symmetry we have the analogous result for h and the proof is complete.

We shall conclude this § by mentioning the following lemma which is an immediate consequence of Lemma 5:

Lemma 11. *If $z \in \mathfrak{L}$, $z \geqslant 0$ and $p(z) = 0$, then any function x such that $|x| \leqslant z$ belongs to $\mathfrak{L}$ and for any such function x we have $p(x) = 0$.*

§ 7. Let $F(x)=p(x)$ for $x \in \mathfrak{L}$. The lemmas of the preceding sections show that the set $\mathfrak{L}$ and the functional $F(z)$ satisfy the theorem stated in § 3. Theorem 1 is thus proved.

It is easily seen that if an $\mathfrak{L}$-integral F_1 defined in a linear set $\mathfrak{L}_1 \supset \mathfrak{L}$ satisfies the condition $f(x) = F_1(x)$ for $x \in \mathfrak{C}$, then $F(x)=F_1(x)$ for all $x \in \mathfrak{L}$. Consequently the functional f determines completely an $\mathfrak{L}$-integral in the set $\mathfrak{L}$.

II. Metrical compact sets.

§ 8. Let now $\boldsymbol{H}$ be a complete and compact metrical space. We shall specify $\mathfrak{C}$ as the set of functions continuous in $\boldsymbol{H}$.

The set $\mathfrak{C}$ satisfies evidently the conditions (i), § 2. It may be shown that any additive and non-negative functional f defined in $\mathfrak{C}$ satisfies the condition (ii_3) [1]).

Theorem 1 permits to define a Lebesgue integral $F(x)$ for all functions x belonging to a certain set $\mathfrak{L} \supset \mathfrak{C}$, in such a manner that the condition R), p. 321, is satisfied and that $F(x)=f(x)$ for $x \in \mathfrak{C}$.

Evidently, every function $x(t)$ which is constant on $\boldsymbol{H}$ belongs to $\mathfrak{C}$. It follows by condition C), p. 320, that every bounded function measurable in the sense of Borel belongs to $\mathfrak{C}$.

We have thus proved the following

Theorem 2. *Every additive and non-negative functional, defined for all functions which are continuous in a complete compact space* $\boldsymbol{H}$, *may by extended to an* $\mathfrak{L}$*-integral defined in a certain linear set (containing all bounded functions measurable in the sense of Borel) so that the condition* R) *be satisfied.*

The values of this $\mathfrak{L}$-integral for functions bounded and measurable ($\mathfrak{B}$) are, of course, determined by the given functional f. Hence the most general $\mathfrak{L}$-integral defined for this class of functions may be obtained by choosing an arbitrary additive non-negative functional defined for all functions which are continuous in $\boldsymbol{H}$ and by extending this functional by means of the method described in Part I of this note.

---

[1]) A functional of this kind is necessarily linear. Every linear functional defined in $\mathfrak{C}$ satisfies the condition (ii_3). See S. Banach [I, p.224].

Any linear functional $f(x)$ defined in the set E is the difference of two additive non-negative functionals $f_1(x)$ and $f_2(x)$ (cf. S. Banach [I, p. 217]). Extending these functionals by means of Theorem 1 over two sets, $\mathfrak{L}_1$ and $\mathfrak{L}_2$ say, respectively, we see that it is possible to extend the functional $f(x)$ over the linear set $\mathfrak{L}=\mathfrak{L}_1\cdot\mathfrak{L}_2$. This set will contain all bounded functions measurable ($\mathfrak{B}$). The extended additive functional $F(x)$ evidently satisfies the conditions C) and R), p. 321, and is non-negative.

III. The Hilbert space.

§ 9. We shall now understand by $\boldsymbol{H}$ the unit sphere of the Hilbert space, i. e. the set of all sequences $\{\vartheta_i\}$ for which $\sum_{i=1}^{\infty}\vartheta_i^2\leqslant 1$. The distance of two points $t=\{\vartheta_i\}$ and $t'=\{\vartheta_i'\}$ is defined, as usually, by the formula

$$\varrho(t,t')=[\sum_{i=1}^{\infty}(\vartheta_i-\vartheta_i')^2]^{\frac{1}{2}}.$$

With regard to this definition of distance the space $\boldsymbol{H}$ is not compact and therefore we cannot apply Theorem 2 directly.

Let $\mathfrak{C}_n$ be the set of functions $x=x(t)=x(\vartheta_1,\vartheta_2,...)$ which are continuous in $\boldsymbol{H}$ and whose values depend only on the first n coordinates ϑ_j, so that $x(\vartheta_1,\vartheta_2,...)=x(\vartheta_1,\vartheta_2,...,\vartheta_n,0,0,...)$ for any $t=\{\vartheta_i\}\epsilon\boldsymbol{H}$. Clearly $\mathfrak{C}_n\subset\mathfrak{C}_{n+1}$.

It is easily seen that the set $\mathfrak{C}=\sum_{n=1}^{\infty}\mathfrak{C}_n$ satisfies the conditions (i), § 2. Any functional f defined in $\mathfrak{C}$ for which the conditions (ii) hold may be extended to an $\mathfrak{L}$-integral defined in a certain set $\mathfrak{L}$ containing $\mathfrak{C}$.

Lemma 12. *The set $\mathfrak{L}$ contains all bounded functions mesurable ($\mathfrak{B}$) defined in $\boldsymbol{H}$.*

Proof. Let x be a bounded continuous function defined in $\boldsymbol{H}$. For any point $t=(\vartheta_1,\vartheta_2,...,\vartheta_n,...)$ and any positive integer n, we write $x_n(t)=x(\vartheta_1,...,\vartheta_n,0,0,...)$. Evidently $x_n\epsilon\mathfrak{C}$ and $\lim_n x_n=x$. If M is the upper bound of $|x(t)|$ for $t\epsilon\boldsymbol{H}$, then $|x_n|\leqslant M$. Since the constant function $z=M$ certainly belongs to $\mathfrak{C}$, it follows from the condition C), p. 320, that $x\epsilon\mathfrak{L}$.

Consequently every bounded and continuous function belongs to $\mathfrak{L}$ and by the condition C) the same is true of any bounded function measurable ($\mathfrak{B}$).

Lemma 13. *Every additive and non-negative functional* $f(x)$ *defined in* $\mathfrak{E}$ *satisfies the condition* (ii₃), § 2.

Proof. We define in **H** a distance $\varrho_1(t, t')$ of two points $t = \{\vartheta_1, \vartheta_2, \ldots\}$, $t' = \{\vartheta'_1, \vartheta'_2, \ldots\}$ by

$$(1) \qquad \varrho_1(t, t') = \sum_{i=1}^{\infty} \frac{1}{2^i} \frac{|\vartheta_i - \vartheta'_i|}{1 + |\vartheta_i - \vartheta'_i|}.$$

We easily verify that with regard to this distance the set **H** is complete and compact.

Let $\widetilde{\mathfrak{E}}$ be the set of all functions defined in **H** which are continuous according to the distance defined by the formula (1). Evidently $\mathfrak{E} \subset \widetilde{\mathfrak{E}}$.

Let f be an additive non-negative functional defined in $\mathfrak{E}$. Let $x_n(t) = x(\vartheta_1, \ldots, \vartheta_n, 0, 0, \ldots)$ for $x \,\epsilon\, \widetilde{\mathfrak{E}}$ and $t = \{\vartheta_1, \vartheta_2, \ldots\} \,\epsilon\, \textbf{H}$.

With regard to the distance (1), **H** is a complete and compact space, and hence the function $x(t) \,\epsilon\, \mathfrak{E}$ is uniformly continuous. It follows that the sequence $\{x_n\}$ uniformly converges to x. This implies the convergence of the sequence $\{f(x_n)\}$ [1]). Let $\widetilde{f}(x) = \lim_{n} f(x_n)$.

If $x \geqslant 0$, then $x_n \geqslant 0$ for each n, and consequently $\widetilde{f}(x) \geqslant 0$. The functional $\widetilde{f}(x)$, clearly additive, is therefore non-negative. The set **H** being compact, it follows, by what has been established in Part II, that $\widetilde{f}$ satisfies in **H** the condition (ii₃) (with $\mathfrak{E}$ and f replaced by $\widetilde{\mathfrak{E}}$ and $\widetilde{f}$ respectively). Since $\mathfrak{E} \subset \widetilde{\mathfrak{E}}$ and $\widetilde{f}(x) = f(x)$ for $x \,\epsilon\, \mathfrak{E}$, the functional f satisfies the condition (ii₃) in $\mathfrak{E}$.

§ 10. Now consider an additive non-negative functional $f(x)$ defined in $\mathfrak{E}$. Let $f_n(x)$ denote the functional defined in $\mathfrak{E}_n$ by the formula

$$(2) \qquad f_n(x) = f(x) \qquad for \quad x \,\epsilon\, \mathfrak{E}_n.$$

We obviously have

$$(3) \qquad f_n(x) = f_{n+1}(x) \qquad for \quad x \,\epsilon\, \mathfrak{E}_n.$$

---

[1]) Indeed if $\varepsilon > 0$, there exists a positive integer N such that $-\varepsilon \leqslant x_p - x_q \leqslant \varepsilon$ whenever $p > N$, $q > N$. Since the constant function $z = 1$ belongs to $\mathfrak{E}$, we have, for $k = f(1)$, the inequality $-k\varepsilon \leqslant f(x_p) - f(x_q) \leqslant k\varepsilon$ which proves the convergence of $\{f(x_n)\}$.

Conversely, if we choose any sequence $\{f_n(x)\}$ of additive non-negative functionals, the functional f_n being defined in $\mathfrak{E}_n$ (where $n=1,2,...$) subject to the condition (3), then the formula (2) determines an additive non-negative functional $f(x)$ in $\mathfrak{E}$. We thus obtain the most general additive non-negative functional $f(x)$ defined in $\mathfrak{E}$, and by what has been established in the preceding §, the most general Lebesgue integral for all functions bounded and measurable ($\mathfrak{B}$).

The set $\mathfrak{E}_n$ may be interpreted as the set of all function of n variables $\vartheta_1,...,\vartheta_n$ which are defined and continuous in the sphere $\vartheta_1^2+...+\vartheta_n^2 \leqslant 1$. It is known that the most general additive and non-negative functional defined in $\mathfrak{E}_n$ may be represented by a Stjeltjes integral.

These general considerations will now be illustrated by the following example. Suppose that the functionals f_n are given by the formula

$$(4) \qquad f_n(x) = \int_{\vartheta_1^2+...+\vartheta_n^2 \leqslant 1} ... \int x(\vartheta_1,...,\vartheta_n,0,0,...) \, \varphi_n(\vartheta_1,...,\vartheta_n) \, d\vartheta_1...d\vartheta_n$$

for $x \,\epsilon\, \mathfrak{E}_n$, where φ_n denotes a fixed non-negative function integrable in the sphere $\vartheta_1^2+...+\vartheta_n^2 \leqslant 1$. The condition (3) may be written in the form

$$\varphi_n(\vartheta_1,...,\vartheta_n) = \int_{-\sqrt{1-\vartheta_1^2-...-\vartheta_n^2}}^{+\sqrt{1-\vartheta_1^2-...-\vartheta_n^2}} \varphi_{n+1}(\vartheta_1,...,\vartheta_n,\vartheta_{n+1}) \, d\vartheta_{n+1}.$$

To satisfy this condition, we may put, for instance, $\varphi_1 = 1/2$ and $\varphi_{n+1} = \varphi_n/2\sqrt{1-\vartheta_1^2-...-\vartheta_n^2}$ for $n \geqslant 1$. We thus obtain

$$(5) \qquad \varphi_n(\vartheta_1,...,\vartheta_n) = \frac{1}{2^n\sqrt{1-\vartheta_1^2}...\sqrt{1-\vartheta_1^2-...-\vartheta_{n-1}^2}}$$

Let x be an arbitrary function bounded and continuous in H. We write again $x_n = x(\vartheta_1,...,\vartheta_n,0,0,...)$. If $|x| \leqslant M$, where M is a constant, then $\lim_n x_n = x$, $|x_n| \leqslant M$.

Now let F be an $\mathfrak{L}$-integral which for functions belonging to $\mathfrak{C}$ coincides with the functional f subject to (2). We then have $F(x) = \lim_n F(x_n) = \lim_n f_n(x_n)$. If further f_n is represented by the formula (4), then

$$F(x) = \lim_n \int_{\vartheta_1^2 + \ldots + \vartheta_n^2 \leqslant 1} \ldots \int x(\vartheta_1, \ldots, \vartheta_n, 0, 0, \ldots)\, \varphi_n(\vartheta_1, \ldots, \vartheta_n)\, d\vartheta_1 \ldots d\vartheta_n$$

and, in particular, if φ_n is given by (5),

$$F(x) = \lim_n \int_{\vartheta_1^2 + \ldots + \vartheta_n^2 \leqslant 1} \ldots \int x(\vartheta_1, \ldots, \vartheta_n, 0, 0, \ldots) \frac{d\vartheta_1 \ldots d\vartheta_n}{2^n \sqrt{1-\vartheta_1^2} \ldots \sqrt{1-\vartheta_1^2 - \ldots - \vartheta_{n-1}^2}}.$$

This formula defines explicitly a certain $\mathfrak{L}$-integral for all functions bounded and continuous in H.

The above considerations may be extended to certain spaces of the type (B) (cf. S. Banach [I, Chap. V]), e. g. the spaces $l^{(p)}$, $L^{(p)}$ with $p > 1$.

BIBLIOGRAPHY.

Adams, C. R. and **Clarkson, J. A.** [1] On definitions of bounded variation for functions of two variables, Trans. Amer. Math. Soc., **35**, 824—854 (1933). — [2] Properties of functions $f(x,y)$ of bounded variation, ibid., **36**, 711—730 (1934).

Alexandroff, P. [1] Über die Äquivalenz des Perronschen und des Denjoyschen Integralbegriffes, Math. Zeitschr., **20**, 213—222 (1924). — [2] L'intégration au sens de M. Denjoy considérée comme recherche des fonctions primitives, Rec. Math. Soc. Math. Moscou, **31**, 465—476 (1924).

Appert, A. [1] Mesures normales dans les espaces distanciés, Bull. Soc. Math. France, **60**, 1—36 (1936).

Auerbach, H. [1] Démonstration nouvelle d'un théorème de M. Banach sur les fonctions dérivées des fonctions mesurables, Fundam. Math., **7**, 263 (1925).

Baire, R. [1] Sur les fonctions de variables réelles, Ann. Mat. Pura e Appl. **(3)**, **3**, 1—122 (1899).

Banach, S. [I] Théorie des opérations linéaires, Monografje Matematyczne **1**, Warszawa 1932. — [1] Sur les ensembles de points où la dérivée est infinie, C. R. Acad. Sci. Paris, **173**, 457—459 (1921). — [2] Sur les fonctions dérivées des fonctions mesurables, Fundam. Math., **3**, 128—132 (1922). — [3] Sur un théorème de M. Vitali, ibid., **5**, 130—136 (1924). — [4] Sur une classe de fonctions d'ensemble, ibid., **6**, 170—188 (1924). — [5] Sur les lignes rectifiables et les surfaces dont l'aire est finie, ibid., **7**, 225—237 (1925). — [6] Sur une classe de fonctions continues, ibid., **8**, 166—173 (1926). — [7] Ueber additive Massfunktionen in abstrakten Mengen, ibid., **15**, 97—101 (1930).

Banach, S. et **Kuratowski, C.** [1] Sur une généralisation du problème de la mesure, Fundam. Math., **14**, 127—131 (1929).

Banach, S. et **Saks, S.** [1] Sur les fonctions absolument continues des fonctions absolument continues, Fundam. Math., **11**, 113—116 (1928).

Bary, N. [1] Sur la représentation analytique d'une classe de fonctions continues, C. R. Acad. Sci. Paris, **183**, 469—471 (1926). — [2] Sur les fonctions jouissant de la propriété (N), ibid., **189**, 441—443 (1929). — [3] Mémoire sur la représentation finie des fonctions continues, Math. Ann., **103**, 185—248 and 598—653 (1930). — [4] Sur une classification des fonctions continues à partir des fonctions à variation bornée, Rec. Math. Soc. Math. Moscou, **40**, 326—370 (1933).

Bary, N. et **Menchoff, D.** [1] Sur l'intégrale de Lebesgue-Stieltjes et les fonctions absolument continues des fonctions absolument continues, Ann. Mat. Pura e Appl. (4), **5**, 19—54 (1928).

Bauer, H. [1] Der Perronsche Integralbegriff und seine Beziehung zum Lebesgueschen, Monatshefte Math. Phys., **26**, 153—198 (1915).

Besicovitch, A. S. [1] On the fundamental geometrical properties of linearly measurable plane sets of points, Math. Ann., **98**, 422—464 (1928). — [2] Discussion der stetigen Funktionen im Zusammenhang mit der Frage über ihre Differenzierbarkeit, Bull. Acad. Sci. URSS, 97—122, 527—540 (1925). — [3] On sufficient conditions for a function to be analytic, and on behaviour of analytic functions in the neighborhood of non-isolated singular points, Proc. London Math. Soc. (2), **32**, 1—9 (1931). — [4] On tangents to general sets of points, Fundam. Math., **22**, 49—53 (1934). — [5] On differentiation of Lebesgue double integrals, ibid., **25**, 209—216 (1935). — [6] On differentiation of functions of two variables, Math. Zeitschr., **41**, 402—404 (1936).

Birkhoff, G. [1] Integration of functions with values in a Banach space, Trans. Amer. Math. Soc., **38**, 357—378 (1935).

Blumberg, H. [1] A theorem on arbitrary functions of two variables with applications, Fundam. Math., **16**, 17—24 (1930). — [2] The measurable boundaries of an arbitrary function, Acta Math., **65**, 263—282 (1935).

Bochner, S. [1] Integration von Funktionen, deren Werte die Elemente eines Vektorraumes sind, Fundam. Math., **20**, 262—276 (1933). — [2] Eine Bemerkung zum Satz von Fubini, ibid., **20**, 277—280 (1933). — [3] Absolut-additive abstrakte Mengenfunktionen, ibid., **21**, 211—213 (1933).

Borel, E. [I] Leçons sur la théorie des fonctions, Paris 1898. — [1] Sur l'intégration des fonctions non bornées et sur les définitions constructives, Ann. Ecole Norm., **36**, 71—91, (1919).

Bourbaki, N. [1] Sur un théorème de Carathéodory et la mesure dans les espaces topologiques, C. R. Acad. Sci. Paris, **201**, 1309—1311 (1935).

Bouligand, G. [I] Introduction à la Géométrie infinitésimale directe, Paris 1932.

Burkill, J. C. [1] The fundamental theorem of Denjoy integration, Proc. Cambridge Philos. Soc., **21**, 659—663 (1923). — [2] Functions of intervals, Proc. London Math. Soc. (2), **22**, 275—310 (1924). — [3] The expressions of area as an integral, ibid. (2), **22**, 311—336 (1924). — [4] The derivates of functions of intervals, Fundam. Math., **5**, 321—327 (1924). — [5] The approximately continuous Perron integral, Math. Zeitschr., **34**, 270—278 (1931). — [6] The Cesàro-Perron integral, Proc. London Math. Soc. (2), **34**, 314—322 (1932). — [7] The Cesàro-Perron scale of integration, ibid., **39**, 541—552 (1935).

Burkill, J. C. and **Haslam-Jones, U. S.** [1] The derivates and approximate derivates of measurable functions, Proc. London Math. Soc. (2), **32**, 346—355 (1931). — [2] Note on the differentiability of functions of two variables, Journ. London Math. Soc., **7**, 297—305 (1932). — [3] Relative measurability and the derivates of non-measurable functions, Quart. Journ. Math., Oxford Ser., **4**,, 233—239 (1933).

Busemann, H. und **Feller, W.** [1] Zur Differentiation der Lebesgueschen Integrale, Fundam. Math., **22**, 226—256 (1934).

Caccioppoli, R. [1] Sul lemma fondamentale del calcolo integrale, Atti Mem. Accad. Sci. Padova, **50**, 93—98 (1934).

Carathéodory, C. [I] Vorlesungen über reelle Funktionen, Leipzig-Berlin 1918. — (II) Vorlesungen über reelle Funktionen, Leipzig-Berlin, 2. Aufl. 1927. — [1] Ueber das lineare Mass von Punktmengen — eine Verallgemeinerung des Längenbegriffs, Nachr. Ges. Wiss. Göttingen, 404—426 (1914).

Cauchy, A. [I] Oeuvres complètes, Paris 1882—1899.

Čelidze, V. G. [1] Ueber derivierte Zahlen einer Funktion zweier Variablen, C. R. Acad. Sci. URSS, **15**, 13—15 (1937).

Clarkson, J. A. [1] Uniformly convex spaces, Trans. Amer. Math. Soc., **40**, 396—414 (1936).

Cohen, L. W. [1] A new proof of Lusin's theorem, Fundam. Math., **9**, 122—123 (1927).

Currier, A. E. [1] Proof of the fundamental theorems on second-order cross partial derivatives, Trans. Amer. Math. Soc., **35**, 245—253 (1933).

Daniell, P. J. [1] A general form of integral, Ann. of Math. (2), **19**, 279—294 (1917—18). — [2] Integrals in an infinite number of dimensions, ibid. (2), **20**, 281—288 (1918). — [3] Functions of limited variation in an infinite number of dimensions, ibid., **21**, 30—38 (1919). — [4] Stieltjes derivatives, Bull. Amer. Math. Soc., **26**, 444—448 (1919). — [5] Further properties of the general integral, Ann. of Math. (2), **21**, 203—220 (1920).

Denjoy, A. [1] Mémoire sur les nombres dérivés des fonctions continues, Journ. Math. Pures et Appl. (7), **1**, 105—240 (1915). — [2] Une extension de l'intégrale de M. Lebesgue, C. R. Acad. Sci. Paris, **154**, 859—862 (1912). — [3] Calcul de la primitive de la fonction dérivée la plus générale, ibid., **154**, 1075—1078 (1912). — [4] Sur la dérivation et son calcul inverse, ibid., **162**, 377—380 (1916). — [5] Sur les fonctions dérivées sommables, Bull. Soc. Math. France, **43**, 161—248 (1915). — [6] Mémoire sur la totalisation des nombres dérivés non-sommables, Ann. Ecole Norm., **33**, 127—222 (1916); **34**, 181—238 (1917). — [7] Sur l'intégration riemannienne, C. R. Acad. Sci. Paris, **169**, 219—220 (1919). — [8] Sur la définition riemannienne de l'intégrale de Lebesgue, ibid., **193**, 695—698 (1931). — [9] Sur l'intégration des coefficients différentiels d'ordre supérieur, Fundam. Math., **25**, 273—326 (1935).

Dini, U. [1] Fondamenti per la teorica delle funzioni di variabili reali, Pisa 1878.

Dunford, N. [1] On a theorem of Plessner, Bull. Amer. Math. Soc., **41**, 356—358 (1935). — [2] Integration in general analysis, Trans. Amer. Math. Soc., **37**, 441—453 (1935) [Corrections, ibid., **38**, 600—601 (1936)]. — [3] Integration and linear operations, ibid., **40**, 474—484 (1936).

Egoroff, D. Th. [1] Sur les suites des fonctions mesurables, C. R. Acad. Sci. Paris, **152**, 244—246 (1911).

Evans, G. C. [1] On potentials of positive mass, I, Trans. Amer. Math. Soc., **37**, 226—253 (1935).

Faber, G. [1] Über stetige Funktionen II., Math. Ann., **69**, 372—433 (1910).

Fatou, P. [1] Séries trigonométriques et séries de Taylor, Acta Math., **30**, 335—400 (1906).

Feller, W. [1] Bemerkungen zur Masstheorie in abstrakten Räumen, Bull. Int. Acad. Yougosl., **28**, 30—45 (1934).

Fichtenholz, G. [1] Sur une fonction de deux variables sans intégrale double, Fundam. Math., **6**, 30—36 (1924). — [2] Sur une généralisation de l'intégrale de Stieltjes, C. R. Acad. Sci. URSS, **3**, 95—100 (1936). — [3] Note sur les fonctions absolument continues, Rec. Math. Soc. Math. Moscou, **31**, 286—295 (1923). — [4] Sur un problème de M. Banach, Fundam. Math., **10**, 302—304 (1927).

Fichtenholz, G. et **Kantorovitch, L.** [1] Sur les opérations dans l'espace des fonctions bornées, Studia Math., **5**, 69—98 (1934).

Fréchet, M. [1] Sur l'intégrale d'une fonctionnelle étendue à un ensemble abstrait, Bull. Soc. Math. France, **43**, 249—267 (1915). — [2] Note on the area of a surface, Proc. London Math. Soc. (2), **24**, XLVIII (1926). — [3] Sur l'aire des surfaces polyédrales, Ann. Soc. Polon. Math., **3**, 1—3 (1925). — [4] Sur le prolongement des fonctionnelles semi-continues et sur l'aire des surfaces courbes, Fundam. Math., **7**, 210—224 (1925). — [5] Sur quelques définitions possibles de l'intégrale de Stieltjes, Duke Math. Journ., **2**, 283—395 (1936).

Fubini, G. [1] Sugli integrali multipli, Atti Accad. Naz. Lincei, Rend., 16_1, 608—614 (1907). — [2] Sulla derivazione per serie, ibid., 24_1, 204—206 (1915).

Geöcze, Z. de [1] Quadrature des surfaces courbes, Math. Naturwiss. Ber. Ungarn, **26**, 1—88 (1910).

Gillis, J. [1] On linearly measurable plane sets of points, C. R. Soc. Sci. Varsovie, **27**, 49—70 (1936).

Goldowsky, G. [1] Note sur les dérivées exactes, Rec. Math. Soc. Math. Moscou, **35**, 35—36 (1928).

Goursat, E. [1] Sur la définition générale des fonctions analytiques d'après Cauchy, Trans. Amer. Math. Soc., **1**, 14—16 (1900).

Gowurin, M. [1] Ueber die Stieltjessche Integration abstrakter Funktionen, Fundam. Math. **27**, 254—268 (1936).

Gross, W. [1] Über das Flächenmass von Punktmengen, Monatshefte Math. Phys., **29**, 145—176 (1918).

Haar, A. [1] Der Massbegriff in der Theorie der kontinuierlichen Gruppen, Ann. of Math. (2), **34**, 147—169 (1933).

Hahn, H. [I] Theorie der reellen Funktionen, 1. Band, Berlin 1921. — [II] Reelle Funktionen, 1. Teil, Leipzig 1932. — [1] Ueber den Fundamentalsatz der Integralrechnung, Monatshefte Math. Phys., **16**, 161—166 (1905). — [2] Ueber die Multiplikation total-additiver Mengenfunktionen, Ann. Scuola Norm. Sup. Pisa **3**, 429—452 (1933).

Hake, H. [1] Ueber de la Vallée Poussins Ober- und Unterfunktionen einfacher Integrale und die Integraldefinition von Perron, Math. Ann., **83**, 119—142 (1921).

Hardy, G. H. and **Littlewood, J. E.** [1] Some properties of fractional integrals, Math. Zeitschr., **27**, 565—606 (1928). — [2] A maximal theorem with function-theoretic applications, Acta Math., **54**, 81—116 (1930).

Harnack, A. [1] Die allgemeinen Sätze über den Zusammenhang der Funktionen einer reellen Variabeln mit ihren Ableitungen, II, Math. Ann., **24**, 217—252 (1884).

Haslam-Jones, U. S. [1] Derivate planes and tangent planes of a measurable function, Quart. Journ. Math., Oxford Ser., **3**, 120—132 (1932). — [2] Tangential properties of a plane set of points, ibid., **7**, 116—123 (1936). — [3] The discontinuities of an arbitrary function of two variables, ibid., **7**, 184—190 (1936).

Hausdorff, F. [I] Grundzüge der Mengenlehre, Leipzig 1914. — [II] Mengenlehre, 3. Aufl., Berlin 1935. — [1] Dimension und äusseres Mass, Math. Ann., **79**, 157—179 (1919).

Heffter, L. [1] Zum Beweis des Cauchy-Goursatschen Integralsatzes, Nachr. Ges. Wiss. Göttingen, 312—316 (1903).

Hildebrandt, T. H. [1] On integrals related to and extensions of the Lebesgue integrals, Bull. Amer. Math. Soc. (2), **24**, 113—144 (1917), 177—202 (1918). — [2] On the interchange of limit and Lebesgue integral for a sequence of functions, Trans. Amer. Math. Soc., **33**, 441—443 (1931).

Hille, J. and **Tamarkin, J. D.** [1] Remarks on a known example of a monotone continuous function, Amer. Math. Monthly, **36**, 255—264 (1929).

Hobson, E. W. [I] The theory of functions of a real variable and the theory of Fourier's series, Vol. I, 3d edition, Cambridge 1927. — [II] The theory of functions of a real variable and the theory of Fourier's series, Vol. II, 2d edition, Cambridge 1926.

Izumi, S. [1] On the F. Riesz' lemma, Tôhoku Math. Journ., **42**, 65—66 (1936).

Jarník, V. [1] Über die Differenzierbarkeit stetiger Funktionen, Fundam. Math., **21**, 48—58 (1933). — [2] Sur les nombres dérivés approximatifs, ibid., **22**, 4—16 (1934). — [3] Sur les fonctions de deux variables réelles, ibid., **27**, 147—150 (1936).

Jeffery, R. L. [1] The integrability of a sequence of functions, Trans. Amer. Math. Soc., **33**, 433—440 (1931). — [2] Non-absolutely convergent integrals with respect to functions of bounded variation, ibid., **34**, 645—675 (1932). — [3] Derived numbers with respect to functions of bounded variation, ibid., **36**, 749—758 (1934).

Jessen, B. [1] Abstrakt Maal- og Integralteori, Mat. Tidsskr. B, 73—84 (1934); 60—74 (1935). — [2] The theory of integration in a space of an infinite number of dimensions, Acta Math., **63**, 249—323 (1934).

Jessen, B., Marcinkiewicz, J. and **Zygmund, A.** [1] Note on the differentiability of multiple integrals, Fundam. Math., **25**, 217—234 (1935).

Kamke, E. [I] Das Lebesgue'sche Integral, Leipzig 1925. —[1] Zur Definition der approximativ stetigen Funktionen, Fundam. Math., **10**, 431—433 (1927).

Kellogg, O. D. [1] An example in potential theory, Proc. Amer. Acad. Arts Sci., **58**, 527—533 (1923).

Kempisty, S. [1] Sur la méthode triangulaire du calcul de l'aire d'une surface courbe, Bull. Soc. Math. France, **64**, 119—132 (1936).

Kennedy, M. D. and **Pollard, S.** [1] Upper and lower integrals, Math. Zeitschr., **39**, 432—454.

Khintchine, A. [1] Sur une extension de l'intégrale de M. Denjoy, C. R. Acad. Sci. Paris, **162**, 287—291 (1916). — [2] Sur le procédé d'intégration de M. Denjoy, Rec. Math. Soc. Math. Moscou, **30**, 543—557 (1918). — [3] Sur la dérivation asymptotique, C. R. Acad. Sci. Paris, **164**, 142—144 (1917). — [4] Recherches sur la structure des fonctions mesurables, Rec. Math. Soc. Math. Moscou, **31**, 265—285 and 377—433 (1924). — [5] Recherches sur la structure des fonctions mesurables, Fundam. Math., **9**, 212—279 (1927).

Kolmogoroff, A. [1] Untersuchungen über den Integralbegriff, Math. Ann., **103**, 654—696 (1930). — [2] La définition axiomatique de l'intégrale, C. R. Acad. Sci. Paris, **180**, 110—111 (1925). — [3] Beiträge zur Masstheorie, Math. Ann., **107**, 351—366 (1932).

Kolmogoroff, A. und **Verčenko, J.** [1] Ueber Unstetigkeitspunkte von Funktionen zweier Veränderlichen, C. R. Acad. Sci. URSS, **1**, 1—3, 105—107 (1934). — [2] Weitere Untersuchungen über Unstetigkeitspunkte von Funktionen zweier Veränderlichen, ibid., **4**, 361—364 (1934).

Kondô, M. [1] Sur les notions de catégorie et de mesure dans la théorie des ensembles de points, Journ. Fac. Sci. Hokkaido Univ., **4**, 123—180 (1936).

Krzyżański, M. [1] Sur les fonctions absolument continues généralisées de deux variables, C. R. Acad. Sci. Paris, **198**, 2058—2060 (1934).

Kuratowski, C. [I] Topologie I (Espaces métrisables, espaces complets), Monografie Matematyczne **4**, Warszawa-Lwów 1933.

Kuratowski, C. et **Ulam, S.** [1] Quelques propriétés topologiques du produit combinatoire, Fundam. Math., **19**, 247—251 (1932).

Lampariello, G. [1] Sulle superficie continue che ammettono area finita, Atti Accad. Naz. Lincei, Rend., $\mathbf{3}_1$, 294—298 (1926).

Lebesgue, H. [I] Leçons sur l'intégration et la recherche des fonctions primitives, Paris 1904. — [II] Leçons sur l'intégration et la recherche des fonctions primitives, 2-me éd., Paris 1928. — [1] Intégrale, Longueur, Aire, Ann. Mat. Pura e Appl. (3), **7**, 231—359 (1902). — [2] Sur les fonctions dérivées, Atti Accad. Naz. Lincei, Rend., $\mathbf{15}_2$, 3—8 (1906). — [3] Encore une observation sur les fonctions dérivées, ibid., **16**, 92—100 (1907). — [4] Sur la recherche des fonctions primitives, ibid., $\mathbf{16}_1$, 283—290 (1907). — [5] Sur l'intégration des fonctions discontinues, Ann. Ecole Norm. (3), **27**, 361—450 (1910). — [6] Remarques sur les théories de la mesure et de l'intégration, ibid., **35**, 191—250 (1918). — [7] Sur la recherche des fonctions primitives, Acta Math., **49**, 245—262 (1926). — [8] Sur le développement de la notion d'intégrale, Mat. Tidsskr. B, 54—74 (1926).

Levi, B. [1] Ricerche sulle funzioni derivate, Atti Accad. Naz. Lincei, Rend., 15_1, 433—438 (1906).

Looman, H. [1] Sur la totalisation des dérivées des fonctions continues de plusieurs variables indépendantes, Fundam. Math., **4**, 246—285 (1923). — [2] Ueber die Cauchy-Riemannschen Differentialgleichungen, Nachr. Ges. Wiss. Göttingen, 97—108 (1923). — [3] Ueber eine Erweiterung des Cauchy-Goursatschen Integralsatzes, Nieuw. Arch. Wiskde (2), **14**, 234—239 (1925). — [4] Ueber die Perronsche Integraldefinition, Math. Ann., **93**, 153—156 (1925).

Lusin, N. [I] Intégrale et série trigonométrique (in Russian), Moscou 1915. — [II] Leçons sur les ensembles analytiques, Paris 1930. — [1] Sur les propriétés des fonctions mesurables, C. R. Acad. Sci. Paris, **154**, 1688—1690 (1912). — [2] Sur les propriétés de l'intégrale de M. Denjoy, ibid., **155**, 1475—1478 (1912). — [3] Sur les ensembles analytiques, Fundam. Math., **10**, 1—95 (1927). — [4] Sur la notion de l'intégrale, Annali Mat. Pura e Appl. (3), **26**, 77—129 (1917).

Lusin, N. et **Sierpiński, W.** [1] Sur quelques propriétés des ensembles (*A*), Bull. Acad. Sci. Cracovie, 35—48 (1918).

Lomnicki, Z. et **Ulam, S.** [1] Sur la théorie de la mesure dans les espaces combinatoires et son application au calcul des probabilités, Fundam. Math., **23**, 237—278 (1934).

Marcinkiewicz, J. [1] Sur les nombres dérivés, Fundam. Math., **24**, 305—308 (1935). — [2] Sur les séries de Fourier, ibid., **27**, 38—69 (1936).

Marcinkiewicz, J. and **Zygmund, A.** [1] On the differentiability of functions and summability of trigonometrical series, Fundam. Math., **26**, 1—43 (1936).

Mazur, S. [1] O metodach sumowalności, Księga pamiątkowa I Polskiego Zjazdu Matematycznego, Lwów 1927, 102—107.

Mazurkiewicz, S. [1] Sur les fonctions qui satisfont à la condition (*N*), Fundam. Math., **16**, 348—352 (1930).

McShane, E. J. [1] Integrals over surfaces in parametric form, Ann. of Math. (2), **34**, 815—838 (1933).

Menchoff, D. [I] Les conditions de monogénéité, Paris 1936. — [1] Sur la généralisation des conditions de Cauchy-Riemann, Fundam. Math., **25**, 59—97 (1935). — [2] Sur la monogénéité asymptotique, Rec. Math. Soc. Math. Moscou, **1**, 189—210 (1936).

Milicer-Grużewska, H. [1] Sur la continuité de la variation, C. R. Soc. Sci. Varsovie, **21**, 165—176 (1928).

Montel, P. [1] Sur les suites infinies de fonctions, Ann. Ecole Norm. (3), **24**, 233—334 (1907). — [2] Sur les différentielles totales et les fonctions monogènes, C. R. Acad. Sci. Paris, **156**, 1820—1822 (1913).

Morera, G. [1] Sulla definizione di funzione di una variabile complessa, Atti Accad. Sci. Torino, **37**, 99—102 (1902).

Morrey, C. B. [1] A class of representations of manifolds I, Amer. J. Math., **55**, 683—707 (1933).

Nalli, P. [I] Esposizione e confronto critico delle diverse definizioni proposte per l'integrale definita di una funzione limitata o no, Palermo 1914.

Neubauer, M. [1] Ueber die partiellen Derivierten unstetiger Funktionen, Monatshefte Math. Phys., **38**, 139—146 (1931).

Nikodym, O. [1] Sur la mesure des ensembles plans dont tous les points sont rectilinéairement accessibles, Fundam. Math., **10**, 116—168 (1927). — [2] Sur une généralisation des intégrales de M. Radon, ibid., **15**, 131—179 (1930).

Osgood, W. F. [1] Zweite Note über analytische Funktionen mehrerer Veränderlichen, Math. Ann., **53**, 461—464 (1900).

Perron, O. [1] Ueber den Integralbegriff, S.-B. Heidelberg. Akad. Wiss., **16** (1914).

Petrovsky, J. [1] Sur l'unicité de la fonction primitive par rapport à une fonction continue arbitraire, Rec. Math. Soc. Math. Moscou, **41**, 48—58 (1934).

Plessner, A. [1] Eine Kennzeichnung der total-stetigen Funktionen, Journ. Reine u. Angew. Math., **160**, 26—32 (1929).

Pollard, S. [1] The Stieltjes integral and its generalisations, Quart. Journ. Math., Oxford Ser., **49**, 87—94 (1920).

Pompeiù, T. [I] Sur la continuité des fonctions de variable complexe, Ann. Fac. Sci. Univ. Toulouse (2), **7**, 264—315 (1905).

Possel, R. de [1] Sur la dérivation abstraite des fonctions d'ensembles, C. R. Acad. Sci. Paris, **201**, 579—581 (1935).

Rademacher, H. [1] Eineindeutige Abbildungen und Messbarkeit, Monatshefte Math. Phys., **27**, 183—291 (1916). — [2] Bemerkungen zu den Cauchy-Riemannschen Differentialgleichungen und zum Moreraschen Satz, Math. Zeitschr., **4**, 177—185 (1919). — [3] Ueber partielle und totale Differenzierbarkeit I, Math. Ann., **79**, 340—359 (1919). — [4] Ueber partielle und totale Differenzierbarkeit II, ibid., **81**, 52—63 (1920).

Radò, T. [I] On the problem of Plateau, Ergebnisse der Mathematik, Berlin 1933. — [1] Sur l'aire des surfaces courbes, Acta Litt. Sci. Szeged, **3**, 131—169 (1927). — [2] Sur le calcul des surfaces courbes, Fundam. Math., **10**, 197—210 (1927). — [3] Sur un problème relatif à un théorème de Vitali, ibid., **11**, 228—229 (1928). — [4] Ueber das Flächenmass rektifizierbarer Flächen, Math. Ann., **100**, 445—479 (1928). — [5] O polu powierzchni krzywych, Mathesis Polska, **7**, 1—18 (1932). — [6] A remark on the area of surfaces, Amer. J. Math., **58**, 598—606 (1936).

Radon, J. [1] Theorie und Anwendungen der absolut additiven Mengenfunktionen, S.-B. Akad. Wiss. Wien, **122**, 1295—1438 (1913).

Rajchman, A. et **Saks, S.** [1] Sur la dérivabilité des fonctions monotones, Fundam. Math. **4**, 204—213 (1923).

Ridder, J. [1] Ueber den Cauchyschen Integralsatz für reelle und komplexe Funktionen, Math. Ann., **102**, 132—156 (1929). — [2] Ueber stetige, additive Intervallfunktionen in der Ebene, Nieuw Arch. Wiskde (2), **16**, 55—69 (1929). — [3] Ueber additive Intervallfunktionen, ibid., **16**, 60—75 (1930). — [4] Ueber Derivierten und Ableitungen, C. R. Soc. Sci. Varsovie, **23**, 1—11 (1930). — [5] Ueber den Perronschen Integralbegriff und seine Beziehung zu den *R*-, *L*- und *D*-Integralen, Math. Zeitschr., **34**, 234—269 (1931). — [6] Ueber approximativ stetige Denjoy-Integrale, Fundam. Math., **21**, 1—10 (1933). — [7] Ueber die gegenseitigen Beziehungen verschiedener approximativ stetiger Denjoy-Perron-Integrale, ibid., **22**, 136—162 (1934). — [8] Ueber die *T*- und *N*-Bedingungen und die approximativ stetigen Denjoy-Perron-Integrale, ibid., **22**, 163—179 (1934). — [9] Ueber Perron-Stieltjessche und Denjoy-Stieltjessche Integrationen, Math. Zeitschr., **40**, 127—160 (1935). — [10] Ueber Denjoy-Perron Integration von Funktionen zweier Variablen, C. R. Soc. Sci. Varsovie, **28**, 5—16 (1935). — [11] Ueber die gegenseitigen Beziehungen einiger »trigonometrischer« Integrationen, Math. Zeitschr., **42**, 322—336 (1937).

Riesz, F. [1] Sur l'intégrale de Lebesgue, Acta Math., [illegible], 1[illegible]1—[illegible] (19[illegible]0). [2] Sur le théorème de M. Egoroff et sur les opérations fonctionnelles linéaires, Acta Litt. Sci. Szeged., **1**, 18—26 (1922). — [3] Elementarer Beweis des Egoroff schen Satzes, Monatshefte Math. Phys., **35**, 243—248 (1928). — [4] Sur les fonctions sousharmoniques et leur rapport à la théorie du potentiel, II, Acta Math., **54**, 321—360 (1930). — [5] Sur un théorème de maximum de MM. Hardy et Littlewood, Journ. London Math. Soc., **7**, 10—13 (1932). — [6] Sur l'existence de la dérivée des fonctions monotones et sur quelques problèmes qui s'y rattachent, Acta Litt. Sci. Szeged, **5**, 208—221 (1932). — [7] Sur l'existence de la dérivée des fonctions d'une variable réelle et des fonctions d'intervalle, Verhandl. Internat. Math. Kongress Zürich 1932, I, 258—269. — [8] Sur les points de densité au sens fort, Fundam. Math., **22**, 221—225 (1934). — [9] Sur l'intégrale de Lebesgue comme l'opération inverse de la dérivation, Ann. Scuola Norm. Sup. Pisa (2), **5**, 191—212 (1936).

Roger, F. [1] Sur quelques applications métriques de la notion de contingent bilatéral, C. R. Acad. Sci. Paris, **201**, 28—30 (1935). — [2] Sur la relation entre les propriétés tangentielles et métriques des ensembles cartésiens, ibid., **201**, 871—873 (1935). — [3] Sur l'extension à la structure locale des ensembles cartésiens les plus généraux des théorèmes de M. Denjoy sur les nombres dérivés des fonctions continues, ibid., **202**, 377—380 (1936).

Romanowski, P. [1] Essai d'une exposition de l'intégrale de Denjoy sans nombres transfinis, Fundam. Math., **19**, 38—44 (1932).

Rosenthal, A. [I] Neuere Untersuchungen über Funktionen reeller Veränderlichen (Sonderabdruck aus der Encyklopädie der Mathematischen Wissenschaften), Leipzig-Berlin 1923 — [1] Ueber die Singularitäten der reellen ebenen Kurven, Math. Ann., **73**, 480—521 (1913).

Roussel, A. [1] Primitive de seconde espèce, C. R. Acad. Sci. Paris, **187**, 926—927 (1928).

Ruziewicz, S. [1] Sur les fonctions qui ont la même dérivée et dont la différence n'est pas constante, Fundam Math., **1**, 148—151 (1920); 2-me éd. 1937.

Saks, S. et **Zygmund, A.** [1] Sur les faisceaux des tangentes à une courbe, Fundam. Math., **6**, 117—121 (1924). — [2] On functions of rectangles and their application to the analytic functions, Ann. Scuola Norm. Sup. Pisa **3**, 1—6 (1934).

Schauder, J. [1] The theory of surface measure, Fundam. Math., **8**, 1—48 (1926).

Schmeiser, M. [1] Some properties of arbitrary functions, Fundam. Math., **22**, 70—76 (1934).

Schoenflies, A. [I] Die Entwickelung der Lehre von den Punktmannigfaltigkeiten, Bericht, erstattet der Deutschen Mathematiker-Vereinigung 1900.

Sierpiński, W. [I] Hypothèse du continu, Monografie Matematyczne **4**, Warszawa—Lwów 1934. — [II] Introduction to General Topology (translated by C. C. Krieger), Toronto 1934. — [1] Démonstration de la dénombrabilité des valeurs extrêmales d'une fonction, C. R. Soc. Sci. Varsovie, **5**, 232—237 (1912). — [2] Sur l'ensemble des points angulaires d'une courbe $y=f(x)$, Bull. Acad. Sci. Cracovie, 850—855 (1912). — [3] Un exemple élémentaire d'une fonction croissante qui a presque partout une dérivée nulle, Giorn. Mat. Battaglini (3), **7**, 314—334 (1916). [4] Un lemme métrique, Fundam. Math., **4**, 201—203 (1923). — [5] Sur un problème concernant les ensembles mesurables superficiellement, ibid., **1**, 112—115 (1920). — [6] Démonstration de quelques théorèmes sur les fonctions mesurables, ibid., **3**, 314—321 (1922). — [7] Sur la densité linéaire des ensembles plans, ibid., **9**, 172—185 (1927). — [8] Sur les fonctions dérivées des fonctions discontinues, ibid., **3**, 123—127 (1922). — [9] Sur une généralisation de la notion de continuité approximative, ibid., **4**, 124—127 (1923). — [10] Démonstration élémentaire du théorème sur la densité des ensembles, ibid., **4**, 167—171 (1923). — [11] Démonstration d'un théorème sur les fonctions additives d'ensemble, ibid., **5**, 262—264 (1924). — [12] Sur la mesurabilité des ensembles analytiques, C. R. Soc. Sci. Varsovie, **22**, 155—159 (1929). — [13] Sur une opération sur les familles d'ensembles, ibid., **22**, 163—167 (1929). — [14] Remarque sur le théorème de M. Egoroff, ibid., **20**, 84—87 (1928). — [15] Sur les constituantes des ensembles analytiques, Fundam. Math., **21**, 29—34 (1933).

Sierpiński, W. et **Szpilrajn, E.** [1] Remarque sur le problème de la mesure, Fundam. Math., **26**, 256—261 (1936).

Singh, A. N. [1] The theory and construction of non-differentiable functions, Lucknow 1935.

Souslin, M. [1] Sur une definition des ensembles mesurables *B* sans nombres transfinis, C. R. Acad. Sci. Paris, **164**, 88—91 (1917).

Steinhaus, H. [1] Sur l'existence de la dérivée, Bull. Acad. Sci. Cracovie, 62—65 (1919). — [2] Sur la probabilité de la convergence des séries, Studia Math., **2**, 21—39 (1930).

Stepanoff, W. [1] Ueber totale Differenzierbarkeit, Math. Ann., **90**, 318—320 (1923). — [2] Sur une propriété caractéristique des fonctions mesurables, Rec. Math. Soc. Math. Moscou, **30**, 487—489 (1924). — [3] Sur les conditions de l'existence de la différentielle totale, ibid., **32**, 511—526 (1925).

Szpilrajn, E. [1] Remarques sur les fonctions complètement additives d'ensembles, Fundam. Math., **22**, 303—311 (1934).

Todd, J. [1] Superpositions of functions (I), Journ. London Math. Soc., **10**, 166—171 (1935). — [2] Superpositions of functions (II), Proc. London Math. Soc. (2), **41**, 433—439 (1936).

Tonelli, L. [1] Sulla rettificazione delle curve, Atti Accad. Sci. Torino, **43**, 399—416 (1908). — [2] Sull'integrazione per parti, Atti Accad. Naz. Lincei (5), $\mathbf{18}_2$, 246—253 (1909). — [3] Successioni di curve e derivazione per serie, ibid., $\mathbf{25}_2$, 22—30, 85—91 (1916). — [4] Sul differenziale dell'arco di curva, ibid., $\mathbf{25}_1$, 207—213 (1916). — [5] Sur la quadrature des surfaces, C. R. Acad. Sci. Paris, **182**, 1198—1200 (1926). — [6] Sulla quadratura delle superficie, Atti Accad. Naz. Lincei (6), $\mathbf{3}_1$, 357—363, 445—450 and 633—658 (1926). — [7] Su un polinomio d'approssimazione e l'area di una superficie, ibid., **5**, 313—318 (1927). — [8] Sulle derivate esatte, Mem. Istit. Bologna (8), **8**, 13—15 (1930/31).

Ulam, S. [1] Zur Masstheorie in der allgemeinen Mengenlehre, Fundam. Math., **16**, 140—150 (1930). — [2] Zum Massbegriff in Produkträumen, Verhandl. Intern. Math. Kongress Zürich 1932, II, 118—119.

Vallée Poussin, Ch. J. de la [I] Intégrales de Lebesgue. Fonctions d'ensemble. Classes de Baire, Paris 1916 (2-me éd., Paris 1936). — [1] Sur l'intégrale de Lebesgue, Trans. Amer. Math. Soc., **16**, 435—501 (1915).

Verblunsky, S. [1] On the theory of trigonometric series, VII, Fundam. Math., **23**, 193—236 (1934).

Vitali, G. [1] Sulle funzioni integrali, Atti Accad. Sci. Torino, **40**, 753—766 (1905). — [2] Una proprietà delle funzioni misurabili, Istit. Lombardo Rend. (2), **38**, 599—603 (1905). — [3] Sui gruppi di punti e sulle funzioni di variabili reali, Atti Accad. Sci. Torino, **43**, 75—92 (1908). — [4] Analisi delle funzioni a variazione limitata, R. C. Circ. Mat. Palermo, **46**, 388—408 (1922). — [5] Sulle funzioni continue, Fundam. Math., **8**, 175—188 (1926).

Volterra, V. [1] Sui principii del calcolo integrale, Giorn. Mat. Battaglini, **19**, 333—372 (1881).

Ward, A. J. [1] On the differential structure of real functions, Proc. London Math. Soc. (2), **39**, 339—362 (1935). — [2] On the differentiation of the additive functions of rectangles, Fundam. Math., **26**, 167—182 (1936). — [3] The Perron-Stieltjes integral, Math. Zeitschr., **41**, 578—604 (1936). — [4] The linear derivates and approximate linear derivates of a function of two variables, Proc. London Math. Soc. (2), **42**, 266—273 (1936). — [5] On the derivation of additive functions of intervals in m-dimensional space, Fundam. Math., **28**, 265—279 (1937). — [6] A sufficient condition for a function of intervals to be monotone, ibid., **29**, 22—25 (1937). — [7] A certain function of rectangles, C. R. Soc. Sci. Varsovie (1937) (to appear).

Ważewski, T. [1] Kontinua prostowalne w związku z funkcjami i odwzorowaniami absolutnie ciągłemi, Ann. Soc. Polon. Math., **3**, Suppl. 9—49 (1927).

Wiener, N. and **Young, R. C.** [1] The total variation of $g(x+h)—g(x)$, Trans. Amer. Math. Soc., **35**, 327—340 (1933).

Wolff, J. [1] Ueber die Loomansche Erweiterung eines Satzes von Pompeiù, Nieuw Arch. Wiskde (2), **14**, 337—339 (1925).

Young, G. C. [1] A note on derivates and differential coefficients, Acta Math., **37**, 141—154 (1916). — [2] On the derivates of a function, Proc. London Math. Soc. (2), **15**, 360—384 (1916).

Young, G. C. and **Young, W. H.** [1] On the existence of a differential coefficient, Proc. London Math. Soc. (2), **9**, 325—335 (1911).

Young, L. C. [I] The theory of integration, Cambridge 1927. — [1] Note on the theory of measure, Proc. Cambridge Philos. Soc., **26**, 88—93 (1930).

Young R. C. [1] On Riemann integration with respect to a continuous increment, Math. Ann., **29**, 217—233 (1928). — [2] Functions of Σ defined by addition or functions of intervals in n-dimensional formulation, ibid., **29**, 171—216 (1928).

Young, W. H. [1] Zur Lehre der nicht abgeschlossenen Punktmengen, Ber. Verh. Sächs. Akad. Leipzig, **55**, 287—293 (1903). — [2] Integration with respect to a function of bounded variation, Proc. London Math. Soc. (2), **13**, 109—150 (1914). — [3] On the general theory of integration, Philos. Trans. Roy. Soc. London, **204**, 221—252 (1905). — [4] On the area of surfaces, Proc. Roy. Soc. London (A), **96**, 72—81 (1920). — [5] On the triangulation method of defining the area of a surface, Proc. London Math. Soc. (2), **19**, 117—152 (1921). — [6] On non-absolutely convergent, not necessarily continuous integrals, ibid., **16**, 175—218 (1918). — [7] The progress of mathematical analysis in the 20th century, ibid., **24**, 421—434 (1926).

Zygmund, A. [I] Trigonometrical Series, Monografie Matematyczne, Warszawa—Lwów 1935. — [1] On the differentiability of multiple integrals, Fundam. Math., **23**, 143—149 (1934) [Corrigenda, ibid., **25**, 234 (1935)].

GENERAL INDEX.

CATALOG OF DOVER BOOKS

BOOKS EXPLAINING SCIENCE AND MATHEMATICS

THE COMMON SENSE OF THE EXACT SCIENCES, W. K. Clifford. Introduction by James Newman, edited by Karl Pearson. For 70 years this has been a guide to classical scientific and mathematical thought. Explains with unusual clarity basic concepts, such as extension of meaning of symbols, characteristics of surface boundaries, properties of plane figures, vectors, Cartesian method of determining position, etc. Long preface by Bertrand Russell. Bibliography of Clifford. Corrected, 130 diagrams redrawn. 249pp. 5⅜ x 8.
T61 Paperbound **$1.60**

SCIENCE THEORY AND MAN, Erwin Schrödinger. This is a complete and unabridged reissue of SCIENCE AND THE HUMAN TEMPERAMENT plus an additional essay: "What is an Elementary Particle?" Nobel Laureate Schrödinger discusses such topics as nature of scientific method, the nature of science, chance and determinism, science and society, conceptual models for physical entities, elementary particles and wave mechanics. Presentation is popular and may be followed by most people with little or no scientific training. "Fine practical preparation for a time when laws of nature, human institutions . . . are undergoing a critical examination without parallel," Waldemar Kaempffert, N. Y. TIMES. 192pp. 5⅜ x 8.
T428 Paperbound **$1.35**

PIONEERS OF SCIENCE, O. Lodge. Eminent scientist-expositor's authoritative, yet elementary survey of great scientific theories. Concentrating on individuals—Copernicus, Brahe, Kepler, Galileo, Descartes, Newton, Laplace, Herschel, Lord Kelvin, and other scientists—the author presents their discoveries in historical order adding biographical material on each man and full, specific explanations of their achievements. The clear and complete treatment of the post-Newtonian astronomers is a feature seldom found in other books on the subject. Index. 120 illustrations. xv + 404pp. 5⅜ x 8. T716 Paperbound **$1.50**

THE EVOLUTION OF SCIENTIFIC THOUGHT FROM NEWTON TO EINSTEIN, A. d'Abro. Einstein's special and general theories of relativity, with their historical implications, are analyzed in non-technical terms. Excellent accounts of the contributions of Newton, Riemann, Weyl, Planck, Eddington, Maxwell, Lorentz and others are treated in terms of space and time, equations of electromagnetics, finiteness of the universe, methodology of science. 21 diagrams. 482pp. 5⅜ x 8. T2 Paperound **$2.00**

THE RISE OF THE NEW PHYSICS, A. d'Abro. A half-million word exposition, formerly titled THE DECLINE OF MECHANISM, for readers not versed in higher mathematics. The only thorough explanation, in everyday language, of the central core of modern mathematical physical theory, treating both classical and modern theoretical physics, and presenting in terms almost anyone can understand the equivalent of 5 years of study of mathematical physics. Scientifically impeccable coverage of mathematical-physical thought from the Newtonian system up through the electronic theories of Dirac and Heisenberg and Fermi's statistics. Combines both history and exposition; provides a broad yet unified and detailed view, with constant comparison of classical and modern views on phenomena and theories. "A must for anyone doing serious study in the physical sciences," JOURNAL OF THE FRANKLIN INSTITUTE. "Extraordinary faculty . . . to explain ideas and theories of theoretical physics in the language of daily life," ISIS. First part of set covers philosophy of science, drawing upon the practice of Newton, Maxwell, Poincaré, Einstein, others, discussing modes of thought, experiment, interpretations of causality, etc. In the second part, 100 pages explain grammar and vocabulary of mathematics, with discussions of functions, groups, series, Fourier series, etc. The remainder is devoted to concrete, detailed coverage of both classical and quantum physics, explaining such topics as analytic mechanics, Hamilton's principle, wave theory of light, electromagnetic waves, groups of transformations, thermodynamics, phase rule, Brownian movement, kinetics, special relativity, Planck's original quantum theory, Bohr's atom, Zeeman effect, Broglie's wave mechanics, Heisenberg's uncertainty, Eigen-values, matrices, scores of other important topics. Discoveries and theories are covered for such men as Alembert, Born, Cantor, Debye, Euler, Foucault, Galois, Gauss, Hadamard, Kelvin, Kepler, Laplace, Maxwell, Pauli, Rayleigh, Volterra, Weyl, Young, more than 180 others. Indexed. 97 illustrations. ix + 982pp. 5⅜ x 8. T3 Volume 1, Paperbound **$2.00**
T4 Volume 2, Paperbound **$2.00**

CONCERNING THE NATURE OF THINGS, Sir William Bragg. Christmas lectures delivered at the Royal Society by Nobel laureate. Why a spinning ball travels in a curved track; how uranium is transmuted to lead, etc. Partial contents: atoms, gases, liquids, crystals, metals, etc. No scientific background needed; wonderful for intelligent child. 32pp. of photos, 57 figures. xii + 232pp. 5⅜ x 8. T31 Paperbound **$1.35**

THE UNIVERSE OF LIGHT, Sir William Bragg. No scientific training needed to read Nobel Prize winner's expansion of his Royal Institute Christmas Lectures. Insight into nature of light, methods and philosophy of science. Explains lenses, reflection, color, resonance, polarization, x-rays, the spectrum, Newton's work with prisms, Huygens' with polarization, Crookes' with cathode ray, etc. Leads into clear statement of 2 major historical theories of light, corpuscle and wave. Dozens of experiments you can do. 199 illus., including 2 full-page color plates. 293pp. 5⅜ x 8. S538 Paperbound **$1.85**

A SURVEY OF PHYSICAL THEORY, Max Planck. One of the greatest scientists of all time, creator of the quantum revolution in physics, writes in non-technical terms of his own discoveries and those of other outstanding creators of modern physics. Planck wrote this book when science had just crossed the threshold of the new physics, and he communicates the excitement felt then as he discusses electromagnetic theories, statistical methods, evolution of the concept of light, a step-by-step description of how he developed his own momentous theory, and many more of the basic ideas behind modern physics. Formerly "A" Survey of Physics." Bibliography. Index. 128pp. 5⅜ x 8. S650 Paperbound **$1.15**

THE NATURE OF LIGHT AND COLOUR IN THE OPEN AIR, M. Minnaert. Why is falling snow sometimes black? What causes mirages, the fata morgana, multiple suns and moons in the sky? How are shadows formed? Prof. Minnaert of the University of Utrecht answers these and similar questions in optics, light, colour, for non-specialists. Particularly valuable to nature, science students, painters, photographers. Translated by H. M. Kremer-Priest, K. Jay. 202 illustrations, including 42 photos. xvi + 362pp. 5⅜ x 8. T196 Paperbound **$1.95**

THE STORY OF X-RAYS FROM RONTGEN TO ISOTOPES, A. R. Bleich. Non-technical history of x-rays, their scientific explanation, their applications in medicine, industry, research, and art, and their effect on the individual and his descendants. Includes amusing early reactions to Röntgen's discovery, cancer therapy, detections of art and stamp forgeries, potential risks to patient and operator, etc. Illustrations show x-rays of flower structure, the gall bladder, gears with hidden defects, etc. Original Dover publication. Glossary. Bibliography. Index. 55 photos and figures. xiv + 186pp. 5⅜ x 8. T662 Paperbound **$1.35**

TEACH YOURSELF ELECTRICITY, C. W. Wilman. Electrical resistance, inductance, capacitance, magnets, chemical effects of current, alternating currents, generators and motors, transformers, rectifiers, much more. 230 questions, answers, worked examples. List of units. 115 illus. 194pp. 6⅞ x 4¼. Clothbound **$2.00**

TEACH YOURSELF HEAT ENGINES, E. De Ville. Measurement of heat, development of steam and internal combustion engines, efficiency of an engine, compression-ignition engines, production of steam, the ideal engine, much more. 318 exercises, answers, worked examples. Tables. 76 illus. 220pp. 6⅞ x 4¼. Clothbound **$2.00**

TEACH YOURSELF MECHANICS, P. Abbott. The lever, centre of gravity, parallelogram of force, friction, acceleration, Newton's laws of motion, machines, specific gravity, gas, liquid pressure, much more. 280 problems, solutions. Tables. 163 illus. 271pp. 6⅞ x 4¼. Clothbound **$2.00**

GREAT IDEAS OF MODERN MATHEMATICS: THEIR NATURE AND USE, Jagjit Singh. Reader with only high school math will understand main mathematical ideas of modern physics, astronomy, genetics, psychology, evolution, etc., better than many who use them as tools, but comprehend little of their basic structure. Author uses his wide knowledge of non-mathematical fields in brilliant exposition of differential equations, matrices, group theory, logic, statistics, problems of mathematical foundations, imaginary numbers, vectors, etc. Original publication. 2 appendixes. 2 indexes. 65 illustr. 322pp. 5⅜ x 8. S587 Paperbound **$1.55**

MATHEMATICS IN ACTION, O. G. Sutton. Everyone with a command of high school algebra will find this book one of the finest possible introductions to the application of mathematics to physical theory. Ballistics, numerical analysis, waves and wavelike phenomena, Fourier series, group concepts, fluid flow and aerodynamics, statistical measures, and meteorology are discussed with unusual clarity. Some calculus and differential equations theory is developed by the author for the reader's help in the more difficult sections. 88 figures. Index. viii + 236pp. 5⅜ x 8. T440 Clothbound **$3.50**

FREE! All you do is ask for it!

A DOVER SCIENCE SAMPLER, edited by George Barkin. 64-page book, sturdily bound, containing excerpts from over 20 Dover books explaining science. Edwin Hubble, George Sarton, Ernst Mach, A. d'Abro, Galileo, Newton, others, discussing island universes, scientific truth, biological phenomena, stability in bridges, etc. Copies limited, no more than 1 to a customer. FREE

THE FOURTH DIMENSION SIMPLY EXPLAINED, edited by H. P. Manning. 22 essays, originally Scientific American contest entries, that use a minimum of mathematics to explain aspects of 4-dimensional geometry: analogues to 3-dimensional space, 4-dimensional absurdities and curiosities (such as removing the contents of an egg without puncturing its shell), possible measurements and forms, etc. Introduction by the editor. Only book of its sort on a truly elementary level, excellent introduction to advanced works. 82 figures. 251pp. 5⅜ x 8. T711 Paperbound **$1.35**

FAMOUS BRIDGES OF THE WORLD, D. B. Steinman. An up-to-the-minute revised edition of a book that explains the fascinating drama of how the world's great bridges came to be built. The author, designer of the famed Mackinac bridge, discusses bridges from all periods and all parts of the world, explaining their various types of construction, and describing the problems their builders faced. Although primarily for youngsters, this cannot fail to interest readers of all ages. 48 illustrations in the text. 23 photographs. 99pp. 6⅛ x 9¼. T161 Paperbound **$1.00**

BRIDGES AND THEIR BUILDERS, David Steinman and Sara Ruth Watson. Engineers, historians, everyone who has ever been fascinated by great spans will find this book an endless source of information and interest. Dr. Steinman, recipient of the [illegible], was one of the great bridge architects and engineers of all time, and his analysis of the great bridges of history is both authoritative and easily followed. Greek and Roman bridges, medieval bridges, Oriental bridges, modern works such as the Brooklyn Bridge and the Golden Gate Bridge, and many others are described in terms of history, constructional principles, artistry, and function. All in all this book is the most comprehensive and accurate semipopular history of bridges in print in English. New, greatly revised, enlarged edition. 23 photographs, 26 line drawings. Index. xvii + 401pp. 5⅜ x 8. T431 Paperbound **$2.00**

FADS AND FALLACIES IN THE NAME OF SCIENCE, Martin Gardner. Examines various cults, quack systems, frauds, delusions which at various times have masqueraded as science. Accounts of hollow-earth fanatics like Symmes; Velikovsky and wandering planets; Hoerbiger; Bellamy and the theory of multiple moons; Charles Fort; dowsing, pseudoscientific methods for finding water, ores, oil. Sections on naturopathy, iridiagnosis, zone therapy, food fads, etc. Analytical accounts of Wilhelm Reich and orgone sex energy; L. Ron Hubbard and Dianetics; A. Korzybski and General Semantics; many others. Brought up to date to include Bridey Murphy, others. Not just a collection of anecdotes, but a fair, reasoned appraisal of eccentric theory. Formerly titled IN THE NAME OF SCIENCE. Preface. Index. x + 384pp. 5⅜ x 8. T394 Paperbound **$1.50**

See also: **A PHILOSOPHICAL ESSAY ON PROBABILITIES, P. de Laplace; ON MATHEMATICS AND MATHEMATICIANS, R. E. Moritz; AN ELEMENTARY SURVEY OF CELESTIAL MECHANICS, Y. Ryabov; THE SKY AND ITS MYSTERIES, E. A. Beet; THE REALM OF THE NEBULAE, E. Hubble; OUT OF THE SKY, H. H. Nininger; SATELLITES AND SCIENTIFIC RESEARCH, D. King-Hele; HEREDITY AND YOUR LIFE, A. M. Winchester; INSECTS AND INSECT LIFE, S. W. Frost; PRINCIPLES OF STRATIGRAPHY, A. W. Grabau; TEACH YOURSELF SERIES.**

HISTORY OF SCIENCE AND MATHEMATICS

DIALOGUES CONCERNING TWO NEW SCIENCES, Galileo Galilei. This classic of experimental science, mechanics, engineering, is as enjoyable as it is important. A great historical document giving insights into one of the world's most original thinkers, it is based on 30 years' experimentation. It offers a lively exposition of dynamics, elasticity, sound, ballistics, strength of materials, the scientific method. "Superior to everything else of mine," Galileo. Trans. by H. Crew, A. Salvio. 126 diagrams. Index. xxi + 288pp. 5⅜ x 8.
S99 Paperbound **$1.65**

A DIDEROT PICTORIAL ENCYCLOPEDIA OF TRADES AND INDUSTRY, Manufacturing and the Technical Arts in Plates Selected from "L'Encyclopédie ou Dictionnaire Raisonné des Sciences, des Arts, et des Métiers" of Denis Diderot. Edited with text by C. Gillispie. This first modern selection of plates from the high point of 18th century French engraving is a storehouse of valuable technological information to the historian of arts and science. Over 2000 illustrations on 485 full page plates, most of them original size, show the trades and industries of a fascinating era in such great detail that the processes and shops might very well be reconstructed from them. The plates teem with life, with men, women, and children performing all of the thousands of operations necessary to the trades before and during the early stages of the industrial revolution. Plates are in sequence, and show general operations, closeups of difficult operations, and details of complex machinery. Such important and interesting trades and industries are illustrated as sowing, harvesting, beekeeping, cheesemaking, operating windmills, milling flour, charcoal burning, tobacco processing, indigo, fishing, arts of war, salt extraction, mining, smelting, casting iron, steel, extracting mercury, zinc, sulphur, copper, etc., slating, tinning, silverplating, gilding, making gunpowder, cannons, bells, shoeing horses, tanning, papermaking, printing, dyeing, and more than 40 other categories. Professor Gillispie, of Princeton, supplies a full commentary on all the plates, identifying operations, tools, processes, etc. This material, presented in a lively and lucid fashion, is of great interest to the reader interested in history of science and technology. Heavy library cloth. 920pp. 9 x 12. T421 Two volume set **$18.50**

DE MAGNETE, William Gilbert. This classic work on magnetism founded a new science. Gilbert was the first to use the word "electricity", to recognize mass as distinct from weight, to discover the effect of heat on magnetic bodies; invent an electroscope, differentiate between static electricity and magnetism, conceive of the earth as a magnet. Written by the first great experimental scientist, this lively work is valuable not only as an historical landmark, but as the delightfully easy to follow record of a perpetually searching, ingenious mind. Translated by P. F. Mottelay. 25 page biographical memoir. 90 figures. lix + 368pp. 5⅜ x 8. S470 Paperbound **$2.00**

CHARLES BABBAGE AND HIS CALCULATING ENGINES, edited by P. Morrison and E. Morrison. Babbage, leading 19th century pioneer in mathematical machines and herald of modern operational research, was the true father of Harvard's relay computer Mark I. His Difference Engine and Analytical Engine were the first machines in the field. This volume contains a valuable introduction on his life and work; major excerpts from his autobiography, revealing his eccentric and unusual personality; and extensive selections from "Babbage's Calculating Engines," a compilation of hard-to-find journal articles by Babbage, the Countess of Lovelace, L. F. Menabrea, and Dionysius Lardner. 8 illustrations, Appendix of miscellaneous papers. Index. Bibliography. xxxviii + 400pp. 5⅜ x 8. T12 Paperbound **$2.00**

A HISTORY OF ASTRONOMY FROM THALES TO KEPLER, J. L. E. Dreyer. (Formerly A HISTORY OF PLANETARY SYSTEMS FROM THALES TO KEPLER.) This is the only work in English to give the complete history of man's cosmological views from prehistoric times to Kepler and Newton. Partial contents: Near Eastern astronomical systems, Early Greeks, Homocentric Spheres of Eudoxus, Epicycles, Ptolemaic system, medieval cosmology, Copernicus, Kepler, etc. Revised, foreword by W. H. Stahl. New bibliography. xvii + 430pp. 5⅜ x 8.
S79 Paperbound **$1.98**

A SHORT HISTORY OF ANATOMY AND PHYSIOLOGY FROM THE GREEKS TO HARVEY, Charles Singer. Corrected edition of THE EVOLUTION OF ANATOMY, classic work tracing evolution of anatomy and physiology from prescientific times through Greek & Roman periods, Dark Ages, Renaissance, to age of Harvey and beginning of modern concepts. Centered on individuals, movements, periods that definitely advanced anatomical knowledge: Plato, Diocles, Aristotle, Theophrastus, Herophilus, Erasistratus, the Alexandrians, Galen, Mondino, da Vinci, Linacre, Sylvius, others. Special section on Vesalius; Vesalian atlas of nudes, skeletons, muscle tabulae. Index of names, 20 plates. 270 extremely interesting illustrations of ancient, medieval, Renaissance, Oriental origin. xii + 209pp. 5⅜ x 8. T389 Paperbound **$1.75**

FROM MAGIC TO SCIENCE, Charles Singer. A great historian examines aspects of medical science from the Roman Empire through the Renaissance. Includes perhaps the best discussion of early herbals, and a penetrating physiological interpretation of "The Visions of Hildegarde of Bingen." Also examined are Arabian and Galenic influences; the Sphere of Pythagoras; Paracelsus; the reawakening of science under Leonardo da Vinci, Vesalius; the Lorica of Gildas the Briton; etc. Frequent quotations with translations. New Introduction by the author. New unabridged, corrected edition. 158 unusual illustrations from classical and medieval sources. Index. xxvii + 365pp. 5⅜ x 8. T390 Paperbound **$2.00**

HISTORY OF MATHEMATICS, D. E. Smith. Most comprehensive non-technical history of math in English. Discusses lives and works of over a thousand major and minor figures, with footnotes supplying technical information outside the book's scheme, and indicating disputed matters. Vol I: A chronological examination, from primitive concepts through Egypt, Babylonia, Greece, the Orient, Rome, the Middle Ages, the Renaissance, and up to 1900. Vol 2: The development of ideas in specific fields and problems, up through elementary calculus. Two volumes, total of 510 illustrations, 1355pp. 5⅜ x 8. Set boxed in attractive container. T429, 430 Paperbound, the set **$5.00**

A SHORT ACCOUNT OF THE HISTORY OF MATHEMATICS, W. W. R. Ball. Most readable non-technical history of mathematics treats lives, discoveries of every important figure from Egyptian, Phoenician mathematicians to late 19th century. Discusses schools of Ionia, Pythagoras, Athens, Cyzicus, Alexandria, Byzantium, systems of numeration; primitive arithmetic; Middle Ages, Renaissance, including Arabs, Bacon, Regiomontanus, Tartaglia, Cardan, Stevinus, Galileo, Kepler; modern mathematics of Descartes, Pascal, Wallis, Huygens, Newton, Leibnitz, d'Alembert, Euler, Lambert, Laplace, Legendre, Gauss, Hermite, Weierstrass, scores more. Index. 25 figures. 546pp. 5⅜ x 8. S630 Paperbound **$2.00**

A SOURCE BOOK IN MATHEMATICS, D. E. Smith. Great discoveries in math, from Renaissance to end of 19th century, in English translation. Read announcements by Dedekind, Gauss, Delamain, Pascal, Fermat, Newton, Abel, Lobachevsky, Bolyai, Riemann, De Moivre, Legendre, Laplace, others of discoveries about imaginary numbers, number congruence, slide rule, equations, symbolism, cubic algebraic equations, non-Euclidean forms of geometry, calculus, function theory, quaternions, etc. Succinct selections from 125 different treatises, articles, most unavailable elsewhere in English. Each article preceded by biographical, historical introduction. Vol. I: Fields of Number, Algebra. Index. 32 illus. 338pp. 5⅜ x 8. Vol. II: Fields of Geometry, Probability, Calculus, Functions, Quaternions. 83 illus. 432pp. 5⅜ x 8.
Vol. 1: S552 Paperbound **$1.85**
Vol. 2: S553 Paperbound **$1.85**
2 vol. set, boxed **$3.50**

A HISTORY OF THE CALCULUS, AND ITS CONCEPTUAL DEVELOPMENT, Carl B. Boyer. Provides laymen and mathematicians a detailed history of the development of the calculus, from early beginning in antiquity to final elaboration as mathematical abstractions. Gives a sense of mathematics not as a technique, but as a habit of mind, in the progression of ideas of Zeno, Plato, Pythagoras, Eudoxus, Arabic and Scholastic mathematicians, Newton, Leibnitz, Taylor, Descartes, Euler, Lagrange, Cantor, Weierstrass, and others. This first comprehensive critical history of the calculus was originally titled "The Concepts of the Calculus." Foreword by R. Courant. Preface. 22 figures. 25-page bibliography. Index. v + 364pp. 5⅜ x 8. S509 Paperbound **$2.00**

A CONCISE HISTORY OF MATHEMATICS, D. Struik. Lucid study of development of mathematical ideas, techniques from Ancient Near East, Greece, Islamic science, Middle Ages, Renaissance, modern times. Important mathematicians are described in detail. Treatment is not anecdotal, but analytical development of ideas. "Rich in content, thoughtful in interpretation," U.S. QUARTERLY BOOKLIST. Non-technical; no mathematical training needed. Index. 60 illustrations, including Egyptian papyri, Greek mss., portraits of 31 eminent mathematicians. Bibliography. 2nd edition. xix + 299pp. 5⅜ x 8. T255 Paperbound **$1.75**

See also: **NON-EUCLIDEAN GEOMETRY, R. Bonola; THEORY OF DETERMINANTS IN HISTORICAL ORDER OF DEVELOPMENT, T. Muir; HISTORY OF THE THEORY OF ELASTICITY AND STRENGTH OF MATERIALS, I. Todhunter and K. Pearson; A SHORT HISTORY OF ASTRONOMY, A. Berry; CLASSICS OF SCIENCE.**

PHILOSOPHY OF SCIENCE AND MATHEMATICS

FOUNDATIONS OF SCIENCE: THE PHILOSOPHY OF THEORY AND EXPERIMENT, N. R. Campbell. A critique of the most fundamental concepts of science in general and physics in particular. Examines why certain propositions are accepted without question, demarcates science from philosophy, clarifies the understanding of the tools of science. Part One analyzes the presuppositions of scientific thought: existence of the material world, nature of scientific laws, multiplication of probabilities, etc.: Part Two covers the nature of experiment and the application of mathematics: conditions for measurement, relations between numerical laws and theories, laws of error, etc. An appendix covers problems arising from relativity, force, motion, space, and time. A classic in its field. Index. xiii + 565pp. 5⅝ x 8⅜. S372 Paperbound **$2.95**

WHAT IS SCIENCE?, Norman Campbell. This excellent introduction explains scientific method, role of mathematics, types of scientific laws. Contents: 2 aspects of science, science & nature, laws of science, discovery of laws, explanation of laws, measurement & numerical laws, applications of science. 192pp. 5⅜ x 8. S43 Paperbound **$1.25**

THE VALUE OF SCIENCE, Henri Poincaré. Many of the most mature ideas of the "last scientific universalist" covered with charm and vigor for both the beginning student and the advanced worker. Discusses the nature of scientific truth, whether order is innate in the universe or imposed upon it by man, logical thought versus intuition (relating to math, through the works of Weierstrass, Lie, Klein, Riemann), time and space (relativity, psychological time, simultaneity), Hertz's concept of force, interrelationship of mathematical physics to pure math, values within disciplines of Maxwell, Carnot, Mayer, Newton, Lorentz, etc. Index. iii + 147pp. 5⅜ x 8. S469 Paperbound **$1.35**

SCIENCE AND METHOD, Henri Poincaré. Procedure of scientific discovery, methodology, experiment, idea-germination—the intellectual processes by which discoveries come into being. Most significant and most interesting aspects of development, application of ideas. Chapters cover selection of facts, chance, mathematical reasoning, mathematics, and logic; Whitehead, Russell, Cantor; the new mechanics, etc. 288pp. 5⅜ x 8. S222 Paperbound **$1.35**

SCIENCE AND HYPOTHESIS, Henri Poincaré. Creative psychology in science. How such concepts as number, magnitude, space, force, classical mechanics were developed, and how the modern scientist uses them in his thought. Hypothesis in physics, theories of modern physics. Introduction by Sir James Larmor. "Few mathematicians have had the breadth of vision of Poincaré, and none is his superior in the gift of clear exposition," E. T. Bell. Index. 272pp. 5⅜ x 8. S221 Paperbound **$1.35**

PHILOSOPHY AND THE PHYSICISTS, L. S. Stebbing. The philosophical aspects of modern science examined in terms of a lively critical attack on the ideas of Jeans and Eddington. Discusses the task of science, causality, determinism, probability, consciousness, the relation of the world of physics to that of everyday experience. Probes the philosophical significance of the Planck-Bohr concept of discontinuous energy levels, the inferences to be drawn from Heisenberg's Uncertainty Principle, the implications of "becoming" involved in the 2nd law of thermodynamics, and other problems posed by the discarding of Laplacean determinism. 285pp. 5⅜ x 8. T480 Paperbound **$1.65**

EXPERIMENT AND THEORY IN PHYSICS, Max Born. A Nobel laureate examines the nature and value of the counterclaims of experiment and theory in physics. Synthetic versus analytical scientific advances are analyzed in the work of Einstein, Bohr, Heisenberg, Planck, Eddington, Milne, and others by a fellow participant. 44pp. 5⅜ x 8. S308 Paperbound **60¢**

BIBLIOGRAPHIES

GUIDE TO THE LITERATURE OF MATHEMATICS AND PHYSICS, N. G. Parke III. Over 5000 entries included under approximately 120 major subject headings, of selected most important books, monographs, periodicals, articles in English, plus important works in German, French, Italian, Spanish, Russian (many recently available works). Covers every branch of physics, math, related engineering. Includes author, title, edition, publisher, place, date, number of volumes, number of pages. A 40-page introduction on the basic problems of research and study provides useful information on the organization and use of libraries, the psychology of learning, etc. This reference work will save you hours of time. 2nd revised edition. Indices of authors, subjects. 464pp. 5⅜ x 8. S447 Paperbound **$2.49**

THE STUDY OF THE HISTORY OF MATHEMATICS & THE STUDY OF THE HISTORY OF SCIENCE, George Sarton. Scientific method & philosophy in 2 scholarly fields. Defines duty of historian of math., provides especially useful bibliography with best available biographies of modern mathematicians, editions of their collected works, correspondence. Observes combination of history & science, will aid scholar in understanding science today. Bibliography includes best known treatises on historical methods. 200-item critically evaluated bibliography. Index. 10 illustrations. 2 volumes bound as one. 113pp. + 75pp. 5⅜ x 8. T240 Paperbound **$1.25**

MATHEMATICAL PUZZLES

AMUSEMENTS IN MATHEMATICS, Henry Ernest Dudeney. The foremost British originator of mathematical puzzles is always intriguing, witty, and paradoxical in this classic, one of the largest collections of mathematical amusements. More than 430 puzzles, problems, and paradoxes. Mazes and games, problems on number manipulation, unicursal and other route problems, puzzles on measuring, weighing, packing, age, kinship, chessboards, joiners' crossing river, plane figure dissection, and many others. Solutions. More than 450 illustrations. vii + 258pp. 5⅜ x 8. T473 Paperbound **$1.25**

THE CANTERBURY PUZZLES, Henry Ernest Dudeney. Chaucer's pilgrims set one another problems in story form. Also Adventures of the Puzzle Club, the Strange Escape of the King's Jester, the Monks of Riddlewell, the Squire's Christmas Puzzle Party, and others. All puzzles are original, based on dissecting plane figures, arithmetic, algebra, elementary calculus, and other branches of mathematics, and purely logical ingenuity. "The limit of ingenuity and intricacy . . ." The Observer. Over 110 puzzles. Full solutions. 150 illustrations. viii + 225pp. 5⅜ x 8. T474 Paperbound **$1.25**

SYMBOLIC LOGIC and THE GAME OF LOGIC, Lewis Carroll. "Symbolic Logic" is not concerned with modern symbolic logic, but is instead a collection of over 380 problems posed with charm and imagination, using the syllogism, and a fascinating diagrammatic method of drawing conclusions. In "The Game of Logic," Carroll's whimsical imagination devises a logical game played with 2 diagrams and counters (included) to manipulate hundreds of tricky syllogisms. The final section, "Hit or Miss" is a lagniappe of 101 additional puzzles in the delightful Carroll manner. Until this reprint edition, both of these books were rarities costing up to $15 each. Symbolic Logic: Index, xxxi + 199pp. The Game of Logic: 96pp. Two vols. bound as one. 5⅜ x 8. T492 Paperbound **$1.50**

PILLOW PROBLEMS and A TANGLED TALE, Lewis Carroll. One of the rarest of all Carroll's works, "Pillow Problems" contains 72 original math puzzles, all typically ingenious. Particularly fascinating are Carroll's answers which remain exactly as he thought them out, reflecting his actual mental processes. The problems in "A Tangled Tale" are in story form, originally appearing as a monthly magazine serial. Carroll not only gives the solutions, but uses answers sent in by readers to discuss wrong approaches and misleading paths, and grades them for insight. Both of these books were rarities until this edition, "Pillow Problems" costing up to $25, and "A Tangled Tale" $15. Pillow Problems: Preface and introduction by Lewis Carroll. xx + 109pp. A Tangled Tale: 6 illustrations. 152pp. Two vols. bound as one. 5⅜ x 8. T493 Paperbound **$1.50**

DIVERSIONS AND DIGRESSIONS OF LEWIS CARROLL. A major new treasure for Carroll fans! Rare privately published puzzles, mathematical amusements and recreations, games. Includes the fragmentary Part III of "Curiosa Mathematica." Also contains humorous and satirical pieces: "The New Belfry," "The Vision of the Three T's," and much more. New 32-page supplement of rare photographs taken by Carroll. Formerly titled "The Lewis Carroll Picture Book." Edited by S. Collingwood. x + 375pp. 5⅜ x 8. T732 Paperbound **$1.50**

MATHEMATICAL PUZZLES OF SAM LOYD, Vol. I, selected and edited by M. Gardner. Puzzles by the greatest puzzle creator and innovator. Selected from his famous "Cyclopedia of Puzzles," they retain the unique style and historical flavor of the originals. There are posers based on arithmetic, algebra, probability, game theory, route tracing, topology, counter, sliding block, operations research, geometrical dissection. Includes his famous "14-15" puzzle which was a national craze, and his "Horse of a Different Color" which sold millions of copies. 117 of his most ingenious puzzles in all, 120 line drawings and diagrams. Solutions. Selected references. xx + 167pp. 5⅜ x 8. T498 Paperbound **$1.00**

MATHEMATICAL PUZZLES OF SAM LOYD, Vol. II, selected and edited by Martin Gardner. The outstanding second selection from the great American innovator's "Cyclopedia of Puzzles": speed and distance problems, clock problems, plane and solid geometry, calculus problems, etc. Analytical table of contents that groups the puzzles according to the type of mathematics necessary to solve them. 166 puzzles, 150 original line drawings and diagrams. Selected references. xiv + 177pp. 5⅜ x 8. T709 Paperbound **$1.00**

CALIBAN'S PROBLEM BOOK: MATHEMATICAL, INFERENTIAL, AND CRYPTOGRAPHIC PUZZLES, H. Phillips ("Caliban"), S. T. Shovelton, G. S. Marshall. 105 ingenious problems by the greatest living creator of puzzles based on logic and inference. Rigorous, modern, piquant, and reflecting their author's unusual personality, these intermediate and advanced puzzles all involve the ability to reason clearly through complex situations; some call for mathematical knowledge, ranging from algebra to number theory. Solutions. xi + 180pp. 5⅜ x 8. T736 Paperbound **$1.25**

MATHEMATICAL PUZZLES FOR BEGINNERS AND ENTHUSIASTS, G. Mott-Smith. 188 mathematical puzzles to test mental agility. Inference, interpretation, algebra, dissection of plane figures, geometry, properties of numbers, decimation, permutations, probability, all enter these delightful problems. Puzzles like the Odic Force, How to Draw an Ellipse, Spider's Cousin, more than 180 others. Detailed solutions. Appendix with square roots, triangular numbers, primes, etc. 135 illustrations. 2nd revised edition. 248pp. 5⅜ x 8. T198 Paperbound **$1.00**

INGENIOUS MATHEMATICAL PROBLEMS AND METHODS, L. A. Graham. 100 best problems from Graham "Dial," at least ¾ absolutely original in book form, submitted by applied mathematicians and math puzzle fans. Posed in practical terms, utilize number theory, statistics, compass geometry, networks, inversion, in proofs. Accent on heuristics (problem-solving technique) with various methods of solution discussed, compared, for each problem. First publication. Full solutions. 254pp. 5⅜ x 8. T545 Paperbound **$1.45**

101 PUZZLES IN THOUGHT AND LOGIC, C. R. Wylie, Jr. Designed for readers who enjoy the challenge and stimulation of logical puzzles without specialized mathematical or scientific knowledge. These problems are entirely new, and range from relatively easy to brain-teasers that will afford hours of subtle entertainment. It contains detective puzzles, how to find the lying fisherman, how a blind man can identify color by logic, and many more. Easy-to-understand introduction to the logic of puzzle solving and general scientific method. 128pp. 5⅜ x 8. T367 Paperbound **$1.00**

MAZES AND LABYRINTHS: A BOOK OF PUZZLES, W. Shepherd. Mazes, formerly associated with mystery and ritual, are still among the most intriguing of intellectual puzzles. This is a novel and different collection of 50 amusements that embody the principle of the maze: mazes in the classical tradition; 3-dimensional, ribbon, and Möbius-strip mazes; hidden messages; spatial arrangements; etc.—almost all built on amusing story situations. 84 illustrations. Essay on maze psychology. Solutions. xv + 122pp. 5⅜ x 8. T731 Paperbound **$1.00**

MATHEMAGIC, MAGIC PUZZLES, AND GAMES WITH NUMBERS, Royal V. Heath. Over 60 new puzzles and stunts based on properties of numbers. Demonstrates easy techniques for multiplying large numbers mentally, identifying unknown numbers, determining date of any day in any year, dozens of similar useful, entertaining applications of mathematics. Entertainments like The Lost Digit, 3 Acrobats, Psychic Bridge, magic squares, triangles, cubes, circles, other material not easily found elsewhere. Edited by J. S. Meyer. 76 illustrations. 128pp. 5⅜ x 8 T110 Paperbound **$1.00**

MATHEMATICAL RECREATIONS, M. Kraitchik. Some 250 puzzles, problems, demonstrations of recreational mathematics for beginners & advanced mathematicians. Unusual historical problems from Greek, Medieval, Arabic, Hindu sources: modern problems based on "mathematics without numbers," geometry, topology, arithmetic, etc. Pastimes derived from figurative numbers, Mersenne numbers, Fermat numbers; fairy chess, latruncles, reversi, many topics. Full solutions. Excellent for insights into special fields of math. 181 illustrations. 330pp. 5⅜ x 8. T163 Paperbound **$1.75**

PUZZLE QUIZ AND STUNT FUN, Jerome Meyer. 238 high-priority puzzles, stunts, and tricks—mathematical puzzles like The Clever Carpenter, Atom Bomb, Please Help Alice; mysteries and deductions like The Bridge of Sighs, Dog Logic, Secret Code; observation puzzlers like The American Flag, Playing Cards, Telephone Dial; more than 200 others involving magic squares, tongue twisters, puns, anagrams, word design. Answers included. Revised, enlarged edition of FUN-TO-DO. Over 100 illustrations. 238 puzzles, stunts, tricks. 256pp. 5⅜ x 8. T337 Paperbound **$1.00**

THE BOOK OF MODERN PUZZLES, G. L. Kaufman. More than 150 word puzzles, logic puzzles. No warmed-over fare but all new material based on same appeals that make crosswords and deduction puzzles popular, but with different principles, techniques. Two-minute teasers, involved word labyrinths, design and pattern puzzles, puzzles calling for logic and observation, puzzles testing ability to apply general knowledge to peculiar situations, many others. Answers to all problems. 116 illustrations. 192pp. 5⅜ x 8. T143 Paperbound **$1.00**

NEW WORD PUZZLES, Gerald L. Kaufman. Contains 100 brand new challenging puzzles based on words and their combinations, never published before in any form. Most are new types invented by the author—for beginners or experts. Chess word puzzles, addle letter anagrams, double word squares, double horizontals, alphagram puzzles, dual acrostigrams, linkogram lapwords—plus 8 other brand new types, all with solutions included. 196 figures. 100 brand new puzzles. vi + 122pp. 5⅜ x 8. T344 Paperbound **$1.00**

MATHEMATICAL RECREATIONS

MATHEMATICS, MAGIC AND MYSTERY, Martin Gardner. Card tricks, feats of mental mathematics, stage mind-reading, other "magic" explained as applications of probability, sets, theory of numbers, topology, various branches of mathematics. Creative examination of laws and their applications with scores of new tricks and insights. 115 sections discuss tricks wtih cards, dice, coins; geometrical vanishing tricks, dozens of others. No sleight of hand needed; mathematics guarantees success. 115 illustrations. xii + 174pp. 5⅜ x 8.
T335 Paperbound **$1.00**

MATHEMATICAL EXCURSIONS, Helen A. Merrill. Fun, recreation, insights into elementary problem-solving. A mathematical expert guides you along by-paths not generally travelled in elementary math courses—how to divide by inspection, Russian peasant system of multiplication; memory systems for pi; building odd and even magic squares; dyadic systems; facts about 37; square roots by geometry; Tchebichev's machine; drawing five-sided figures; dozens more. Solutions to more difficult ones. 50 illustrations. 145pp. 5⅜ x 8.
T350 Paperbound **$1.00**

CRYPTOGRAPHY, L. D. Smith. Excellent elementary introduction to enciphering, deciphering secret writing. Explains transposition, substitution ciphers; codes; solutions. Geometrical patterns, route transcription, columnar transposition, other methods. Mixed cipher systems; single-alphabet, polyalphabetical substitution; mechanical devices; Vigenere system, etc. Enciphering Japanese; explanation of Baconian Biliteral cipher; frequency tables. More than 150 problems provide practical application. Bibliography. Index. 164pp. 5⅜ x 8.
T247 Paperbound **$1.00**

CRYPTANALYSIS, Helen F. Gaines. (Formerly ELEMENTARY CRYPTANALYSIS.) A standard elementary and intermediate text for serious students. It does not confine itself to old material, but contains much that is not generally known, except to experts. Concealment, Transposition, Substitution ciphers; Vigenere, Kasiski, Playfair, multafid, dozens of other techniques. Appendix with sequence charts, letter frequencies in English, 5 other languages, English word frequencies. Bibliography. 167 codes. New to this edition: solution to codes. vi + 230pp. 5⅜ x 8. T97 Paperbound **$1.95**

MAGIC SQUARES AND CUBES, W. S. Andrews. Only book-length treatment in English, a thorough non-technical description and analysis. Here are nasik, overlapping, pandiagonal, serrated squares; magic circles, cubes, spheres, rhombuses. Try your hand at 4-dimensional magical figures! Much unusual folklore and tradition included. High school algebra is sufficient. 754 diagrams and illustrations. viii + 419pp. 5⅜ x 8. T658 Paperbound **$1.85**

PAPER FOLDING FOR BEGINNERS, W. D. Murray and F. J. Rigney. A delightful introduction to the varied and entertaining Japanese art of origami (paper folding), with a full crystal-clear text that anticipates every difficulty; over 275 clearly labeled diagrams of all important stages in creation. You get results at each stage, since complex figures are logically developed from simpler ones. 43 different pieces are explained: place mats, drinking cups, bonbon boxes, sailboats, frogs, roosters, etc. 6 photographic plates. 279 diagrams. 95pp. 5⅝ x 8⅜.
T713 Paperbound **$1.00**

CHESS, CHECKERS, GAMES, GO

A TREASURY OF CHESS LORE, edited by Fred Reinfeld. A delightful collection of anecdotes, short stories, aphorisms by and about the masters, poems, accounts of games and tournaments, photographs. Hundreds of humorous, pithy, satirical, wise, and historical episodes, comments, and word portraits. A fascinating "must" for chess players; revealing and perhaps seductive to those who wonder what their friends see in the game. 49 photographs (14 full page plates). 12 diagrams. xi + 306pp. 5⅜ x 8. T458 Paperbound **$1.75**

THE ADVENTURE OF CHESS, Edward Lasker. A lively story of the history of chess, from its ancient beginnings in the Indian four-handed game of Chaturanga, through to the great players of our own day, as told by one of America's finest chess masters. He introduces such unusual sidelights and amusing addition as Maelzel's chess playing automaton that beat Napoleon three times. One of the most valuable features of this work is the author's personal recollections of men he has played against and known—Nimzovich, Emanuel Lasker, Capablanca, Alekhine, etc. Lasker's discussion of chess-playing machines (revised for this edition) is particularly knowledgeable, since he is an electrical engineer by profession. 5 page chess primer. 11 illustrations; 53 diagrams. 296pp. 5⅜ x 8.
T510 Paperbound **$1.45**

FREE! All you do is ask for it!

HOW DO YOU PLAY CHESS?, Fred Reinfeld. A 40-page book of 86 lively questions and answers explaining all aspects of chess to beginners, by a noted writer on chess. Copies limited, no more than 1 to a customer.

THE PLEASURES OF CHESS, Assiac. Internationally-known British writer, influential chess columnist, writes wittily about wide variety of chess subjects: Anderssen's "Immortal Game;" only game in which both opponents resigned at once; psychological tactics of Reshevsky, Lasker; varieties played by masters for relaxation, such as "losing chess;" sacrificial orgies; etc. These anecdotes, witty observations will give you fresh appreciation of game. 43 problems. 150 diagrams. 139pp. 5⅜ x 8. T597 Paperbound **$1.25**

WIN AT CHESS, Fred Reinfeld. 300 practical chess situations enable you to sharpen your chess eye and test your skill against the masters. You start with simple examples and progress at your own pace to complex positions. This selected series of crucial moments in chess will stimulate your imagination and enable you to develop a stronger more versatile game. A simple grading system enables you to judge your progress through the course of the book. 300 diagrams. Notes and solutions to every situation. Formerly entitled CHESS QUIZ. vi + 120pp. 5⅜ x 8. T438 Paperbound **$1.00**

THE ART OF CHESS, James Mason. An unabridged reprinting of the latest revised edition of the most famous general study of chess ever written. Also included, a complete supplement by Fred Reinfeld, "How Do You Play Chess?", invaluable to beginners for its lively question and answer method. Mason, an early 20th century master, teaches the beginning and intermediate player more than 90 openings, middle game, end game, how to see more moves ahead, to plan purposefully, attack, sacrifice, defend, exchange, and govern general strategy. Supplement. 448 diagrams. 1947 Reinfeld-Bernstein text. Bibliography. xvi + 340pp. 5⅜ x 8. T463 Paperbound **$1.85**

THE PRINCIPLES OF CHESS, James Mason. This "great chess classic" (N. Y. Times) is a general study covering all aspects of the game: basic forces, resistance, obstruction, opposition, relative values, mating, typical end game situations, combinations, much more. The last section discusses openings, with 50 games illustrating modern master play of Rubinstein, Spielmann, Lasker, Capablanca, etc., selected and annotated by Fred Reinfeld. Will improve the game of any intermediate-skilled player. 1946 Reinfeld edition. 166 diagrams. 378pp. 5⅜ x 8. T646 Paperbound **$1.85**

LASKER'S MANUAL OF CHESS, Dr. Emanuel Lasker. World Champion 28 years, perhaps greatest modern player, writes one of most thorough studies on all facets of chess. How to gain advantage, value of pieces, combinations, etc. Dozens of openings analyzed. Valuable illumination, elaboration of theories of Steinitz. For intermediate-skilled player, but may be read by beginner. Introduction. Indexes. 308 illus. 397pp. 5⅜ x 8. T533 Paperbound **$1.00**

THE ART OF CHESS COMBINATION, E. Znosko-Borovsky. Proves that combinations, perhaps the most aesthetically satisfying, successful technique in chess, can be an integral part of your game, instead of a haphazard occurrence. Games of Capablanca, Rubinstein, Nimzovich, Bird, etc. grouped according to common features, perceptively analyzed to show that every combination begins in certain simple ideas. Will help you to plan many moves ahead. Technical terms almost completely avoided. "In the teaching of chess he may claim to have no superior," P. W. Sergeant. Introduction. Exercises. Solutions. Index. 223pp. 5⅜ x 8.
T583 Paperbound **$1.45**

CHESS STRATEGY, Edward Lasker. Classic study has taught 2 generations of players, including Grandmasters Fine, Keres. Emphasis is on general strategy, not memorization. How to formulate general strategy in terms of opponent's weaknesses, how to form "pawn skeleton," objects of attack, backward pawns, etc. 48 major tournament games analyzed. "The finest book I know of in the English language," J. R. Capablanca. Introduction. Index. 167 illus. 5⅜ x 8. T528 Paperbound **$1.50**

REINFELD ON THE END GAME IN CHESS, Fred Reinfeld. Analyzes 62 end games by Alekhine, Flohr, Tarrasch, Morphy, Bogolyubov, Capablanca, Vidmar, Rubinstein, Lasker, Reshevsky, other masters. Only first-rate book with extensive coverage of error; of immense aid in pointing out errors you might have made. Centers around transitions from middle play to various types of end play. King & pawn endings, minor piece endings, queen endings, bad bishops, blockage, weak pawns, passed pawns, etc. Formerly titled PRACTICAL END-GAME PLAY. 62 figures. vi + 177pp. 5⅜ x 8. T417 Paperbound **$1.25**

HOW TO FORCE CHECKMATE, Fred Reinfeld. If you have trouble finishing off your opponent, this book is for you. It is a collection of lightning strokes and combinations from actual tournament play. Starting with one-move checkmates and working up to three-move mates, you develop the ability to look ahead, and gain new insights into combinations, complex or deceptive positions, and ways of estimating both your own and your opponent's strengths and weaknesses. 300 diagrams. Solutions to all positions. Formerly entitled CHALLENGE TO CHESS PLAYERS. 111pp. 5⅜ x 8. T439 Paperbound **$1.25**

CHESSBOARD MAGIC! A COLLECTION OF 160 BRILLIANT ENDINGS, compiled, annotated by Irving Chernev. Illustrate not only ingenuity of composition, method of solution, but inherent beauty of solution. Many, by foremost Russian chess authorities, have won first prize in Russian chess magazines; are unavailable in this country. "Marvelous . . . sheer magic," Emanuel Lasker. "An endless feast of delight," Reuben Fine. Introduction. 160 diagrams. Index. 184pp. 5⅜ x 8. T607 Paperbound **$1.00**

LEARN CHESS FROM THE MASTERS, Fred Reinfeld. Improve your chess, rate your improvement, by playing against Marshall, Znosko-Borovsky, Bronstein, Najdorf, others. Formerly titled CHESS BY YOURSELF, this book contains 10 games in which you move against masters, and grade your moves by an easy system. Games selected for interest, clarity, easy principles; illustrate common openings, both classical and modern. Ratings for 114 extra playing situations that might have arisen. Full annotations. 91 diagrams. viii + 144pp. 5⅜ x 8. T362 Paperbound **$1.00**

MORPHY'S GAMES OF CHESS, edited by Philip W. Sergeant. You can put boldness into your game by following the brilliant, forceful moves of the man who has been called the greatest chess player of all time. Here are 300 of Morphy's best games, carefully annotated to reveal Morphy's principles. 54 classics against masters like Anderssen, Harrwitz, Bird, Paulsen, and others. 52 games at odds; 54 blindfold games; plus over 100 others. Unabridged reissue of the latest revised edition. Bibliography. New introduction by Fred Reinfeld. Annotations and introduction by Sergeant. Index. 235 diagrams. x + 352pp. 5⅜ x 8. T386 Paperbound **$1.75**

MODERN IDEAS IN CHESS, R. Réti. Clearest and most readable explanation of major developments in chess styles. Concentrates on the games of the master most closely associated with each major advance of the last hundred years. Seven world champions (Anderssen, Morphy, Steinitz, Lasker, Capablanca, Alekhine, and Euwe) are analyzed by a modern master. 34 diagrams. 192pp. 5⅜ x 8. T638 Paperbound **$1.25**

THE BOOK OF THE NEW YORK INTERNATIONAL CHESS TOURNAMENT, 1924, annotated by A. Alekhine and edited by H. Helms. Long a rare collector's item, this is the book of one of the most brilliant tournaments of all time, during which Capablanca, Dr. Lasker, Alekhine, Reti, and others immeasurably enriched chess theory in a thrilling contest. All 110 games played, with Alekhine's unusually penetrating notes. 15 photographs. xi + 271pp. 5⅜ x 8. T752 Paperboard **$1.85**

KERES' BEST GAMES OF CHESS, selected, annotated by F. Reinfeld. 90 best games, 1931-1948, by one of boldest, most exciting players of modern chess. Games against Alekhine, Bogolyubov, Capablanca, Euwe, Fine, Reshevsky, other masters, show his treatments of openings such as Giuoco Piano, Alekhine Defense, Queen's Gambit Declined; attacks, sacrifices, alternative methods. Preface by Keres gives personal glimpses, evaluations of rivals. 110 diagrams. 272pp. 5⅜ x 8. T593 Paperbound **$1.35**

THE DEVELOPMENT OF A CHESS GENIUS: 100 INSTRUCTIVE GAMES OF ALEKHINE, by Fred Reinfeld. Games from vital formative years 1905-1914, most of them never before in book form, show a future great master being shaped by experience and challenge in matches against Bernstein, Bogolyubov, Capablanca, Marshall, Rubinstein, Tarrasch, others. Interesting as chess biography, instructive as a master's increasingly adept responses to problems of every player. Annotated by F. Reinfeld. "One of America's most significant contributions," Chess Life. Formerly "The Unknown Alekhine." Introduction. Indexes of players, openings. 204 illustrations. 242pp. 5⅜ x 8. T551 Paperbound **$1.35**

RESHEVSKY'S BEST GAMES OF CHESS, Samuel Reshevsky. One time 4-year old chess genius, 5-time winner U. S. Chess Championship, selects, annotates 110 of his best games, illustrating theories, favorite methods of play against Capablanca, Alekhine, Bogolyubov, Kashdan, Vidmar, Botvinnik, others. Clear, non-technical style. Personal impressions of opponents, autobiographical material, tournament match record. Formerly, "Reshevsky on Chess." 309 diagrams, 2 photos. 288pp. 5⅜ x 8. T606 Paperbound **$1.25**

HYPERMODERN CHESS as developed in the games of its greatest exponent, ARON NIMZOVICH, edited by Fred Reinfeld. An intensely original player and analyst, Nimzovich's extraordinary approaches startled and often angered the chess world. This volume, designed for the average player, shows in his [illegible] Alekhine, Lasker, Marshall, Rubinstein, Spielmann, and others, how his iconoclastic methods infused new life into the game. Use Nimzovich to invigorate your play and startle opponents. Introduction. Indices of players and openings. 180 diagrams. viii + 220pp. 5⅜ x 8. T448 Paperbound **$1.35**

ONE HUNDRED SELECTED GAMES, Mikhail Botvinnik. Author's own choice of his best games before becoming World Champion in 1948, beginning with first big tournament, the USSR Championship, 1927. Shows his great powers of analysis as he annotates these games, giving strategy, technique against Alekhine, Capablanca, Euwe, Keres, Reshevsky, Smyslov, Vidmar, many others. Discusses his career, methods of play, system of training, 6 studies of endgame positions. 221 diagrams. 272pp. 5⅜ x 8. T620 Paperbound **$1.50**

RUBINSTEIN'S CHESS MASTERPIECES, selected and annotated by H. Kmoch. Thoroughgoing mastery of opening, middle game; faultless technique in endgame, particularly rook and pawn endings; ability to switch from careful positional play to daring combinations; all distinguish the play of Rubinstein. 100 best games, against Janowski, Nimzowitch, Tarrasch, Vidmar, Capablanca, other greats, carefully annotated, will improve your game rapidly. Biographical introduction, B. F. Winkelman, 103 diagrams. 192pp. 5⅜ x 8. T617 Paperbound **$1.25**

TARRASCH'S BEST GAMES OF CHESS, selected & annotated by Fred Reinfeld. First definitive collection of games by Siegbert Tarrasch, winner of 7 international tournaments, and the leading theorist of classical chess. 183 games cover 50 years of play against Mason, Mieses, Paulsen, Teichmann, Pillsbury, Janowski, others. Reinfeld includes Tarrasch's own analyses of many of these games. A careful study and replaying of the games will give you a sound understanding of classical methods, and many hours of enjoyment. Introduction. Indexes. 183 diagrams. xxiv + 386pp. 5⅜ x 8. T644 Paperbound **$2.00**

MARSHALL'S BEST GAMES OF CHESS, F. J. Marshall. Grandmaster, U. S. champion for 27 years, tells story of career; presents magnificent collection of 140 of best games, annotated by himself. Games against Capablanca, Alekhine, Emanuel Lasker, Janowski, Rubinstein, Pillsbury, etc. Special section analyzes openings such as King's Gambit, Ruy Lopez, Alekhine's Defence, Giuoco Piano, others. A study of Marshall's brilliant "swindles," slashing attacks, extraordinary sacrifices, will rapidly improve your game. Formerly "My Fifty Years of Chess." Introduction. 19 diagrams. 13 photos. 250pp. 5⅜ x 8. T604 Paperbound **$1.35**

THE ENJOYMENT OF CHESS PROBLEMS, K. S. Howard. A classic treatise on this minor art by an internationally recognized authority that gives a basic knowledge of terms and themes for the everyday chess player as well as the problem fan: 7 chapters on the two-mover; 7 more on 3- and 4-move problems; a chapter on selfmates; and much more. "The most important one-volume contribution originating solely in the U.S.A.", Alain White. 200 diagrams. Index. Solutions. viii + 212pp. 5⅜ x 8. T742 Paperbound **$1.25**

HOW TO SOLVE CHESS PROBLEMS, K. S. Howard. Full of practical suggestions for the fan or the beginner—who need only know the moves of the chessmen. Contains preliminary section and 58 two-move, 46 three-move, and 8 four-move problems composed by 27 outstanding American problem creators in the last 30 years. Explanation of all terms and exhaustive index. "Just what is wanted for the student," Brian Warley. 112 problems, solutions. vi + 171pp. 5⅜ x 8. T748 Paperbound **$1.00**

CHESS AND CHECKERS: THE WAY TO MASTERSHIP, Edward Lasker. Complete, lucid instructions for the beginner—and valuable suggestions for the advanced player! For both games the great master and teacher presents fundamentals, elementary tactics, and steps toward becoming a superior player. He concentrates on general principles rather than a mass of rules, comprehension rather than brute memory. Historical introduction. 118 diagrams. xiv + 167pp. 5⅜ x 8. T657 Paperbound **$1.15**

WIN AT CHECKERS, M. Hopper. (Formerly CHECKERS). The former World's Unrestricted Checker Champion discusses the principles of the game, expert's shots and traps, problems for the beginner, standard openings, locating your best move, the end game, opening "blitzkrieg" moves, ways to draw when you are behind your opponent, etc. More than 100 detailed questions and answers anticipate your problems. Appendix. 75 problems with solutions and diagrams. Index. 79 figures. xi + 107pp. 5⅜ x 8. T363 Paperbound **$1.00**

GAMES ANCIENT AND ORIENTAL, AND HOW TO PLAY THEM, E. Falkener. A connoisseur's selection of exciting and different games: Oriental varieties of chess, with unusual pieces and moves (including Japanese shogi); the original pachisi; go; reconstructions of lost Roman and Egyptian games; and many more. Full rules and sample games. Now play at home the games that have entertained millions, not on a fad basis, but for millennia. 345 illustrations and figures. iv + 366pp. 5⅜ x 8. T739 Paperbound **$1.85**

GO AND GO-MOKU: THE ORIENTAL BOARD GAMES, Edward Lasker. Best introduction to Go and its easier sister game, Go-Moku—games new to western world, but ancient in China, Japan. Extensively revised work by famed chess master Lasker, Go-player for over 50 years, stresses theory rather than brute memory, presents step-by-step explanation of strategy, gives examples of world championship matches, in game which has replaced chess as favorite of many physicists, mathematicians. 72 diagrams. xix + 215 pp. 5⅜ x 8.
T613 Paperbound **$1.45**

FICTION

FLATLAND, E. A. Abbott. A science-fiction classic of life in a 2-dimensional world that is also a first-rate introduction to such aspects of modern science as relativity and hyperspace. Political, moral, satirical, and humorous overtones have made FLATLAND fascinating reading for thousands. 7th edition. New introduction by Banesh Hoffmann. 16 illustrations. 128pp. 5⅜ x 8.
T1 Paperbound **$1.00**

THE WONDERFUL WIZARD OF OZ, L. F. Baum. Only edition in print with all the original W. W. Denslow illustrations in full color—as much a part of "The Wizard" as Tenniel's drawings are of "Alice in Wonderland." "The Wizard" is still America's best-loved fairy tale, in which, as the author expresses it, "The wonderment and joy are retained and the heartaches and nightmares left out." Now today's young readers can enjoy every word and wonderful picture of the original book. New introduction by Martin Gardner. A Baum bibliography. 23 full-page color plates. viii + 268pp. 5⅜ x 8. T691 Paperbound **$1.45**

THE MARVELOUS LAND OF OZ, L. F. Baum. This is the equally enchanting sequel to the "Wizard," continuing the adventures of the Scarecrow and the Tin Woodman. The hero this time is a little boy named Tip, and all the delightful Oz magic is still present. This is the book with the Animated Saw-horse, the Woggle-Bug, and Jack Pumpkinhead. All the original John R. Neill illustrations, 16 in full color. 287pp. 5⅜ x 8. T692 Paperbound **$1.45**

FIVE GREAT DOG NOVELS, edited by Blanche Cirker. The complete original texts of five classic dog novels that have delighted and thrilled millions of children and adults throughout the world with stories of loyalty, adventure, and courage. Full texts of Jack London's "The Call of the Wild"; John Brown's "Rab and His Friends"; Alfred Ollivant's "Bob, Son of Battle"; Marshall Saunders' "Beautiful Joe"; and Ouida's "A Dog of Flanders." 21 illustrations from the original editions. 495pp. 5⅜ x 8. T777 Paperbound **$1.50**

3 ADVENTURE NOVELS by H. Rider Haggard. Complete texts of "She," "King Solomon's Mines," "Allan Quatermain." Qualities of discovery; desire for immortality; search for primitive, for what is unadorned by civilization, have kept these novels of African adventure exciting, alive to readers from R. L. Stevenson to George Orwell. 636pp. 5⅜ x 8.
T584 Paperbound **$2.00**

The Space Novels of Jules Verne

TO THE SUN? and OFF ON A COMET!, Jules Verne. Complete texts of two of the most imaginative flights into fancy in world literature display the high adventure that have kept Verne's novels read for nearly a century. Only unabridged edition of the best translation, by Edward Roth. Large, easily readable type. 50 illustrations selected from first editions. 462pp. 5⅜ x 8.
T634 Paperbound **$1.75**

FROM THE EARTH TO THE MOON and ALL AROUND THE MOON, Jules Verne. Complete editions of two of Verne's most successful novels, in finest Edward Roth translations, now available after many years out of print. Verne's visions of submarines, airplanes, television, rockets, interplanetary travel; of scientific and not-so-scientific beliefs; of peculiarities of Americans; all delight and engross us today as much as when they first appeared. Large, easily readable type. 42 illus. from first French edition. 476pp. 5⅜ x 8.
T633 Paperbound **$1.75**

THE CASTING AWAY OF MRS. LECKS AND MRS. ALESHINE, F. R. Stockton. A charming light novel by Frank Stockton, one of America's finest humorists (and author of "The Lady, or the Tiger?"). This book has made millions of Americans laugh at the reflection of themselves in two middle-aged American women involved in some of the strangest adventures on record. You will laugh, too, as they endure shipwreck, desert island, and blizzard with maddening tranquility. Also contains complete text of "The Dusantes," sequel to "The Casting Away." 49 original illustrations by F. D. Steele. vii + 142pp. 5⅜ x 8. T743 Paperbound **$1.00**

GESTA ROMANORUM, trans. by Charles Swan, ed. by Wynnard Hooper. 181 tales of Greeks, Romans, [illegible], Biblical characters, comprise one of greatest medieval story collections, source plots for writers including Shakespeare, Chaucer, Gower, etc. Imaginative tales of wars, incest, thwarted love, magic, fantasy, allegory, humor, tell about kings, prostitutes, philosophers, fair damsels, knights, Noah, pirates, all walks and stations of life. Introduction. Notes. 500pp. 5⅜ x 8. T535 Paperbound **$1.85**

THREE PROPHETIC NOVELS BY H. G. WELLS, edited by E. F. Bleiler. Complete texts of "When the Sleeper Wakes" (1st book printing in 50 years), "A Story of the Days to Come," "The Time Machine" (1st complete printing in book form). Exciting adventures in the future are as enjoyable today as 50 years ago when first printed. Predict TV, movies, intercontinental airplanes, prefabricated houses, air-conditioned cities, etc. First important author to foresee problems of mind control, technological dictatorships. "Absolute best of imaginative fiction," N. Y. Times. Introduction. 335pp. 5⅜ x 8. T605 Paperbound **$1.45**

SEVEN SCIENCE FICTION NOVELS, H. G. Wells. Full unabridged texts of 7 science-fiction novels of the master. Ranging from biology, physics, chemistry, astronomy to sociology and other studies, Mr. Wells extrapolates whole worlds of strange and intriguing character. "One will have to go far to match this for entertainment, excitement, and sheer pleasure . . . ," NEW YORK TIMES. Contents: The Time Machine, The Island of Dr. Moreau, First Men in the Moon, The Invisible Man, The War of the Worlds, The Food of the Gods, In the Days of the Comet. 1015pp. 5⅜ x 8. T264 Clothbound **$3.95**

28 SCIENCE FICTION STORIES OF H. G. WELLS. Two full unabridged novels, MEN LIKE GODS and STAR BEGOTTEN, plus 26 short stories by the master science-fiction writer of all time. Stories of space, time, invention, exploration, future adventure—an indispensable part of the library of everyone interested in science and adventure. PARTIAL CONTENTS: Men Like Gods, The Country of the Blind, In the Abyss, The Crystal Egg, The Man Who Could Work Miracles, A Story of the Days to Come, The Valley of Spiders, and 21 more! 928pp. 5⅜ x 8. T265 Clothbound **$3.95**

DAVID HARUM, E. N. Westcott. This novel of one of the most lovable, humorous characters in American literature is a prime example of regional humor. It continues to delight people who like their humor dry, their characters quaint, and their plots ingenuous. First book edition to contain complete novel plus chapter found after author's death. Illustrations from first illustrated edition. 192pp. 5⅜ x 8. T580 Paperbound **$1.15**

HUMOR

THE WIT AND HUMOR OF OSCAR WILDE, ed. by Alvin Redman. Wilde at his most brilliant, in 1000 epigrams exposing weaknesses and hypocrisies of "civilized" society. Divided into 49 categories—sin, wealth, women, America, etc.—to aid writers, speakers. Includes excerpts from his trials, books, plays, criticism. Formerly "The Epigrams of Oscar Wilde." Introduction by Vyvyan Holland, Wilde's only living son. Introductory essay by editor. 260pp. 5⅜ x 8. T602 Paperbound **$1.00**

A NONSENSE ANTHOLOGY, collected by **Carolyn Wells.** 245 of the best nonsense verses ever written, including nonsense puns, absurd arguments, mock epics and sagas, nonsense ballads, odes, "sick" verses, dog-Latin verses, French nonsense verses, songs. By Edward Lear, Lewis Carroll, Gelett Burgess, W. S. Gilbert, Hilaire Belloc, Peter Newell, Oliver Herford, etc., 83 writers in all plus over four score anonymous nonsense verses. A special section of limericks, plus famous nonsense such as Carroll's "Jabberwocky" and Lear's "The Jumblies" and much excellent verse virtually impossible to locate elsewhere. For 50 years considered the best anthology available. Index of first lines specially prepared for this edition. Introduction by Carolyn Wells. 3 indexes: Title, Author, First lines. xxxiii + 279pp. 5⅜ x 8. T499 Paperbound **$1.25**

THE BAD CHILD'S BOOK OF BEASTS, MORE BEASTS FOR WORSE CHILDREN, and A MORAL ALPHABET, H. Belloc. Hardly an anthology of humorous verse has appeared in the last 50 years without at least a couple of these famous nonsense verses. But one must see the entire volumes—with all the delightful original illustrations by Sir Basil Blackwood—to appreciate fully Belloc's charming and witty verses that play so subacidly on the platitudes of life and morals that beset his day—and ours. A great humor classic. Three books in one. Total of 157pp. 5⅜ x 8. T749 Paperbound **$1.00**

THE DEVIL'S DICTIONARY, Ambrose Bierce. Sardonic and irreverent barbs puncturing the pomposities and absurdities of American politics, business, religion, literature, and arts, by the country's greatest satirist in the classic tradition. Epigrammatic as Shaw, piercing as Swift, American as Mark Twain, Will Rogers, and Fred Allen. Bierce will always remain the favorite of a small coterie of enthusiasts, and of writers and speakers whom he supplies with "some of the most gorgeous witticisms of the English language." (H. L. Mencken) Over 1000 entries in alphabetical order. 144pp. 5⅜ x 8. T487 Paperbound **$1.00**

THE PURPLE COW AND OTHER NONSENSE, Gelett Burgess. The best of Burgess's early nonsense, selected from the first edition of the "Burgess Nonsense Book." Contains many of his most unusual and highly original pieces: 37 nonsense quatrains, the Poems of Patagonia, Alphabet of Famous Goops, and the other hilarious (and rare) adult nonsense that places him in the forefront of American humorists. All pieces are accompanied by the original Burgess illustrations. 123 illustrations. xiii + 113pp. 5⅜ x 8.
T772 Paperbound **$1.00**

THE HUMOROUS VERSE OF LEWIS CARROLL. Almost every poem Carroll ever wrote, the largest collection ever published, including much never published elsewhere: 150 parodies, burlesques, riddles, ballads, acrostics, etc., with 130 original illustrations by Tenniel, Carroll, and others. "Addicts will be grateful . . . there is nothing for the faithful to do but sit down and fall to the banquet," N. Y. Times. Index to first lines. xiv + 446pp. 5 x 8.
T654 Paperbound **$1.85**

DIVERSIONS AND DIGRESSIONS OF LEWIS CARROLL. A major new treasure for Carroll fans! Rare privately published humor, fantasy, puzzles, and games by Carroll at his whimsical best, with a new vein of frank satire. Includes many new mathematical amusements and recreations, among them the fragmentary Part III of "Curiosa Mathematica." Contains "The Rectory Umbrella," "The New Belfry," "The Vision of the Three T's," and much more. New 32-page supplement of rare photographs taken by Carroll. x + 375pp. 5⅜ x 8.
T732 Paperbound **$1.50**

THE COMPLETE NONSENSE OF EDWARD LEAR. This is the only complete edition of this master of gentle madness available at a popular price. A BOOK OF NONSENSE, NONSENSE SONGS, MORE NONSENSE SONGS AND STORIES in their entirety with all the old favorites that have delighted children and adults for years. The Dong With A Luminous Nose, The Jumblies, The Owl and the Pussycat, and hundreds of other bits of wonderful nonsense. 214 limericks, 3 sets of Nonsense Botany, 5 Nonsense Alphabets. 546 drawings by Lear himself, and much more. 320pp. 5⅜ x 8.
T167 Paperbound **$1.00**

PECK'S BAD BOY AND HIS PA, George W. Peck. The complete edition, containing both volumes, one of the most widely read of all American humor books. The endless ingenious pranks played by bad boy "Hennery" on his pa and the grocery man, the outraged pomposity of Pa, the perpetual ridiculing of middle class institutions, are as entertaining today as they were in 1883. No pale sophistications or subtleties, but rather humor vigorous, raw, earthy, imaginative, and, as folk humor often is, sadistic. This peculiarly fascinating book is also valuable to historians and students of American culture as a portrait of an age. 100 original illustrations by True Williams. Introduction by E. F. Bleiler. 347pp. 5⅜ x 8.
T497 Paperbound **$1.35**

FABLES IN SLANG & MORE FABLES IN SLANG, George Ade. 2 complete books of major American humorist in pungent colloquial tradition of Twain, Billings. 1st reprinting in over 30 years includes "The Two Mandolin Players and the Willing Performer," "The Base Ball Fan Who Took the Only Known Cure," "The Slim Girl Who Tried to Keep a Date that was Never Made," 42 other tales of eccentric, perverse, but always funny characters. "Touch of genius," H. L. Mencken. New introduction by E. F. Bleiler. 86 illus. 203pp. 5⅜ x 8.
T533 Paperbound **$1.00**

SINGULAR TRAVELS, CAMPAIGNS, AND ADVENTURES OF BARON MUNCHAUSEN, R. E. Raspe, with 90 illustrations by Gustave Doré. The first edition in over 150 years to reestablish the deeds of the Prince of Liars exactly as Raspe first recorded them in 1785—the genuine Baron Munchausen, one of the most popular personalities in English literature. Included also are the best of the many sequels, written by other hands. Introduction on Raspe by J. Carswell. Bibliography of early editions. xliv + 192pp. 5⅜ x 8. T698 Paperbound **$1.00**

HOW TO TELL THE BIRDS FROM THE FLOWERS, R. W. Wood. How not to confuse a carrot with a parrot, a grape with an ape, a puffin with nuffin. Delightful drawings, clever puns, absurd little poems point out farfetched resemblances in nature. The author was a leading physicist. Introduction by Margaret Wood White. 106 illus. 60pp. 5⅜ x 8.
T523 Paperbound **75¢**

MATHEMATICS, ELEMENTARY TO INTERMEDIATE

HOW TO CALCULATE QUICKLY, Henry Sticker. This handy volume offers a tried and true method for helping you in the basic mathematics of daily life—addition, subtraction, multiplication, division, fractions, etc. It is designed to awaken your "number sense" or the ability to see relationships between numbers as whole quantities. It is not a collection of tricks working only on special numbers, but a serious course of over 9,000 problems and their solutions, teaching special techniques not taught in schools: left-to-right multiplication, new fast ways of division, etc. 5 or 10 minutes daily use will double or triple your calculation speed. Excellent for the scientific worker who is at home in higher math, but is not satisfied with his speed and accuracy in lower mathematics. 256pp. 5 x 7¼. T295 Paperbound **$1.00**

TEACH YOURSELF books. For adult self-study, for refresher and supplementary study.

The most effective series of home study mathematics books on the market! With absolutely no outside help, they will teach you as much as any similar college or high-school course, or will helpfully supplement any such course. Each step leads directly to the next, each question is anticipated. Numerous lucid examples and carefully-wrought practice problems illustrate meanings. Not skimpy outlines, not surveys, not usual classroom texts, these 204- to 380-page books are packed with the finest instruction you'll find anywhere for adult self-study.

TEACH YOURSELF ALGEBRA, P. Abbott. Formulas, coordinates, factors, graphs of quadratic functions, quadratic equations, logarithms, ratio, irrational numbers, arithmetical, geometrical series, much more. 1241 problems, solutions. Tables. 52 illus. 307pp. 6⅞ x 4¼.
Clothbound **$2.00**

TEACH YOURSELF GEOMETRY, P. Abbott. Solids, lines, points, surfaces, angle measurement, triangles, theorem of Pythagoras, polygons, loci, the circle, tangents, symmetry, solid geometry, prisms, pyramids, solids of revolution, etc. 343 problems, solutions. 268 illus. 334pp. 6⅞ x 4¼.
Clothbound **$2.00**

TEACH YOURSELF TRIGONOMETRY, P. Abbott. Geometrical foundations, indices, logarithms, trigonometrical ratios, relations between sides, angles of triangle, circular measure, trig. ratios of angles of any magnitude, much more. Requires elementary algebra, geometry. 465 problems, solutions. Tables. 102 illus. 204pp. 6⅞ x 4¼.
Clothbound **$2.00**

TEACH YOURSELF THE CALCULUS, P. Abbott. Variations in functions, differentiation, solids of revolution, series, elementary differential equations, areas by integral calculus, much more. Requires algebra, trigonometry. 970 problems, solutions. Tables. 89 illus. 380pp. 6⅞ x 4¼.
Clothbound **$2.00**

TEACH YOURSELF THE SLIDE RULE, B. Snodgrass. Fractions, decimals, A-D scales, log-log scales, trigonometrical scales, indices, logarithms. Commercial, precision, electrical, dualistic, Brighton rules. 80 problems, solutions. 10 illus. 207pp. 6⅞ x 4¼. Clothbound **$2.00**

See also: **TEACH YOURSELF ELECTRICITY, C. W. Wilman; TEACH YOURSELF HEAT ENGINES, E. De Ville; TEACH YOURSELF MECHANICS, P. Abbott.**

* * *

HOW DO YOU USE A SLIDE RULE? by A. A. Merrill. Not a manual for mathematicians and engineers, but a lucid step-by-step explanation that presents the fundamental rules clearly enough to be understood by anyone who could benefit by the use of a slide rule in his work or business. This work concentrates on the 2 most important operations: multiplication and division. 10 easy lessons, each with a clear drawing, will save you countless hours in your banking, business, statistical, and other work. First publication. Index. 2 Appendixes. 10 illustrations. 78 problems, all with answers. vi + 36pp. 6⅛ x 9¼. T62 Paperbound **60¢**

THEORY OF OPERATION OF THE SLIDE RULE, J. P. Ellis. Not a skimpy "instruction manual", but an exhaustive treatment that will save you uncounted hours throughout your career. Supplies full understanding of every scale on the Log Log Duplex Decitrig type of slide rule. Shows the most time-saving methods, and provides practice useful in the widest variety of actual engineering situations. Each operation introduced in terms of underlying logarithmic theory. Summary of prerequisite math. First publication. Index. 198 figures. Over 450 problems with answers. Bibliography. 12 Appendices. ix + 289pp. 5⅜ x 8.
S727 Paperbound **$1.50**

ARITHMETICAL EXCURSIONS: AN ENRICHMENT OF ELEMENTARY MATHEMATICS, H. Bowers and J. Bowers. For students who want unusual methods of arithmetic never taught in school; for adults who want to increase their number sense. Little known facts about the most simple numbers, arithmetical entertainments and puzzles, figurate numbers, number chains, mysteries and folklore of numbers, the "Hin-dog-abic" number system, etc. First publication. Index. 529 numbered problems and diversions, all with answers. Bibliography. 50 figures. xiv + 320pp. 5⅜ x 8.
T770 Paperbound **$1.65**

APPLIED MATHEMATICS FOR RADIO AND COMMUNICATIONS ENGINEERS, C. E. Smith. No extraneous material here!—only the theories, equations, and operations essential and immediately useful for radio work. Can be used as refresher, as handbook of applications and tables, or as full home-study course. Ranges from simplest arithmetic through calculus, series, and wave forms, hyperbolic trigonometry, simultaneous equations in mesh circuits, etc. Supplies applications right along with each math topic discussed. 22 useful tables of functions, formulas, logs, etc. Index. 166 exercises, 140 examples, all with answers. 95 diagrams. Bibliography. x + 336pp. 5⅜ x 8.
S141 Paperbound **$1.75**

FAMOUS PROBLEMS OF ELEMENTARY GEOMETRY, Felix Klein. Expanded version of the 1894 Easter lectures at Göttingen. 3 problems of classical geometry, in an excellent mathematical treatment by a famous mathematician: squaring the circle, trisecting angle, doubling cube. Considered with full modern implications: transcendental numbers, pi, etc. Notes by R. Archibald. 16 figures. xi + 92pp. 5⅜ x 8. T348 Clothbound **$1.50**
T298 Paperbound **$1.00**

* * *

ELEMENTARY MATHEMATICS FROM AN ADVANCED STANDPOINT, Felix Klein.

This classic text is an outgrowth of Klein's famous integration and survey course at Göttingen. Using one field of mathematics to interpret, adjust, illuminate another, it covers basic topics in each area, illustrating its discussion with extensive analysis. It is especially valuable in considering areas of modern mathematics. "Makes the reader feel the inspiration of . . . a great mathematician, inspiring teacher . . . with deep insight into the foundations and interrelations," BULLETIN, AMERICAN MATHEMATICAL SOCIETY.

Vol. 1. ARITHMETIC, ALGEBRA, ANALYSIS. Introducing the concept of function immediately, it enlivens abstract discussion with graphical and geometrically perceptual methods. Partial contents: natural numbers, extension of the notion of number, special properties, complex numbers. Real equations with real unknowns, complex quantities. Logarithmic, exponential functions, goniometric functions, infinitesimal calculus. Transcendence of e and pi, theory of assemblages. Index. 125 figures. ix + 274pp . 5⅜ x 8. S150 Paperbound **$1.75**

Vol. 2. GEOMETRY. A comprehensive view which accompanies the space perception inherent in geometry with analytic formulas which facilitate precise formulation. Partial contents: Simplest geometric manifolds: line segment, Grassmann determinant principles, classification of configurations of space, derivative manifolds. Geometric transformations: affine transformations, projective, higher point transformations, theory of the imaginary. Systematic discussion of geometry and its foundations. Indexes. 141 illustrations. ix + 214pp. 5⅜ x 8.
S151 Paperbound **$1.75**

* * *

COORDINATE GEOMETRY, L. P. Eisenhart. Thorough, unified introduction. Unusual for advancing in dimension within each topic (treats together circle, sphere; polar coordinates, 3-dimensional coordinate systems; conic sections, quadric surfaces), affording exceptional insight into subject. Extensive use made of determinants, though no previous knowledge of them is assumed. Algebraic equations of 1st degree, 2 and 3 unknowns, carried further than usual in algebra courses. Over 500 exercises. Introduction. Appendix. Index. Bibliography. 43 illustrations. 310pp. 5⅜ x 8. S600 Paperbound **$1.65**

MONOGRAPHS ON TOPICS OF MODERN MATHEMATICS, edited by **J. W. A. Young.** Advanced mathematics for persons who haven't gone beyond or have forgotten high school algebra. 9 monographs on foundation of geometry, modern pure geometry, non-Euclidean geometry, fundamental propositions of algebra, algebraic equations, functions, calculus, theory of numbers, etc. Each monograph gives proofs of important results, and descriptions of leading methods, to provide wide coverage. New introduction by Prof. M. Kline, N. Y. University. 100 diagrams. xvi + 416pp. 6⅛ x 9¼. S289 Paperbound **$2.00**

MATHEMATICS, INTERMEDIATE TO ADVANCED

Geometry

THE FOUNDATIONS OF EUCLIDEAN GEOMETRY, H. G. Forder. The first rigorous account of Euclidean geometry, establishing propositions without recourse to empiricism, and without multiplying hypotheses. Corrects many traditional weaknesses of Euclidean proofs, and investigates the problems imposed on the axiom system by the discoveries of Bolya and Lobatchefsky. Some topics discussed are Classes and Relations; Axioms for Magnitudes; Congruence and Similarity; Algebra of Points; Hessenberg's Theorem; Continuity; Existence of Parallels; Reflections; Rotations; Isometries; etc. Invaluable for the light it throws on foundations of math. Lists: Axioms employed, Symbols, Constructions. 295pp. 5⅜ x 8.
S481 Paperbound **$2.00**

ADVANCED EUCLIDEAN GEOMETRY, R. A. Johnson. For years the standard textbook on advanced Euclidean geometry, requires only high school geometry and trigonometry. Explores in unusual detail and gives proofs of hundreds of relatively recent theorems and corollaries, many formerly available only in widely scattered journals. Covers tangent circles, the theorem of Miquel, symmedian point, pedal triangles and circles, the Brocard configuration, and much more. Formerly "Modern Geometry." Index. 107 diagrams. xiii + 319pp. 5⅜ x 8.
S669 Paperbound **$1.65**

NON-EUCLIDEAN GEOMETRY, Roberto Bonola. The standard coverage of non-Euclidean geometry. It examines from both a historical and mathematical point of view the geometries which have arisen from a study of Euclid's 5th postulate upon parallel lines. Also included are complete texts, translated, of Bolyai's THEORY OF ABSOLUTE SPACE, Lobachevsky's THEORY OF PARALLELS. 180 diagrams. 431pp. 5⅜ x 8. S27 Paperbound **$1.95**

ELEMENTS OF NON-EUCLIDEAN GEOMETRY, D. M. Y. Sommerville. Unique in proceeding step-by-step, in the manner of traditional geometry. Enables the student with only a good knowledge of high school algebra and geometry to grasp elementary hyperbolic, elliptic, analytic non-Euclidean geometries; space curvature and its philosophical implications; theory of radical axes; homothetic centres and systems of circles; parataxy and parallelism; absolute measure; Gauss' proof of the defect area theorem; geodesic representation; much more, all with exceptional clarity. 126 problems at chapter endings provide progressive practice and familiarity. 133 figures. Index. xvi + 274pp. 5⅜ x 8. S460 Paperbound **$1.50**

HIGHER GEOMETRY: AN INTRODUCTION TO ADVANCED METHODS IN ANALYTIC GEOMETRY, F. S. Woods. Exceptionally thorough study of concepts and methods of advanced algebraic geometry (as distinguished from differential geometry). Exhaustive treatment of 1-, 2-, 3-, and 4-dimensional coordinate systems, leading to n-dimensional geometry in an abstract sense. Covers projectivity, tetracyclical coordinates, contact transformation, pentaspherical coordinates, much more. Based on M.I.T. lectures, requires sound preparation in analytic geometry and some knowledge of determinants. Index. Over 350 exercises. References. 60 figures. x + 423pp. 5⅜ x 8. S737 Paperbound **$2.00**

ELEMENTS OF PROJECTIVE GEOMETRY, L. Cremona. Outstanding complete treatment of projective geometry by one of the foremost 19th century geometers. Detailed proofs of all fundamental principles, stress placed on the constructive aspects. Covers homology, law of duality, anharmonic ratios, theorems of Pascal and Brianchon, foci, polar reciprocal figures, etc. Only ordinary geometry necessary to understand this honored classic. Index. Over 150 fully worked out examples and problems. 252 diagrams. xx + 302pp. 5⅜ x 8. S668 Paperbound **$1.75**

A TREATISE ON THE DIFFERENTIAL GEOMETRY OF CURVES AND SURFACES, L. P. Eisenhart. Introductory treatise especially for the graduate student, for years a highly successful textbook. More detailed and concrete in approach than most more recent books. Covers space curves, osculating planes, moving axes, Gauss' method, the moving trihedral, geodesics, conformal representation, etc. Last section deals with deformation of surfaces, rectilinear congruences, cyclic systems, etc. Index. 683 problems. 30 diagrams. xii + 474pp. 5⅜ x 8. S667 Paperbound **$2.75**

A TREATISE ON ALGEBRAIC PLANE CURVES, J. L. Coolidge. Unabridged reprinting of one of few full coverages in English, offering detailed introduction to theory of algebraic plane curves and their relations to geometry and analysis. Treats topological properties, Riemann-Roch theorem, all aspects of wide variety of curves including real, covariant, polar, containing series of a given sort, elliptic, polygonal, rational, the pencil, two parameter nets, etc. This volume will enable the reader to appreciate the symbolic notation of Aronhold and Clebsch. Bibliography. Index. 17 illustrations. xxiv + 513pp. 5⅜ x 8. S543 Paperbound **$2.45**

AN INTRODUCTION TO THE GEOMETRY OF N DIMENSIONS, D. M. Y. Sommerville. An introduction presupposing no prior knowledge of the field, the only book in English devoted exclusively to higher dimensional geometry. Discusses fundamental ideas of incidence, parallelism, perpendicularity, angles between linear space; enumerative geometry; analytical geometry from projective and metric points of view; polytopes; elementary ideas in analysis situs; content of hyper-spacial figures. Bibliography. Index. 60 diagrams. 196pp. 5⅜ x 8. S494 Paperbound **$1.50**

GEOMETRY OF FOUR DIMENSIONS, H. P. Manning. Unique in English as a clear, concise introduction. Treatment is synthetic, and mostly Euclidean, although in hyperplanes and hyperspheres at infinity, non-Euclidean geometry is used. Historical introduction. Foundations of 4-dimensional geometry. Perpendicularity, simple angles. Angles of planes, higher order. Symmetry, order, motion; hyperpyramids, hypercones, hyperspheres; figures with parallel elements; volume, hypervolume in space; regular polyhedroids. Glossary. 78 figures. ix + 348pp. 5⅜ x 8. S182 Paperbound **$1.95**

ELEMENTARY CONCEPTS OF TOPOLOGY, P. Alexandroff. First English translation of the famous brief introduction to topology for the beginner or for the mathematician not undertaking extensive study. This unusually useful intuitive approach deals primarily with the concepts of complex, cycle, and homology, and is wholly consistent with current investigations. Ranges from basic concepts of set-theoretic topology to the concept of Betti groups. "Glowing example of harmony between intuition and thought," David Hilbert. Translated by A. E. Farley. Introduction by D. Hilbert. Index. 25 figures. 73pp. 5⅜ x 8. S747 Paperbound **$1.00**

THE WORKS OF ARCHIMEDES, edited by **T. L. Heath.** All the known works of the great Greek mathematician are contained in this one volume, including the recently discovered Method of Archimedes. Contains: On Sphere & Cylinder, Measurement of a Circle, Spirals, Conoids, Spheroids, etc. This is the definitive edition of the greatest mathematical intellect of the ancient world. 186-page study by Heath discusses Archimedes and the history of Greek mathematics. Bibliography. 563pp. 5⅜ x 8. S9 Paperbound **$2.00**

THE THIRTEEN BOOKS OF EUCLID'S ELEMENTS, edited by **Sir Thomas Heath.** Definitive edition of one of the very greatest classics of Western world. Complete English translation of Heiberg text, together with spurious Book XIV. Detailed 150-page introduction discussing aspects of Greek and Medieval mathematics. Euclid, texts, commentators, etc. Paralleling the text is an elaborate critical apparatus analyzing each definition, proposition, postulate, covering textual matters, mathematical analysis, commentators of all times, refutations, supports, extrapolations, etc. This is the FULL EUCLID. Unabridged reproduction of Cambridge U. 2nd edition. 3 volumes. Total of 995 figures, 1426pp. 5⅜ x 8.
S88,89,90, 3 volume set, paperbound **$6.00**

THE GEOMETRY OF RENE DESCARTES. With this book Descartes founded analytical geometry. Excellent Smith-Latham translation, plus original French text with Déscartes' own diagrams. Contains Problems the Construction of Which Requires Only Straight Lines and Circles; On the Nature of Curved Lines; On the Construction of Solid or Supersolid Problems. Notes. Diagrams. 258pp. 5⅜ x 8. S68 Paperbound **$1.50**

See also: **FOUNDATIONS OF GEOMETRY, B. Russell; THE PHILOSOPHY OF SPACE AND TIME, H. Reichenbach; FAMOUS PROBLEMS OF ELEMENTARY GEOMETRY, F. Klein; MONOGRAPHS ON TOPICS OF MODERN MATHEMATICS, ed. by J. W. Young.**

Calculus and function theory, Fourier theory, real and complex functions, determinants

A COLLECTION OF MODERN MATHEMATICAL CLASSICS, edited by R. Bellman. 13 classic papers, complete in their original languages, by Hermite, Hardy and Littlewood, Tchebychef, Fejér, Fredholm, Fuchs, Hurwitz, Weyl, van der Pol, Birkhoff, Kellogg, von Neumann, and Hilbert. Each of these papers, collected here for the first time, triggered a burst of mathematical activity, providing useful new generalizations or stimulating fresh investigations. Topics discussed include classical analysis, periodic and almost periodic functions, analysis and number theory, integral equations, theory of approximation, non-linear differential equations, and functional analysis. Brief introductions and bibliographies to each paper. xii + 292pp. 6 x 9.
S730 Paperbound **$2.00**

MATHEMATICS OF MODERN ENGINEERING, E. G. Keller and R. E. Doherty. Written for the Advanced Course in Engineering of the General Electric Corporation, deals with the engineering use of determinants, tensors, the Heaviside operational calculus, dyadics, the calculus of variations, etc. Presents underlying principles fully, but purpose is to teach engineers to deal with modern engineering problems, and emphasis is on the perennial engineering attack of set-up and solve. Indexes. Over 185 figures and tables. Hundreds of exercises, problems, and worked-out examples. References. Two volume set. Total of xxxiii + 623pp. 5⅜ x 8.
S734 Vol I Paperbound **$1.65**
S735 Vol II Paperbound **$1.65**
The set **$3.30**

MATHEMATICAL METHODS FOR SCIENTISTS AND ENGINEERS, L. P. Smith. For scientists and engineers, as well as advanced math students. Full investigation of methods and practical description of conditions under which each should be used. Elements of real functions, differential and integral calculus, space geometry, theory of residues, vector and tensor analysis, series of Bessel functions, etc. Each method illustrated by completely-worked-out examples, mostly from scientific literature. 368 graded unsolved problems. 100 diagrams. x + 453pp. 5⅝ x 8⅜. S220 Paperbound **$2.00**

THEORY OF FUNCTIONS AS APPLIED TO ENGINEERING PROBLEMS, edited by R. Rothe, F. Ollendorff, and K. Pohlhausen. A series of lectures given at the Berlin Institute of Technology that shows the specific applications of function theory in electrical and allied fields of engineering. Six lectures provide the elements of function theory in a simple and practical form, covering complex quantities and variables, integration in the complex plane, residue theorems, etc. Then 5 lectures show the exact uses of this powerful mathematical tool, with full discussions of problem methods. Index. Bibliography. 108 figures. x + 189pp. 5⅜ x 8.
S733 Paperbound **$1.35**

ADVANCED CALCULUS, E. B. Wilson. An unabridged reprinting of the work which continues to be recognized as one of the most comprehensive and useful texts in the field. It contains an immense amount of well-presented, fundamental material, including chapters on vector functions, ordinary differential equations, special functions, calculus of variations, etc., which are excellent introductions to these areas. For students with only one year of calculus, more than 1300 exercises cover both pure math and applications to engineering and physical problems. For engineers, physicists, etc., this work, with its 54 page introductory review, is the ideal reference and refresher. Index. ix + 566pp. 5⅜ x 8.
S504 Paperbound **$2.45**

CALCULUS OF VARIATIONS, A. R. Forsyth. Methods, solutions, rather than determination of weakest valid hypotheses. Over 150 examples completely worked-out show use of Euler, Legendre, Jacobi, Weierstrass tests for maxima, minima. Integrals with one original dependent variable; with derivatives of 2nd order; two dependent variables, one independent variable; double integrals involving 1 dependent variable, 2 first derivatives; double integrals involving partial derivatives of 2nd order; triple integrals; much more. 50 diagrams. 678pp. 5⅝ x 8⅜. S622 Paperbound **$2.95**

LECTURES ON THE CALCULUS OF VARIATIONS, O. Bolza. Analyzes in detail the fundamental concepts of the calculus of variations, as developed from Euler to Hilbert, with sharp formulations of the problems and rigorous demonstrations of their solutions. More than a score of solved examples; systematic references for each theorem. Covers the necessary and sufficient conditions; the contributions made by Euler, Du Bois Reymond, Hilbert, Weierstrass, Legendre, Jacobi, Erdmann, Kneser, and Gauss; and much more. Index. Bibliography. xi + 271pp. 5⅜ x 8. S218 Paperbound **$**

A TREATISE ON THE CALCULUS OF FINITE DIFFERENCES, G. Boole. A classic in the literature of the calculus. Thorough, clear discussion of basic principles, theorems, methods. Covers MacLaurin's and Herschel's theorems, mechanical quadrature, factorials, periodical constants, Bernoulli's numbers, difference-equations (linear, mixed, and partial), etc. Stresses analogies with differential calculus. 236 problems, answers to the numerical ones. viii + 336pp. 5⅜ x 8. S695 Paperbound **$1.85**

THE ANALYTICAL THEORY OF HEAT, Joseph Fourier. This book, which revolutionized mathematical physics, is listed in the Great Books program, and many other listings of great books. It has been used with profit by generations of mathematicians and physicists who are interested in either heat or in the application of the Fourier integral. Covers cause and reflection of rays of heat, radiant heating, heating of closed spaces, use of trigonometric series in the theory of heat, Fourier integral, etc. Translated by Alexander Freeman. 20 figures. xxii + 466pp. 5⅜ x 8. S93 Paperbound **$2.00**

AN INTRODUCTION TO FOURIER METHODS AND THE LAPLACE TRANSFORMATION, Philip Franklin. Concentrates upon essentials, enabling the reader with only a working knowledge of calculus to gain an understanding of Fourier methods in a broad sense, suitable for most applications. This work covers complex qualities with methods of computing elementary functions for complex values of the argument and finding approximations by the use of charts; Fourier series and integrals with half-range and complex Fourier series; harmonic analysis; Fourier and Laplace transformations, etc.; partial differential equations with applications to transmission of electricity; etc. The methods developed are related to physical problems of heat flow, vibrations, electrical transmission, electromagnetic radiation, etc. 828 problems with answers. Formerly entitled "Fourier Methods." Bibliography. Index. x + 289pp. 5⅜ x 8. S452 Paperbound **$1.75**

THE FOURIER INTEGRAL AND CERTAIN OF ITS APPLICATIONS, Norbert Wiener. The only book-length study of the Fourier integral as link between pure and applied math. An expansion of lectures given at Cambridge. Partial contents: Plancherel's theorem, general Tauberian theorem, special Tauberian theorems, generalized harmonic analysis. Bibliography. viii + 201pp. 5⅜ x 8. S272 Paperbound **$1.50**

INTRODUCTION TO THE THEORY OF FOURIER'S SERIES AND INTEGRALS, H. S. Carslaw. 3rd revised edition. This excellent introduction is an outgrowth of the author's courses at Cambridge. Historical introduction, rational and irrational numbers, infinite sequences and series, functions of a single variable, definite integral, Fourier series, Fourier integrals, and similar topics. Appendixes discuss practical harmonic analysis, periodogram analysis. Lebesgues theory. Indexes. 84 examples, bibliography. xiii + 368pp. 5⅜ x 8. S48 Paperbound **$2.00**

FOURIER'S SERIES AND SPHERICAL HARMONICS, W. E. Byerly. Continues to be recognized as one of most practical, useful expositions. Functions, series, and their differential equations are concretely explained in great detail; theory is applied constantly to practical problems, which are fully and lucidly worked out. Appendix includes 6 tables of surface zonal harmonics, hyperbolic functions, Bessel's functions. Bibliography. 190 problems, approximately half with answers. ix + 287pp. 5⅜ x 8. S536 Paperbound **$1.75**

ASYMPTOTIC EXPANSIONS, A. Erdélyi. The only modern work available in English, this is an unabridged reproduction of a monograph prepared for the Office of Naval Research. It discusses various procedures for asymptotic evaluation of integrals containing a large parameter and solutions of ordinary linear differential equations. Bibliography of 71 items. vi + 108pp. 5⅜ x 8. S318 Paperbound **$1.35**

LINEAR INTEGRAL EQUATIONS, W. V. Lovitt. Systematic survey of general theory, with some application to differential equations, calculus of variations, problems of math, physics. Partial contents: integral equation of 2nd kind by successive substitutions; Fredholm's equation as ratio of 2 integral series in lambda, applications of the Fredholm theory, Hilbert-Schmidt theory of symmetric kernels, application, etc. Neumann, Dirichlet, vibratory problems. Index. ix + 253pp. 5⅜ x 8. S175 Clothbound **$3.50**
S176 Paperbound **$1.60**

THEORY OF FUNCTIONALS AND OF INTEGRAL AND INTEGRO-DIFFERENTIAL EQUATIONS, Vito Volterra. Unabridged republication of the only English translation. An exposition of the general theory of the functions depending on a continuous set of values of another function, based on the author's fundamental notion of the transition from a finite number of variables to a continually infinite number. Though dealing primarily with integral equations, much material on calculus of variations is included. The work makes no assumption of previous knowledge on the part of the reader. It begins with fundamental material and proceeds to Generalization of Analytic Functions, Integro-Differential Equations, Functional Derivative Equations, Applications, Other Directions of Theory of Functionals, etc. New introduction by G. C. Evans. Bibliography and criticism of Volterra's work by E. Whittaker. Bibliography. Index of authors cited. Index of subjects. xxxx + 226pp. 5⅜ x 8. S502 Paperbound **$1.75**

AN ELEMENTARY TREATISE ON ELLIPTIC FUNCTIONS, A. Cayley. Still the fullest and clearest text on the theories of Jacobi and Legendre for the advanced student (and an excellent supplement for the beginner). A masterpiece of exposition by the great 19th century British mathematician (creator of the theory of matrices and abstract geometry), it covers the addition-theory, Landen's theorem, the 3 kinds of elliptic integrals, transformations, the q-functions, reduction of a differential expression, and much more. Index. xii + 386pp. 5⅜ x 8. S728 Paperbound **$2.00**

THE APPLICATIONS OF ELLIPTIC FUNCTIONS, A. G. Greenhill. Modern books forgo detail for sake of brevity—this book offers complete exposition necessary for proper understanding, use of elliptic integrals. Formulas developed from definite physical, geometric problems; examples representative enough to offer basic information in widely useable form. Elliptic integrals, addition theorem, algebraical form of addition theorem, elliptic integrals of 2nd, 3rd kind, double periodicity, resolution into factors, series, transformation, etc. Introduction. Index. 25 illus. xi + 357pp. 5⅜ x 8. S603 Paperbound **$1.75**

THE THEORY OF FUNCTIONS OF REAL VARIABLES, James Pierpont. A 2-volume authoritative exposition, by one of the foremost mathematicians of his time. Each theorem stated with all conditions, then followed by proof. No need to go through complicated reasoning to discover conditions added without specific mention. Includes a particularly complete, rigorous presentation of theory of measure; and Pierpont's own work on a theory of Lebesgue integrals, and treatment of area of a curved surface. Partial contents, Vol. 1: rational numbers, exponentials, logarithms, point aggregates, maxima, minima, proper integrals, improper integrals, multiple proper integrals, continuity, discontinuity, indeterminate forms. Vol. 2: point sets, proper integrals, series, power series, aggregates, ordinal numbers, discontinuous functions, sub-, infra-uniform convergence, much more. Index. 95 illustrations. 1229pp. 5⅜ x 8. S558-9, 2 volume set, paperbound **$4.90**

FUNCTIONS OF A COMPLEX VARIABLE, James Pierpont. Long one of best in the field. A thorough treatment of fundamental elements, concepts, theorems. A complete study, rigorous, detailed, with carefully selected problems worked out to illustrate each topic. Partial contents: arithmetical operations, real term series, positive term series, exponential functions, integration, analytic functions, asymptotic expansions, functions of Weierstrass, Legendre, etc. Index. List of symbols. 122 illus. 597pp. 5⅜ x 8. S560 Paperbound **$2.45**

ELEMENTS OF THE THEORY OF REAL FUNCTIONS, J. E. Littlewood. Based on lectures given at Trinity College, Cambridge, this book has proved to be extremely successful in introducing graduate students to the modern theory of functions. It offers a full and concise coverage of classes and cardinal numbers, well-ordered series, other types of series, and elements of the theory of sets of points. 3rd revised edition. vii + 71pp. 5⅜ x 8.
S171 Clothbound **$2.85**
S172 Paperbound **$1.25**

TRANSCENDENTAL AND ALGEBRAIC NUMBERS, A. O. Gelfond. First English translation of work by leading Soviet mathematician. Thue-Siegel theorem, its p-adic analogue, on approximation of algebraic numbers by numbers in fixed algebraic field; Hermite-Lindemann theorem on transcendency of Bessel functions, solutions of other differential equations; Gelfond-Schneider theorem on transcendency of alpha to power beta; Schneider's work on elliptic functions, with method developed by Gelfond. Translated by L. F. Boron. Index. Bibliography. 200pp. 5⅜ x 8. S615 Paperbound **$1.75**

THEORY OF MAXIMA AND MINIMA, H. Hancock. Fullest treatment ever written; only work in English with extended discussion of maxima and minima for functions of 1, 2, or n variables, problems with subsidiary constraints, and relevant quadratic forms. Detailed proof of each important theorem. Covers the Scheeffer and von Dantscher theories, homogeneous quadratic forms, reversion of series, fallacious establishment of maxima and minima, etc. Unsurpassed treatise for advanced students of calculus, mathematicians, economists, statisticians. Index. 24 diagrams. 39 problems, many examples. 193pp. 5⅜ x 8. S665 Paperbound **$1.50**

DICTIONARY OF CONFORMAL REPRESENTATIONS, H. Kober. Laplace's equation in 2 dimensions solved in this unique book developed by the British Admiralty. Scores of geometrical forms & their transformations for electrical engineers, Joukowski aerofoil for aerodynamists, Schwartz-Christoffel transformations for hydrodynamics, transcendental functions. Contents classified according to analytical functions describing transformation. Twin diagrams show curves of most transformations with corresponding regions. Glossary. Topological index. 447 diagrams. 244pp. 6⅛ x 9¼. S160 Paperbound **$2.00**

THE TAYLOR SERIES, AN INTRODUCTION TO THE THEORY OF FUNCTIONS OF A COMPLEX VARIABLE, P. Dienes. This book investigates the entire realm of analytic functions. Only ordinary calculus is needed, except in the last two chapters. Starting with an introduction to real variables and complex algebra, the properties of infinite series, elementary functions, complex differentiation and integration are carefully derived. Also biuniform mapping, a thorough two part discussion of representation and singularities of analytic functions, overconvergence and gap theorems, divergent series, Taylor series on its circle of convergence, divergence and singularities, etc. Unabridged, corrected reissue of first edition. Preface and index. 186 examples, many fully worked out. 67 figures. xii + 555pp. 5⅜ x 8.
S391 Paperbound **$2.75**

INTRODUCTION TO BESSEL FUNCTIONS, Frank Bowman. A rigorous self-contained exposition providing all necessary material during the development, which requires only some knowledge of calculus and acquaintance with differential equations. A balanced presentation including applications and practical use. Discusses Bessel Functions of Zero Order, of Any Real Order; Modified Bessel Functions of Zero Order; Definite Integrals; Asymptotic Expansions; Bessel's Solution to Kepler's Problem; Circular Membranes; much more. "Clear and straightforward . . . useful not only to students of physics and engineering, but to mathematical students in general," Nature. 226 problems. Short tables of Bessel functions. 27 figures. Index. x + 135pp. 5⅜ x 8.
S462 Paperbound **$1.35**

MODERN THEORIES OF INTEGRATION, H. Kestelman. Connected and concrete coverage, with fully-worked-out proofs for every step. Ranges from elementary definitions through theory of aggregates, sets of points, Riemann and Lebesgue integration, and much more. This new revised and enlarged edition contains a new chapter on Riemann-Stieltjes integration, as well as a supplementary section of 186 exercises. Ideal for the mathematician, student, teacher, or self-studier. Index of Definitions and Symbols. General Index. Bibliography. x + 310pp. 5⅝ x 8⅜.
S572 Paperbound **$2.00**

A TREATISE ON THE THEORY OF DETERMINANTS, T. Muir. Unequalled as an exhaustive compilation of nearly all the known facts about determinants up to the early 1930's. Covers notation and general properties, row and column transformation, symmetry, compound determinants, adjugates, rectangular arrays and matrices, linear dependence, gradients, Jacobians, Hessians, Wronskians, and much more. Invaluable for libraries of industrial and research organizations as well as for student, teacher, and mathematician; very useful in the field of computing machines. Revised and enlarged by W. H. Metzler. Index. 485 problems and scores of numerical examples. iv + 766pp. 5⅜ x 8.
S670 Paperbound **$2.95**

THEORY OF DETERMINANTS IN THE HISTORICAL ORDER OF DEVELOPMENT, Sir Thomas Muir. Unabridged reprinting of this complete study of 1,859 papers on determinant theory written between 1693 and 1900. Most important and original sections reproduced, valuable commentary on each. No other work is necessary for determinant research: all types are covered—each subdivision of the theory treated separately; all papers dealing with each type are covered; you are told exactly what each paper is about and how important its contribution is. Each result, theory, extension, or modification is assigned its own identifying numeral so that the full history may be more easily followed. Includes papers on determinants in general, determinants and linear equations, symmetric determinants, alternants, recurrents, determinants having invariant factors, and all other major types. "A model of what such histories ought to be," NATURE. "Mathematicians must ever be grateful to Sir Thomas for his monumental work," AMERICAN MATH MONTHLY. Four volumes bound as two. Indices. Bibliographies. Total of lxxxiv + 1977pp. 5⅜ x 8.
S672-3 The set, Clothbound **$10.00**

A COURSE IN MATHEMATICAL ANALYSIS, Edouard Goursat. Trans. by E. R. Hedrick, O. Dunkel. Classic study of fundamental material thoroughly treated. Exceptionally lucid exposition of wide range of subject matter for student with 1 year of calculus. Vol. 1: Derivatives and Differentials, Definite Integrals, Expansion in Series, Applications to Geometry. Problems. Index. 52 illus. 556pp. Vol. 2, Part I: Functions of a Complex Variable, Conformal Representations, Doubly Periodic Functions, Natural Boundaries, etc. Problems. Index. 38 illus. 269pp. Vol. 2, Part 2: Differential Equations, Cauchy-Lipschitz Method, Non-linear Differential Equations, Simultaneous Equations, etc. Problems. Index. 308pp. 5⅜ x 8.
Vol. 1 S554 Paperbound **$2.25**
Vol. 2 part 1 S555 Paperbound **$1.65**
Vol. 2 part 2 S556 Paperbound **$1.65**
3 vol. set **$5.00**

INFINITE SEQUENCES AND SERIES, Konrad Knopp. First publication in any language! Excellent introduction to 2 topics of modern mathematics, designed to give the student background to penetrate farther by himself. Sequences & sets, real & complex numbers, etc. Functions of a real & complex variable. Sequences & series. Infinite series. Convergent power series. Expansion of elementary functions. Numerical evaluation of series. Bibliography. v + 186pp. 5⅜ x 8.
S152 Clothbound **$3.50**
S153 Paperbound **$1.75**

TRIGONOMETRICAL SERIES, Antoni Zygmund. Unique in any language on modern advanced level. Contains carefully organized analyses of trigonometric, orthogonal, Fourier systems of functions, with clear adequate descriptions of summability of Fourier series, proximation theory, conjugate series, convergence, divergence of Fourier series. Especially valuable for Russian, Eastern European coverage. Bibliography. 329pp. 5⅜ x 8.
S290 Paperbound **$1.50**

COLLECTED WORKS OF BERNHARD RIEMANN. This important source book is the first to contain the complete text of both 1892 Werke and the 1902 supplement, unabridged. It contains 31 monographs, 3 complete lecture courses, 15 miscellaneous papers, which have been of enormous importance in relativity, topology, theory of complex variables, and other areas of mathematics. Edited by R. Dedekind, H. Weber, M. Noether, W. Wirtinger. German text. English introduction by Hans Lewy. 690pp. 5⅜ x 8. S226 Paperbound **$2.85**

See also: **A HISTORY OF THE CALCULUS, C. B. Boyer; CALCULUS REFRESHER FOR TECHNICAL MEN, A. A. Klaf; MONOGRAPHS ON TOPICS OF MODERN MATHEMATICS, ed. by J. W. A. Young; THE CONTINUUM AND OTHER TYPES OF SERIAL ORDER, E. V. Huntington.**

Symbolic logic

AN INTRODUCTION TO SYMBOLIC LOGIC, Susanne K. Langer. Probably the clearest book ever written on symbolic logic for the philosopher, general scientist and layman. It will be particularly appreciated by those who have been rebuffed by other introductory works because of insufficient mathematical training. No special knowledge of mathematics is required. Starting with the simplest symbols and conventions, you are led to a remarkable grasp of the Boole-Schroeder and Russell-Whitehead systems clearly and quickly. PARTIAL CONTENTS: Study of forms, Essentials of logical structure, Generalization, Classes, The deductive system of classes, The algebra of logic, Abstraction of interpretation, Calculus of propositions, Assumptions of PRINCIPIA MATHEMATICA, Logistics, Logic of the syllogism, Proofs of theorems. "One of the clearest and simplest introductions to a subject which is very much alive. The style is easy, symbolism is introduced gradually, and the intelligent non-mathematician should have no difficulty in following the argument," MATHEMATICS GAZETTE. Revised, expanded second edition. Truth-value tables. 368pp. 5⅜ x 8.
S164 Paperbound **$1.75**

THE ELEMENTS OF MATHEMATICAL LOGIC, Paul Rosenbloom. First publication in any language. This book is intended for readers who are mature mathematically, but have no previous training in symbolic logic. It does not limit itself to a single system, but covers the field as a whole. It is a development of lectures given at Lund University, Sweden, in 1948. Partial contents: Logic of classes, fundamental theorems, Boolean algebra, logic of propositions, logic of propositional functions, expressive languages, combinatory logics, development of mathematics within an object language, paradoxes, theorems of Post and Goedel, Church's theorem, and similar topics. iv + 214pp. 5⅜ x 8. S227 Paperbound **$1.45**

A SURVEY OF SYMBOLIC LOGIC: THE CLASSIC ALGEBRA OF LOGIC, C. I. Lewis. Classic survey of the field, comprehensive and thorough. Indicates content of major systems, alternative methods of procedure, and relation of these to the Boole-Schroeder algebra and to one another. Contains historical summary, as well as full proofs and applications of the classic, or Boole-Schroeder, algebra of logic. Discusses diagrams for the logical relations of classes, the two-valued algebra, propositional functions of two or more variables, etc. Chapters 5 and 6 of the original edition, which contained material not directly pertinent, have been omitted in this edition at the author's request. Appendix. Bibliography. Index. viii + 352pp. 5⅝ x 8⅜.
S643 Paperbound **$2.00**

INTRODUCTION TO SYMBOLIC LOGIC AND ITS APPLICATIONS, R. Carnap. One of the clearest, most comprehensive, and rigorous introductions to modern symbolic logic by perhaps its greatest living master. Symbolic languages are analyzed and one constructed. Applications to math (symbolic representation of axiom systems for set theory, natural numbers, real numbers, topology, Dedekind and Cantor explanations of continuity), physics (the general analysis of concepts of determination, causality, space-time-topology, based on Einstein), biology (symbolic representation of an axiom system for basic concepts). "A masterpiece," Zentralblatt für Mathematik und ihre Grenzgebiete. Over 300 exercises. 5 figures. Bibliography. Index. xvi + 241pp. 5⅜ x 8. S453 Paperbound **$1.85**
Clothbound **$4.00**